D1455188

ИЗДАТЕЛЬСТВО
МИР

В. П. Минорский

СБОРНИК ЗАДАЧ ПО ВЫСШЕЙ МАТЕМАТИКЕ

Издательство «Наука»
Москва

V. P. Minořsky

PROBLEMS

IN HIGHER MATHEMATICS

Translated from the Russian by
Yuri Ermolyev

Mir Publishers Moscow

First published 1975
Revised from the 1969 Russian edition

На английском языке

CONTENTS

CHAPTER 1

PLANE ANALYTIC GEOMETRY

1.1. Coordinates of a Point on a Straight Line and in a Plane. The Distance Between Two Points

1°. The distance d between two points $A(x_1)$ and $B(x_2)$ on an axis:

$$d=|x_2-x_1|=\sqrt{(x_2-x_1)^2}. \quad (1)$$

2°. The value AB (algebraic) of a *directed segment of an axis:*

$$AB=x_2-x_1. \quad (2)$$

3°. The distance d between two points $A(x_1, y_1)$ and $B(x_2, y_2)$ in a plane:

$$d=\sqrt{(x_2-x_1)^2+(y_2-y_1)^2}. \quad (3)$$

4°. The projections of a *directed segment* having $A(x_1, y_1)$ as its initial point and $B(x_2, y_2)$ as its terminal point on the coordinate axes, or those of a vector $\overrightarrow{AB}$ in a plane

$$\mathrm{pr}_{OX}\overrightarrow{AB}=X=x_2-x_1, \quad \mathrm{pr}_{OY}\overrightarrow{AB}=Y=y_2-y_1. \quad (4)$$

1. Plot the points $A(-5)$, $B(+4)$, and $C(-2)$ on the number axis, and find the values AB, BC, and AC of the segments on the axis. Check that $AB+BC=AC$.

2. Do the same exercise for the points $A(+1)$, $B(-4)$, and $C(+5)$.

3. Construct a triangle with the vertices $A(-4, 2)$, $B(0, -1)$, and $C(3, 3)$ and determine its perimeter and angles.

4. Prove that the triangle with the vertices $A(-3, 2)$, $B(0, -1)$, and $C(-2, 5)$ is a right triangle.

5. Plot the points $A(-4, 0)$, $B(-1, 4)$ and A_1, B_1 which are symmetric to the given ones with respect to the axis OY. Calculate the perimeter of the trapezoid ABB_1A_1.

6. Point B is symmetric to $A(4, -1)$ with respect to the bisector of the first quadrant. Find the length of AB.

7. Find the point 5 units distant both from the point $A(2, 1)$ and the axis OY.

8. On the axis of ordinates find the point 5 units distant from the point $A(4, -1)$. Explain by construction why two solutions are possible.

9. On the axis of abscissas find the point c units distant from the point $A(a, b)$. Analyse the solution for $c > |b|$, $c = |b|$, and $c < |b|$.

10. On the axis OX find the point equidistant from the origin of coordinates and from the point $A(8, 4)$.

11. Find the centre and the radius of the circle circumscribed about a triangle with the vertices $A(4, 3)$, $B(-3, 2)$, and $C(1, -6)$.

12. Given the points $A(2, 6)$ and $B(0, 2)$; construct the vector $\overrightarrow{AB}$, its components on the axes and compute $\text{pr}_{OX}\overrightarrow{AB}$, $\text{pr}_{OY}\overrightarrow{AB}$ and the length AB.

13. Applied at the point $A(2, 5)$ is a force whose projections on the coordinate axes are $X = 3$ and $Y = 3$. Determine the end-point of the vector $\overrightarrow{AB}$ representing the force, and the magnitude of the force.

14. Applied at the point $A(-3, -2)$ is a force whose projection $Y = -1$, and the projection X is positive. Determine the end-point of the vector $\overrightarrow{AB}$ representing the force if its magnitude is equal to $5\sqrt{2}$.

15*. Plot the points $A(1)$, $B(-3)$, and $C(-2)$ on the number axis and find the values AB, BC and CA of the segments on the axis. Check that $AB + BC + CA = 0$.

---

* Each section of the present book is supplied by a stock of problems which are recommended for home tasks or recapitulation purposes. They are given below a separating line.

16. Plot in a plane the points $A(-7, 0)$, $B(0, 1)$ and points A_1, B_1 which are symmetric to A and B with respect to the bisectors of the first and third quadrants. Compute the perimeter of the trapezoid ABB_1A_1.

17. On the axis of ordinates find the point equidistant from the origin and from the point $A(-2, 5)$.

18. On the axis of abscissas find the point $3\sqrt{5}$ units distant from the point $A(-2, 3)$.

19. Determine the centre and the radius of the circle circumscribed about a triangle with the vertices $A(-3, -1)$, $B(5, 3)$, and $C(6, -4)$.

20. Given the points $A(x_1, y_1)$ and $B(x_2, y_2)$. Applied at the origin are two forces represented by the vectors $\overrightarrow{OA}$ and $\overrightarrow{OB}$. Construct the resultant force $\overrightarrow{OC}$ and prove that its projection on the coordinate axis is equal to the sum of the projections of the components on the same axis.

21. Given the points $A(1, 2)$, $B(3, 5)$, $C(5, 2)$, and $D(2, -2)$. Applied at the point A are forces $\overrightarrow{AB}$, $\overrightarrow{AC}$ and $\overrightarrow{AD}$. Find the projections of the resultant force on the coordinate axes and its value.

1.2. Dividing a Line Segment in a Given Ratio. The Area of a Triangle and a Polygon

1°. Dividing a line segment in a given ratio. Given two points $A(x_1, y_1)$ and $B(x_2, y_2)$. The coordinates of the point $M(x, y)$ that divides the segment AB in the ratio $AM:MB=\lambda$ are determined by the formulas

$$x=\frac{x_1+\lambda x_2}{1+\lambda}, \quad y=\frac{y_1+\lambda y_2}{1+\lambda}. \tag{1}$$

In a particular case when M is the midpoint of the segment AB (i.e. when $\lambda=1:1=1$)

$$x=\frac{x_1+x_2}{2}, \quad y=\frac{y_1+y_2}{2}. \tag{2}$$

2°. The area S of a polygon with the vertices $A(x_1, y_1)$, $B(x_2, y_2)$, $C(x_3, y_3)$, $\ldots$, $F(x_n, y_n)$ is given by the formula

$$S = \pm\frac{1}{2}\left[\begin{vmatrix} x_1 & y_1 \\ x_2 & y_2 \end{vmatrix} + \begin{vmatrix} x_2 & y_2 \\ x_3 & y_3 \end{vmatrix} + \dots + \begin{vmatrix} x_n & y_n \\ x_1 & y_1 \end{vmatrix}\right]. \qquad (3)$$

The expression $\begin{vmatrix} x_1 & y_1 \\ x_2 & y_2 \end{vmatrix}$ equals $x_1y_2 - x_2y_1$ and is called a *determinant* of the second order *.

22. Plot the points $A(-2, 1)$, and $B(3, 6)$ and find the point M which divides AB in the ratio $AM:MB = 3:2$.

23. Given the points $A(-2, 1)$ and $B(3, 6)$. "Divide" the segment AB in the ratio $AM:MB = -3:2$.

24. Masses m_1 and m_2 are placed at the points $A(x_1)$ and $B(x_2)$ on the axis OX. Find the centre of mass of this system.

25. Masses m_1, m_2, and m_3 are placed on the axis OX at the points $A(x_1)$, $B(x_2)$, and $C(x_3)$ respectively. Show that the centre of mass of this system is found at the point $x = \frac{m_1x_1 + m_2x_2 + m_3x_3}{m_1 + m_2 + m_3}$.

26. The ends of a 40 cm 500 g uniform bar are fitted with balls weighing 100 g and 400 g. Determine the centre of gravity of this system.

27. Masses of 60 g, 40 g, and 100 g are placed at the points $A(-2, 4)$, $B(3, -1)$, and $C(2, 3)$ respectively. Determine the centre of mass of this system.

28. Determine the midpoints of the sides of a triangle with the vertices $A(2, -1)$, $B(4, 3)$, and $C(-2, 1)$.

29. In a triangle with the vertices $O(0, 0)$, $A(8, 0)$, and $B(0, 6)$ determine the lengths of the median OC and of the bisector OD.

30. Find the centre of gravity of a triangle with the vertices $A(1, -1)$, $B(6, 4)$, and $C(2, 6)$.

Hint. The centre of gravity of a triangle is found at the point of intersection of its medians.

31. Compute the surface area of a triangle whose vertices are $A(2, 0)$, $B(5, 3)$, and $C(2, 6)$.

---

* For more detail see Chapter 4.

32. Show that the points $A(1, 1)$, $B(-1, 7)$, and $C(0, 4)$ belong to one straight line.

33. Calculate the area of a quadrangle with the vertices $A(3, 1)$, $B(4, 6)$, $C(6, 3)$, and $D(5, -2)$.

---

34. Two parallel forces equal to 300 N and 400 N are applied at the points $A(-3, -1)$ and $B(4, 6)$ respectively. Find the point of application of the resultant force.

35. Masses of 500 g, 200 g, and 100 g are placed at the points $O(0, 0)$, $A(2, -5)$, and $B(4, 2)$ respectively. Determine the centre of mass of this system.

36. In a triangle with the vertices $A(-2, 0)$, $B(6, 6)$, and $C(1, -4)$ determine the length of the bisector AE.

37. Find the centre of gravity of a triangle with the vertices $A(x_1, y_1)$, $B(x_2, y_2)$, and $C(x_3, y_3)$.

38. Find the centre of gravity of a uniform quadrangular board with the vertices $A(-2, 1)$, $B(3, 6)$, $C(5, 2)$, and $D(0, -6)$.

Hint. Using the formulas obtained in Problem 37 find the centres of gravity of the triangles ABC and ADC and divide the distance between the centres in the ratio reversely equal to the ratio of the areas of the triangles.

39. Given the points $A(1, 2)$ and $B(4, 4)$. On the axis OX determine a point C so that the area of the triangle ABC is equal to 5 square units. Construct the triangle ABC.

40. In a triangle with the vertices $A(-2, 2)$, $B(1, -4)$, and $C(4, 5)$ each side is extended by one third of its length in the direction corresponding to the counterclockwise traverse of the perimeter of the triangle. Determine the end-points M, N, and P of the extensions and find the ratio k of the areas of triangles MNP and ABC.

1.3. The Equation of a Line as a Locus of Points

The *equation of a line* is defined as the *equation which relates the variables x and y if and only if the coordinates of any point of this line satisfy the equation.*

The variables x and y entering the equation of a line are called *running (moving, or current) coordinates*, and the literal constants—parameters. For instance, in the equation of a circle (Problem 41) $x^2+y^2=R^2$ the variables x and y are the running coordinates, and the constant R is a parameter.

To set up an equation of a line as a locus of points possessing one and the same property we have to:

(1) take an arbitrary (running) point $M(x, y)$ on the line,

(2) express the general property of all the points M of the line through an equation,

(3) express the line segments (and angles) entering this equation in terms of the running coordinates of the point $M(x, y)$ and through the coordinates given in the specific problem.

41. Show that $x^2+y^2=R^2$ is the equation of a circle of radius R and with the origin as centre.

42. Write the equation of a circle with the centre at $C(3, 4)$ and radius $R=5$. Do the points $A(-1, 1)$, $B(2, 3)$, $O(0, 0)$, and $D(4, 1)$ lie on this circle?

43. Write the equation of a line generated by a moving point $M(x, y)$ which is equidistant from the points $A(0, 2)$ and $B(4, -2)$. Do the points $C(-1, 1)$, $D(1, -1)$, $E(0, -2)$, and $F(2, 2)$ lie on this line?

44. Write the equation of the trajectory of a moving point $M(x, y)$ which always remains three times farther from the point $A(0, 9)$ than from the point $B(0, 1)$.

45. Write the equation of the trajectory of a moving point $M(x, y)$ which always remains twice nearer to the point $A(-1, 1)$ than to the point $B(-4, 4)$.

46. Write the equations of the bisectors of all the quadrants.

47. Write the equation of the locus of points the sum of the distances between each of them and the points $F(2, 0)$ and $F_1(-2, 0)$ being equal to $2\sqrt{5}$. Construct the line by its equation.

48. Write the equation of the locus of points equidistant from the point $F(2, 2)$ and the axis OX. Construct the line by its equation.

49. Write the equation of the line along which a point $M(x, y)$ moves remaining twice farther from the axis OX than from the axis OY.

50. Construct the following lines: (1) $y=2x+5$; (2) $y=7-2x$; (3) $y=2x$; (4) $y=4$; (5) $y=4-x^2$.

51. Determine the points of intersection of the line $y=x^2-4x+3$ and the axes of coordinates and plot them.

52. Determine the points of intersection of the axes of coordinates and the following lines: (1) $3x-2y=12$; (2) $y=x^2+4x$; (3) $y^2=2x+4$. Construct these lines.

53. Write the equation of the locus of points equidistant from the axis OY and the point $F(4, 0)$. Construct the line on the basis of its equation.

---

54. Write the equation of the line along which a point $M(x, y)$ moves remaining equidistant from the origin and the point $A(-4, 2)$. Do the points $B(-2, 1)$, $C(2, 3)$, $D(1, 7)$ belong to this line?

55. Write the equation of the trajectory of a moving point $M(x, y)$ which all the time remains twice nearer to the point $A(0, -1)$ than to the point $B(0, 4)$. Construct the trajectory of its motion.

56. Determine the points of intersection of the axes of coordinates with the following lines: (1) $2x+5y+10=0$; (2) $y=3-2x-x^2$; (3) $y^2=4-x$. Construct these lines.

57. Write the equation of the locus of points equidistant from the axis OX and the point $F(0, 2)$. Construct the line by its equation.

58. Write the equation of the locus of points the difference between the distances of each of which from the points $F_1(-2, -2)$ and $F(2, 2)$ is equal to 4. Construct the line on the basis of its equation.

1.4. The Equation of a Straight Line: (1) Slope-Intercept Form, (2) General Form, (3) Intercept Form

1°. The slope-intercept equation of the straight line:

$$y=kx+b. \quad (1)$$

The parameter k is equal to the tangent of the inclination angle α of a straight line with respect to the axis OX ($k=\tan\alpha$) and is called the *slope* of the line. The parameter b is the length of the intercept on the axis OY or the *initial ordinate*.

2°. The general equation of the straight line

$$Ax+By+C=0. \tag{2}$$

Particular cases:

(a) if $C=0$, then $y=-\frac{A}{B}x$—the straight line passes through the origin;

(b) if $B=0$, then $x=-\frac{C}{A}=a$—the straight line is parallel to the axis OY;

(c) if $A=0$, then $y=-\frac{C}{B}=b$—the straight line is parallel to the axis OX;

(d) if $B=C=0$, then $Ax=0$, $x=0$—the axis OY;

(e) if $A=C=0$, then $By=0$, $y=0$—the axis OX.

3°. The intercept equation of the straight line:

$$\frac{x}{a}+\frac{y}{b}=1, \tag{3}$$

where a and b are the intercepts cut off by the line on the OX- and OY-axis respectively.

59. Construct a straight line cutting off an intercept $b=3$ on the axis OY and forming with the axis OX an angle of: (1) 45°; (2) 135°. Write the equations of the lines.

60. Construct a straight line cutting off an intercept $b=-3$ on the axis OY and forming with the axis OX an angle of: (1) 60°; (2) 120°. Write the equations of the lines.

61. Write the equation of a straight line passing through the origin and inclined to the OX-axis at an angle of: (1) 45°; (2) 60°; (3) 90°; (4) 120°; (5) 135°.

62. Construct the straight line passing through the origin and the point (—2, 3) and write its equation.

63. Determine the parameters k and b for each of the following straight lines: (1) $2x-3y=6$; (2) $2x+3y=0$; (3) $y=-3$; (4) $\frac{x}{4}+\frac{y}{3}=1$.

64. Construct the following straight lines: (1) $3x+4y=12$; (2) $3x-4y=0$; (3) $2x-5=0$; (4) $2y+5=0$.

65. Determine the parameters k and b of the straight line passing through the point $A(2, 3)$ and forming an angle of 45° with the axis OX. Write the equation of this line.

66. Reduce the following equations of the straight lines to the intercept form: (1) $2x-3y=6$; (2) $3x-2y+4=0$.

67. Given the points $O(0, 0)$ and $A(-3, 0)$. Constructed on the segment OA is a parallelogram whose diagonals intersect at the point $B(0, 2)$. Write the equations of the sides and diagonals * of the parallelogram.

68. Write the equation of the straight line passing through the point $A(4, 3)$ and cutting off from the corresponding quadrant a triangle whose area equals 3 square units.

69. The straight lines $y=-2$ and $y=4$ intersect the straight line $3x-4y-5=0$ at the points A and B respectively. Construct the vector $\overrightarrow{AB}$; determine its length and its projections on the axes of coordinates.

70. Are the points $A(3, 5)$, $B(2, 7)$, $C(-1, -3)$, and $D(-2, -6)$ on the straight line $y=2x-1$ or are they above or below this line?

71. What is the geometrical meaning of the inequalities: (1) $y>3x+1$; (2) $y<3x+1$; (3) $2x+y-4\geqslant 0$; (4) $2x+y-4<0$?

72. Construct the domains ** containing the points whose coordinates satisfy the inequalities:

(1) $y<2-x, \quad x>-2, \quad y>-2$;

(2) $y>2-x, \quad x<4, \quad y<0$;

(3) $\frac{x}{4}+\frac{y}{2}\leqslant 1, \quad y\geqslant x+2, \quad x\geqslant -4$.

73. A point $M(x, y)$ moves so that the difference of the squares of its distances from the points $A(-a, a)$ and $B(a, -a)$ remains equal to $4a^2$. Write the equation of its trajectory.

74. Write the equation of the trajectory of the point $M(x, y)$ whose projection on the axis OX moves at the

* The expression "the equations of the sides and diagonals", as used in this book, means "the equations of the straight lines on which the sides and diagonals lie".

** The term "domain" here means a portion of the plane XOY containing points such that the coordinates of each of them satisfy certain conditions (say, inequalities). If a domain contains the boundary points, then it is called a *closed domain*. Otherwise it is called an *open domain*.

velocity of m units per second, and the projection on the axis OY at n units per second. The starting position of the point is $M_0(a, b)$.

---

75. Construct the straight lines given by the parameters: (1) $b=-2$, $\varphi=60°$ and (2) $b=-2$, $\varphi=120°$ and write their equations.

76. Determine the parameters k and b of the straight line passing through the point $(-2, 3)$ and forming an angle of 45° with the axis OX. Construct this line and write its equation.

77. An isosceles trapezoid with bases of 8 cm and 2 cm has an acute angle of 45°. Write the equations of the sides of the trapezoid taking its greater base for the axis OX and the axis of symmetry of the trapezoid for the axis OY.

78. Write the equations of the sides of a rhombus with the diagonals 10 cm and 6 cm long, taking the greater diagonal for the axis OX and the smaller for OY.

79. Write the equation of the straight line passing through the point $(-4, 6)$ and cutting from the coordinate axes a triangle whose area is equal to 6 square units.

80. Write the equation of the line along which a point $M(x, y)$ moves remaining twice farther from the axis OX than from the straight line $x=-3$.

81. The straight lines $x=-1$ and $x=3$ intersect the straight line $y=2x+1$ at the points A and B respectively. Determine the length of the vector $\overrightarrow{AB}$ and its projections on the coordinate axes.

1.5. The Angle Between Two Straight Lines. The Equation of a Pencil of Straight Lines Passing Through a Given Point. The Equation of a Straight Line Passing Through Two Given Points. The Point of Intersection of Two Straight Lines

1°. The angle φ between the two straight lines $y=k_1x+b_1$ and $y=k_2x+b_2$, as measured counterclockwise is determined by the formula

$$\tan \varphi = \frac{\overset{\curvearrowright}{k_2-k_1}}{1+k_1k_2}. \qquad (1)$$

For two straight lines given by the equations

$$A_1x+B_1y+C_1=0 \quad \text{and} \quad A_2x+B_2y+C_2=0$$

the above formula takes the form

$$\tan\varphi=\frac{A_1B_2-A_2B_1}{A_1A_2+B_1B_2}.$$

The condition for the *parallelism* of two straight lines is the equality of their slopes

$$k_1=k_2 \quad \text{or} \quad \frac{A_1}{A_2}=\frac{B_1}{B_2}.$$

The condition for the *perpendicularity* of two straight lines is given by the relation

$$k_2=-\frac{1}{k_1} \quad \text{or} \quad A_1A_2+B_1B_2=0.$$

2°. The equation of a pencil of straight lines passing through a given point $A(x_1, y_1)$

$$y-y_1=k(x-x_1). \tag{2}$$

3°. The equation of a straight line passing through two given points $A(x_1, y_1)$ and $B(x_2, y_2)$

$$\frac{y-y_1}{y_2-y_1}=\frac{x-x_1}{x_2-x_1}. \tag{3}$$

4°. The point of intersection of two non-parallel straight lines $A_1x+B_1y+C_1=0$ and $A_2x+B_2y+C_2=0$ is found by solving the system of their equations. We get

$$x=\frac{\begin{vmatrix}-C_1 & B_1\\ -C_2 & B_2\end{vmatrix}}{\begin{vmatrix}A_1 & B_1\\ A_2 & B_2\end{vmatrix}}, \quad y=\frac{\begin{vmatrix}A_1 & -C_1\\ A_2 & -C_2\end{vmatrix}}{\begin{vmatrix}A_1 & B_1\\ A_2 & B_2\end{vmatrix}}.$$

82. Determine the angle between two straight lines:

(1) $\begin{cases} y=2x-3, \\ y=\frac{1}{2}x+1; \end{cases}$ (2) $\begin{cases} 5x-y+7=0, \\ 2x-3y+1=0; \end{cases}$ (3) $\begin{cases} 2x+y=0, \\ y=3x-4; \end{cases}$

(4) $\begin{cases} 3x+2y=0, \\ 6x+4y+9=0; \end{cases}$ (5) $\begin{cases} 3x-4y=6, \\ 8x+6y=11; \end{cases}$ (6) $\begin{cases} \frac{x}{a}+\frac{y}{b}=1, \\ \frac{x}{b}+\frac{y}{a}=1. \end{cases}$

83. Which of the straight lines $3x-2y+7=0$, $6x-4y-9=0$, $6x+4y-5=0$, $2x+3y-6=0$ are parallel or perpendicular to each other?

84. Write the equation of a pencil of straight lines passing through the point $A(2, 3)$. Choose out of this pencil the straight lines inclined to the axis OX at angles: (1) 45°, (2) 60°, (3) 135°, (4) 0°, and construct them.

85. Plot the point $A(-2, 5)$ and the straight line $2x-y=0$. Write the equation of a pencil of straight lines passing through the point A, and choose from the pencil: (1) the straight line parallel to the given one, (2) the straight line perpendicular to the given one.

86. At the points of intersection of the straight line $2x-5y-10=0$ with the coordinate axes perpendiculars are erected to this line. Write their equations.

87. Write the equation of the straight line passing through the points $A(-1, 3)$ and $B(4, -2)$.

88. In a triangle with the vertices $A(-2, 0)$, $B(2, 6)$, and $C(4, 2)$ the altitude BD and the median BE are drawn. Write the equations of the side AC, the median BE, and the altitude BD.

89. Find the interior angles of a triangle whose sides are given by the equations: $x+2y=0$, $x+4y-6=0$, $x-4y-6=0$.

Hint. To find the interior angles of a triangle it is necessary to arrange the angular coefficients of the sides in the decreasing order: $k_1>k_2>k_3$, and then to compute tangents of the angles using the formulas: $\frac{k_1-k_2}{1+k_1k_2}$, $\frac{k_2-k_3}{1+k_2k_3}$, and $\frac{k_3-k_1}{1+k_1k_3}$. Check the solution by making a drawing and placing one of the vertices at the origin.

90. Write the equations of the straight lines passing through the origin at an angle of 45° to the straight line $y=4-2x$.

91. Write the equations of the straight lines passing through the point $A(-1, 1)$ at an angle of 45° to the straight line $2x+3y=6$.

92. A light beam emanates from the point $A(5, 4)$ at an angle $\varphi = \arctan 2$ to the OX-axis and is reflected by the latter. Write the equations of the incident and reflected beams.

93. Determine the vertices and the angles of a triangle whose sides are given by the equations: $x+3y=0$, $x=3$, $x-2y+3=0$.

94. A segment of the straight line $3x+2y=6$ cut off by the coordinate axes serves as the hypotenuse of a right triangle. Find the vertex of the right angle if it is known that it is situated above the given line.

---

95. Given a triangle with the vertices $A(-2, 0)$, $B(2, 4)$, and $C(4, 0)$. Write the equations of the sides of the triangle, the median AE, the altitude AD and find the length of the median AE.

96. Write the equations of the sides and find the angles of a triangle with the vertices $A(0, 7)$, $B(6, -1)$, and $C(2, 1)$.

97. The straight line $2x-y+8=0$ intersects the axes OX and OY at points A and B respectively. A point M divides AB in the ratio $AM:MB=3:1$. Write the equation of the perpendicular erected to AB at the point M.

98. Construct a triangle whose sides are given by the equations: $x+y=4$, $3x-y=0$, $x-3y-8=0$; find the angles and the area of the triangle.

99. Find the point of intersection of the medians and the point of intersection of the altitudes of a triangle whose vertices are the points $A(-4, 2)$, $B(2, -5)$, and $C(5, 0)$.

100. A light beam emanates from the point $A(-5, 6)$ at an angle $\varphi = \arctan(-2)$ to the axis OX and is reflected by this axis and then by the axis OY. Write the equations of all three beams.

1.6. The Normal Equation of a Straight Line. The Distance of a Point from a Straight Line. Equations of Bisectors. The Equations of a Pencil of Straight Lines Passing Through the Point of Intersection of Two Given Straight Lines

1°. The normal equation of a straight line:

$$x\cos\beta+y\sin\beta-p=0, \qquad (1)$$

where p is the length of the perpendicular (the normal) dropped from the origin to the straight line and β is the angle of inclination of this perpendicular to the axis OX. In order to reduce the general equation of the straight line $Ax+By+C=0$ to the normal form we have to multiply all its terms by the normalizing factor $M=\pm\frac{1}{\sqrt{A^2+B^2}}$ taken with the sign opposite to that of the constant term C.

2°. The distance d of a point (x_0, y_0) from a straight line *is found by substituting the coordinates* (x_0, y_0) *for the current coordinates in the left-hand member of the normal equation of the straight line. The resulting number is taken by the absolute value:*

$$d=|x_0\cos\beta+y_0\sin\beta-p|, \qquad (2)$$

or

$$d=\frac{|Ax_0+By_0+C|}{\sqrt{A^2+B^2}}. \qquad (2')$$

3°. The equations of the bisectors of the angles between the straight lines $Ax+By+C=0$ and $A_1x+B_1y+C_1=0$:

$$\frac{Ax+By+C}{\sqrt{A^2+B^2}}=\pm\frac{A_1x+B_1y+C_1}{\sqrt{A_1^2+B_1^2}}. \qquad (3)$$

4°. The equation of a pencil of straight lines passing through the point of intersection of two given straight lines:

$$\alpha(Ax+By+C)+\beta(A_1x+B_1y+C_1)=0. \qquad (4)$$

Putting $\alpha=1$ we thus exclude the second straight line from the two given out of the pencil (4).

101. Reduce the following equations of straight lines to the normal form:

(1) $3x-4y-20=0$, (2) $x+y+3=0$, (3) $y=kx+b$.

102. Construct the straight line if the length of the normal $p=2$, and the angle β of its inclination to the axis OX is equal to: (1) 45°, (2) 135°, (3) 225°, (4) 315°. Write the equations of these straight lines.

103. Find the distances of the points $A(4, 3)$, $B(2, 1)$, and $C(1, 0)$ from the straight line $3x+4y-10=0$. Plot the points and the straight line.

104. Find the distance between the origin and the straight line $12x-5y+39=0$.

105. Show that the straight lines $2x-3y=6$ and $4x-6y=25$ are parallel, and find the distance between them.

Hint. Take an arbitrary point on one of the lines and find its distance from the other line.

106. Find k from the condition that the distance between the straight line $y=kx+5$ and the origin is $d=\sqrt{5}$.

107. Write the equation of the locus of points 4 units distant from the straight line $4x-3y=0$.

108. Set up the equation of the straight line 4 units distant from the point $A(4, -2)$ and parallel to the straight line $8x-15y=0$.

109. Write the equations of the bisectors of the angles between the straight lines $2x+3y=10$ and $3x+2y=10$.

110. Write the equations of the bisectors of the angles between the straight lines $3x+4y=12$ and $y=0$.

111. Write the equation of the trajectory of a moving point $M(x, y)$ which, during its motion, remains three times farther from the straight line $y=2x-4$ than from the straight line $y=4-2x$.

112. Write the equation of the straight line passing through the point M of intersection of the straight lines $2x+y+6=0$ and $3x+5y-15=0$ and the point $N(1, -2)$ (without finding the point M).

113. Write the equation of the straight line passing through the point M of intersection of the straight lines $5x-y+10=0$ and $8x+4y+9=0$ parallel to the straight line $x+3y=0$ (without finding the point M).

114. Find the altitude BD in a triangle with the vertices $A(-3, 0)$, $B(2, 5)$, and $C(3, 2)$.

115. Write the equation of the straight line passing through the point $A(2, 4)$ at a distance of $d=2$ from the origin.

116. Check to make sure that the points $A(-4, -3)$, $B(-5, 0)$, $C(5, 6)$, and $D(1, 0)$ serve as the vertices of a trapezoid, and find its altitude.

117. A straight line is drawn through the origin at equal distances from the points $A(2, 2)$ and $B(4, 0)$. Find this distance.

118. Write the equations of a locus of points $\sqrt{5}$ distant from the straight line $x+2y-5=0$.

119. Write the equation of the trajectory of a moving point $M(x, y)$ which, while in motion, remains twice as far from the straight line $y=x$ as from the straight line $y=-x$.

120. Write the equation of a straight line passing through the point M of intersection of the straight lines $2x-3y+$ $+5=0$ and $3x+y-7=0$ perpendicular to the straight line $y=2x$ (without finding the point M).

1.7. Miscellaneous Problems

121. Through the origin draw a straight line forming with the straight lines $x+y=a$ and $x=0$ a triangle whose area is a^2.

122. Given the points $A(-4, 0)$ and $B(0, 6)$. Through the midpoint of the line segment AB draw a straight line cutting off an x-intercept twice as long as the y-intercept.

123. Given the points $A(-2, 0)$ and $B(2, -2)$. Constructed on the line segment OA is a parallelogram $OACD$ whose diagonals intersect at the point B. Write the equations of the sides and diagonals of the parallelogram and find the angle CAD.

124. Find the angles and the area of the triangle formed by the straight lines $y=2x$, $y=-2x$, and $y=x+b$.

125. Drawn from the origin are two mutually perpendicular straight lines forming an isosceles triangle together with the straight line $2x+y=a$. Find the area of this triangle.

126. Find the interior angles of a triangle given the equations of its sides: $(AB)\ x-3y+3=0$ and $(AC)\ x+3y+3=0$, and the foot $D(-1, 3)$ of the altitude AD.

127. Given the equations of the lateral sides of an isosceles triangle: $3x+y=0$ and $x-3y=0$, and a point $(5; 0)$ on its base. Find the perimeter and the area of the triangle.

128. Given in a triangle ABC: (1) the equation of the side $(AB)\ 3x+2y=12$, (2) the equation of the altitude $(BM)\ x+2y=4$, (3) the equation of the altitude $(AM)\ 4x+y=6$, where M is the point of intersection of the altitudes. Write the equations of the sides AC, BC and the altitude CM.

129. Two sides of a parallelogram are given by the equations $y=x-2$ and $5y=x+6$. Its diagonals intersect at the origin. Write the equations of two other sides of the parallelogram and its diagonals.

130. Given a triangle with the vertices $A(0, -4)$, $B(3, 0)$, and $C(0, 6)$. Find the distance between the vertex C and the bisector of the angle A.

131. Write the equation of the trajectory of a point $M(x, y)$ moving so that the sum of its distances from the straight lines $y=2x$ and $y=-\frac{x}{2}$ remains constant and is equal to $\sqrt{5}$.

132. Construct the domains the coordinates of the points of which satisfy the inequalities:

(1) $x-2<y<0$, and $x>0$;

(2) $-2\leqslant y\leqslant x\leqslant 2$;

(3) $2<2x+y<8$, $x>0$, and $y>0$.

133. The sides AB and BC of a parallelogram are given by the equations $2x-y+5=0$ and $x-2y+4=0$; its diagonals intersect at the point $M(1, 4)$. Find its altitudes.

134. Find the vertices of a right isosceles triangle given the vertex of the right angle $C(3, -1)$ and the equation of the hypotenuse $3x-y+2=0$.

135. Given two vertices of a triangle $A(-4, 3)$ and $B(4, -1)$ and the point of intersection of the altitudes $M(3, 3)$. Find the third vertex C.

136. Compute the coordinates of the vertex of a rhombus given the equations of two of its sides: $x+2y=4$ and $x+2y=10$, and the equation of one of its diagonals: $y=x+2$.

137. Set up the equations of the sides of a triangle knowing one of its vertices $A(0, 2)$ and the equations of the altitudes $(BM)\ x+y=4$ and $(CM)\ y=2x$, where M is the point of intersection of the altitudes.

138. Given the straight line $x+2y-4=0$ and the point $A(5, 7)$. Find: (1) the projection B of the point A on the given line, (2) the reflection C of the point A in the given straight line.

Hint. Writing the equation of the perpendicular AB and solving it together with the equation of the given line, find the point B which is the midpoint of AC.

139. Given the straight line $2x+y-6=0$ and two points on it A and B with the ordinates $y_A=6$ and $y_B=-2$ respectively. Write the equation of the altitude AD of the triangle AOB, find its length and the angle DAB.

1.8. The Circle

A circle of radius R with centre at the point $C(a, b)$ is given by the equation

$$(x-a)^2+(y-b)^2=R^2. \tag{1}$$

It may be rewritten as

$$x^2+y^2+mx+ny+p=0. \tag{2}$$

To pass over from Eq. (2) again to the equation of the form (1) we have to single out perfect squares in the left-hand member of equation (2):

$$\left(x+\frac{m}{2}\right)^2+\left(y+\frac{n}{2}\right)^2=\frac{m^2}{4}+\frac{n^2}{4}-p. \tag{3}$$

140. Write the equation of a circle of radius $R=5$ with centre $C(-4, 3)$ and construct the circle. Do the points $A(-1, -1)$, $B(3, 2)$, $O(0, 0)$ lie on this circle?

141. Given the point $A(-4, 6)$. Write the equation of a circle for which the line segment OA serves as the diameter.

142. Construct the circles: (1) $x^2+y^2-4x+6y-3=0$; (2) $x^2+y^2-8x=0$; (3) $x^2+y^2+4y=0$.

143. Construct the circle $x^2+y^2+5x=0$, the straight line $x+y=0$ and find the points of intersection.

144. Write the equation of a circle tangent to the coordinate axes and passing through the point $A(1, 2)$.

145. Find the angle between the radii of the circle $x^2+y^2+4x-6y=0$ drawn to the points of intersection of the circle and the axis OY.

146. Write the equation of a circle passing through the points $A(-1, 3)$, $B(0, 2)$, and $C(1, -1)$.

Hint. Write the equation of the required circle in the form $x^2+y^2+mx+ny+p=0$, substitute the coordinates of each point into it, and then find m, n, and p.

147. Write the equation of a circle passing through the points of intersection of the circle $x^2+y^2+4x-4y=0$ and the straight line $y=-x$, and through the point $A(4, 4)$.

148. Determine the location of the curve $y=-\sqrt{-x^2-4x}$. Construct the curve.

149. Write the equations of the straight lines drawn from the origin and tangent to the circle x^2+y^2-8x- $-4y+16=0$.

150. Given the point $A(a, 0)$. A point M moves so that the angle OMA in the triangle OMA remains right. Determine the trajectory of the point M.

151. Given the points $A(-6, 0)$ and $B(2, 0)$. Find the locus of points wherefrom the line segments OA and OB are seen at equal angles.

152. Determine the trajectory of a point $M(x, y)$ which moves so that the sum of its squared distances from the points $A(-a, 0)$, $B(0, a)$, and $C(a, 0)$ remains equal to $3a^2$.

153. Determine the trajectory of a point $M(x, y)$ which moves so that the sum of its squared distances from the bisectors of the quadrants remains equal to a^2.

154. Given the circle $x^2+y^2=a^2$. From the point $A(a, 0)$ belonging to this circle all possible chords are drawn. Determine the locus of the midpoints of the chords.

---

155. Given the points $A(-3, 0)$ and $B(3, 6)$. Write the equation of the circle for which the line segment AB is the diameter.

156. Find the centres and the radii of the circles: (1) $x^2+y^2-6x+4y-23=0$; (2) $x^2+y^2+5x-7y+2.5=0$; (3) $x^2+y^2+7y=0$. Construct the circles.

157. A circle is tangent to the axis OX at the origin and passes through the point $A(0, -4)$. Write the equation of the circle and find the points at which it intersects the bisectors of the quadrants.

158. Write the equation of a circle passing through the origin and the points of intersection of the straight line $x+y+a=0$ with the circle $x^2+y^2=a^2$.

159. Write the equations of the tangent lines drawn from the origin to the circle passing through the points $A(1, -2)$, $B(0, -1)$, and $C(-3, 0)$.

160. Find the angle between the radii of the circle $x^2+y^2-4x+6y-5=0$ drawn to the points at which it intersects the axis OX.

161. Show that the point $A(3, 0)$ is located inside the circle $x^2+y^2-4x+2y+1=0$ and write the equation of the chord bisected at the point A.

Hint. The required chord is perpendicular to CA where C is the centre of the circle.

162. A point $M(x, y)$ moves so that the sum of its squared distances from the origin and the point $A(-a, 0)$ remains equal to a^2. Determine the trajectory of the point M.

163. Given the circle $x^2+y^2=4$. From the point $A(-2, 0)$ belonging to it a chord AB is drawn and extended by a distance $BM=AB$. Determine the locus of points M.

164. A line segment $AM=a$ moves in the plane XOY remaining parallel to OX so that its left end-point A slides along the circle $x^2+y^2=a^2$. Determine the trajectory of the point M.

1.9. The Ellipse

An ellipse is the *locus of points, the sum of the distances of which from two given points F and F_1* (called the foci) *is a constant*, $2a$. This constant is required to be *greater* than the distance between the foci (F_1F) (the focal length).

The *canonical* (standard) form of the equation of the ellipse:

$$\frac{x^2}{a^2}+\frac{y^2}{b^2}=1. \qquad (1)$$

The ellipse given by equation (1) is symmetrical with respect to both the axis OX and the axis OY (Fig. 1). The parameters a and b are called the *semi-axes* of the ellipse. Let $a > b$, then the foci F and F_1 are found on the axis OX at a distance $c=\sqrt{a^2-b^2}$ from the centre. The ratio $\frac{c}{a}=\varepsilon < 1$ is called the *eccentricity* of the ellipse. The distances of a point $M(x, y)$ of the ellipse from its

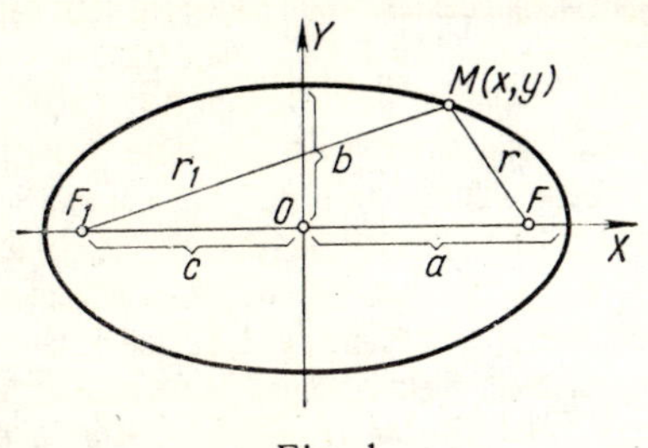

Fig. 1

foci (the so-called *focal radius vectors*) are determined by the formulas

$$r=a-\varepsilon x, \quad r_1=a+\varepsilon x. \tag{2}$$

If $a < b$, then the foci are located on the axis OY, $c=\sqrt{b^2-a^2}$, $\varepsilon=\frac{c}{b}$, $r=b\pm\varepsilon y$.

165. Construct the ellipse $x^2+4y^2=16$; find its foci and the eccentricity.

166. Write the canonical equation of the ellipse knowing that (1) the focal length is equal to 8 and the minor semi-axis $b=3$; (2) the major semi-axis $a=6$ and the eccentricity $\varepsilon=0.5$.

167. Find the minor semi-axis b and the eccentricity ε of the ellipse whose major semi-axis $a=5$ and the parameter c is equal to: (1) 4.8; (2) 4; (3) 3; (4) 1.4; (5) 0. Construct each of the ellipses.

168. The earth orbits the sun forming an ellipse, the sun being situated at one of its foci. The minimum distance of the earth from the sun is approximately equal to 147.5 million kilometres and the maximum distance to 152.5 million kilometres. Find the major semi-axis and the eccentricity of the earth's orbit.

169. An ellipse symmetrical with respect to the coordinate axes passes through the points $M(2, \sqrt{3})$ and $B(0, 2)$. Write its equation and find the focal radius vectors of the point M.

170. An ellipse, symmetrical with respect to the coordinate axes and whose foci are found on the x-axis, passes through the point $M(-4, \sqrt{21})$ and has the eccentricity $\varepsilon=\frac{3}{4}$. Write the equation of the ellipse and find the focal radius vectors of the point M.

171. Find the length of the chord which bisects the angle between the axes of the ellipse $x^2+2y^2=18$.

172. Find the eccentricity of an ellipse whose focal length is equal to the distance between the end-points of the major and minor semi-axes.

173. Inscribed in the ellipse $x^2+4y^2=4$ is a regular triangle one of whose vertices coincides with the end-point of the major semi-axis. Determine the coordinates of two other vertices of the triangle.

Hint. Write the equation of one of the sides having the slope $k=\tan 30°$, and find the points at which it intersects the ellipse.

174. On the ellipse $9x^2+25y^2=225$ find the point whose distance from the right-hand focus is four times the distance from the left-hand focus.

175. The ordinates of all the points of the circle $x^2+y^2=36$ are reduced by $\frac{1}{3}$. Write the equation of the new curve.

176. Determine the trajectory of a moving point M which all the time remains twice nearer to the point $F(-1, 0)$ than to the straight line $x=-4$.

177. A line segment AB of a constant length $a+b$ moves so that its end-point A slides along the axis OX, and the end-point B slides along the axis OY. Determine the trajectory of a moving point M of the segment which divides the latter into the following portions: $BM=a$ and $MA=b$ (Leonardo da Vinci's elliptic compass).

178. Given the circles $x^2+y^2=b^2$ and $x^2+y^2=a^2$ $(b < a)$. An arbitrary ray OBA intersects them at points B and A

respectively, wherefrom straight lines are drawn parallel to the coordinate axes to intersect at point M. Determine the locus of points M.

---

179. Write the simplest equation of the ellipse in which the distances of one of the foci from the ends of the major axis are equal to 5 and 1.

180. An ellipse symmetrical with respect to the coordinate axes passes through the points $M(2\sqrt{3}, \sqrt{6})$ and $A(6, 0)$. Write its equation, find its eccentricity and the distances of the point M from the foci.

181. Find the length of the chord of the ellipse $\frac{x^2}{a^2}+\frac{y^2}{b^2}=1$ directed along the diagonal of the rectangle constructed on the axes of the ellipse.

182. Find the points common for the ellipse $x^2+4y^2=4$ and a circle passing through the foci of the ellipse and having its centre at the upper vertex of the ellipse.

183. On the straight line $x=-5$ find the point equidistant from the left-hand focus and upper vertex of the ellipse $x^2+5y^2=20$.

184. On the ellipse $x^2+5y^2=20$ find the point whose radius vectors are mutually perpendicular.

Hint. The required points are the points at which the ellipse is intersected by the circle passing through the foci of the ellipse and having its centre at the origin.

185. The abscissas of the points of the circle $x^2+y^2=4$ are doubled. Determine the curve thus obtained.

186. Determine the trajectory of a moving point M which all the time remains three times nearer to the point $A(1, 0)$ than to the straight line $x=9$.

1.10. The Hyperbola

The hyperbola is the *locus of points whose distances from two fixed points* F *and* F_1 (called the foci) *have a constant difference* $2a$ $(0 < 2a < F_1F)$.

The canonical (standard) equation of the hyperbola:

$$\frac{x^2}{a^2}-\frac{y^2}{b^2}=1. \qquad (1)$$

The hyperbola given by equation (1) is symmetric about the coordinate axes (Fig. 2). It intersects the axis OX at two points $A(a, 0)$ and $A_1(-a, 0)$. These points are the vertices of the hyperbola. The axis OY is not intersected by the hyperbola. The parameter a is called the *transverse* semi-axis; b, is the *conjugate* semi-axis. The parameter $c=\sqrt{a^2+b^2}$ is the distance of the focus from the centre. The ratio $\frac{c}{a}=\varepsilon>1$ is called the *eccentricity* of the hyperbola. The straight lines $y=\pm\frac{b}{a}x$ are called the *asymptotes* of the hyperbola. The distances of a point $M(x, y)$

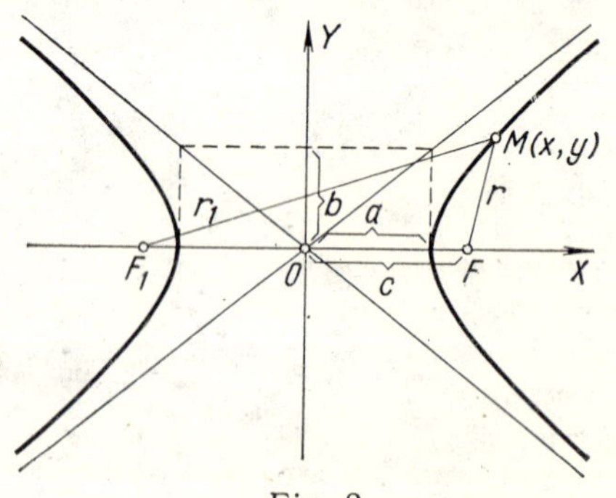

Fig. 2

of the hyperbola from its foci (called the *focal radius vectors*) are determined by the formulas

$$r=|\varepsilon x-a|, \quad r_1=|\varepsilon x+a|. \tag{2}$$

The hyperbola in which $a=b$ is termed *equilateral*, equiangular, or rectangular; its equation is $x^2-y^2=a^2$, and the equations of the asymptotes are $y=\pm x$. The hyperbolas $\frac{x^2}{a^2}-\frac{y^2}{b^2}=1$ and $\frac{y^2}{b^2}-\frac{x^2}{a^2}=1$ are called *conjugate*.

187. Construct the hyperbola $x^2-4y^2=18$ and its asymptotes. Find the foci, the eccentricity, and the angle between the asymptotes.

188. A point M with the ordinate equal to unity is taken on the hyperbola $x^2-4y^2=16$. Find the distances of the point M from the foci.

189. Write the canonical equation of the hyperbola given (1) the focal length $2c=10$ and the distance between the vertices $2a=8$; (2) the transverse semi-axis $a=2\sqrt{5}$ and the eccentricity $\varepsilon=\sqrt{1.2}$.

190. A hyperbola is symmetric about the coordinate axes, passes through the point $M(6, -2\sqrt{2})$, and has the conjugate axis $b=2$. Write its equation and find the distances of the point M from the foci.

191. Write the equation of a hyperbola whose vertices are situated at the foci, and the latter at the vertices of the ellipse $\frac{x^2}{25}+\frac{y^2}{9}=1$.

192. Write the equation of the hyperbola which has the eccentricity $\varepsilon=\sqrt{2}$, passes through the point $(2a, a\sqrt{3})$ and is symmetric about the coordinate axes.

193. Construct the hyperbola $y^2=a^2+x^2$, find the coordinates of its foci and the angle between the asymptotes.

194. Write the equations of the straight lines drawn from the point $A(0, -2)$ tangent to the hyperbola $x^2-4y^2=16$.

195. Find the distance of the focus of the hyperbola $\frac{x^2}{a^2}-\frac{y^2}{b^2}=1$ from its asymptotes, and the angles between the asymptotes.

196. Find the side of the square inscribed in the hyperbola $\frac{x^2}{a^2}-\frac{y^2}{b^2}=1$ and analyse in which hyperbolas a square can be inscribed.

197. Find the eccentricity of the hyperbola whose asymptote forms with the transverse (real) axis an angle of: (1) 60°, (2) α.

198. Determine the location of the curve $y=-\sqrt{9+x^2}$. Construct this curve.

199. Determine the trajectory of a moving point $M(x, y)$ which all the time remains twice nearer to the straight line $x=1$ than to the point $F(4, 0)$.

200. Given the points $A(-1, 0)$ and $B(2, 0)$. A point M moves so that in the triangle AMB the angle B all the time remains twice the magnitude of the angle A. Determine the trajectory of the point M.

201. Given the point $A(a, 0)$. A point B moves along the axis OY. On a straight line BE, which is parallel to the axis OX, line segments BM and BM_1 are laid off, each of them being equal to AB. Determine the locus of the points M and M_1.

202. Given the straight lines $x = \pm b$ and $x = \pm a$ $(b < a)$. An arbitrary ray OA (Fig. 3) intersects the line $x = b$ (or $x = -b$) at point B, and the line $x = a$ (or $x = -a$) at

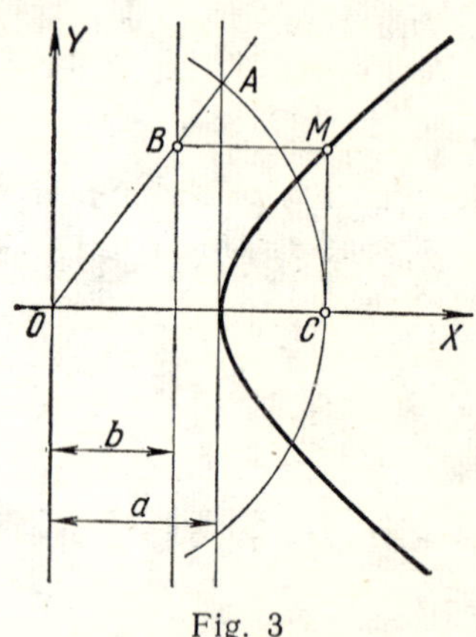

Fig. 3

point A. With OA as radius an arc is drawn to intersect OX at point C. Through the points B and C straight lines are drawn parallel to OX and OY, respectively, to intersect at point M. Determine the locus of points M.

---

203. Write the canonical equation of a hyperbola knowing that the distances of one of its vertices from the foci are equal to 9 and 1.

204. Find the points of intersection of the asymptotes of the hyperbola $x^2 - 3y^2 = 12$ and a circle having its centre at the right-hand focus of the hyperbola and passing through the origin.

205. A hyperbola passes through the point $M\left(6, \frac{3}{2}\sqrt{5}\right)$, is symmetric about the coordinate axes, and has a transverse semi-axis $a=4$. Write the equations of the perpendiculars dropped from the left-hand focus of the hyperbola to its asymptotes.

206. On the hyperbola $9x^2-16y^2=144$ find the point twice as far from the right focus as from the left one.

207. On the hyperbola $x^2-y^2=4$ find the point whose focal radius vectors are mutually perpendicular (see the hint to Problem 184).

208. A point M divides the focal length of the hyperbola $9x^2-16y^2=144$ in the ratio $F_1M:MF=2:3$, where F_1 is the left-hand focus of the hyperbola. Through the point M a straight line is drawn at an angle of 135° to the axis OX. Find the points at which this line intersects the asymptotes of the hyperbola.

209. Determine the trajectory of a point M which moves so that it remains twice as far from the point $F(-8, 0)$ as from the straight line $x=-2$.

210. Given the points $A(-a, 0)$ and $B(2a, 0)$. A point M moves so that the angle MAB remains one third the exterior angle AMC of the triangle AMB. Determine the trajectory of point M.

1.11. The Parabola

The parabola is the *locus of points* (M) *equidistant from a given point* (the focus) *and a given straight line* (the directrix).

The *canonical* equation of the parabola has two forms: (1) $y^2=2px$ if the parabola is symmetric about the axis OX (as in Fig. 4);

(2) $x^2=2py$ if the parabola is symmetric about the axis OY (as in Fig. 5).

In both cases the vertex of the parabola, i.e. the point lying on the axis of symmetry, is found at the coordinate origin.

The parabola $y^2=2px$ has the focus $F\left(\frac{p}{2}, 0\right)$ and the directrix $x=-\frac{p}{2}$; the focal radius vector of a point $M(x, y)$ on it is $r=x+\frac{p}{2}$.

The parabola $x^2=2py$ has the focus $F\left(0, \frac{p}{2}\right)$ and the directrix $y=-\frac{p}{2}$; the focal radius vector of a point $M(x, y)$ on it is $r=y+\frac{p}{2}$.

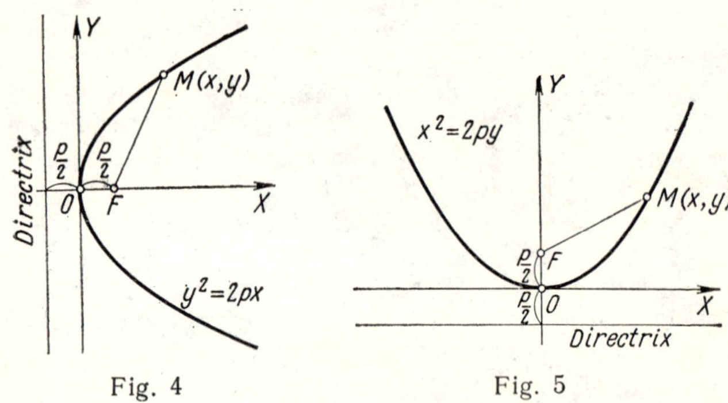

Fig. 4 Fig. 5

211. Set up the equation of the locus of points equidistant from the point $F(0, 2)$ and the straight line $y=4$. Find the points at which this curve intersects the coordinate axes and construct it.

212. Set up the equation of the locus of points equidistant from the coordinate origin and the straight line $x=-4$. Find the points at which this curve intersects the coordinate axes and construct it.

213. Construct the parabolas given by the equations: (1) $y^2=4x$; (2) $y^2=-4x$; (3) $x^2=4y$; (4) $x^2=-4y$, and also their foci and directrices; write the equations of the directrices.

214. Write the equation of a parabola: (1) which passes through the points (0, 0) and (1, —3) and is symmetric about the axis OX; (2) which passes through the points (0, 0) and (2, —4) and is symmetric about the axis OY.

215. The cable of a suspension bridge has the form of the parabola (Fig. 6). Write its equation with respect to the axes shown in the drawing if the cable deflection $OA=a$ and the span $BC=2b$.

216. Write the equation of a circle tangent to the directrix of the parabola $y^2=2px$, the centre of the circle lying in the focus of the parabola. Find the points of intersection of the parabola and the circle.

217. Write the equation of the parabola and its directrix if the parabola passes through the points of intersection of a straight line $x+y=0$ and a circle $x^2+y^2+4y=0$,

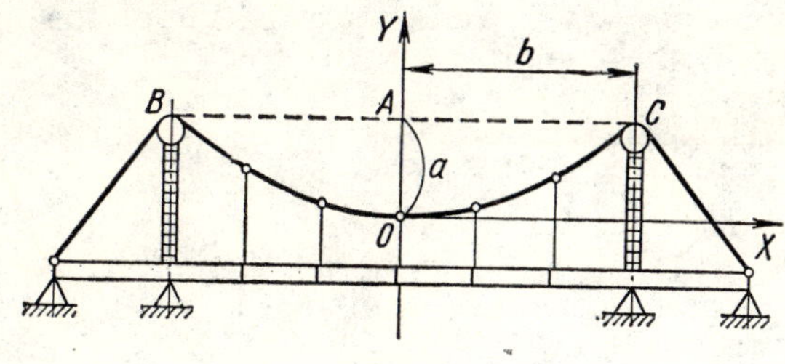

Fig. 6

and is symmetric about the axis OY. Construct the circle, the straight line, and the parabola.

218. On the parabola $y^2=6x$ find the point whose focal radius vector is equal to 4.5.

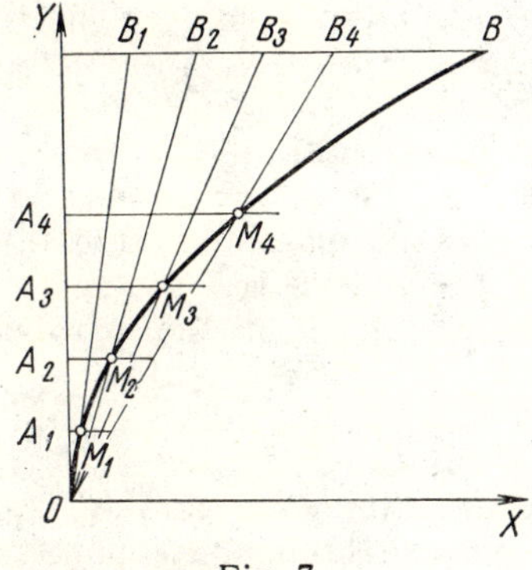

Fig. 7

219. The mirror surface of a searchlight is generated by revolving a parabola about its axis of symmetry. The diameter of the mirror is equal to 80 cm; its depth, to 10 cm. At what distance from the vertex of the parabola should a light source be placed?

Hint. In order to reflect the light as a parallel beam the source should be placed in the focus of the parabola.

220. Determine the location of the curve $y=-\sqrt{-x}$. Construct this curve.

221. All possible chords are drawn from the vertex of the parabola $y^2=2px$. Write the equation of the locus of midpoints of these chords.

222. Determine the locus of the centres of circles tangent to the circle $x^2+y^2=2ax$ and the axis OY.

223. Given the points $A(0, a)$ and $B(a, a)$. The line segments OA and AB are divided into n equal parts by points $A_1, A_2, A_3, \ldots$ and $B_1, B_2, B_3, \ldots$ (Fig. 7). Let M_k be the point of intersection of the ray OB_k and the straight line A_kM_k which is parallel to OX. Show that such points M_k lie on the parabola $y^2=ax$. Construct the parabolas $y^2=4x$, $y^2=5x$, and $y^2=3x$ using this method.

---

224. Derive the equation of the locus of points equidistant from the origin and the straight line $x=4$. Find the points at which this curve intersects the coordinate axes and construct it.

225. Derive the equation of the locus of points equidistant from the point $F(2, 0)$ and the straight line $y=2$. Find the vertex of the parabola and the points of its intersection with the axis OX. Construct the parabola.

226. Write the equation of the parabola: (1) passing through the points (0, 0), (—1, 2) and symmetric about the axis OX; (2) passing through the points (0, 0), (2, 4) and symmetric about the axis OY.

227. Write the equation of a parabola and its directrix if the parabola passes through the points of intersection of the straight line $y=x$ and the circle $x^2+y^2+6x=0$ and is symmetric about the axis OX. Construct the straight line, circle, and parabola.

228. A regular triangle is inscribed in the parabola $y^2=2x$. Determine its vertices (see the hint to Problem 173).

229. Write the equations of the tangent lines to the parabola $y^2=8x$ drawn from the point $A(0, -2)$.

230. A straight line is drawn through the focus of the parabola $y^2=-4x$ at an angle of 120° to the OX-axis. Write the equation of the straight line and find the length of the chord thus obtained.

1.12. Directrices, Diameters, and Tangents to Curves of the Second Order

1°. The directrices of the ellipse $\frac{x^2}{a^2}+\frac{y^2}{b^2}=1$ (for $a>b$) and hyperbola $\frac{x^2}{a^2}-\frac{y^2}{b^2}=1$ are defined as the straight lines parallel to the axis OY and drawn at a distance $\frac{a}{\varepsilon}$ from this axis, where ε is the eccentricity.

The equation of the directrices:

$$x=\pm\frac{a}{\varepsilon}. \tag{1}$$

For any point of the ellipse or hyperbola the *ratio of its distance from the focus to the distance from the corresponding directrix is equal to the eccentricity:*

$$\frac{r}{d}=\varepsilon. \tag{2}$$

2°. The locus of the midpoints of parallel chords is called the *diameter of a curve of the second order*. The diameters of the ellipse and hyperbola turn out to be all the segments and rays of the straight lines passing through the centre, and the diameters of the parabola are the rays parallel to its axis.

This is the equation of the diameter bisecting the chords with the slope $\tan\alpha=k$:

for the curves $\frac{x^2}{a^2}\pm\frac{y^2}{b^2}=1$ (ellipse and hyperbola)

$$y=\mp\frac{b^2}{a^2k}x; \tag{3}$$

for the parabola $y^2=2px$

$$y=\frac{p}{k}. \tag{4}$$

Two diameters of the ellipse or hyperbola such that

each one bisects the chords parallel to the other one are called *conjugate*. Their slopes k and k_1 are connected by the relation $kk_1=-\frac{b^2}{a^2}$ (for the ellipse) and $kk_1=\frac{b^2}{a^2}$ (for the hyperbola).

3°. The equations of lines tangent to:

the ellipse $\left(\frac{x^2}{a^2}+\frac{y^2}{b^2}=1\right)$ $\frac{xx_0}{a^2}+\frac{yy_0}{b^2}=1$;

the hyperbola $\left(\frac{x^2}{a^2}-\frac{y^2}{b^2}=1\right)$ $\frac{xx_0}{a^2}-\frac{yy_0}{b^2}=1$;

the parabola $(y^2=2px)$ $yy_0=p(x+x_0)$,

where (x_0, y_0) is the point of tangency.

231. Construct the ellipse $\frac{x^2}{25}+\frac{y^2}{9}=1$, its directrices and find the distances of the point with the abscissa $x=-3$ from the right-hand focus and right-hand directrix.

232. Construct the hyperbola $\frac{x^2}{16}-\frac{y^2}{9}=1$, its directrices and find the distances of the point with the abscissa $x=5$ from the left-hand focus and left-hand directrix.

233. Write the canonical equation of the ellipse whose directrices are the straight lines $x=\pm\frac{4}{\sqrt{3}}$ and whose major semi-axis is equal to 2.

234. Write the equation of the hyperbola whose asymptotes are $y=\pm x$, and the directrices are $x=\pm\sqrt{6}$.

235. Construct the ellipse $x^2+4y^2=16$, the diameter $y=\frac{x}{2}$ and its conjugate diameter, and find the lengths a_1 and b_1 of the constructed semi-diameters.

236. Construct the hyperbola $x^2-4y^2=4$, the diameter $y=-x$ and its conjugate diameter. Find the angle between the diameters.

237. Find the length of the diameter of the ellipse $\frac{x^2}{a^2}+\frac{y^2}{b^2}=1$ which is equal to its conjugate diameter.

238. The asymptote of the hyperbola $\frac{x^2}{a^2}-\frac{y^2}{b^2}=1$ forms an angle of 60° with the axis OX. Write the equation of the diameter conjugate to the diameter $y=2x$. Choose an arbitrary line segment a and construct the curve, the diameters, and the chords parallel to the given diameter.

239. Determine the locus of the midpoints of chords of the parabola $y^2=4x$ which form an angle of 45° with the axis OX.

240. Given the ellipse $\frac{x^2}{9}+\frac{y^2}{4}=1$. Through the point $(-2, 1)$ draw a chord bisected at this point.

241. Given the parabola $y^2=-4x$. Through the point $(-2, -1)$ draw a chord bisected at this point.

242. Making use of Problem 235 check the Apollonius theorem: $a_1^2+b_1^2=a^2+b^2$ and $a_1b_1\sin\varphi=ab$, here a_1 and b_1 are the lengths of the conjugate semi-diameters, a and b, the semi-axes of the ellipse, and φ, the angle between the conjugate diameters.

243. Write the equations of the straight lines tangent to the curves: (1) $x^2+4y^2=16$; (2) $3x^2-y^2=3$; (3) $y^2=2x$ at the point with the abscissa $x_0=2$.

244. Show that if the straight line $Ax+By+C=0$ is tangent to the ellipse $\frac{x^2}{a^2}+\frac{y^2}{b^2}=1$, then $A^2a^2+B^2b^2=C^2$.

Hint. From the proportionality of the coefficients of the equations $\frac{xx_0}{a^2}+\frac{yy_0}{b^2}=1$ and $Ax+By+C=0$ determine x_0 and y_0 and substitute them in the equation $\frac{x^2}{a^2}+\frac{y^2}{b^2}=1$.

245. Write the equations of the tangent lines to the ellipse $x^2+4y^2=20$ which are parallel to the bisector of the first quadrant.

246. Write the equations of the tangent lines to the ellipse $x^2+2y^2=8$ drawn from the point $(0, 6)$.

247. Write the equation of a tangent line to the ellipse $\frac{x^2}{a^2}+\frac{y^2}{b^2}=1$ cutting off equal positive intercepts on the coordinate axes.

248. Show that if the straight line $Ax+By+C=0$ is tangent to the hyperbola $\frac{x^2}{a^2}-\frac{y^2}{b^2}=1$, then $A^2a^2-B^2b^2=C^2$ (see the hint to Problem 244).

249. Write the equations of the straight lines tangent to the hyperbola $4x^2-9y^2=36$ and perpendicular to the straight line $x+2y=0$.

250. Prove that a normal to an ellipse is the bisector of the angle between the radius vectors of the corresponding point of the ellipse.

251. Prove that a tangent to a hyperbola is the bisector of the angle between the radius vectors of the point of tangency.

252. Prove that the rays emanating from the focus of a parabola are reflected from the parabola along straight lines parallel to its axis.

Hint. Write the equation of the normal MN, find the point N at which it intersects the axis of the parabola, and prove that $FM=FN$, where F is the focus of the parabola.

253. Find the points of intersection of the asymptotes of the hyperbola $\frac{x^2}{16}-\frac{y^2}{9}=1$ and its directrices.

254. Construct the ellipse $x^2+4y^2=16$, its diameter $y=x$ and the conjugate diameter, and find the angle between these diameters.

255. Determine the locus of midpoints of the chords drawn in the hyperbola $x^2-4y^2=16$ which form an angle of 45° with the axis OX.

256. Given the hyperbola $4x^2-y^2=4$. Through the point (2, 2) draw a chord bisected at this point.

257. Taken on the ellipse $x^2+2y^2=6$ is a point M with the ordinate equal to unity and a negative abscissa. Find the angle between the straight line tangent to the ellipse at the point M and the line OM.

258. Show that if the straight line $Ax+By+C=0$ is tangent to the parabola $y^2=2px$ then $B^2p=2AC$ (see the hint to Problem 244).

259. Write the equation of the straight line tangent to the parabola $y^2=8x$ and parallel to the straight line $x+y=0$.

1.13. Transformation of Cartesian Coordinates. The Parabolas $y=ax^2+bx+c$ and $x=ay^2+by+c$. The Hyperbola $xy=k$.

1°. The coordinates (x, y) in a given "old" system are transformed to the coordinates (X, Y) in a "new" system by the following formulas:

(1) *for translating the coordinate axes and displacing the origin* to the point $O_1(\alpha, \beta)$

$$x = X + \alpha, \quad y = Y + \beta; \tag{1}$$

(2) *for rotating the axes* by an angle φ

$$x = X\cos\varphi - Y\sin\varphi, \quad y = X\sin\varphi + Y\cos\varphi. \tag{2}$$

2°. By carrying the origin to the point $O_1(\alpha, \beta)$, the equation $y = a(x-\alpha)^2 + \beta$ is transformed to the form

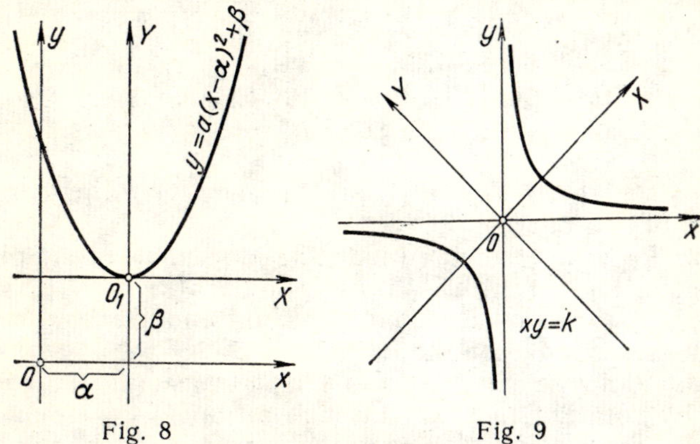

Fig. 8 Fig. 9

$Y = aX^2$ and, consequently, defines a parabola with the vertex $O_1(\alpha, \beta)$ and an axis of symmetry parallel to the Oy-axis (Fig. 8). By singling out a perfect square in the right-hand member, the equation $y = ax^2 + bx + c$ is transformed to the previous one and, therefore, also defines a parabola. For $a > 0$ the parabola is directed "upwards" from the vertex, for $a < 0$, "downwards".

3°. By rotating the coordinate axes through an angle $\varphi = 45°$ the equation $xy = k$ is transformed to the form $X^2 - Y^2 = 2k$ and consequently defines an *equilateral hyperbola* whose asymptotes coincide with the coordinate axes (Fig. 9). By translating the origin to the point $O_1(\alpha, \beta)$ the equation $(x-\alpha)(y-\beta) = k$ is brought to the form $XY = k$ and therefore also defines an equilateral hyperbola.

260. (1) As a result of a translation of the coordinate axes the point $A(3, 1)$ attains new coordinates $(2, -1)$.

Construct both the given and the new coordinate axes and plot the point A.

(2) Find the acute angle through which the coordinate axes should be rotated for the point $A(2, 4)$ to attain the new abscissa 4. Construct both systems of coordinates and plot the point A.

261. Translating the coordinate origin, simplify the following equations:

(1) $\frac{(x-2)^2}{4}+(y+1)^2=1$; (2) $\frac{(x+3)^2}{9}-\frac{(y-1)^2}{4}=1$;

(3) $(y+2)^2=4(x-3)$; (4) $2y=-(x+2)^2$;

(5) $x^2+4y^2-6x+8y=3$; (6) $y^2-8y=4x$;

(7) $x^2-4y^2+8x-24y=24$; (8) $x^2+6x+5=2y$.

Construct both the old and the new coordinate axes and plot the curves.

262. Rotating the coordinate axes through 45°, simplify the equations: (1) $5x^2-6xy+5y^2=32$; (2) $3x^2-10xy+3y^2+32=0$. Construct both the old and the new coordinate axes and plot the curves.

263. Plot the curve $xy=-4$ and transform the equation by rotating the axes through an angle $\varphi=-45°$.

264. Translating the coordinate origin, bring to the form $xy=k$ the equations of the following curves:

(1) $xy-2x=6$; (2) $xy-2x-y+8=0$; (3) $xy-x+2y=6$; (4) $xy+2x=3y$.

Hint. Write the equation $xy+Ax+By+C=0$ in the form $(x+B)(y+A)=AB-C$.

265. Construct the parabolas:

(1) $y=(x-2)^2$; (2) $y=(x-2)^2+3$;
(3) $y=(x+2)^2$; (4) $y=(x+2)^2-3$.

266. Construct the parabolas:

(1) $y=x^2-4x+5$; (2) $y=x^2+2x+3$; (3) $y=-x^2+2x-2$ by singling out perfect squares in the right-hand members of the above equations.

267. Construct the parabolas: (1) $y=4x-x^2$ and (2) $2y=3+2x-x^2$ finding the points at which they intersect the axis OX.

268. A water jet from a fountain reaches its maximum height of 4 m at a distance of 0.5 m from the vertical passing through the point O of water outlet. Find the height of the jet above the horizontal OX at a distance of 0.75 m from the point O.

269. Derive the equation of the parabola which is symmetric about the axis OY and cuts off on it an intercept b, and on the axis OX, intercepts a and $-a$.

Hint. Substitute the given coordinates of the points on the parabola $(-a, 0)$, $(a, 0)$, and $(0, b)$ in the equation of the form $y=Ax^2+Bx+C$ and then find A, B, and C.

270. The parabola $y=ax^2+bx+c$ passes through the points $O(0, 0)$, $A(-1, -3)$, and $B(-2, -4)$. Write the equation of the circle whose diameter is the x-intercept cut off by the parabola.

271. Through what angle is it necessary to rotate the coordinate axes in order to eliminate the term containing xy in the equations: (1) $x^2-xy+y^2-3=0$; (2) $5x^2-4xy+$ $+2y^2-24=0$? Construct both the old and the new coordinate axes and plot the curves.

272. Determine the trajectory of a bullet shot at an angle of φ to the horizon with the initial velocity v_0. Determine also the bullet range and the highest point of the trajectory (air resistance should be neglected).

273. Write the equation of the locus of points $M(x, y)$, the ratio of the distances of which from the point $F(4, 0)$ to the distances from the straight line $x=-2$ is equal to 2.

274. Show that, by translating the coordinate origin in the left-hand vertex of the ellipse $\frac{x^2}{a^2}+\frac{y^2}{b^2}=1$ or in the right-hand vertex of the hyperbola $\frac{x^2}{a^2}-\frac{y^2}{b^2}=1$ both equations are brought to the same form $y^2=2px+qx^2$, where $p=\frac{b^2}{a}$ and $q=\varepsilon^2-1$.

275. Using the results of Problem 274, determine the eccentricity and the type of the curve (1) $y^2=x-\frac{1}{4}x^2$;

(2) $y^2=x+\frac{1}{4}x^2$; (3) $y^2=x$. Construct the curves finding for the first two of them the points of their intersection with the axis OX and the parameters a and b.

---

276. Singling out perfect squares and translating the coordinate origin, simplify the following equations of lines:

(1) $2x^2+5y^2-12x+10y+13=0$;
(2) $x^2-y^2+6x+4y-4=0$;
(3) $y^2+4y=2x$;
(4) $x^2-10x=4y-13$.

Construct both the old and the new axes and plot the curves.

277. By rotating the coordinate axes through 45° simplify the equation $3x^2-2xy+3y^2-8=0$. Determine the coordinates of the foci in the old system.

278. Write the equation of the circle whose diameter is the x-intercept cut off by the parabola $y=3-2x-x^2$. Construct both curves.

279. Write the equation of the circle whose diameter is the segment of the straight line $x+y=6$ cut off by the hyperbola $xy=8$. Construct each of the three lines.

280. A is the vertex of the parabola $y=x^2+6x+5$, B is the point of intersection of the parabola and the OY-axis. Write the equation of the perpendicular erected at the midpoint of the line segment AB.

281. Derive the equation of the parabola which is symmetric about the axis OX and cuts off on it an intercept -4, and on the axis OY, intercepts 4 and -4.

Hint. The equation of the parabola must be of the form $x=ay^2+c$ (why?).

282. Using the points of intersection with the coordinate axes, construct the parabolas:

(1) $3y=9-x^2$; (2) $y^2=9-3x$; (3) $y^2=4+x$; (4) $x^2=4+2y$.

283. Write the equation of the locus of points $M(x, y)$, the ratio of the distances of each from the point $F(4, 0)$ to the distances from the straight line $x=10$ being equal to $\frac{1}{2}$.

1.14. Miscellaneous Problems on Second-Order Curves

284. Write the equation of the circle whose diameter is a segment of the straight line $\frac{x}{a}+\frac{y}{b}=1$ intercepted by the coordinate axes.

285. Find the distance of the centre of the circle $x^2+y^2+ay=0$ from the straight line $y=2(a-x)$.

286. A straight line is drawn through the centre of the circle $x^2+y^2=2ax$ parallel to the straight line $x+2y=0$ and intersecting the circle at the points A and B. Find the area of the triangle AOB.

287. Show that the locus of points M, which are m times farther from a given point A than from another given point B, is a straight line at $m=1$ and a circle if $m\neq 1$.

288. A line segment AB is divided into two parts: $AO=a$ and $OB=b$. Show that the locus of points, from which the segments AO and OB are seen at equal angles, is a straight line at $a=b$, and a circle when $a\neq b$ (the circle of Apollonius).

289. Determine the trajectory of a point $M(x, y)$ moving in such a manner that the sum of the squares of its distances from the straight lines $y=kx$ and $y=-kx$ remains constant and equal to a^2.

290. An ellipse symmetric about the axis OX and the straight line $x=-5$ passes through the points $(-1, 1.8)$ and $(-5, 3)$. Write the equation of the ellipse and construct it.

291. Find the area of an equilateral triangle inscribed in the hyperbola $x^2-y^2=a^2$.

292. Find the angle between the diagonals of a rectangle whose vertices are found at the points of intersection of the ellipse $x^2+3y^2=12l^2$ and the hyperbola $x^2-3y^2=6l^2$.

293. A circle with the centre at the coordinate origin passes through the foci of the hyperbola $x^2-y^2=a^2$. Find the points of intersection of the circle and the asymptotes of the hyperbola.

294. Construct the hyperbolas $xy=-4$ and $x^2-y^2=6$ and find the area of the triangle ABC, where A and B

are the vertices of two intersecting branches of the hyperbolas and C is the point of intersection of the two other branches of the hyperbolas.

295. Prove that the product of the distances of any point of the hyperbola from its asymptotes is a constant equal to $\frac{a^2b^2}{c^2}$.

296. Find the length and the equation of a perpendicular dropped from the focus of the parabola $y=-\frac{x^2}{8}$ onto a straight line cutting off the intercepts $a=b=2$ on the coordinate axes.

297. Construct the ellipse $x^2+4y^2=4$ and the parabola $x^2=6y$ and find the area of the trapezoid whose bases are the major axis of the ellipse and a common chord of the ellipse and parabola.

298. From the focus of the parabola $y^2=2px$ as centre a circle is described so that a common chord of the curves is equidistant from the vertex and the focus of the parabola. Write the equation of the circle.

299. Find the length and the equation of the perpendicular dropped from the vertex of the parabola $by=x^2+2ax+a^2+b^2$ onto the straight line cutting off intercepts a and b on the coordinate axes.

300. Plotting the points of intersection with the coordinate axes, construct the parabolas $4y=12-x^2$ and $4x=12-y^2$ and find the length of their common chord.

301. Find the area of a quadrilateral whose vertices lie in the points of intersection of the parabola $y=4-x^2$ and the axis OX and the straight line $y=3x$.

302. Write the equation of a circle passing through the coordinate origin and the points of intersection of the parabola $y=\frac{x^2}{a}-2x+a$ with the coordinate axes.

303. Given the ellipse $x^2+4y^2=16$. From its vertex $A(4, 0)$ all possible chords are drawn. Determine the locus of midpoints of these chords and construct the curves.

304. Determine the trajectory of a point $M(x, y)$ moving so that the difference of the squares of its distances from the bisectors of the quadrants remains equal to 8.

305. Derive the equation of the locus of centres of the

circles passing through the point $A(3, 4)$ tangent to the axis OX.

306. Singling out perfect squares and translating the origin, simplify the equation of the curve $x^2-y^2-4x-6y-9=0$. Construct both the old and the new coordinate axes and plot the curve.

307. Find the locus of midpoints of the focal radius vectors drawn from the right-hand focus to all points of the hyperbola $\frac{x^2}{9}-\frac{y^2}{16}=1$.

308. Write the equation of the ellipse passing through the point $A(a, -a)$ if its foci are found at the points $F(a, a)$ and $F_1(-a; -a)$.

Simplify the equation by rotating the coordinate axes through an angle of 45°.

309. By rotating the coordinate axes through an angle $\varphi=\arctan\frac{1}{2}$ simplify the equation of the curve $3x^2+8xy-3y^2=20$. Construct both the old and the new coordinate axes and plot the curve.

310. Write the equation of the locus of points, the difference of the squares of whose distances from the straight line $3x+4y=0$ and from the axis OX remains constant and equals 2.4.

311. Write the equation of the locus of points $M(x, y)$, the ratio of whose distances from the point $F\left(\frac{p}{\varepsilon+1}, 0\right)$ to the distances from the straight line $x=-\frac{p}{\varepsilon(\varepsilon+1)}$ is ε.

312. Construct the domains, the coordinates of whose points satisfy the following inequalities:

(1) $R^2<x^2+y^2<4R^2$ and $x^2>\frac{R^2}{4}$;

(2) $x^2-y^2>a^2$ and $x^2<4a^2$;

(3) $xy>a^2$ and $|x+y|<4a$;

(4) $2x<y^2+4y$ and $x^2+y^2+4x+4y<0$.

1.15. General Equation of a Second-Order Curve

1°. A curve which is represented by an equation of the second degree in a Cartesian coordinate system is called a curve of the second order. The general equation of the second degree is usually written as

$$Ax^2+2Bxy+Cy^2+2Dx+2Ey+F=0. \tag{1}$$

Let us form two determinants using the coefficients of equation (1):

$$\delta=\begin{vmatrix} A & B \\ B & C \end{vmatrix} \text{ and } \Delta=\begin{vmatrix} A & B & D \\ B & C & E \\ D & E & F \end{vmatrix}.$$

The determinant Δ is called the *discriminant of equation* (1), and δ, the *discriminant of its senior terms.* Depending on the magnitudes of δ and Δ, equation (1) defines the following geometric image:

	$\Delta\neq 0$	$\Delta=0$
$\delta>0$	Ellipse (real or imaginary)	Point
$\delta<0$	Hyperbola	A pair of intersecting straight lines
$\delta=0$	Parabola	A pair of parallel straight lines (real or imaginary)

2°. Transforming equation (1) to the centre. If $\delta=\begin{vmatrix} A & B \\ B & C \end{vmatrix}\neq 0$, then the curve has a centre whose coordinates are found from the equations

$$\Phi'_x(x,\ y)=0,\quad \Phi'_y(x,\ y)=0, \tag{2}$$

where $\Phi(x,\ y)$ is the left-hand member of equation (1). By translating the origin to the centre O_1 $(x_0,\ y_0)$ (see Fig. 10), we reduce equation (1) to the form

$$Ax_1^2+2Bx_1y_1+Cy_1^2+F_1=0, \tag{3}$$

where

$$F_1=Dx_0+Ey_0+F=\frac{\Delta}{\delta}. \tag{4}$$

3°. Transforming equation (3) to the axes of symmetry. By rotating the axes O_1x_1 and O_1y_1 through some angle φ (Fig. 10), equation (3) is transformed to the canonical form

$$A_1X^2+C_1Y^2+F_1=0. \qquad (5)$$

The coefficients A_1 and C_1 are the roots of the equation

$$\lambda^2-(A+C)\lambda+\delta=0. \qquad (6)$$

The angle of rotation φ is found by the formula

$$\tan\varphi=\frac{B}{A_1-C}. \qquad (7)$$

4°. Transforming the equation of a second-order curve having no centre. If $\delta=0$, the curve has no centre or

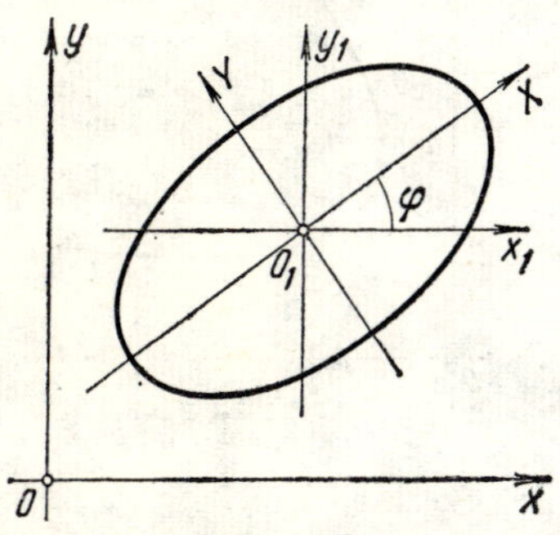

Fig. 10

has no defined centre. Its equation then may be written in the form

$$(\alpha x+\beta y)^2+2Dx+2Ey+F=0. \qquad (8)$$

Case I. D and E are proportional to α and β: $D=m\alpha$, $E=m\beta$. Equation (8) takes on the form $(\alpha x+\beta y)^2+$ $+2m\cdot(\alpha x+\beta y)+F=0$, whence $\alpha x+\beta y=-m\pm\sqrt{m^2-F}$, i.e. a pair of straight lines.

Case II. D and E are not proportional to α and β. Equation (8) may be rewritten as

$$(\alpha x+\beta y+n)^2+2m(\beta x-\alpha y+q)=0. \qquad (9)$$

The parameters m, n, and q are found by comparing the coefficients of equations (8) and (9). Taking then the straight line $\alpha x+\beta y+n=0$ for the axis O_1X and the straight line $\beta x-\alpha y+q=0$ for the axis O_1Y (Fig. 11), we find:

$$Y=\frac{\alpha x+\beta y+n}{\pm\sqrt{\alpha^2+\beta^2}},\quad X=\frac{\beta x-\alpha y+q}{\pm\sqrt{\alpha^2+\beta^2}}.$$

Now equation (9) takes on the form $Y^2=2pX$, where $p=\frac{|m|}{\sqrt{\alpha^2+\beta^2}}$. The axis O_1X is directed towards the half-

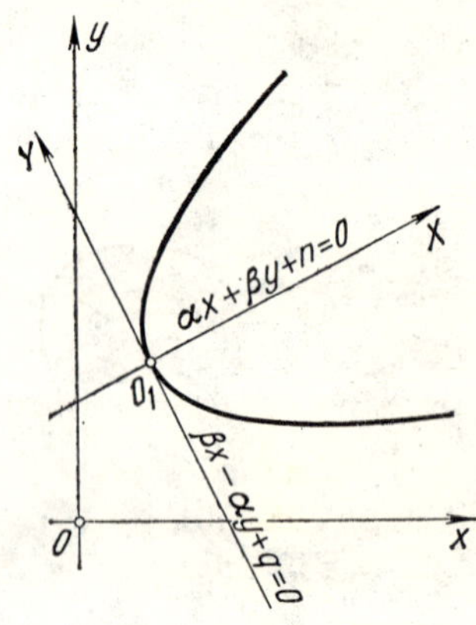

Fig. 11

plane in which $\beta x-\alpha y+q$ has the sign opposite to that of m, as is obvious from equation (9).

313. Determine the geometric objects represented by the following equations:

(1) $4x^2-y^2=0$; (2) $4x^2+y^2=0$; (3) $x^2+y^2+2x+2=0$;
(4) $x^2+y^2-6x-8y+25=0$; (5) $x^2+xy=0$;
(6) $y^2-16=0$; (7) $x^2-3xy+2y^2=0$.

314. Find the centres and transform to them the equations of the curves:

(1) $2x^2+3y^2-4x+6y-7=0$;
(2) $x^2-y^2-4x+2y-4=0$;
(3) $2x^2+5xy+2y^2-6x-3y-8=0$.

315. By rotating the coordinate axes, bring the equations to the canonical form and construct the curves:

(1) $5x^2-4xy+2y^2=24$; (2) $2x^2+4xy-y^2=12$.

316. Reduce the equations to the canonical form and construct the curves:

(1) $3x^2-2xy+3y^2-4x-4y-12=0$;
(2) $x^2-6xy+y^2-4x-4y+12=0$.

317. Transform the equations to the canonical form:

(1) $x^2+4xy+4y^2-20x+10y-50=0$;
(2) $x^2-4xy+4y^2-6x+12y+8=0$;

and construct the curves represented by them.

318. Making use of the discriminants δ and Δ, determine the geometric objects represented by the following equations:

(1) $x^2-4xy+3y^2-8x+14y+15=0$;
(2) $x^2+2xy+4y^2-2x+4y+4=0$;
(3) $x^2+4xy+4y^2+3x+6y+2=0$.

On solving the first and third equations with respect to y, construct the curves determined by these equations.

319. Bring to the canonical form the equation of the curve $y=\frac{3x^2-12x+4}{4x-8}$ and construct it.

320. Write the equation of the second-order curve whose centre is the point O_1 (1, 2) and which passes through the coordinate origin and the points (0, 4) and (1, —1).

321. Show that the equation $\sqrt{x}+\sqrt{y}=\sqrt{a}$ defines an arc of the parabola, construct this parabola and find its vertex.

Hint. Rotate the coordinate axes through an angle $\varphi=-45°$.

322. Write the equation of the locus of points $M(x, y)$, the ratio of the distances of each of which from the point $F(m, n)$ to its distance from the straight line $x\cos\alpha+$ $+y\sin\alpha-q=0$ is ε. Denoting the coefficients of the obtained equation by $A, B, C, \ldots$, determine the invariants $A+C$ and $\delta=\begin{vmatrix} A & B \\ B & C \end{vmatrix}$.

323. Determine the geometric objects represented by the following equations:

(1) $x^2-4y^2=0$;
(2) $x^2+2y^2+4x-8y+12=0$;
(3) $x^2+5xy-6y^2=0$.

324. Transform to the canonical form the equations and construct the curves:

(1) $x^2-xy+y^2-2x-2y-2=0$;
(2) $3x^2+10xy+3y^2-12x-12y+4=0$.

325. Transform to the canonical form the equations:

(1) $x^2-2xy+y^2-10x-6y+25=0$;
(2) $x^2+2xy+y^2-4x-4y+3=0$

and construct the curves represented by them.

326. Making use of the discriminants δ and Δ determine the geometric objects represented by the equations:

(1) $x^2-2xy+y^2-4x+4y+3=0$;
(2) $x^2-2xy-3y^2+6x+10y-7=0$.

After solving each equation with respect to y construct the curve determined by it.

327. Write the equation of the locus of points $M(x, y)$, the ratio of whose distances from the point $F(3, 3)$ to the distances from the straight line $x+y=0$ is equal to:

(1) $\varepsilon=\frac{1}{2}$; (2) $\varepsilon=2$.

328. Write the equation of the locus of points $M(x, y)$ equidistant from the point $F\left(\frac{a}{2}, \frac{a}{2}\right)$ and the straight line $x+y=0$ and reduce it to the canonical form.

329. Write the equation of the locus of points the difference of the squared distances of each from the straight line $x-2y=2$ and from the axis OX remaining constant and equal to 3.2. Transform it to the canonical form and construct the curve.

1.16. Polar Coordinates

In a plane (Fig. 12) take an arbitrary point O (pole) and draw a ray OP (polar axis). Then the position of any point M in the plane may be specified by

(1) *the polar angle* $\varphi = \angle MOP$;
(2) *the radius vector* $r = OM$.

The numbers φ and r are termed the polar coordinates of the point M.

When studying the equations associated with r and φ it is useful to consider the polar coordinates φ and r as

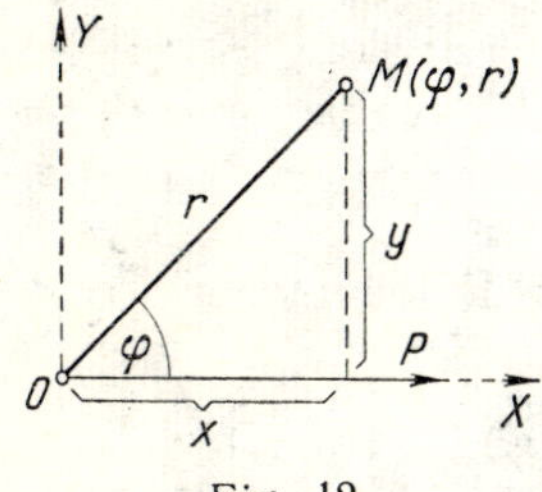

Fig. 12

attaining any positive and negative values. Negative angles φ are usually measured clockwise, and negative r are laid off not on the ray but on its extension beyond the pole.

If we take the pole for the origin of the Cartesian rectangular coordinates and the polar axis OP for the axis OX, then the cartesian coordinates (x, y) of the point M and its polar coordinates (φ, r) will be related as follows:

$$x = r\cos\varphi, \qquad y = r\sin\varphi; \tag{1}$$

$$r = \sqrt{x^2 + y^2}, \qquad \tan\varphi = \frac{y}{x}. \tag{2}$$

If we now take the focus of the ellipse, hyperbola, or parabola for the pole, and the focal axis of symmetry for the polar axis drawn in the direction opposite to the nearest vertex, then the equation in polar coordinates for all the three curves will be the same:

$$r = \frac{p}{1 - \varepsilon\cos\varphi}, \tag{3}$$

where ε is the eccentricity, and p, the parameter. For the ellipse and hyperbola $p=\frac{b^2}{a}$.

330. Construct the following points using polar coordinates (φ, r): $A(0, 3)$, $B\left(\frac{\pi}{4}, 2\right)$, $C\left(\frac{\pi}{2}, 3\right)$, $D(\pi, 2)$, $E\left(\frac{3\pi}{2}, 3\right)$.

331. Construct the following points: $A\left(\frac{\pi}{2}, -2\right)$, $B\left(-\frac{\pi}{2}, 3\right)$, $C\left(-\frac{\pi}{4}, -4\right)$, $D\left(\frac{2\pi}{3}, -3\right)$.

332. Construct the line $r=2+2\cos\varphi$.

Hint. Tabulate the values of r for $\varphi=0$; $\pm\frac{\pi}{3}$; $\pm\frac{\pi}{2}$; $\pm\frac{2\pi}{3}$; π.

333. Construct the following curves (Figs. 84, 85, and 90):

(1) $r=a\varphi$ (the *spiral of Archimedes*)
(2) $r=a(1-\cos\varphi)$ (the *cardioid*)
(3) $r^2=a^2\cos 2\varphi$ (the *lemniscate*)
(4) $r=\frac{a}{\varphi}$ (the *hyperbolic spiral*)
(5) $r=a(1+2\cos\varphi)$ (the *limaçon of Pascal*)

334. Construct the lines: (1) $r=a$; (2) $\varphi=\frac{\pi}{4}$; (3) $r=\frac{b}{\sin\varphi}$.

335. Write in polar coordinates the equation of the (1) straight line cutting off an intercept a on the polar axis and perpendicular to it; (2) straight line passing through the point $A(\alpha; a)$ and parallel to the polar axis.

336. Write in polar coordinates the equation of the straight line passing through the point $A(\alpha, a)$ at an angle β to the polar axis.

337. Write in polar coordinates the equation of the circle whose centre lies at the point $C(0, a)$ and the radius equals a.

338. Construct the curves:

(1) $r=3-2\sin 2\varphi$; (2) $r=2+\cos 3\varphi$; (3) $r=1-\sin 3\varphi$.

Hint. First determine the angles at which we have r_{max} and r_{min}.

339. Construct the curves (see Figs. 86 and 87 on page 386):

(1) $r = a \sin 3\varphi$ (three-leafed rose);

(2) $r = a \sin 2\varphi$ (four-leafed rose).

340. Transform the following equations of the lines to polar coordinates:

(1) $x^2 - y^2 = a^2$; (2) $x^2 + y^2 = a^2$; (3) $x \cos \alpha + y \sin \alpha - p = 0$;
(4) $y = x$; (5) $x^2 + y^2 = ax$; (6) $(x^2 + y^2)^2 = a^2 (x^2 - y^2)$.

341. Transform the following equations to the Cartesian-coordinate form and construct the corresponding lines:

(1) $r \cos \varphi = a$; (2) $r = 2a \sin \varphi$; (3) $r^2 \sin 2\varphi = 2a^2$;
(4) $r \sin\left(\varphi + \frac{\pi}{4}\right) = a\sqrt{2}$; (5) $r = a(1 + \cos \varphi)$.

342. Write the canonical equations of the second-order curves:

(1) $r = \frac{9}{5 - 4 \cos \varphi}$; (2) $r = \frac{9}{4 - 5 \cos \varphi}$; (3) $r = \frac{3}{1 - \cos \varphi}$.

343. *Conchoid*. Draw a straight line through the point $A\left(\frac{\pi}{2}, a\right)$ and parallel to the polar axis. An arbitrary ray OB intersects this straight line at point B. On OB lay off, on either side of B, the line segments $BM = BM_1 = b$. Determine the locus of points M and M_1 in polar coordinates and construct the curve.

344. *Strophoid*. A straight line $x = a$ intersects the axis OX at point A and an arbitrary ray OB at point B. On OB lay off, on either side of B, the line segments BM_1 and BM_2 equal to AB. Write the equation of the locus of points M_1 and M_2 both in polar and Cartesian coordinates (see Fig. 88).

345. *Cassinian curve* (*oval of Cassini*). A point $M(\varphi, r)$ moves so that the product of its distances from the points $F(0, a)$ and $F_1(\pi, a)$ remains equal to b^2. Write in polar coordinates the equation of the path covered by the point M.

346. *Cardioid.* An arbitrary ray OA intersects the circle $r = a\cos\varphi$ at point A. On OA lay off, on either side of A, the line segments $AM = AM_1 = a$. Derive the equation of the locus of points M and M_1 both in polar and Cartesian coordinates.

347. *Epicycloid.* A circle of diameter a rolls without sliding along a circle of the same diameter outside this circle. Write the equation of the curve described by a point M on the rolling circle if the point of tangency of circles is taken for the pole and the starting position of the point M, and the polar axis is drawn through the centres of the circles (in the starting position).

---

348. Construct the curves: (1) $r = 3 + 2\cos 2\varphi$; (2) $r = 3 - \sin 3\varphi$; (3) $r = a\cos 2\varphi$ (see the hint to Problem 338).

349. Construct: (1) $r = 4(1 + \cos\varphi)$; (2) $r = 2 - \sin\varphi$.

350. Write in polar coordinates the equation of a straight line passing through the given points $A(\alpha;\ a)$ and $B(\beta;\ b)$.

Hint: Consider the relationship among the areas of the triangles AOM, BOM, and AOB, where $M(\varphi,\ r)$ is an arbitrary point of the straight line.

351. Write the canonical equations of the curves of the second order:

$$(1)\ r = \frac{1}{2 - \sqrt{3}\cos\varphi};\quad (2)\ r = \frac{1}{2 - \sqrt{5}\cos\varphi};\quad (3)\ r = \frac{1}{2 - 2\cos\varphi}.$$

352. *Lemniscate of Bernoulli.* A point $M(\varphi,\ r)$ moves so that the product of its distances from the points $F(0,\ c)$ and $F_1(\pi,\ c)$ remains equal to c^2. Write the equation of the path traversed by M both in polar and Cartesian coordinates.

Hint. According to the law of cosines $FM^2 = r^2 + c^2 - 2rc\cos\varphi$ and $F_1M^2 = r^2 + c^2 + 2rc\cos\varphi$, and, by hypothesis, $FM^2 \cdot F_1M^2 = c^4$.

353. *Limaçon of Pascal*. Draw an arbitrary ray OA. From the point A where OA intersects the circle $r = a\cos\varphi$ lay off, on both sides of A, the line segments $AM = AM_1 = b$.

Derive the equation of the locus of points M in polar coordinates.

354. *Four-leafed rose.* The ends of a line segment $AB = 2a$ slide along the axes of the Cartesian coordinates. A perpendicular OM is dropped from the origin onto AB. Write the equation of the locus of points $M(x, y)$ for all possible positions of AB.

1.17. Algebraic Curves of the Third and Higher Orders

355. Construct the following curves (see Figs. 70 to 73 on pages 383, 384):

(1) $y = \frac{x^3}{3}$ (*cubical parabola*);

(2) $y^2 = x^3$ }
(3) $y^3 = x^2$ } (*semicubical parabola*);

(4) $y^2 = x(x-4)^2$ (*loop parabola*).

356. Construct the curves:

(1) $x^{\frac{2}{3}} + y^{\frac{2}{3}} = a^{\frac{2}{3}}$ (*equilateral astroid*);

(2) $\left(\frac{x}{a}\right)^{\frac{2}{3}} + \left(\frac{y}{b}\right)^{\frac{2}{3}} = 1$, $b \neq a$ (*non-equilateral astroid*).

Hint. Find the points of intersection of the curves and the axes OX and OY and also the points at which the first curve intersects the straight lines $y = \pm x$, and the second curve the straight lines $y = \pm \frac{b}{a} x$ (see Fig. 82 on page 386).

357. On the line segment $[-1, 1]$ construct the following curves: (1) $y = x^{2n+1}$; (2) $y = x^{2n}$; (3) $x^{2n} + y^{2n} = 1$ if $n = 1, 2, 4$. What polygonal lines do these curves approach as $n \to \infty$?

Hint. Find the points at which the first curve intersects the straight line $y = \frac{x}{2n}$; the second, the straight line $y = \frac{1}{2n}$, and the third, the straight line $y = x$. Ten squares of squared paper should be taken for a scale unit.

358. *Astroid.* The end-points of a line segment $AB = a$ slide along the axes of the Cartesian coordinates. Two straight lines AC and BC parallel to the coordinate axes intersect at point C. A perpendicular CM is dropped from C onto AB. Write the equation of the locus of points $M(x, y)$ for all possible positions of the line segment AB.

359. Construct the curves:

(1) $y^2 = \frac{x^3}{a-x}$ (*cissoid*, Fig. 89 on page 387);

(2) $y = \frac{8a^3}{x^2+4a^2}$ (*versiera*, Fig. 80 on page 385).

360. Each point $P(x_0, y_0)$ of the parabola $y^2 = 2px$ is displaced parallel to the axis OX by a distance $PM = \pm OP$. Find the locus of points M.

361. A bar $OA = a$ rotates about the origin O. Hinged to it at point A is another bar $AB = 2a$, whose end-point slides along the axis OX. Write the equation of the line described by the midpoint M of the line segment AB.

362. *Cissoid.* An arbitrary ray OA (Fig. 89 on page 387) intersects the circle $x^2 + y^2 = ax$ at point A and the straight line $x = a$ at point B. A line segment $OM = AB$ is laid off on the ray. Derive the equation of the locus of points M.

363. An arbitrary ray OB (Fig. 89 on page 387) intersects the straight line $x = a$ at point B. Point C is the projection of B on the axis OY, and M is the projection of C on OB. Show that the locus of points M is a cissoid.

364. Prove that, if from the vertex of the parabola $y^2 = -4ax$ perpendiculars are drawn to the tangent lines to this curve, then the locus of the feet of the perpendiculars is a cissoid.

365. *Versiera.* An arbitrary ray OA intersects the circle $x^2 + y^2 = 2ay$ and the straight line $y = 2a$ at points A and B respectively. From these points two straight lines are drawn: one parallel to the axis OX, the other to the axis OY to intersect each other at a point M. Determine the locus of points M.

366. *Folium of Descartes*: $x^3 + y^3 - 3axy = 0$. Show that, by rotating the coordinate axes through an angle of 45°, this equation is reduced to the form $Y^2=\frac{X^3(3b-X)}{3(b+X)}$, where $b=\frac{a}{\sqrt{2}}$. Construct the curve, determining the location of the curve and its symmetry, the points of intersection with the straight line $y=x$ and the asymptote. Show that the equation of the asymptote in the new system of coordinates will be $X=-b$, while in the old one $x+y+a=0$ (see Fig. 83 on page 386).

1.18. Transcendental Curves

367. *Cycloid.* A circle of radius a rolls along a straight line OX without sliding. Derive parametric equations of the curve described by point M of the circle, taking the angle of rotation of the rolling circle for the parameter t and putting that at $t=0$ the point M is found at the origin.

368. *Involute of a Circle.* This is a curve described by the extremity of a taut string unwinding from (or winding onto) a circular spool, the equation of the circle being $x^2+y^2=a^2$. Set up parametric equations of the curve if the starting point of the extremity is $(a, 0)$. Take the length of the unwound arc (in radians) for the parameter t.

369. *Quadratrix.* An arbitrary ray OM, forming an angle t (in radians) with the axis OY, intersects the straight line $x=at$ at point M. Write the equation of the locus of points M.

370. *Epicycloid.* A circle of radius r rolls without sliding along a circle of radius R outside it. Set up parametric equations of the curve described by point M of the rolling circle. (At $r=R$ an epicycloid turns into a cardioid. See Problem 347.)

371. *Hypocycloid.* A circle of radius r rolls without sliding along a circle of radius $R>r$ inside it. Set up parametric equations of the curve described by point M of the rolling circle. $\left(\text{At } r=\frac{R}{4}\right.$ a hypocycloid turns into an astroid $\left.x^{\frac{2}{3}}+y^{\frac{2}{3}}=a^{\frac{2}{3}}.\right)$

CHAPTER 2

VECTOR ALGEBRA

2.1. Addition of Vectors. Multiplication of a Vector by a Scalar

1°. Definitions. A *vector quantity*, or a *vector* (in the broad sense of the word), is any quantity possessing direction. A *scalar quantity* (or *scalar*) is a quantity that does not possess direction.

In geometry, a *vector* (in the narrow sense) is any directed line segment.

A vector with initial point A and terminal point B is denoted as $\overrightarrow{AB}$ (Fig. 13).

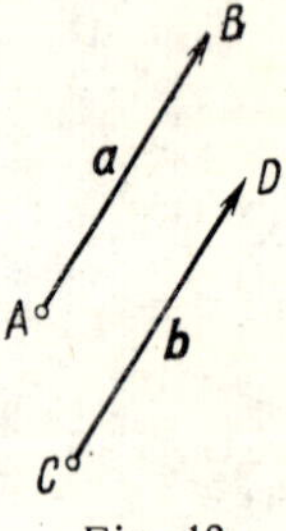

Fig. 13

A vector can also be denoted by a single letter as in Fig. 13. In printing this letter is given in boldface type ($\boldsymbol{a}$), in writing it is given with a bar ($\bar{a}$).

The length of a vector is also called the *absolute value* (or *modulus*) of the vector. The absolute value of a vector is a *scalar quantity*.

The absolute value of a vector is denoted by two vertical lines: $|\overrightarrow{AB}|$ or $|\boldsymbol{a}|$ or $|\bar{a}|$.

In the two-letter notation of a vector, its absolute value is sometimes denoted by the same letters without an arrow (AB is the absolute value of the vector $\overrightarrow{AB}$), in the single-letter notation, the absolute value is denoted by a normal weight letter (b is the absolute value of the vector $\boldsymbol{b}$).

Vectors parallel to one straight line are termed *collinear*. Vectors parallel to one plane are called *coplanar*. Two vectors $\boldsymbol{a}$ and $\boldsymbol{b}$ (Fig. 13) are equal if they (1) have the *same modulus*, (2) are *collinear*, (3) are *in the same direction*.

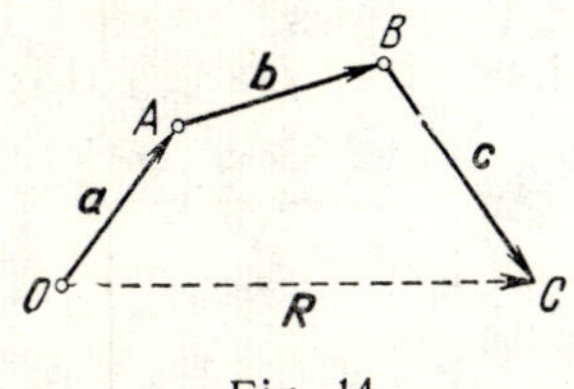

Fig. 14

2°. Multiplication of a vector by a scalar. *To multiply a vector* $\boldsymbol{a}$ (multiplicand) *by a number* (scalar) m means to construct a new vector (product) the absolute value of which is obtained by multiplying the absolute value of the vector $\boldsymbol{a}$ by the absolute value of the number m, the direction coinciding with the direction of the vector $\boldsymbol{a}$ or being in the opposite sense, depending on whether the number m is positive or negative. If $m=0$, the product is the null vector.

3°. Addition of vectors. The *sum of the vectors* $\boldsymbol{a}+\boldsymbol{b}+\boldsymbol{c}$ is a fourth vector $\boldsymbol{R}=\overrightarrow{OC}$ (Fig. 14) joining the initial point O of the vector $\boldsymbol{a}$ to the terminal point of the vector $\boldsymbol{c}$, i.e. connecting the end-points of the polygonal line $OABC$ constructed from the given vectors. In particular, in a parallelogram, constructed from the given vectors $\overrightarrow{OA}=\boldsymbol{a}$ and $\overrightarrow{OB}=\boldsymbol{b}$, one vector-diagonal $\overrightarrow{OC}$ is the sum $\boldsymbol{a}+\boldsymbol{b}$, the other $\overrightarrow{BA}$ being the difference $\boldsymbol{a}-\boldsymbol{b}$ of the given vectors.

4°. The projection of a vector on an axis. Let a vector $\boldsymbol{a}$ form an angle φ with the axis OX. Then the projection of the vector on this axis is determined by the formula

$$\mathrm{pr}_{OX}\boldsymbol{a} = |\boldsymbol{a}|\cos\varphi = a\cos(\widehat{\boldsymbol{a}, OX}).$$

The *projection of a sum of vectors* on some axis is *equal to the sum of the projections* of those vectors on the same axis:

$$\mathrm{pr}_{OX}(\boldsymbol{a}+\boldsymbol{b}) = \mathrm{pr}_{OX}\boldsymbol{a} + \mathrm{pr}_{OX}\boldsymbol{b}.$$

372. Laid off on the sides OA and OB of a rectangle $OACB$ are the unit vectors $\boldsymbol{i}$ and $\boldsymbol{j}$ (Fig. 15). Express the

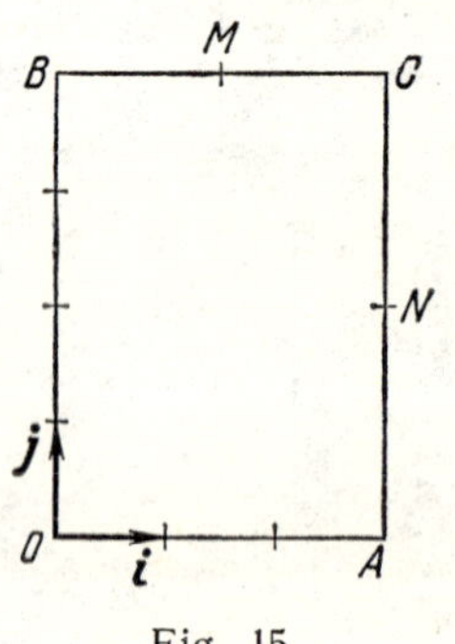

Fig. 15

vectors $\overrightarrow{OA}$, $\overrightarrow{AC}$, $\overrightarrow{CB}$, $\overrightarrow{BO}$, $\overrightarrow{OC}$, and $\overrightarrow{BA}$ in terms of $\boldsymbol{i}$ and $\boldsymbol{j}$ if the length $OA=3$ and $OB=4$.

373. Let M be the midpoint of BC and N, the midpoint of AC (Fig. 15). Determine the vectors $\overrightarrow{OM}$, $\overrightarrow{ON}$, and $\overrightarrow{MN}$ if $OA=3$ and $OB=4$.

374. Given in a plane are the points $A(0, -2)$, $B(4, 2)$, and $C(4, -2)$. Forces $\overrightarrow{OA}$, $\overrightarrow{OB}$, and $\overrightarrow{OC}$ are applied at the coordinate origin. Construct the resultant force $\overrightarrow{OM}$, and find its projections on the coordinate axes and its magnitude. Express the forces $\overrightarrow{OA}$, $\overrightarrow{OB}$, $\overrightarrow{OC}$, and $\overrightarrow{OM}$ in terms of the unit vectors $\boldsymbol{i}$ and $\boldsymbol{j}$ of the coordinate axes.

375. Given three coplanar unit vectors $\boldsymbol{m}$, $\boldsymbol{n}$, and $\boldsymbol{p}$,

$(\widehat{\boldsymbol{m}, \boldsymbol{n}}) = 30°$ and $(\widehat{\boldsymbol{n}, \boldsymbol{p}}) = 60°$. Construct the vector $\boldsymbol{u} = \boldsymbol{m} + 2\boldsymbol{n} - 3\boldsymbol{p}$ and compute its modulus.

Hint. In the polygonal line constructed from the vectors $\boldsymbol{m}$, $2\boldsymbol{n}$ and $-3\boldsymbol{p}$ extend the first line segment to intersect the third one.

376. Check analytically and geometrically the vector identities:

$$(1)\ \boldsymbol{a} + \frac{\boldsymbol{b}-\boldsymbol{a}}{2} = \frac{\boldsymbol{a}+\boldsymbol{b}}{2}; \quad (2)\ \boldsymbol{a} - \frac{\boldsymbol{a}+\boldsymbol{b}}{2} = \frac{\boldsymbol{a}-\boldsymbol{b}}{2}.$$

377. A parallelepiped is constructed on three non-coplanar vectors $\overrightarrow{OA} = \boldsymbol{a}$, $\overrightarrow{OB} = \boldsymbol{b}$, and $\overrightarrow{OC} = \boldsymbol{c}$. Indicate those of its vector-diagonals which are equal to $\boldsymbol{a}+\boldsymbol{b}-\boldsymbol{c}$, $\boldsymbol{a}-\boldsymbol{b}+\boldsymbol{c}$, $\boldsymbol{a}-\boldsymbol{b}-\boldsymbol{c}$, and $\boldsymbol{b}-\boldsymbol{a}-\boldsymbol{c}$ respectively.

378. With the aid of the drawing of Problem 377 check the commutative property of the vector sum:

$$\boldsymbol{a}+\boldsymbol{b}-\boldsymbol{c} = \boldsymbol{a}-\boldsymbol{c}+\boldsymbol{b} = \boldsymbol{b}+\boldsymbol{a}-\boldsymbol{c} = \boldsymbol{b}-\boldsymbol{c}+\boldsymbol{a}.$$

379. Given vectors $\overrightarrow{OA} = \boldsymbol{a}$ and $\overrightarrow{OB} = \boldsymbol{b}$. Vector $\overrightarrow{OC} = \boldsymbol{c}$ is a median of the triangle OAB. Resolve analytically and geometrically (1) the vector $\boldsymbol{c}$ into $\boldsymbol{a}$ and $\boldsymbol{b}$; (2) the vector $\boldsymbol{a}$ into $\boldsymbol{b}$ and $\boldsymbol{c}$.

380. In a rectangle $OACB$ (Fig. 15) M and N are the midpoints of the sides $BC = 3$ and $AC = 4$. Resolve geometrically and analytically the vector $\overrightarrow{OC} = \boldsymbol{c}$ into the vectors $\overrightarrow{OM} = \boldsymbol{a}$ and $\overrightarrow{ON} = \boldsymbol{b}$.

Hint. Substitute the expressions of $\boldsymbol{a}$, $\boldsymbol{b}$, and $\boldsymbol{c}$ in terms of $\boldsymbol{i}$ and $\boldsymbol{j}$ into the condition $\boldsymbol{c} = m\boldsymbol{a} + n\boldsymbol{b}$ and compare the coefficients of $\boldsymbol{i}$ and $\boldsymbol{j}$ in the left-hand and right-hand members.

381. Given a regular hexagon $OABCDE$ with side $OA = 3$. Denoting the unit vectors of the directions $\overrightarrow{OA}$, $\overrightarrow{AB}$, $\overrightarrow{BC}$ in terms of $\boldsymbol{m}$, $\boldsymbol{n}$, and $\boldsymbol{p}$, find the relationship among them (for instance, by considering the trapezoid $OABC$). Express then the vectors $\overrightarrow{OB}$, $\overrightarrow{BC}$, $\overrightarrow{EO}$, $\overrightarrow{OD}$, and $\overrightarrow{DA}$ in terms of $\boldsymbol{m}$ and $\boldsymbol{n}$.

---

382. In an isosceles trapezoid $OACB$ (Fig. 16) the angle $BOA = 60°$, $OB = BC = CA = 2$, M and N are the midpoints of the sides BC and AC. Express the vectors $\overrightarrow{AC}$, $\overrightarrow{OM}$, $\overrightarrow{ON}$, and $\overrightarrow{MN}$ in terms of $\boldsymbol{m}$ and $\boldsymbol{n}$ which are the unit vectors of the directions of $\overrightarrow{OA}$ and $\overrightarrow{OB}$.

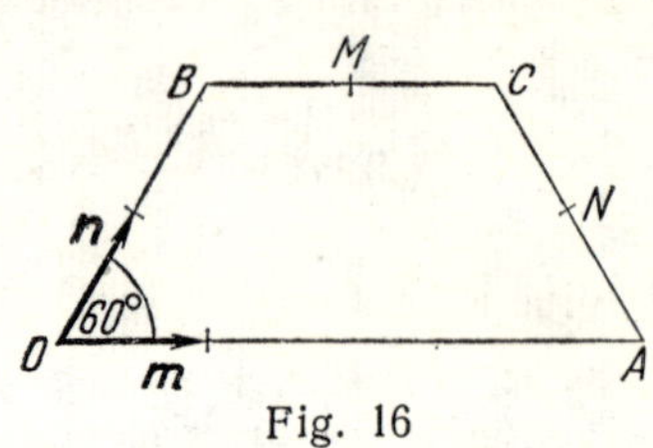

Fig. 16

383. Given vectors $\boldsymbol{a}$ and $\boldsymbol{b}$ the angle between which equals 120°. Construct the vector $\boldsymbol{c} = 2\boldsymbol{a} - 1.5\boldsymbol{b}$ and determine its modulus if $a = 3$ and $b = 4$.

384. Given in a plane are the points $A(3, 3)$, $B(-3, 3)$, and $C(-3, 0)$. Applied at the coordinate origin are forces $\overrightarrow{OA}$, $\overrightarrow{OB}$, and $\overrightarrow{OC}$. Construct the resultant force $\overrightarrow{OM}$ and find its projections on the coordinate axes and its magnitude. Express the forces $\overrightarrow{OA}$, $\overrightarrow{OB}$, $\overrightarrow{OC}$, and $\overrightarrow{OM}$ in terms of the unit vectors $\boldsymbol{i}$ and $\boldsymbol{j}$ of the coordinate axes.

385. (1) In a trapezoid $OACB$: $BC = \frac{1}{3} OA$ and $BC \parallel OA$. Resolve geometrically and analytically the vector $\overrightarrow{OA} = \boldsymbol{a}$ into the vectors $\overrightarrow{OC} = \boldsymbol{c}$ and $\overrightarrow{OB} = \boldsymbol{b}$.

Hint. In the triangle OBC express $\boldsymbol{c}$ in terms of $\boldsymbol{b}$ and $\boldsymbol{a}$ and then solve the obtained equation with respect to $\boldsymbol{a}$.

(2) Point B divides a circular arc $\overset{\frown}{AC} = 90°$ in the ratio 1:2. O is the centre of the circle. Resolve the vector $\overrightarrow{OC} = \boldsymbol{c}$ into vectors $\overrightarrow{OA} = \boldsymbol{a}$ and $\overrightarrow{OB} = \boldsymbol{b}$.

2.2 Rectangular Coordinates of a Point and a Vector in Space

1°. Definition. Let there be given three mutually perpendicular coordinate axes with a common origin O and a point M (Fig. 17). The *projections* of its *radius vector*

$\overrightarrow{OM}=\boldsymbol{r}$ on the coordinate axes $OM_1=x$, $OM_2=y$, and $OM_3=z$ are called the *rectangular coordinates* of the point M or the vector $\boldsymbol{r}=\overrightarrow{OM}$.

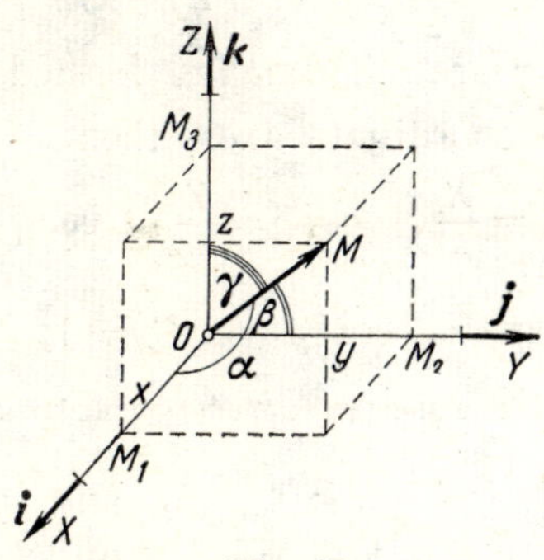

Fig. 17

2°. The radius vector of a point in space. The *modulus* or the length of the *radius vector* $\overrightarrow{OM}=\boldsymbol{r}$ is expressed in terms of its coordinates by the formula

$$r=\sqrt{x^2+y^2+z^2}. \tag{1}$$

The unit vectors of the coordinate axes $\boldsymbol{i}$, $\boldsymbol{j}$, and $\boldsymbol{k}$ are called the *basis vectors*. The radius vectors are expressed in terms of the basis vectors

$$\boldsymbol{r}=x\boldsymbol{i}+y\boldsymbol{j}+z\boldsymbol{k}. \tag{2}$$

3°. A vector given by the coordinates of the initial and terminal points. Let there be given points $A(x_1, y_1, z_1)$ and $B(x_2, y_2, z_2)$. The projections of the vector $\boldsymbol{u}=\overrightarrow{AB}$ on the coordinate axes will be

$$\left.\begin{aligned}\mathrm{pr}_{OX}\overrightarrow{AB}&=X=x_2-x_1,\\ \mathrm{pr}_{OY}\overrightarrow{AB}&=Y=y_2-y_1,\\ \mathrm{pr}_{OZ}\overrightarrow{AB}&=Z=z_2-z_1.\end{aligned}\right\} \tag{3}$$

We may write formulas analogous to formulas (1) and (2):

$$u=\sqrt{X^2+Y^2+Z^2}=\sqrt{(x_2-x_1)^2+(y_2-y_1)^2+(z_2-z_1)^2}, \quad (4)$$

$$\boldsymbol{u}=\overrightarrow{AB}=X\boldsymbol{i}+Y\boldsymbol{j}+Z\boldsymbol{k}. \quad (5)$$

If α, β, and γ are the angles formed by the vector $\boldsymbol{u}=\overrightarrow{AB}$ with the coordinate axes, then

$$\cos\alpha=\frac{X}{u}, \quad \cos\beta=\frac{Y}{u}, \quad \cos\gamma=\frac{Z}{u}, \quad (6)$$

and

$$\cos^2\alpha+\cos^2\beta+\cos^2\gamma=1, \quad (7)$$

i.e. the *sum of the squared direction cosines of a vector is equal to 1.*

It follows from formulas (4), (5), and (6) that the vector $\boldsymbol{u}$ is completely determined by the three numbers: X, Y, and Z, i.e. by its projections, or its *coordinates*. Therefore, we sometimes write or say: Given a vector $\boldsymbol{u}\{X, Y, Z\}$.

386. Construct the point $M(5, -3, 4)$ and determine the length and the direction of its radius vector.

387. Construct the vector $\boldsymbol{r}=\overrightarrow{OM}=2\boldsymbol{i}+3\boldsymbol{j}+6\boldsymbol{k}$ and determine its length and direction (check using formula (7)).

388. A vector is inclined to the axis OX at an angle of 40° and to OZ at 80°. Find the angle between the vector and the axis OY.

389. The radius vector of a point M forms an angle of 45° with the axis OX and of 60° with OY. Its length $r=6$. Determine the coordinates of the point M, if its coordinate z is negative, and express the vector $\overrightarrow{OM}=\boldsymbol{r}$ in terms of the basis vectors $\boldsymbol{i}$, $\boldsymbol{j}$, $\boldsymbol{k}$.

390. Given the points $A(1, 2, 3)$ and $B(3, -4, 6)$. Construct the vector $\overrightarrow{AB}=\boldsymbol{u}$, its projections on the coordinate axes and determine the length and the direction of the vector. Construct the angles formed by the vector $\boldsymbol{u}$ with the coordinate axes.

391. Construct a parallelogram on the vectors $\overrightarrow{OA}=\boldsymbol{i}+\boldsymbol{j}$ and $\overrightarrow{OB}=\boldsymbol{k}-3\boldsymbol{j}$, and determine its diagonals.

392. A force $R=7$ is applied at the point $A(2, 1, -1)$. Given two coordinates of the force $X=2$ and

$Y=-3$, determine the direction and the terminal point of the vector representing the force.

393. Given in a plane XOY are the points $A(4, 2)$, $B(2, 3)$, and $C(0, 5)$ and constructed on it are the vectors $\overrightarrow{OA}=\boldsymbol{a}$, $\overrightarrow{OB}=\boldsymbol{b}$, and $\overrightarrow{OC}=\boldsymbol{c}$. Resolve geometrically and analytically the vector $\boldsymbol{a}$ into the vectors $\boldsymbol{b}$ and $\boldsymbol{c}$.

---

394. Given the points $A(2, 2, 0)$ and $B(0, -2, 5)$. Construct the vector $\overrightarrow{AB}=\boldsymbol{u}$ and determine its length and direction.

395. A vector $\overrightarrow{OM}=\boldsymbol{r}$ forms equal acute angles with the coordinate axes. Determine these angles and construct the vector $\boldsymbol{r}$ if its length is $2\sqrt{3}$.

396. A vector forms angles of 60° and 120° with the axes OY and OZ respectively. What is the angle between the vector and the axis OX?

397. Given three consecutive vertices of a parallelogram $A(1, -2, 3)$, $B(3, 2, 1)$, and $C(6, 4, 4)$, find its fourth vertex D.

Hint. It follows from the equality $\overrightarrow{AD}=\overrightarrow{BC}$ that the coordinates of these vectors are also equal: $x-1=6-3$, etc.

398. Construct the vectors $\overrightarrow{OA}=\boldsymbol{a}=2\boldsymbol{i}$, $\overrightarrow{OB}=\boldsymbol{b}=3\boldsymbol{i}+3\boldsymbol{j}$, and $\overrightarrow{OC}=\boldsymbol{c}=2\boldsymbol{i}+6\boldsymbol{j}$ in the plane XOY. Resolve geometrically and analytically the vector $\boldsymbol{c}$ into the vectors $\boldsymbol{a}$ and $\boldsymbol{b}$.

2.3. Scalar Product of Two Vectors

1°. Definition. The *scalar product* of two vectors is the *product of their absolute values by the cosine of the angle between them.*

The scalar product of a vector $\boldsymbol{a}$ by a vector $\boldsymbol{b}$ is denoted: $\boldsymbol{a}\cdot\boldsymbol{b}$ or $\boldsymbol{ab}$. By definition,

$$\boldsymbol{a}\cdot\boldsymbol{b}=ab\cos\varphi. \qquad (1)$$

As is obvious from Fig. 18, $b\cos\varphi=\text{pr}_{\boldsymbol{a}}\boldsymbol{b}$. Therefore

$$\boldsymbol{a}\cdot\boldsymbol{b}=ab\cos\varphi=a\,\text{pr}_{\boldsymbol{a}}\boldsymbol{b}=b\,\text{pr}_{\boldsymbol{b}}\boldsymbol{a}. \qquad (2)$$

2°. Properties of a scalar product.

I. $\boldsymbol{a}\cdot\boldsymbol{b}=\boldsymbol{b}\cdot\boldsymbol{a}$ (*commutative property*).

II. $\boldsymbol{a}\cdot(\boldsymbol{b}+\boldsymbol{c})=\boldsymbol{a}\cdot\boldsymbol{b}+\boldsymbol{a}\cdot\boldsymbol{c}$ (*distributive property*).

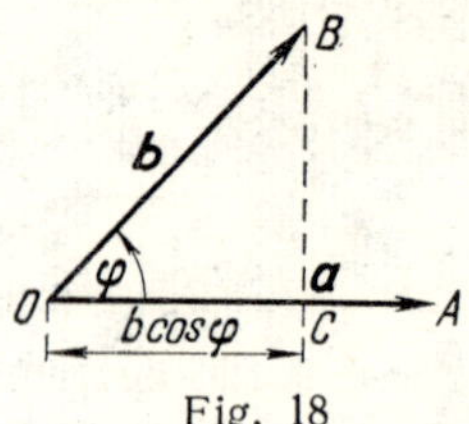

Fig. 18

III. If $\boldsymbol{a}\parallel\boldsymbol{b}$, then $\boldsymbol{a}\cdot\boldsymbol{b}=\pm ab$. In particular, $\boldsymbol{a}^2=\boldsymbol{a}\cdot\boldsymbol{a}= aa\cos 0°=a^2$; hence

$$a=\sqrt{\boldsymbol{a}^2}. \tag{3}$$

IV. If $\boldsymbol{a}\perp\boldsymbol{b}$, then $\boldsymbol{a}\cdot\boldsymbol{b}=ab\cos 90°=0$.

V. The scalar products of basis vectors:

$$\boldsymbol{i}\cdot\boldsymbol{j}=0,\quad \boldsymbol{j}\cdot\boldsymbol{k}=0,\quad \boldsymbol{i}\cdot\boldsymbol{k}=0,\quad \boldsymbol{i}\cdot\boldsymbol{i}=1,\ \boldsymbol{j}\cdot\boldsymbol{j}=1,\quad \boldsymbol{k}\cdot\boldsymbol{k}=1.$$

VI. If vectors are given by coordinates $\boldsymbol{a}\{a_x, a_y, a_z\}$ and $\boldsymbol{b}\{b_x, b_y, b_z\}$, then

$$\boldsymbol{a}\cdot\boldsymbol{b}=a_xb_x+a_yb_y+a_zb_z. \tag{4}$$

3°. The angle between vectors:

$$\cos\varphi=\frac{\boldsymbol{a}\cdot\boldsymbol{b}}{ab}=\frac{a_xb_x+a_yb_y+a_zb_z}{\sqrt{a_x^2+a_y^2+a_z^2}\sqrt{b_x^2+b_y^2+b_z^2}}. \tag{5}$$

The *condition of parallelism* of vectors: $\boldsymbol{b}=m\boldsymbol{a}$ or $\frac{b_x}{a_x}=\frac{b_y}{a_y}=\frac{b_z}{a_z}=m$.

The *condition of perpendicularity* of vectors: $\boldsymbol{a}\cdot\boldsymbol{b}=0$ or

$$a_xb_x+a_yb_y+a_zb_z=0.$$

399. Determine the angle between the vectors $\boldsymbol{a}=-\boldsymbol{i}+\boldsymbol{j}$ and $\boldsymbol{b}=\boldsymbol{i}-2\boldsymbol{j}+2\boldsymbol{k}$.

400. Determine the angles of a triangle ABC with the vertices $A(2, -1, 3)$, $B(1, 1, 1)$ and $C(0, 0, 5)$.

401. Given the points $A(a, 0, 0)$, $B(0, 0, 2a)$, and

$C(a, 0, a)$. Construct the vectors $\overrightarrow{OC}$ and $\overrightarrow{AB}$ and find the angle between them.

402. Given in a plane is a triangle with the vertices $O(0, 0)$, $A(2a, 0)$, and $B(a, -a)$. Find the angle formed by the side OB and median OM of this triangle.

403. Find the angle between the bisectors of the angles XOY and YOZ.

404. Drawn from a vertex of a square are two straight lines bisecting the opposite sides. Find the angle between these lines.

405. Find the angle between the diagonals of a parallelogram constructed on the vectors $\boldsymbol{a}=2\boldsymbol{i}+\boldsymbol{j}$ and $\boldsymbol{b}=-2\boldsymbol{j}+\boldsymbol{k}$.

406. Given the vectors $\boldsymbol{a}=\boldsymbol{i}+\boldsymbol{j}+2\boldsymbol{k}$ and $\boldsymbol{b}=\boldsymbol{i}-\boldsymbol{j}+4\boldsymbol{k}$. Determine $\text{pr}_{\boldsymbol{b}}\,\boldsymbol{a}$ and $\text{pr}_{\boldsymbol{a}}\,\boldsymbol{b}$.

407. Remove the parentheses in the expression

$$(2\boldsymbol{i}-\boldsymbol{j})\cdot\boldsymbol{j}+(\boldsymbol{j}-2\boldsymbol{k})\cdot\boldsymbol{k}+(\boldsymbol{i}-2\boldsymbol{k})^2.$$

408. Compute: (1) $(\boldsymbol{m}+\boldsymbol{n})^2$ if $\boldsymbol{m}$ and $\boldsymbol{n}$ are unit vectors and the angle between them is equal to 30°; (2) $(\boldsymbol{a}-\boldsymbol{b})^2$ if $a=2\sqrt{2}$, $b=4$ and $(\widehat{\boldsymbol{a}, \boldsymbol{b}})=135°$.

409. Remove the parentheses in the expressions

$$(1)\ (\boldsymbol{a}+\boldsymbol{b})^2;\quad 2)\ (\boldsymbol{a}+\boldsymbol{b})^2+(\boldsymbol{a}-\boldsymbol{b})^2$$

and find out the geometrical meaning of the formulas obtained.

410. Given coplanar vectors $\boldsymbol{a}$, $\boldsymbol{b}$, and $\boldsymbol{c}$; $a=3$, $b=2$, $c=5$, $(\widehat{\boldsymbol{a}, \boldsymbol{b}})=60°$, and $(\widehat{\boldsymbol{b}, \boldsymbol{c}})=60°$. Construct the vector $\boldsymbol{u}=\boldsymbol{a}+\boldsymbol{b}-\boldsymbol{c}$ and compute its absolute value, using the formula

$$u=\sqrt{(\boldsymbol{a}+\boldsymbol{b}-\boldsymbol{c})^2}.$$

411. Find the resultant of four coplanar forces applied at point O if each of them is equal to 100 N and the angle between two consecutive forces equals 45°.

412. Determine the lengths of the diagonals of a parallelogram constructed on the vectors $\boldsymbol{a}=2\boldsymbol{m}+\boldsymbol{n}$ and $\boldsymbol{b}=\boldsymbol{m}-2\boldsymbol{n}$, where $\boldsymbol{m}$ and $\boldsymbol{n}$ are unit vectors forming an angle of 60°.

413. Given the vector $\boldsymbol{a}=2\boldsymbol{m}-\boldsymbol{n}$, where $\boldsymbol{m}$ and $\boldsymbol{n}$ are unit vectors and the angle between them is 120°. Find $\cos(\widehat{\boldsymbol{a}, \boldsymbol{m}})$ and $\cos(\widehat{\boldsymbol{a}, \boldsymbol{n}})$.

414. Determine the angle between the bisectors of two plane angles of a regular tetrahedron drawn from one of its vertices.

Hint. If $\boldsymbol{m}$, $\boldsymbol{n}$ and $\boldsymbol{p}$ are the unit vectors of the edges, then $\boldsymbol{m}+\boldsymbol{n}$ and $\boldsymbol{m}+\boldsymbol{p}$ are vectors directed along the bisectors.

---

415. Lay off equal line segments $a=4$ on the axes OX, OY, and OZ and construct a cube on them. Let M be the centre of the upper face, and N the centre of the right-hand lateral face of the cube. Determine the vectors $\overrightarrow{OM}$ and $\overrightarrow{ON}$ and the angle between them.

416. Given the vectors $\overrightarrow{OA}=\boldsymbol{a}$ and $\overrightarrow{OB}=\boldsymbol{b}$; $a=2$, $b=4$, and $(\widehat{\boldsymbol{a}, \boldsymbol{b}})=60°$. Determine the angle between the median $\overrightarrow{OM}$ of the triangle AOB and the side $\overrightarrow{OA}$.

417. Drawn from a vertex of a rectangle with the sides 6 cm and 4 cm long are two straight lines bisecting the opposite sides. Find the angle φ between them.

418. Given the three consecutive vertices of a parallelogram: $A(-3, -2, 0)$, $B(3, -3, 1)$, and $C(5, 0, 2)$. Find its fourth vertex D and the angle between the vectors $\overrightarrow{AC}$ and $\overrightarrow{BD}$.

419. Given the points $A(3, 3, -2)$, $B(0, -3, 4)$, $C(0, -3, 0)$, and $D(0, 2, -4)$. Construct the vectors $\overrightarrow{AB}=\boldsymbol{a}$ and $\overrightarrow{CD}=\boldsymbol{b}$ and find $\text{pr}_{\boldsymbol{a}}\boldsymbol{b}$.

420. In an isosceles trapezoid $OACB$ (Fig. 16) M and N are the midpoints of the sides $BC=2$ and $AC=2$. The acute angle of the trapezoid is equal to 60°. Determine the angle between the vectors $\overrightarrow{OM}$ and $\overrightarrow{ON}$.

421. Find the angle between the vectors $\boldsymbol{a}=2\boldsymbol{m}+4\boldsymbol{n}$ and $\boldsymbol{b}=\boldsymbol{m}-\boldsymbol{n}$, where $\boldsymbol{m}$ and $\boldsymbol{n}$ are unit vectors forming an angle of 120°.

422. Show that the angle between the diagonals of a rectangle constructed on vectors $\boldsymbol{a}$ and $\boldsymbol{b}\,(\boldsymbol{a}\perp\boldsymbol{b})$ is determined by the formula $\cos\varphi=\pm\frac{a^2-b^2}{a^2+b^2}$.

423. The projections of the displacement of a moving point on the coordinate axes are $s_x=2$ m, $s_y=1$ m, $s_z=-2$ m. The projections of an acting force $\boldsymbol{F}$ on the coordinate axes are $F_x=50$ N, $F_y=40$ N, and $F_z=30$ N. Compute the work A of the force $\boldsymbol{F}\,(A=\boldsymbol{F}\cdot\boldsymbol{s})$ and the angle between the force $\boldsymbol{F}$ and the displacement $\boldsymbol{s}$.

424. Applied to a vertex of a regular tetrahedron with the edge a are three forces represented by its vector edges. Determine the absolute value of the resultant force.

Hint. The required value is equal to $a\sqrt{(\boldsymbol{m}+\boldsymbol{n}+\boldsymbol{p})^2}$, where $\boldsymbol{m}$, $\boldsymbol{n}$, and $\boldsymbol{p}$ are the unit vectors of the given forces.

425. A square is divided into three strips of equal widths and then made up into a regular triangular prism. Find the angle between two adjacent segments of the polygonal line formed by the diagonal of the square.

2.4. Vector Product of Two Vectors

1°. Definition. The *vector product* of a vector $\boldsymbol{a}$ by a vector $\boldsymbol{b}$ is a *third vector* $\boldsymbol{c}$ (Fig. 19), which is constructed as follows:

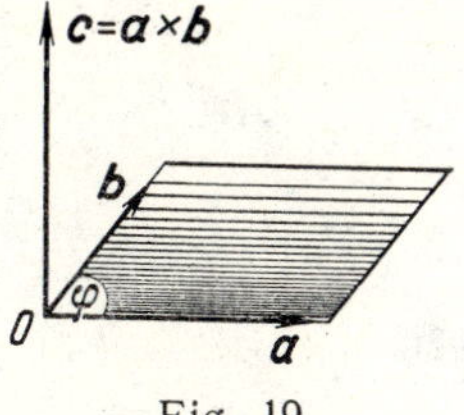

Fig. 19

(1) its *absolute value* is numerically *equal to the area of a parallelogram* constructed on the vectors $\boldsymbol{a}$ and $\boldsymbol{b}$;

(2) its direction is *perpendicular* to the plane of the parallelogram;

(3) the direction of the vector $\boldsymbol{c}$ is chosen (from two possible directions) so that the vectors a, b, c form a so-called *right-handed system*, in which the shortest rotation from $\boldsymbol{a}$ to $\boldsymbol{b}$ is considered as being carried out counterclockwise.

Notation: $$\boldsymbol{c}=\boldsymbol{a}\times\boldsymbol{b}$$

$$\text{if}\begin{cases}(1)\ \ c=|\boldsymbol{a}\times\boldsymbol{b}|=ab\sin\varphi,\\(2)\ \ \boldsymbol{c}\perp\boldsymbol{a}\text{ and }\boldsymbol{c}\perp\boldsymbol{b},\\(3)\ \ \boldsymbol{a},\ \boldsymbol{b},\ \boldsymbol{c}\text{ form a } \textit{right-handed system}.\end{cases}$$

2°. Properties of a vector product:

I. $\boldsymbol{a}\times\boldsymbol{b}=-\boldsymbol{b}\times\boldsymbol{a}$.

II. $\boldsymbol{a}\times(\boldsymbol{b}+\boldsymbol{c})=\boldsymbol{a}\times\boldsymbol{b}+\boldsymbol{a}\times\boldsymbol{c}$ (*distributive property*).

III. If $\boldsymbol{a}\parallel\boldsymbol{b}$, then $\boldsymbol{a}\times\boldsymbol{b}=0$; in particular, $\boldsymbol{a}\times\boldsymbol{a}=0$.

3°. The vector products of basis vectors:

$$\boldsymbol{i}\times\boldsymbol{j}=\boldsymbol{k},\quad \boldsymbol{j}\times\boldsymbol{k}=\boldsymbol{i},\quad \boldsymbol{k}\times\boldsymbol{i}=\boldsymbol{j}.$$

In general, a product of any two adjacent vectors in the sequence

$$\begin{array}{c}\longrightarrow +\\ \boldsymbol{ijkij}\\ -\longleftarrow\end{array}$$

yields the next vector with the plus sign, in case of the reversed sequence with the minus sign.

4°. Expressing a vector product in terms of the coordinates of the factors $\boldsymbol{a}\{a_x, a_y, a_z\}$ and $\boldsymbol{b}\{b_x, b_y, b_z\}$:

$$\boldsymbol{a}\times\boldsymbol{b}=\begin{vmatrix}\boldsymbol{i} & \boldsymbol{j} & \boldsymbol{k}\\ a_x & a_y & a_z\\ b_x & b_y & b_z\end{vmatrix}. \tag{2}$$

5°. The area of a parallelogram constructed on the vectors $\boldsymbol{a}$ and $\boldsymbol{b}$:

$$S_{\square}=|\boldsymbol{a}\times\boldsymbol{b}|, \tag{3}$$

and the area of a triangle constructed on the vectors $\boldsymbol{a}$ and $\boldsymbol{b}$:

$$S_{\Delta}=\frac{1}{2}|\boldsymbol{a}\times\boldsymbol{b}|. \tag{4}$$

426. Determine and construct the vector $\boldsymbol{c}=\boldsymbol{a}\times\boldsymbol{b}$ if (1) $\boldsymbol{a}=3\boldsymbol{i}$, $\boldsymbol{b}=2\boldsymbol{k}$; (2) $\boldsymbol{a}=\boldsymbol{i}+\boldsymbol{j}$, $\boldsymbol{b}=\boldsymbol{i}-\boldsymbol{j}$; (3) $\boldsymbol{a}=2\boldsymbol{i}+3\boldsymbol{j}$, $\boldsymbol{b}=3\boldsymbol{j}+2\boldsymbol{k}$. For each case find the area of a parallelogram constructed on the vectors $\boldsymbol{a}$ and $\boldsymbol{b}$.

427. Compute the area of a triangle with the vertices $A(7, 3, 4)$, $B(1, 0, 6)$, and $C(4, 5, -2)$.

428. Construct a parallelogram on the vectors $\boldsymbol{a}=2\boldsymbol{j}+\boldsymbol{k}$ and $\boldsymbol{b}=\boldsymbol{i}+2\boldsymbol{k}$ and compute its area and altitude.

429. Remove the parentheses and simplify the expressions:

(1) $\boldsymbol{i}\times(\boldsymbol{j}+\boldsymbol{k})-\boldsymbol{j}\times(\boldsymbol{i}+\boldsymbol{k})+\boldsymbol{k}\times(\boldsymbol{i}+\boldsymbol{j}+\boldsymbol{k})$;

(2) $(\boldsymbol{a}+\boldsymbol{b}+\boldsymbol{c})\times\boldsymbol{c}+(\boldsymbol{a}+\boldsymbol{b}+\boldsymbol{c})\times\boldsymbol{b}+(\boldsymbol{b}-\boldsymbol{c})\times\boldsymbol{a}$;

(3) $(2\boldsymbol{a}+\boldsymbol{b})\times(\boldsymbol{c}-\boldsymbol{a})+(\boldsymbol{b}+\boldsymbol{c})\times(\boldsymbol{a}+\boldsymbol{b})$;

(4) $2\boldsymbol{i}\cdot(\boldsymbol{j}\times\boldsymbol{k})+3\boldsymbol{j}\cdot(\boldsymbol{i}\times\boldsymbol{k})+4\boldsymbol{k}\cdot(\boldsymbol{i}\times\boldsymbol{j})$.

430. Prove that $(\boldsymbol{a}-\boldsymbol{b})\times(\boldsymbol{a}+\boldsymbol{b})=2\boldsymbol{a}\times\boldsymbol{b}$, and find out the geometrical meaning of this identity.

431. Vectors $\boldsymbol{a}$ and $\boldsymbol{b}$ form an angle of 45°. Find the area of a triangle constructed on the vectors $\boldsymbol{a}-2\boldsymbol{b}$ and $3\boldsymbol{a}+2\boldsymbol{b}$ if $|\boldsymbol{a}|=|\boldsymbol{b}|=5$.

432. Find the area of a parallelogram whose diagonals are the vectors $2\boldsymbol{m}-\boldsymbol{n}$ and $4\boldsymbol{m}-5\boldsymbol{n}$, where $\boldsymbol{m}$ and $\boldsymbol{n}$ are the unit vectors forming an angle of 45°.

Hint. $\boldsymbol{a}+\boldsymbol{b}=2\boldsymbol{m}-\boldsymbol{n}$ and $\boldsymbol{a}-\boldsymbol{b}=4\boldsymbol{m}-5\boldsymbol{n}$, where $\boldsymbol{a}$ and $\boldsymbol{b}$ are the vector sides of the parallelogram. Multiplying we find the vector $2\boldsymbol{b}\times\boldsymbol{a}$ whose modulus is equal to twice the required area.

---

433. Construct the vectors $\boldsymbol{a}=3\boldsymbol{k}-2\boldsymbol{j}$, $\boldsymbol{b}=3\boldsymbol{i}-2\boldsymbol{j}$, and $\boldsymbol{c}=\boldsymbol{a}\times\boldsymbol{b}$. Compute the absolute value of the vector $\boldsymbol{c}$ and the area of a triangle constructed on the vectors $\boldsymbol{a}$ and $\boldsymbol{b}$.

434. Construct a triangle with the vertices $A(1, -2, 8)$, $B(0, 0, 4)$, and $C(6, 2, 0)$. Compute its area and the altitude BD.

435. Compute the diagonals and the area of a parallelogram constructed on the vectors $\boldsymbol{a}=\boldsymbol{k}-\boldsymbol{j}$ and $\boldsymbol{b}=\boldsymbol{i}+\boldsymbol{j}+\boldsymbol{k}$.

436. Prove that $(2\boldsymbol{a}+\boldsymbol{b})\times(\boldsymbol{a}+2\boldsymbol{b})=3\boldsymbol{a}\times\boldsymbol{b}$.

437. Find the area of a parallelogram constructed on the vectors $\boldsymbol{a}=\boldsymbol{m}+2\boldsymbol{n}$ and $\boldsymbol{b}=2\boldsymbol{m}+\boldsymbol{n}$, where $\boldsymbol{m}$ and $\boldsymbol{n}$ are the unit vectors forming an angle of 30°.

2.5. Scalar Triple Product

1°. Definition. The *scalar triple product* of three vectors $\boldsymbol{a}$, $\boldsymbol{b}$, and $\boldsymbol{c}$ is the expression $(\boldsymbol{a}\times\boldsymbol{b})\cdot\boldsymbol{c}$, i.e. the scalar product of the vector product $\boldsymbol{a}\times\boldsymbol{b}$ by the vector $\boldsymbol{c}$.

If the vectors $\boldsymbol{a}$, $\boldsymbol{b}$, and $\boldsymbol{c}$ are given by their coordinates, then

$$(\boldsymbol{a}\times\boldsymbol{b})\cdot\boldsymbol{c}=\begin{vmatrix} a_x & a_y & a_z \\ b_x & b_y & b_z \\ c_x & c_y & c_z \end{vmatrix}. \qquad (1)$$

2°. The properties of a scalar triple product.

I. An interchange of any two factors reverses its sign:

$$(\boldsymbol{a}\times\boldsymbol{b})\cdot\boldsymbol{c}=-(\boldsymbol{a}\times\boldsymbol{c})\cdot\boldsymbol{b}=-(\boldsymbol{c}\times\boldsymbol{b})\cdot\boldsymbol{a}. \qquad (2)$$

II. A triple product having at least two equal or parallel vectors is zero.

III. The signs of operations may be interchanged: $(\boldsymbol{a}\times\boldsymbol{b})\cdot\boldsymbol{c}=\boldsymbol{a}\cdot(\boldsymbol{b}\times\boldsymbol{c})$, therefore the scalar triple product is usually written as $\boldsymbol{abc}$, i.e. without the signs of operations and without parentheses.

3°. The volume of a parallelepiped constructed on the vectors $\boldsymbol{a}$, $\boldsymbol{b}$, and $\boldsymbol{c}$:

$$V_{\text{par}}=\pm\,\boldsymbol{abc}\begin{cases} + \text{for a right-handed system} \\ - \text{for a left-handed system.} \end{cases}$$

The volume of a pyramid constructed on the vectors $\boldsymbol{a}$, $\boldsymbol{b}$, $\boldsymbol{c}$:

$$V_{\text{pyr}}=\pm\frac{1}{6}\,\boldsymbol{abc}.$$

4°. Criterion of coplanarity. If the system $\boldsymbol{a}$, $\boldsymbol{b}$, $\boldsymbol{c}$ is right-handed, then $\boldsymbol{abc}>0$; if it is left-handed, then $\boldsymbol{abc}<0$. But if the vectors $\boldsymbol{a}$, $\boldsymbol{b}$, $\boldsymbol{c}$ are *coplanar*, then

$abc=0$. In other words, the vanishing of the triple product abc is a criterion of the coplanarity of the vectors a, b, c. There exists a *linear dependence* of a, b, and c of the form $c=ma+nb$.

438. Construct a parallelepiped on the vectors $a=3i+4j$, $b=-3j+k$, $c=2j+5k$ and calculate its volume. Will the system (a, b, c) be right-handed or left-handed?

439. Construct a pyramid with the vertices $O(0, 0, 0)$, $A(5, 2, 0)$, $B(2, 5, 0)$, and $C(1, 2, 4)$ and compute its volume, the area of the face ABC and the altitude of the pyramid dropped onto this face.

440. Show that the points $A(2, -1, -2)$, $B(1, 2, 1)$, $C(2, 3, 0)$, and $D(5, 0, -6)$ lie in one and the same plane.

441. Show that the vectors $a=-i+3j+2k$, $b=2i-3j-4k$, $c=-3i+12j+6k$ are coplanar and resolve the vector c into the vectors a and b.

442. Show that: (1) $(a+b)\cdot[(a+c)\times b]=-abc$; (2) $(a+2b-c)\cdot[(a-b)\times(a-b-c)]=3abc$.

443. Find the volume of a tetrahedron constructed on the vectors $\overrightarrow{OA}$, $\overrightarrow{OB}$, and $\overrightarrow{OC}$ if they are directed along the bisectors of the corresponding quadrants, the length of each vector being equal to 2.

---

444. Construct a pyramid with the vertices $A(2, 0, 0)$, $B(0, 3, 0)$, $C(0, 0, 6)$, and $D(2, 3, 8)$, compute its volume and the altitude dropped onto the face ABC.

445. Construct the vectors $a=i+j+4k$, $b=i-2j$, and $c=3i-3j+4k$, show that they are coplanar, and find the linear dependence of them.

446. Show that the volume of a parallelepiped constructed on the diagonals of the faces of the given parallelepiped is twice the volume of the given parallelepiped.

447. Given the unit vectors m, n, and p. The angle $\widehat{(m, n)}=\widehat{[p, (m\times n)]}=\alpha$. Prove that then $(m\times n)\cdot p=\frac{1}{2}\sin 2a$.

448. For any vectors a, b, and c the vectors $a-b$, $b-c$, and $c-a$ are coplanar. Prove this analytically and geometrically (by considering the parallelepiped constructed on the vectors $\boldsymbol{a}$, $\boldsymbol{b}$, and $\boldsymbol{c}$).

449. Compute the volume of a parallelepiped $OABCO_1A_1B_1C_1$ given three vertices of its lower base $O(0, 0, 0)$, $A(2, -3, 0)$, and $C(3, 2, 0)$ and the vertex of the upper base $B_1(3, 0, 4)$ which lies on the lateral edge BB_1, the latter being opposite to the edge OO_1.

CHAPTER 3

SOLID ANALYTIC GEOMETRY

3.1. *The Equation of a Plane*

1°. The equation of a plane which passes through a point $M_1(x_1, y_1, z_1)$ and is perpendicular to a vector $\mathbf{N}\{A, B, C\}$.

Let $M(x, y, z)$ be an arbitrary point of a plane (Fig. 20).

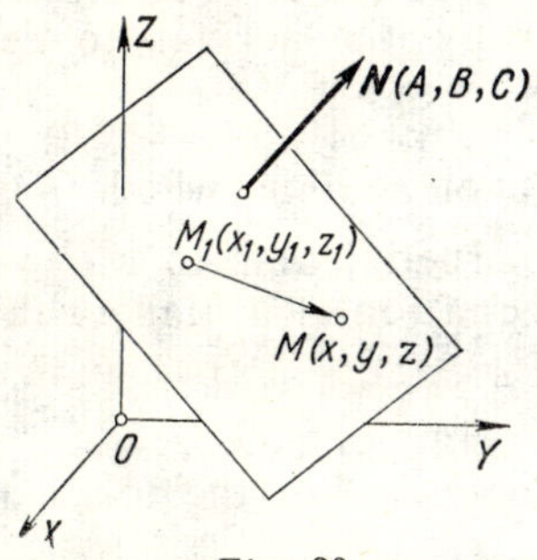

Fig. 20

Then $\overrightarrow{M_1M} \perp \mathbf{N}$, and, by the condition of perpendicularity of vectors,

$$A(x-x_1)+B(y-y_1)+C(z-z_1)=0. \qquad (1)$$

2°. The general equation of a plane:

$$Ax+By+Cz+D=0. \qquad (2)$$

The vector $N\{A, B, C\}$ is called the *normal* vector of plane (2) or (1).

3°. Particular cases of the equation $Ax+By+Cz+D=0$.

I. The equation $Ax+By+Cz=0$ (constant term $D=0$) represents a plane passing through the origin.

II. The equation $Ax+By+D=0$ (coefficient $C=0$) is a plane parallel to the axis OZ.

III. The equation $Ax+By=0$ $(C=D=0)$ represents a plane passing through the axis OZ.

IV. The equation $Ax+D=0$ $(B=C=0)$ is a plane parallel to the plane YOZ.

V. The equations of the coordinate planes: $x=0$, $y=0$, $z=0$.

4°. The intercept form of the equation of a plane:

$$\frac{x}{a}+\frac{y}{b}+\frac{z}{c}=1. \tag{3}$$

450. Construct the planes: (1) $5x-2y+3z-10=0$; (2) $3x+2y-z=0$; (3) $3x+2z=6$; (4) $2z-7=0$.

451. Construct the plane $2x+3y+6z-12=0$ and find the angles formed by the normal to the plane and the coordinate axes.

452. Given the points $M_1(0, -1, 3)$ and $M_2(1, 3, 5)$. Write the equation of a plane which passes through the point M_1 and is perpendicular to the vector $\boldsymbol{N}=\overrightarrow{M_1M_2}$.

453. Write the equation of a plane which passes through the point $M(a, a, 0)$ and is perpendicular to the vector $\overrightarrow{OM}$. Construct this plane.

454. Write the equation of the locus of points equidistant from the points $A\left(a, -\frac{a}{2}, a\right)$ and $B\left(0, \frac{a}{2}, 0\right)$.

455. Write the equation of a plane which is parallel to the axis OX and passes through the points $M_1(0, 1, 3)$ and $M_2(2, 4, 5)$ and construct this plane.

456. Write the equation of a plane passing through the axis OX and point $M_1(0, -2, 3)$. Construct the plane.

457. Write the equation of a plane passing through the axis OZ and point $M_1(2, -4, 3)$. Construct the plane.

458. Write the equation of a plane which is parallel to the axis OY and cuts off intercepts a and c on the axes OX and OZ respectively. Construct the plane.

459. Write the equation of a plane passing through the point $M(2, -1, 3)$ and intercepting equal line segments on the coordinate axes.

460. Write the equation of a plane passing through the point $M_1(-4, 0, 4)$ and intercepting the line segments $a=4$ and $b=3$ on the axes OX and OY respectively.

---

461. Construct the following planes: (1) $2x+y-z+6=0$; (2) $x-y-z=0$; (3) $y-2z+8=0$; (4) $2x-5=0$; (5) $x+z=1$; (6) $y+z=0$.

462. Construct the plane $2x-2y+z-6=0$ and find the angles formed by its normal and the coordinate axes.

463. Through the point $M(-1, 2, 3)$ a plane is drawn perpendicular to OM. Write its equation.

464. Write the equation of a plane passing through the axis OY and through the point $(4, 0, 3)$. Construct the plane.

465. Write the equation of a plane which is parallel to the axis OZ and passes through the points $M_1(2, 2, 0)$ and $M_2(4, 0, 0)$. Construct the plane.

466. Write the equation of a plane which passes through the point $M_1(1, -3, 5)$ and intercepts on the axes OY and OZ line segments twice as long as one on the axis OX.

3.2. Basic Problems Involving the Equation of a Plane

1°. An angle formed by two planes:

$$\cos\varphi = \pm\frac{\mathbf{N}\cdot\mathbf{N}_1}{NN_1} = \pm\frac{AA_1+BB_1+CC_1}{NN_1}, \tag{1}$$

where $\mathbf{N}$ and $\mathbf{N}_1$ are the normal vectors to the planes $Ax+By+Cz+D=0$ and $A_1x+B_1y+C_1z+D_1=0$.

The condition of parallelism of planes:

$$\frac{A}{A_1}=\frac{B}{B_1}=\frac{C}{C_1}. \tag{2}$$

The condition of perpendicularity of planes:

$$AA_1+BB_1+CC_1=0. \tag{3}$$

2°. The distance from a point $M_0(x_0, y_0, z_0)$ to a plane $Ax+By+Cz+D=0$

$$d=\frac{|Ax_0+By_0+Cz_0+D|}{N}. \tag{4}$$

3°. The equation of a pencil of all planes passing through the line of intersection of two given planes:

$$\alpha(Ax+By+Cz+D)+\beta(A_1x+B_1y+C_1z+D_1)=0. \quad (5)$$

We may put $\alpha=1$, thus eliminating the second of the given planes from pencil (5).

467. Find the angle between the planes:

(1) $x-2y+2z-8=0$ and $x+z-6=0$;
(2) $x+2z-6=0$ and $x+2y-4=0$.

468. Find the plane passing through a point (2, 2, —2) parallel to the plane $x-2y-3z=0$.

469. Write the equation of a plane passing through a point (—1, —1, 2) perpendicular to the planes $x-2y+z-4=0$ and $x+2y-2z+4=0$.

470. Write the equation of a plane passing through a point (0, 0, a) perpendicular to the planes $x-y-z=0$ and $2y=x$.

471. Write the equation of a plane passing through the points $M_1(-1, -2, 0)$ and $M_2(1, 1, 2)$ perpendicular to the plane $x+2y+2z-4=0$.

472. Write the equation of a plane passing through the points $M_1(1, -1, 2)$, $M_2(2, 1, 2)$, and $M_3(1, 1, 4)$.

473. Through the axis OZ draw a plane at an angle of 60° to the plane $2x+y-\sqrt{5}z=0$.

474. Find the distance from the point (5, 1, —1) to the plane $x-2y-2z+4=0$.

475. Find the distance from the point (4, 3, 0) to a plane passing through the points $M_1(1, 3, 0)$, $M_2(4, -1, 2)$, and $M_3(3, 0, 1)$.

476. Find the distance between the two parallel planes

$$4x+3y-5z-8=0 \quad \text{and} \quad 4x+3y-5z+12=0.$$

Hint. Take an arbitrary point on one plane, say (2, 0, 0), and find its distance from the other plane.

477. (1) Write the equations of planes parallel to the plane $x-2y+2z-5=0$ and 2 units distant from it.

(2) Write the equations of planes bisecting the dihedral angle formed by the planes $2x+2y=z$ and $z=0$, and construct both the given and the required planes.

478. (1) Write the equation of a plane passing through the line of intersection of the planes $2x-y+3z-6=0$, $x+2y-z+3=0$ and through the point (1, 2, 4).

(2) Find two mutually perpendicular planes passing through the straight line of intersection of the planes $x=y$ and $z=0$ if one of the required planes passes through the point (0, 4, 2). Construct the straight line and the required planes.

479. Find the point of intersection of the planes: $2x-y+3z-9=0$; $x+2y+2z-3=0$; $3x+y-4z+6=0$.

---

480. Write the equation of a plane passing through a point (2, —1, 1) perpendicular to the planes $3x+2y-z+4=0$ and $x+y+z-3=0$. Construct this plane.

481. Write the equation of a plane that passes through the two points (0, —5, 0) and (0, 0, 2) perpendicular to the plane $x+5y+2z-10=0$. Construct the plane.

482. Find the angle between the plane passing through the points $O(0, 0, 0)$, $M_1(a, -a, 0)$, and $M_2(a, a, a)$ and the plane XOY.

483. Find the distance from the coordinate origin to the plane passing through the points $M_1(a, 0, 0)$, $M_2(0, a, 0)$, and $M_3(a, a, a)$.

484. Write the equation of a plane passing through the axis OX at an angle of 60° to the plane $y=x$.

485. Find the distance from a point (a, b, c) to the plane intercepting the line segments a, b, c on the coordinate axes.

486. Write the equations of planes parallel to the plane $2x+2y+z-8=0$ and located at a distance $d=4$ from it.

487. Write the equation of a plane passing through the line of intersection of the planes $4x-y+3z-6=0$ and $x+5y-z+10=0$ perpendicular to the plane $2x-y+5z-5=0$.

3.3. Equations of a Straight Line in Space

1°. Equations of a straight line passing through a point $A(a, b, c)$ parallel to the vector $\mathbf{P}\{m, n, p\}$. Let $M(x, y, z)$ be an arbitrary point of the straight line (Fig. 21), then $\overrightarrow{AM} \parallel \mathbf{P}$ and, by virtue of the condition of parallelism of vectors, we have

$$\frac{x-a}{m}=\frac{y-b}{n}=\frac{z-c}{p}. \tag{1}$$

Equations (1) are called the *canonical* equations of the straight line. Vector $\mathbf{P}\{m, n, p\}$ is called the *direction* vector of that line.

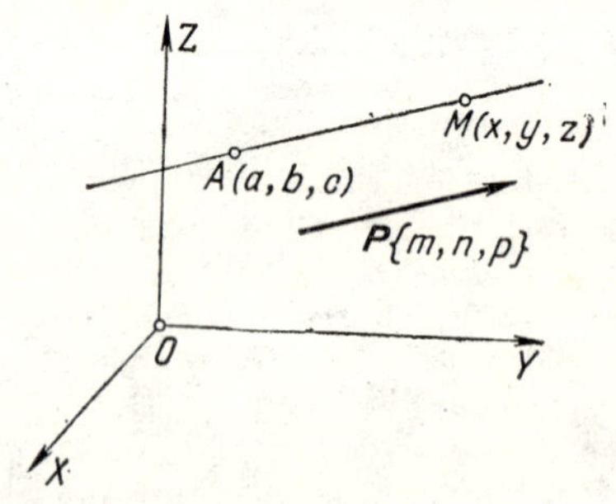

Fig. 21

2°. Parametric equations of a straight line are obtained by equating each of ratios (1) to the parameter t:

$$\left.\begin{aligned} x&=mt+a,\\ y&=nt+b,\\ z&=pt+c. \end{aligned}\right\} \tag{2}$$

3°. Equations of a straight line passing through *two points*:

$$\frac{x-x_1}{x_2-x_1}=\frac{y-y_1}{y_2-y_1}=\frac{z-z_1}{z_2-z_1}. \tag{3}$$

4°. The general equations of a straight line:

$$\left.\begin{aligned} Ax+By+Cz+D&=0,\\ A_1x+B_1y+C_1z+D_1&=0. \end{aligned}\right\} \tag{4}$$

5°. Equations of a straight line represented by its projections are obtained by eliminating first y and then x from general equations (4):

$$\left.\begin{aligned} x &= mz + a, \\ y &= nz + b. \end{aligned}\right\} \qquad (5)$$

Equations (5) can be written in the *canonical* form:

$$\frac{x-a}{m} = \frac{y-b}{n} = \frac{z-0}{1}.$$

488. Find the traces of the straight lines

$$(1)\ \begin{cases} x = z + 5 \\ y = 4 - 2z \end{cases} \quad \text{and} \quad (2)\ \frac{x-3}{1} = \frac{y-2}{2} = \frac{z-3}{1}$$

on the planes XOY and XOZ, and construct the lines.

Hint. Put in the equations (a) $z = 0$; (b) $y = 0$.

489. Write the equation of the straight line $\begin{cases} x + 2y + 3z - 13 = 0 \\ 3x + y + 4z - 14 = 0 \end{cases}$ (1) in projections; (2) in the canonical form. Find the traces of the straight line on the coordinate planes; construct the line and its projections.

490. Write the equations of the straight line passing through the point $A(4,\ 3,\ 0)$ parallel to the vector $\mathbf{P}\{-1,\ 1,\ 1\}$. Find the trace of the straight line on the plane YOZ and construct this line.

491. Construct the straight line $x = 4$, $y = 3$ and find its direction vector.

492. Construct the straight lines

$$(1)\ \begin{cases} y = 3 \\ z = 2, \end{cases} \quad (2)\ \begin{cases} y = 2 \\ z = x + 1, \end{cases} \quad (3)\ \begin{cases} x = 4 \\ z = y \end{cases}$$

and determine their direction vectors.

493. Write the equations of the straight line passing through the points $A(-1,\ 2,\ 3)$ and $B(2,\ 6,\ -2)$, and find its direction cosines.

494. Construct the straight line passing through the points $A(2,\ -1,\ 3)$ and $B(2,\ 3,\ 3)$, and write its equations.

495. Write the equations of the path of a point $M(x, y, z)$ which starts from the point $A(4, -3, 1)$ and moves with velocity $\boldsymbol{v}\{2, 3, 1\}$.

496. Write the parametric equations of the straight line (1) passing through the point $(-2, 1, -1)$ parallel to the vector $\boldsymbol{P}\{1, -2, 3\}$;

(2) passing through the points $A(3, -1, 4)$ and $B(1, 1, 2)$.

497. Write the equations of a straight line passing through the point (a, b, c) (1) parallel to the axis OZ; (2) perpendicular to the axis OZ.

498. Find the angle between the straight line $x=2z-1$, $y=-2z+1$ and the straight line passing through the coordinate origin and the point $(1, -1, -1)$.

499. Find the angle between the straight lines:

$$\begin{cases} x-y+z-4=0 \\ 2x+y-2z+5=0 \end{cases} \quad \text{and} \quad \begin{cases} x+y+z-4=0 \\ 2x+3y-z-6=0. \end{cases}$$

Hint. The direction vector of each line can be determined as a vector product of the normal vectors of the planes $(\boldsymbol{P}=\boldsymbol{N}\times\boldsymbol{N}_1)$.

500. Show that the straight line $\frac{x}{2}=\frac{y}{3}=\frac{z}{1}$ is perpendicular to the straight line $x=z+1$, $y=1-z$.

501. Write the equations of a straight line passing through the point $(-4, 3, 0)$ parallel to the straight line

$$\begin{cases} x-2y+z=4 \\ 2x+y-z=0. \end{cases}$$

502. Write the equations of the perpendicular dropped from the point $(2, -3, 4)$ onto the axis OZ.

Hint. The required straight line also passes through the point $(0, 0, 4)$.

503. Find the distance between the point $M(2, -1, 3)$ and the straight line $\frac{x+1}{3}=\frac{y+2}{4}=\frac{z-1}{5}$.

Hint. $A(-1, -2, 1)$ is a point belonging to the straight line; $\boldsymbol{P}\{3, 4, 5\}$ is the direction vector of the straight line. Then

$$d=AM\sin\alpha=\frac{AM\,|\boldsymbol{P}\times\overrightarrow{AM}|}{P\cdot AM}=\frac{|\boldsymbol{P}\times\overrightarrow{AM}|}{P}.$$

504. Find the distance between the parallel straight lines

$$\frac{x-2}{1}=\frac{y+1}{2}=\frac{z+3}{2} \text{ and } \frac{x-1}{1}=\frac{y-1}{2}=\frac{z+1}{2}.$$

---

505. Find the traces of the straight line $\frac{x-4}{1}=\frac{y-2}{2}=\frac{z}{-2}$ on the coordinate planes and construct the line.

506. Write the equations of the straight line $\begin{cases} 2x+y+8z-16=0 \\ x-2y-z+2=0 \end{cases}$ (1) in projections; (2) in the canonical form. Find its traces on the coordinate planes, construct the straight line and its projections.

507. Write the equations of the straight line passing through the point $A(0, -4, 0)$ parallel to the vector $\boldsymbol{P}\{1, 2, 3\}$, find the trace of the straight line on the plane XOZ and construct this line.

508. Construct the straight line $x=3$, $z=5$ and find its direction vector.

509. Find the direction vector of the straight line $x+y-z=0$, $y=x$ and angles formed by this line and the coordinate axes (see the hint to Problem 499).

510. Write the equations of the perpendicular dropped from the point $(2, -3, 4)$ onto the axis OY.

511. Find the angle between the straight lines:

$$\begin{cases} 2x-y-7=0 \\ 2x-z+5=0 \end{cases} \text{ and } \begin{cases} 3x-2y+8=0 \\ z=3x. \end{cases}$$

512. Write the equations of a straight line passing through the point $(-1, 2, -2)$ parallel to the straight line $x-y=2$, $y=2z+1$.

513. Find the distance from the point $M(3, 0, 4)$ to the straight line $y=2x+1$, $z=2x$ (see Problem 503).

3.4. A Straight Line and a Plane

1°. The angle between the straight line $\frac{x-a}{m}=\frac{y-b}{n}=\frac{z-c}{p}$ and the plane $Ax+By+Cz+D=0$:

$$\sin\theta=\frac{|\boldsymbol{N}\cdot\boldsymbol{P}|}{NP}=\frac{|Am+Bn+Cp|}{NP}. \quad (1)$$

The condition of their parallelism ($N \perp P$):

$$Am+Bn+Cp=0. \qquad (2)$$

The condition of their perpendicularity ($N \parallel P$):

$$\frac{A}{m}=\frac{B}{n}=\frac{C}{p}. \qquad (3)$$

2°. The point of intersection of a straight line and a plane. Write the parametric equations of the straight line $x=mt+a$, $y=nt+b$, $z=pt+c$, and in the equation of the plane $Ax+By+Cz+D=0$ replace x, y, z by their expressions in terms of t. Find t_0, and then x_0, y_0, z_0 which are the coordinates of the point of intersection.

3°. The condition for two straight lines lying in a single plane:

$$\begin{vmatrix} a-a_1 & b-b_1 & c-c_1 \\ m & n & p \\ m_1 & n_1 & p_1 \end{vmatrix}=0. \qquad (4)$$

514. Find the angle between the straight line $y=3x-1$, $2z=-3x+2$ and the plane $2x+y+z-4=0$.

515. Show that (1) the straight line $\frac{x+1}{2}=\frac{y+1}{-1}=\frac{z-3}{3}$ is parallel to the plane $2x+y-z=0$, (2) the straight line $\frac{x+1}{2}=\frac{y+1}{-1}=\frac{z+3}{3}$ lies in this plane.

516. Write the equation of a plane passing through the point $(-1, 2, -3)$ perpendicular to the straight line $x=2$, $y-z=1$.

517. Write the equation of a plane passing through the straight line $\frac{x-2}{1}=\frac{y-3}{2}=\frac{z+1}{3}$ and the point $(3, 4, 0)$.

518. Write the equation of a plane passing through the straight line $\frac{x-1}{1}=\frac{y+1}{2}=\frac{z+2}{2}$ perpendicular to the plane $2x+3y-z=4$.

519. Write the equation of a plane passing through two parallel straight lines $\frac{x-3}{2}=\frac{y}{1}=\frac{z-1}{2}$ and $\frac{x+1}{2}=\frac{y-1}{1}=\frac{z}{2}$.

520. Write the equations of a straight line passing through the coordinate origin and forming equal angles with the planes $4y=3x$, $y=0$, and $z=0$. Find these angles.

521. Find the point of intersection of the straight line $x=2t-1$, $y=t+2$, $z=1-t$ and the plane $3x-2y+z=3$.

522. Find the point of intersection of the straight line $\frac{x}{2}=\frac{y-1}{1}=\frac{z+1}{2}$ and the plane $x+2y+3z-29=0$.

523. Find the projection of the point $(3, 1, -1)$ on the plane $x+2y+3z-30=0$.

524. Find the projection of the point $(2, 3, 4)$ on the straight line $x=y=z$.

525. Find the shortest distance between the non-parallel straight lines:

(1) $\frac{x-a}{m}=\frac{y-b}{n}=\frac{z-c}{p}$ and $\frac{x-a_1}{m_1}=\frac{y-b_1}{n_1}=\frac{z-c_1}{p_1}$;

(2) $\frac{x+1}{1}=\frac{y}{1}=\frac{z-1}{2}$ and $\frac{x}{1}=\frac{y+1}{3}=\frac{z-2}{4}$.

Hint. Assuming that in the general case the straight lines are skew, let us draw parallel planes in which the lines are contained. From the points $A(a, b, c)$ and $A_1(a_1, b_1, c_1)$ draw the vectors $\overrightarrow{AB}=\overrightarrow{A_1B_1}=\mathbf{P}\{m, n, p\}$ and $\overrightarrow{AC}=\overrightarrow{A_1C_1}=\mathbf{P}_1\{m_1, n_1, p_1\}$. The altitude of the prism $ABCA_1B_1C_1$ is then the required distance.

526. Show that the straight lines

$$\begin{cases} x=z-2 \\ y=2z+1 \end{cases} \text{ and } \frac{x-2}{3}=\frac{y-4}{1}=\frac{z-2}{1}$$

intersect, and write the equation of the plane in which they are contained.

527. Write the equations of a perpendicular dropped from the point $(2, 1, 0)$ onto the straight line $x=3z-1$, $y=2z$.

---

528. Construct the plane $x+y-z=0$ and the straight line passing through the points $A(0, 0, 4)$ and $B(2, 2, 0)$. Find the point of intersection of the line and the plane and the angle between them.

529. Construct the plane $y=z$, the straight line $\begin{cases} x=-z+1 \\ y=2 \end{cases}$ and find (1) the point at which they intersect; (2) the angle between them.

530. Find the projection of the point (3, 1, —1) on the plane $3x+y+z-20=0$.

531. Find the projection of the point (1, 2, 8) on the straight line $\frac{x-1}{2}=\frac{y}{-1}=z$.

532. Write the equation of a plane passing through the parallel straight lines $\frac{x-1}{1}=\frac{y+1}{-2}=\frac{z-2}{3}$ and $\frac{x}{1}=\frac{y+1}{-2}=\frac{z-1}{3}$.

533. Show that the straight lines $\frac{x+3}{1}=\frac{y+1}{2}=\frac{z+1}{1}$ and $\begin{cases} x=3z-4 \\ y=z+2 \end{cases}$ intersect; find the point of intersection.

534. Write the equation of the perpendicular dropped from the point (1, 0, —1) onto the straight line $\frac{x+1}{1}=\frac{y-1}{2}=\frac{z}{-3}$.

535. Find the shortes distance between the straight lines $x=-2y=z$ and $x=y=2$.

3.5. Spherical and Cylindrical Surfaces

1°. The equation of a spherical surface of radius R with $C(a, b, c)$ as centre:

$$(x-a)^2+(y-b)^2+(z-c)^2=R^2. \qquad (1)$$

2°. The equation $F(x, y)=0$, which does not have the z-coordinate, defines a *cylindrical* surface whose *generatrix* is *parallel* to the axis OZ. Analogously, each of the equations $F(y, z)=0$ and $F(x, z)=0$ determines a cylindrical surface whose generatrix is parallel to OX and OY respectively.

3°. The equation of a cylindrical surface with the directrix $F(x, y)=0$, $z=0$ and the generatrix parallel to the vector $\mathbf{P}\{m, n, p\}$. The equation of an arbitrary generatrix will be $\frac{x-x_0}{m}=\frac{y-y_0}{n}=\frac{z}{p}$, where $(x_0, y_0, 0)$ is a point belonging to the directrix.

Determining x_0 and y_0 and substituting them into the equation of the directrix, we get the equation of a cylindrical surface:

$$F\left(x-\frac{m}{p}z,\quad y-\frac{n}{p}z\right)=0. \qquad (2)$$

536. Find the centre and he radius of the sphere (1) $x^2+y^2+z^2-3x+5y-4z=0$; (2) $x^2+y^2+z^2=2az$ and construct the second sphere.

537. Write the equation of a spherical surface inscribed in a tetrahedron generated by the planes

$$3x-2y+6z-18=0,\quad x=0,\ y=0,\ z=0.$$

538. Write the equation of the locus of points situated twice as near to the point $A(2, 0, 0)$ as to the point $B(-4, 0, 0)$.

539. Write the equation of a sphere passing through the circle $\begin{cases} x^2+y^2+z^2=a^2 \\ x+y+z=a \end{cases}$ and through the point (a, a, a).

Hint. The required equation must be of the form:

$$x^2+y^2+z^2-a^2+\lambda(x+y+z-a)=0.$$

540. Construct in the left-handed system of coordinates the following surfaces:

(1) $y^2+z^2=4$; (2) $y^2=ax$; (3) $xz=4$; (4) $x^2+y^2=ax$.

541. Write the equation of the locus of points equidistant from the straight line $x=a$, $y=0$ and the plane YOZ. Construct this surface.

542. Write the equations of three cylindrical surfaces circumscribed about the sphere $x^2+y^2+z^2-2ax=0$ whose generatrices are parallel to (1) the axis OX; (2) the axis OY; (3) the axis OZ respectively.

543. Draw *the curve of Viviani*

$$\begin{cases} x^2+y^2+z^2=16 \\ x^2+y^2\qquad\ \ =4x \end{cases}$$

in the first octant of a left-handed coordinate system, constructing the points at $x=0$; 2; and 4. Show that the projection of the curve on the plane XOZ is a parabola.

544. Find the centre and the radius of the circle

$$\begin{cases} x^2+y^2+z^2 = 10y \\ x+2y+2z-19=0. \end{cases}$$

Hint. The centre of a circle is the projection of the centre of a sphere onto a plane (see Problem 530).

545. Write the equation of a cylindrical surface whose directrix is $y^2=4x$, $z=0$ and the generatrix is parallel to the vector $\boldsymbol{P}\{1, 2, 3\}$.

546. Construct the surface $(x+y)^2+az=a^2$ in the first octant using the sections by the planes $x=0$, $y=0$, $z=0$, $z=h\leqslant a$, and show that this is a cylindrical surface whose generatrix is parallel to the straight line $x+y=a$, $z=0$.

547. The sphere $x^2+y^2+z^2=4z$ is illuminated by rays parallel to the straight line $x=0$, $y=z$. Find the shape of the shadow cast on the plane XOY.

Hint. Write the equation of the cylindrical surface generated by the rays tangent to the sphere. Its directrix will be the line cut from the sphere by a plane passing through the centre of the sphere perpendicular to the rays.

---

548. Write the equation of a plane passing through the centre C of the surface $x^2+y^2+z^2-2x+y-3z=0$ perpendicular to the straight line OC.

549. Write the equation of the locus of points situated twice as far from the coordinate origin as from the point $(0, -3, 0)$.

550. Find the projection onto the plane $z=0$ of the section of a spherical surface $x^2+y^2+z^2=4(x-2y-2z)$ by a plane passing through the centre of the sphere perpendicular to the straight line $x=0$, $y+z=0$.

551. Construct the following surfaces in the left-handed coordinate system:

(1) $z=4-x^2$; (2) $y^2+z^2=4z$; (3) $y^2=x^3$.

552. Construct the line of intersection of the cylinders $x^2+z^2=a^2$ and $x^2+y^2=a^2$ in the first octant of a left-handed coordinate system.

Hint. In the planes XOZ and XOY construct quarters of the director circles, divide them approximately into equal parts (for instance, into 4), and through the points of division draw the generatrices of the cylinders to obtain the points of their intersection (see Fig. 64 on page 372).

553. Write the equation of a cylindrical surface whose generatrix is parallel to the vector $\boldsymbol{P}\{1, 1, 1\}$ and the directrix is $x^2+y^2=4x$, $z=0$.

554. Construct a solid bounded by the surfaces $y^2=x$, $z=0$, $z=4$, $x=4$, and write the equations of the diagonals of the face contained in the plane $x=4$.

3.6. Conical Surfaces and Surfaces of Revolution

1°. Conical surfaces. Let a *conical surface* have the vertex at the coordinate origin, and the *directrix* $F(x, y)=0$ on the plane $z=h$. Then the equation of the *generatrix* will be $\frac{x}{x_0}=\frac{y}{y_0}=\frac{z}{h}$, where (x_0, y_0, h) is a point belonging to the directrix. Determining x_0 and y_0 and substituting them into the equation $F(x, y)=0$, we get the *equation of a conical surface with the vertex at the coordinate origin:*

$$F\left(\frac{xh}{z}, \frac{yh}{z}\right)=0. \tag{1}$$

If the vertex of a cone is situated at a point (a, b, c), then equation (1) takes the form

$$F\left[\frac{(x-a)(h-c)}{z-c}+a, \quad \frac{(y-b)(h-c)}{z-c}+b\right]=0. \tag{2}$$

Equation (1) is *homogeneous* with respect to x, y, z, and equation (2) is homogeneous with respect to $(x-a)$, $(y-b)$, and $(z-c)$. Thus, the *equation of a conical surface* is recognized by its *homogeneity*.

2°. Surfaces of revolution.

Equation of the curve	Axis of revolution	Equation of the surface of revolution
$\begin{cases} F(x, y)=0 \\ z=0 \end{cases}$	OX OY	$F(x, \sqrt{y^2+z^2})=0$ $F(\sqrt{x^2+z^2}, y)=0$
$\begin{cases} F(x, z)=0 \\ y=0 \end{cases}$	OX OZ	$F(x, \sqrt{y^2+z^2})=0$ $F(\sqrt{x^2+y^2}, z)=0$
$\begin{cases} F(y, z)=0 \\ x=0 \end{cases}$	OY OZ	$F(y, \sqrt{x^2+z^2})=0$ $F(\sqrt{x^2+y^2}, z)=0$

555. Write the equation of a conical surface with the vertex at the coordinate origin and the directrix $x^2+y^2=a^2$, $z=c$. Construct the surface.

556. Write the equation of a conical surface with the vertex at the point $A(0, -a, 0)$ and the directrix $x^2=2py$, $z=h$. Construct the surface.

557. Determine the vertex of the cone $x^2+(y-a)^2-z^2=0$, its directrix in the plane $z=a$, and construct the cone.

558. Determine the vertex of the cone $x^2=2yz$, its directrix in the plane $z=h$, and construct the cone.

559. Analyse the surface of the *conoid** or *wedge* $(a^2-x^2)y^2=h^2z^2$ using the sections by the planes $z=0$, $y=h$, $x=\pm c$ $(c \leqslant a)$ and construct the conoid in the domain $z \geqslant 0$.

560. Write the equation of the surface generated by revolving the curve $z=x^2$, $y=0$ (a) about the axis OZ; (b) about the axis OX. Construct both surfaces.

561. Write the equation of the surface generated by revolving about the axis OZ (1) the curve $z=e^{-x^2}$, $y=0$; (2) the curve $z=\frac{4}{x^2}$, $y=0$. Construct both surfaces (in the left-handed coordinate system).

---

* *Conoid* is a surface generated by a moving straight line parallel to a given plane and intersecting a given curve and a given straight line.

562. Write the equation of a conical surface with the vertex $O(0, 0, 0)$, the directrix $\begin{cases} x^2+(y-6)^2+z^2=25 \\ y=3 \end{cases}$, and draw the surface.

563. Write the equation of a conical surface with the vertex $C(0, -a, 0)$, the directrix $\begin{cases} x^2+y^2+z^2=a^2 \\ y+z=a \end{cases}$, and draw the surface.

564. Write the equation of a surface generated by revolving the straight line $z=y$, $x=0$ (a) about the axis OY; (b) about the axis OZ, and draw both surfaces.

565. Show that the section of the cone $z^2=xy$ by the plane $x+y=2a$ is an ellipse, and find its semiaxes.

3.7. The Ellipsoid, Hyperboloids, and Paraboloids

1°. Canonical equations. Besides cylindrical surfaces, there are six basic types of second-order surfaces determined by the following canonical (standard) equations:

I. *Ellipsoid* $\frac{x^2}{a^2}+\frac{y^2}{b^2}+\frac{z^2}{c^2}=1$.

II. *Hyperboloids:* $\begin{cases} \frac{x^2}{a^2}+\frac{y^2}{b^2}-\frac{z^2}{c^2}=1 \text{ (of one sheet)}, \\ \frac{x^2}{a^2}+\frac{y^2}{b^2}-\frac{z^2}{c^2}=-1 \text{ (of two sheets)}. \end{cases}$

III. *Quadric conical surface* $\frac{x^2}{a^2}+\frac{y^2}{b^2}-\frac{z^2}{c^2}=0$.

IV. *Paraboloids* $(pq>0)$: $\begin{cases} \frac{x^2}{p}+\frac{y^2}{q}=2z \text{ (elliptic)}, \\ \frac{x^2}{p}-\frac{y^2}{q}=2z \text{ (hyperbolic)}. \end{cases}$

2°. Rectilinear generatrices. *Two rectilinear generatrices* pass through each point of the *hyperboloid of one sheet:*

$$\begin{cases} \alpha\left(\frac{x}{a}+\frac{z}{c}\right)=\beta\left(1+\frac{y}{b}\right) \\ \beta\left(\frac{x}{a}-\frac{z}{c}\right)=\alpha\left(1-\frac{y}{b}\right) \end{cases} \text{ and } \begin{cases} \gamma\left(\frac{x}{a}+\frac{z}{c}\right)=\delta\left(1-\frac{y}{b}\right) \\ \delta\left(\frac{x}{a}-\frac{z}{c}\right)=\gamma\left(1+\frac{y}{b}\right). \end{cases}$$

4—1895

The same in the *hyperbolic paraboloid* (for $p > 0$ and $q > 0$):

$$\begin{cases} \alpha\left(\dfrac{x}{\sqrt{p}}+\dfrac{y}{\sqrt{q}}\right)=2\beta \\ \beta\left(\dfrac{x}{\sqrt{p}}-\dfrac{y}{\sqrt{q}}\right)=\alpha z \end{cases} \text{ and } \begin{cases} \gamma\left(\dfrac{x}{\sqrt{p}}+\dfrac{y}{\sqrt{q}}\right)=\delta z \\ \delta\left(\dfrac{x}{\sqrt{p}}-\dfrac{y}{\sqrt{q}}\right)=2\gamma. \end{cases}$$

3°. Circular sections. All the surfaces having *elliptic* sections also have *circular* sections. The greatest circular sections of the ellipsoid $\frac{x^2}{a^2}+\frac{y^2}{b^2}+\frac{z^2}{c^2}=1$ (for $a>b>c$) are found on the sphere $x^2+y^2+z^2=b^2$. The circular sections of an elliptical paraboloid $\frac{x^2}{p}+\frac{y^2}{q}=2z$ passing through the vertex are found on the sphere $x^2+y^2+z^2=$ $=2pz\ (p>q)$.

566. Write the equation of the surface generated by revolving the ellipse $\frac{x^2}{a^2}+\frac{z^2}{c^2}=1$, $y=0$ about the axis OZ.

567. Construct the surface $\frac{x^2}{9}+\frac{y^2}{4}+\frac{z^2}{25}=1$ and find the areas of its sections by the plane (a) $z=3$; (b) $y=1$.

568. Write the equation of a surface generated by revolving the curve $\frac{x^2}{a^2}-\frac{z^2}{c^2}=1$, $y=0$ (a) about the axis OZ; (b) about the axis OX. Construct both surfaces (in the left-handed system of coordinates).

569. Construct the surfaces:

$$(1)\ x^2+y^2-z^2=4; \quad (2)\ x^2-y^2+z^2+4=0.$$

570. Construct the hyperboloid $\frac{x^2}{16}+\frac{y^2}{4}-\frac{z^2}{36}=1$ and find its generatrices passing through the point (4, 1, —3).

571. A thread model of a cylinder is twisted by turning the upper base circle through an angle α (Fig. 22). Determine the equation of the ruled surface thus obtained if its base circles lie in the planes $z=\pm c$, their centres on the axis OZ, and their radii equal $2a$. Consider particular cases at $\alpha=90°$, $120°$, $180°$.

Hint. Point $M(x, y, z)$ divides the distance between the points $A(2a\cos t, 2a\sin t, -c)$, $B[2a\cos(t+\alpha), 2a\sin(t+\alpha), c]$ in the ratio $AM:MB=(c+z):(c-z)$.

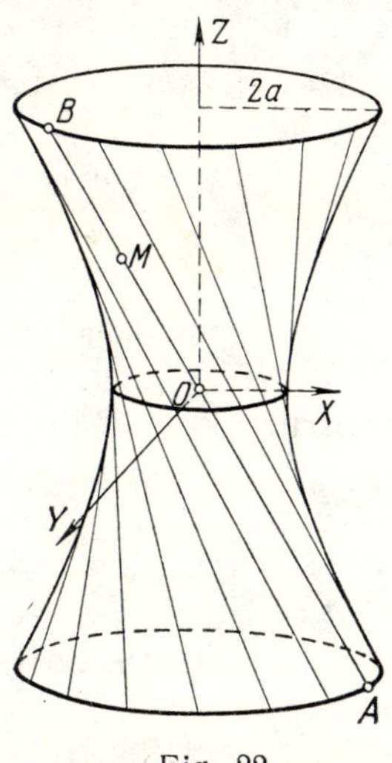

Fig. 22

572. Write the equation of the surface generated by revolving the parabola $az=x^2$, $y=0$ about the axis OZ. Construct the surface using the sections by the planes $z=a$, $x=0$, $y=0$.

573. Construct the surfaces:

$$(1)\ 2z=x^2+\frac{y^2}{2};\quad (2)\ z=c\left(1-\frac{x^2}{a^2}-\frac{y^2}{b^2}\right).$$

574. Construct (in the left-handed system of coordinates) the surface $x^2-y^2=4z$ and find its generatrices passing through the point (3, 1, 2).

575. Write the equation of the locus of points the ratio of the distances of each of which from the plane $x=2a$ to the distances from the point $F(a, 0, 0)$ is equal to $\sqrt{2}$. Construct the surface.

576. Write the equation of the locus of points the ratio of the distances of each of which from the point $F(0, 0, 2a)$

to the distances from the plane $z=a$ is equal to $\sqrt{2}$. Construct the surface.

577. Write the equation of the locus of points equidistant from the point $F(-a, 0, 0)$ and from the plane $x=a$. Construct the surface.

578. Find the greatest circular sections of the ellipsoid $\frac{x^2}{169}+\frac{y^2}{25}+\frac{z^2}{9}=1$.

579. Determine the circular sections of the elliptic paraboloid $\frac{x^2}{25}+\frac{y^2}{9}=z$ passing through the coordinate origin.

---

580. Name and construct each of the following surfaces:

(1) $x^2+y^2+z^2=2az$;
(2) $x^2+y^2=2az$;
(3) $x^2+z^2=2az$;
(4) $x^2-y^2=2az$;
(5) $x^2-y^2=z^2$;
(6) $x^2=2az$;
(7) $x^2=2yz$;
(8) $z=2+x^2+y^2$;
(9) $(z-a)^2=xy$;
(10) $(z-2x)^2+4(z-2x)=y^2$.

581. Write the equations of the rectilinear generatrices of the hyperboloid $x^2-y^2+z^2=4$, the generatrices passing through the point $(2, 4, 4)$.

582. Write the equations of the locus of points equidistant from the point $F\left(0, 0, \frac{a}{2}\right)$ and from the plane $z=-\frac{a}{2}$. Construct the surface.

583. Write the equation of the locus of points equidistant from the point $F\left(0, 0, \frac{a}{2}\right)$ and from the plane $z=\frac{3a}{2}$. Construct the surface.

584. Find the least circular sections of the hyperboloid

$$\frac{x^2}{25}+\frac{y^2}{9}-\frac{3z^2}{25}=1.$$

585. Write the equations of the rectilinear generatrices of the hyperbolic paraboloid $\frac{x^2}{16}-\frac{y^2}{9}=2z$, the generatrices passing through the point $(4, 3, 0)$.

CHAPTER 4

HIGHER ALGEBRA

4.1. Determinants

1°. Determinants. The *second-order determinant* is a number denoted by the symbol $\begin{vmatrix} a_1 & b_1 \\ a_2 & b_2 \end{vmatrix}$ and given by the equality

$$\begin{vmatrix} a_1 & b_1 \\ a_2 & b_2 \end{vmatrix} = a_1b_2 - a_2b_1. \qquad (1)$$

The *third-order determinant* is a number denoted by the symbol $\begin{vmatrix} a_1 & b_1 & c_1 \\ a_2 & b_2 & c_2 \\ a_3 & b_3 & c_3 \end{vmatrix}$ and determined by the equality

$$\begin{vmatrix} a_1 & b_1 & c_1 \\ a_2 & b_2 & c_2 \\ a_3 & b_3 & c_3 \end{vmatrix} = a_1\begin{vmatrix} b_2 & c_2 \\ b_3 & c_3 \end{vmatrix} - b_1\begin{vmatrix} a_2 & c_2 \\ a_3 & c_3 \end{vmatrix} + c_1\begin{vmatrix} a_2 & b_2 \\ a_3 & b_3 \end{vmatrix}. \qquad (2)$$

The second-order determinants entering the right-hand member of equality (2) are obtained from the given third-order determinant by deleting one row and one column and are called its *minors*. Formula (2) presents an expansion of a third-order determinant in terms of the elements of the first row.

2°. Properties of determinants.

I. The magnitude of a determinant does not change if each of the rows is substituted by a column of the same position number.

II. If any two rows or any two columns are interchanged, the absolute value of a determinant remains unaltered, while the sign is reversed.

It follows from I and II, that a determinant can be expanded in terms of any row, since the latter can change its place to occupy the first row.

III. A determinant with two identical rows (columns) is equal to zero.

IV. A common factor of all the elements of one row (or of one column) may be taken outside the sign of the determinant.

V. If to all the elements of some column we add terms proportional to the corresponding elements of another column, then the new determinant is equal to the old one. The same holds true for rows. For instance:

$$\begin{vmatrix} a_1 & b_1 & c_1 \\ a_2 & b_2 & c_2 \\ a_3 & b_3 & c_3 \end{vmatrix} = \begin{vmatrix} a_1+mc_1 & b_1+nc_1 & c_1 \\ a_2+mc_2 & b_2+nc_2 & c_2 \\ a_3+mc_3 & b_3+nc_3 & c_3 \end{vmatrix}.$$

Taking advantage of this property, we can get two zeros in any column (or row) of a third-order determinant. The latter is then evaluated in simpler fashion.

3°. The area of a triangle with the vertices $A(x_1, y_1)$, $B(x_2, y_2)$, $C(x_3, y_3)$:

$$S = \pm\frac{1}{2}\begin{vmatrix} x_1 & y_1 & 1 \\ x_2 & y_2 & 1 \\ x_3 & y_3 & 1 \end{vmatrix}. \qquad (3)$$

Evaluate the determinants:

586. $\begin{vmatrix} 3 & -2 \\ 4 & 6 \end{vmatrix}$. **587.** $\begin{vmatrix} 2 & 3 \\ 6 & -10 \end{vmatrix}$. **588.** $\begin{vmatrix} 3 & -2 \\ -4 & 5 \end{vmatrix}$.

589. $\begin{vmatrix} \sqrt{a} & -1 \\ a & \sqrt{a} \end{vmatrix}$. **590.** $\begin{vmatrix} \sin\alpha & \cos\alpha \\ -\cos\alpha & \sin\alpha \end{vmatrix}$.

591. $\begin{vmatrix} \sin^2\alpha & \cos^2\alpha \\ \sin^2\beta & \cos^2\beta \end{vmatrix}$.

Evaluate the determinants, expanding them in terms of the elements of the first column:

592. $\begin{vmatrix} 2 & 3 & 4 \\ 5 & -2 & 1 \\ 1 & 2 & 3 \end{vmatrix}$. **593.** $\begin{vmatrix} a & 1 & a \\ -1 & a & 1 \\ a & -1 & a \end{vmatrix}$.

Evaluate the determinants, expanding them in terms of the row containing the maximum number of zeros:

594. $\begin{vmatrix} 1 & b & 1 \\ 0 & b & 0 \\ b & 0 & -b \end{vmatrix}$. **595.** $\begin{vmatrix} -x & 1 & x \\ 0 & -x & -1 \\ x & 1 & -x \end{vmatrix}$.

Simplify and evaluate the determinants:

596. $\begin{vmatrix} a & -a & a \\ a & a & -a \\ a & -a & -a \end{vmatrix}$. **597.** $\begin{vmatrix} 1 & 2 & 5 \\ 3 & -4 & 7 \\ -3 & 12 & -15 \end{vmatrix}$.

598. $\begin{vmatrix} 12 & 6 & -4 \\ 6 & 4 & 4 \\ 3 & 2 & 8 \end{vmatrix}$. **599.** $\begin{vmatrix} x^2 & x & 1 \\ y^2 & y & 1 \\ z^2 & z & 1 \end{vmatrix}$.

600. $\begin{vmatrix} 1+\cos\alpha & 1+\sin\alpha & 1 \\ 1-\sin\alpha & 1+\cos\alpha & 1 \\ 1 & 1 & 1 \end{vmatrix}$.

601. $\begin{vmatrix} 2\cos^2\frac{\alpha}{2} & \sin\alpha & 1 \\ 2\cos^2\frac{\beta}{2} & \sin\beta & 1 \\ 1 & 0 & 1 \end{vmatrix}$.

602. Find the area of a triangle with the vertices

$$A(2, 3), \quad B(4, -1) \text{ and } C(6, 5).$$

603. Do the following points belong to one straight line:

$$A(1, 3), \quad B(2, 4) \quad \text{and} \quad C(3, 5)?$$

604. With the aid of a third-order determinant write the equation of the straight line passing through the points

(1) (x_1, y_1) and (x_2, y_2); (2) (2, 3) and (—1, 5).

Simplify and evaluate the determinants:

605. $\begin{vmatrix} 2 & -3 & 1 \\ 6 & -6 & 2 \\ 2 & -1 & 2 \end{vmatrix}$. **606.** $\begin{vmatrix} m+a & m-a & a \\ n+a & 2n-a & a \\ a & -a & a \end{vmatrix}$.

607. $\begin{vmatrix} ax & a^2+x^2 & 1 \\ ay & a^2+y^2 & 1 \\ az & a^2+z^2 & 1 \end{vmatrix}$. **608.** $\begin{vmatrix} \sin 3\alpha & \cos 3\alpha & 1 \\ \sin 2\alpha & \cos 2\alpha & 1 \\ \sin\alpha & \cos\alpha & 1 \end{vmatrix}$.

Hint. In Problem 607 take a outside the sign of the determinant, then subtract the third row from the first and the second ones and take $(x-z)$ and $(y-z)$ outside the sign of the determinant.

609. Prove that

$$\begin{vmatrix} \frac{x_1+x_2}{2} & \frac{y_1+y_2}{2} & 1 \\ \frac{x_1-x_2}{2} & \frac{y_1-y_2}{2} & 1 \\ x_1 & y_1 & 1 \end{vmatrix} = \frac{1}{2}\begin{vmatrix} x_1 & y_1 \\ x_2 & y_2 \end{vmatrix}.$$

610. Find x from the equations:

(1) $\begin{vmatrix} x^2 & 4 & 9 \\ x & 2 & 3 \\ 1 & 1 & 1 \end{vmatrix} = 0$; (2) $\begin{vmatrix} x^2 & 3 & 2 \\ x & -1 & 1 \\ 0 & 1 & 4 \end{vmatrix} = 0$

and check the solution by substituting the roots into the determinant.

4.2. *Systems of First-Degree Equations*

1°. A system of two equations of the first degree in two unknowns

$$\left.\begin{aligned} a_1x+b_1y=c_1, \\ a_2x+b_2y=c_2 \end{aligned}\right\} \qquad (1)$$

has the solution

$$x=\frac{\begin{vmatrix} c_1 & b_1 \\ c_2 & b_2 \end{vmatrix}}{\begin{vmatrix} a_1 & b_1 \\ a_2 & b_2 \end{vmatrix}}, \qquad y=\frac{\begin{vmatrix} a_1 & c_1 \\ a_2 & c_2 \end{vmatrix}}{\begin{vmatrix} a_1 & b_1 \\ a_2 & b_2 \end{vmatrix}}, \tag{2}$$

provided its determinant $\Delta=\begin{vmatrix} a_1 & b_1 \\ a_2 & b_2 \end{vmatrix}\neq 0.$

2°. A system of two homogeneous equations of the first degree in three unknowns

$$\left.\begin{array}{l} a_1x+b_1y+c_1z=0, \\ a_2x+b_2y+c_2z=0 \end{array}\right\} \tag{3}$$

has solutions determined by the formulas

$$x=k\begin{vmatrix} b_1 & c_1 \\ b_2 & c_2 \end{vmatrix}, \quad y=-k\begin{vmatrix} a_1 & c_1 \\ a_2 & c_2 \end{vmatrix}, \quad z=k\begin{vmatrix} a_1 & b_1 \\ a_2 & b_2 \end{vmatrix}, \tag{4}$$

where k is an arbitrary number.

3°. A system of three homogeneous equations of the first degree in three unknowns

$$\left.\begin{array}{l} a_1x+b_1y+c_1z=0, \\ a_2x+b_2y+c_2z=0, \\ a_3x+b_3y+c_3z=0 \end{array}\right\} \tag{5}$$

has non-zero solutions if the determinant of the system

$$\Delta=\begin{vmatrix} a_1 & b_1 & c_1 \\ a_2 & b_2 & c_2 \\ a_3 & b_3 & c_3 \end{vmatrix}=0, \text{ and conversely.}$$

4°. A system of three equations of the first degree in two unknowns

$$\left.\begin{array}{l} a_1x+b_1y=c_1, \\ a_2x+b_2y=c_2, \\ a_3x+b_3y=c_3 \end{array}\right\} \tag{6}$$

is *compatible*, when $\Delta=\begin{vmatrix} a_1 & b_1 & c_1 \\ a_2 & b_2 & c_2 \\ a_3 & b_3 & c_3 \end{vmatrix}=0$ and it contains no pairwise contradictory equations.

5°. A system of three equations of the first degree in three unknowns

$$\left.\begin{aligned} a_1x+b_1y+c_1z&=d_1, \\ a_2x+b_2y+c_2z&=d_2, \\ a_3x+b_3y+c_3z&=d_3 \end{aligned}\right\} \tag{7}$$

has the following unique solution:

$$x=\frac{\Delta_x}{\Delta}, \quad y=\frac{\Delta_y}{\Delta}, \quad z=\frac{\Delta_z}{\Delta}, \tag{8}$$

where

$$\Delta_x=\begin{vmatrix} d_1 & b_1 & c_1 \\ d_2 & b_2 & c_2 \\ d_3 & b_3 & c_3 \end{vmatrix}, \quad \Delta_y=\begin{vmatrix} a_1 & d_1 & c_1 \\ a_2 & d_2 & c_2 \\ a_3 & d_3 & c_3 \end{vmatrix}, \quad \Delta_z=\begin{vmatrix} a_1 & b_1 & d_1 \\ a_2 & b_2 & d_2 \\ a_3 & b_3 & d_3 \end{vmatrix},$$

provided the determinant of the system

$$\Delta=\begin{vmatrix} a_1 & b_1 & c_1 \\ a_2 & b_2 & c_2 \\ a_3 & b_3 & c_3 \end{vmatrix} \neq 0$$

6°. Incompatible and indeterminate systems. Let us denote the left-hand members of equations (7) by X_1, X_2, and X_3. Let the determinant of system (7) $\Delta=0$. In this case two suppositions are possible.

I. The elements of two rows (columns) of the determinant Δ are *proportional*, for instance, $\frac{a_2}{a_1}=\frac{b_2}{b_1}=\frac{c_2}{c_1}=m$. Then $X_2=mX_1$, and

(1) if $d_2\neq md_1$, then the *system is incompatible* (the first two equations are contradictory);

(2) if $d_2=md_1$, then the *system is indeterminate* (if the first and the third equations are not contradictory).

II. The determinant Δ has no rows (columns) with proportional elements. Then there exist non-zero numbers m and n such that $mX_1+nX_2=X_3$, and

(1) if $md_1+nd_2\neq d_3$, then the *system is incompatible*;

(2) if $md_1+nd_2=d_3$, then the *system is indeterminate*.

The numbers m and n can be chosen accordingly, or found from the equations $a_1m+a_2n=a_3$; $b_1m+b_2n=b_3$; $c_1m+c_2n=c_3$.

Using determinants, solve the following systems of equations:

611. $\begin{cases} 3x+2y=7 \\ 4x-5y=40. \end{cases}$ **612.** $\begin{cases} ax-3y=1 \\ ax-2y=2. \end{cases}$

613. $\begin{cases} 5x+2y=4 \\ 7x+4y=8. \end{cases}$ **614.** $\begin{cases} mx-ny=(m-n)^2 \\ 2x-y=n \text{ (for } m\neq 2n). \end{cases}$

Solve the systems of equations:

615. $\begin{cases} 2x-3y+z-2=0 \\ x+5y-4z+5=0 \\ 4x+y-3z+4=0. \end{cases}$ **616.** $\begin{cases} 2x-4y+3z=1 \\ x-2y+4z=3 \\ 3x-y+5z=2. \end{cases}$

617. $\begin{cases} 2x-5y+2z=0 \\ x+4y-3z=0. \end{cases}$ **618.** $\begin{cases} 3x+2y-z=0 \\ 2x-y+3z=0 \\ x+3y-4z=0. \end{cases}$

619. $\begin{cases} 3x+3y-z=0 \\ 2x-y+3z=0 \\ x+y-z=0. \end{cases}$ **620.** $\begin{cases} x+2y+3z=4 \\ 2x+4y+6z=3 \\ 3x+y-z=1. \end{cases}$

621. $\begin{cases} x+2y+3z=4 \\ 2x+y-z=3 \\ 3x+3y+2z=7. \end{cases}$ **622.** $\begin{cases} x+2y+3z=4 \\ 2x+y-z=3 \\ 3x+3y+2z=10. \end{cases}$

623. Do the following straight lines intersect at one point?

(1) $\begin{cases} 2x-3y=6 \\ 3x+y=9 \\ x+4y=3 \end{cases}$ and (2) $\begin{cases} 2x-3y=6 \\ x+2y=4 \\ x-5y=5. \end{cases}$

Construct these lines.

Solve the systems of equations:

624. $\begin{cases} 2x - y + z = 2 \\ 3x + 2y + 2z = -2 \\ x - 2y + z = 1. \end{cases}$ **625.** $\begin{cases} x + 2y + 3z = 5 \\ 2x - y - z = 1 \\ x + 3y + 4z = 6. \end{cases}$

626. $\begin{cases} 3x + 2y + 2z = 0 \\ 5x + 2y + 3z = 0. \end{cases}$ **627.** $\begin{cases} 3x - y + 2z = 0 \\ 2x + 3y - 5z = 0 \\ x + y + z = 0. \end{cases}$

628. $\begin{cases} 2x - y + 3z = 0 \\ x + 2y - 5z = 0 \\ 3x + y - 2z = 0. \end{cases}$ **629.** $\begin{cases} x - 2y + z = 4 \\ 2x + 3y - z = 3 \\ 4x - y + z = 11. \end{cases}$

4.3. *Complex Numbers*

1°. Definitions. The *complex number* is an expression of the form $x+yi$, where x and y are real numbers and i is a certain symbol, the following conditions being observed:

(1) $x+0i=x$, $0+yi=yi$ and $1i=i$, $(-1)i=-i$;
(2) $x+yi=x_1+y_1i$ if and only if $x=x_1$ and $y=y_1$;
(3) $(x+yi)+(x_1+y_1i)=(x+x_1)+(y+y_1)i$;
(4) $(x+yi)(x_1+y_1i)=(xx_1-yy_1)+(xy_1+x_1y)i$.

From conditions (1) and (4) the powers of the number i are obtained:

$$i^2=-1, \quad i^3=-i, \quad i^4=1, \quad i^5=i, \text{ etc.} \tag{1}$$

A complex number $x+yi$, in which $y\neq 0$, is called an *imaginary number*, where i is the so-called *imaginary unit*.

2°. Operations on complex numbers. Addition, subtraction, multiplication, and involution of complex numbers may be performed according to the rules for these operations on polynomials, the powers of i being replaced in accordance with formulas (1).

Division and evolution of complex numbers are defined as inverse operations.

3°. The trigonometric form of a complex number. A complex number $x+yi$ is determined by a pair of real numbers (x, y), and therefore is depicted by a point $M(x, y)$ in a plane or by its radius vector $\boldsymbol{r}=\overrightarrow{OM}$ (see Fig. 12 on p. 57).

The length of this vector $r=\sqrt{x^2+y^2}$ is called the *modulus* of the complex number, and the angle φ between the vector and the axis OX is called the *argument* of the complex number. Since $x=r\cos\varphi$, $y=r\sin\varphi$, we have

$$x+yi=r(\cos\varphi+i\sin\varphi). \quad (2)$$

4°. Operations on complex numbers expressed in the trigonometric form:

$$r=(\cos\varphi+i\sin\varphi)\,r_1(\cos\varphi_1+i\sin\varphi_1)=$$
$$=(rr_1)[\cos(\varphi+\varphi_1)+i\sin(\varphi+\varphi_1)], \quad (3)$$
$$\frac{r(\cos\varphi+i\sin\varphi)}{r_1(\cos\varphi_1+i\sin\varphi_1)}=\frac{r}{r_1}[\cos(\varphi-\varphi_1)+i\sin(\varphi-\varphi_1)], \quad (4)$$
$$[r(\cos\varphi+i\sin\varphi)]^n=r^n(\cos n\varphi+i\sin n\varphi), \quad (5)$$
$$\sqrt[n]{r(\cos\varphi+i\sin\varphi)}=\sqrt[n]{r}\left(\cos\frac{\varphi+2k\pi}{n}+i\sin\frac{\varphi+2k\pi}{n}\right), \quad (6)$$

where $k=0, 1, 2, \ldots, (n-1)$.

Formula (5) is called de Moivre's formula.

5°. Euler's formula: $e^{i\varphi}=\cos\varphi+i\sin\varphi \quad (7)$

6°. Logarithm of a complex number:

$$\ln z=\ln r+i\varphi_0+i2k\pi, \quad (8)$$

where φ_0 is the value of the argument φ satisfying the inequalities $-\pi<\varphi_0\leqslant\pi$. The expression $\ln r+i\varphi_0$ is called the *principal branch* of the logarithm.

630. Perform the following operations: (1) $(2+3i)(3-2i)$; (2) $(a+bi)(a-bi)$; (3) $(3-2i)^2$; (4) $(1+i)^3$; (5) $\frac{1+i}{1-i}$; (6) $\frac{2i}{1+i}$.

631. Solve the equations: (1) $x^2+25=0$; (2) $x^2-2x+5=0$; (3) $x^2+4x+13=0$, and verify the solutions by substituting the roots into the corresponding equation.

Represent the following complex numbers as vectors, determine their moduli and arguments, and write them in the trigonometric form:

632. (1) $z=3$; (2) $z=-2$; (3) $z=3i$; (4) $z=-2i$.

633. (1) $z=2-2i$; (2) $z=1+i\sqrt{3}$; (3) $z=-\sqrt{3}-i$.

634. (1) $-\sqrt{2}+i\sqrt{2}$; (2) $\sin\alpha+i(1-\cos\alpha)$.

635. Write the numbers given in Problems 632 to 634 in the form $re^{i\varphi}$ (for $-\pi < \varphi \leqslant \pi$).

636. Construct the domains of points z, given the following conditions:

(1) $|z| < 3$; (2) $|z| < 2$ and $\frac{\pi}{2} < \varphi < \pi$;

(3) $2 < |z| < 4$ and $-\pi < \varphi < -\frac{\pi}{2}$.

637. Show that $|z_1 - z_2|$ is the distance between the points z_1 and z_2.

638. Given the point $z_0 = -2 + 3i$. Construct the domain of points z for which $|z - z_0| < 1$.

639. The number conjugate with z is denoted by $\bar{z}$. Prove that $z \cdot \bar{z} = |z|^2$.

640. Compute, using de Moivre's formula:

(1) $(1+i)^{10}$; (2) $(1-i\sqrt{3})^6$; (3) $(-1+i)^5$;

(4) $\left(1+\cos\frac{\pi}{4}+i\sin\frac{\pi}{4}\right)^4$; (5) $(\sqrt{3}+i)^3$.

641. Express $\sin 3\alpha$ and $\cos 3\alpha$ in terms of functions of the angle α, using the identity $(\cos\alpha + i\sin\alpha)^3 = \cos 3\alpha + i\sin 3\alpha$.

642. Find all the values of $z = \sqrt[6]{1}$ and represent them by radius vectors for which purpose construct a circle of radius equal to 1.

643. Find (1) $\sqrt[3]{1}$; (2) $\sqrt[3]{i}$; (3) $\sqrt[6]{-1}$; (4) $\sqrt[3]{-2+2i}$.

644. Find (1) $\sqrt{i}$; 2) $\sqrt[3]{-1+i}$; (3) $\sqrt[4]{-8+8i\sqrt{3}}$.

645. Solve the binomial equations: (1) $x^3 + 8 = 0$; (2) $x^4 + 4 = 0$.

646. Find the principal branch of the logarithm (1) $\ln(-2)$; (2) $\ln(1+i)$; (3) $\ln i$; (4) $\ln(x+yi)$; (5) $\ln(2-2i)$.

647. Find the sum $\sin x + \sin 2x + \sin 3x + \ldots + \sin nx$.

Hint. Applying Euler's formula, substitute $\frac{e^{ix} - e^{-ix}}{2i}$ for $\sin x$, and so forth.

648. Find the sum $\cos x + \cos 2x + \cos 3x + \ldots + \cos nx$.

649. Prove the identity $x^5 - 1 = (x-1)(x^2 - 2x\cos 72° + 1) \times (x^2 - 2x\cos 144° + 1)$.

650. Compute:

(1) $\frac{4-3i}{4+3i}$; (2) $(a+bi)^3-(a-bi)^3$.

Represent the following complex numbers as vectors, determine their moduli and arguments, and write them both in the trigonometric form and in the form $re^{i\varphi}$ (for $-\pi<\varphi\leqslant\pi$):

651. (1) $z=4+4i$; (2) $z=-1+i\sqrt{3}$; (3) $z=1-i$.

652. (1) $z=5$; (2) $z=-i$; (3) $z=-\sqrt{2}-\sqrt{-2}$.

653. Construct the domain of points z according to the conditions

$$1<|z|<3 \text{ and } \frac{\pi}{4}<\varphi<\frac{3\pi}{4}.$$

654. Given the point $z_0=3-4i$. Construct the domain of points z for which $|z-z_0|<5$.

655. Using de Moivre's formula, compute:

$$(1)\ (1-i)^6;\quad (2)\ (2+i\sqrt{12})^5;\quad (3)\ \left(1+\cos\frac{\pi}{3}+i\sin\frac{\pi}{3}\right)^6.$$

656. Express $\sin 4\alpha$ and $\cos 4\alpha$ in terms of functions of the angle α using the identity $(\cos\alpha+i\sin\alpha)^4=\cos 4\alpha+ i\sin 4\alpha$.

657. Find all the values of the radicals (1) $\sqrt[4]{-1}$ and (2) $\sqrt[5]{1}$ and represent them by radius vectors.

658. Solve the equations: (1) $x^3-8=0$; (2) $x^6+64=0$; (3) $x^4-81=0$.

659. Find the sum

$$\cos x+\cos 3x+\cos 5x+\ldots+\cos(2n-1)x$$

(see Problem 647).

4.4. Higher-Degree Equations. Approximate Solution of Equations

1°. Cubic equation:

$$x^3+ax^2+bx+c=0. \tag{1}$$

If x_1, x_2, x_3 are the roots of equation (1), then the latter may be rewritten as $(x-x_1)(x-x_2)(x-x_3)=0$.

Hence, $a = -(x_1 + x_2 + x_3)$, $b = x_1x_2 + x_1x_3 + x_2x_3$, $c = -x_1x_2x_3$.

The equation $x^3 + ax^2 + bx + c = 0$ is reduced to the form $z^3 + pz + q = 0$ by the substitution $x = z - \frac{a}{3}$. The equation $z^3 + pz + q = 0$ is solved using Cardan's formula

$$z = \sqrt[3]{-\frac{q}{2} + \sqrt{\frac{q^2}{4} + \frac{p^3}{27}}} + \sqrt[3]{-\frac{q}{2} - \sqrt{\frac{q^2}{4} + \frac{p^3}{3}}} = u + v.$$

I. If $\Delta = \frac{q^2}{4} + \frac{p^3}{27} > 0$, then $z_1 = u_1 + v_1$, $z_{2,3} = -\frac{u_1 + v_1}{2} \pm \frac{u_1 - v_1}{2} i\sqrt{3}$, where u_1 and v_1 are real values of the roots u and v.

II. If $\Delta = \frac{q^2}{4} + \frac{p^3}{27} = 0$, then $z_1 = \frac{3q}{p}$, $z_{2,3} = -\frac{3t}{2p} = -\frac{z_1}{2}$.

III. If $\Delta = \frac{q^2}{4} + \frac{p^3}{27} < 0$, then $z_1 = 2\sqrt{\frac{-p}{3}} \cos\frac{\varphi}{3}$, $z_{2,3} = 2\sqrt{\frac{-p}{3}} \cos\left(\frac{\varphi}{3} \pm 120^\circ\right)$, where $\cos\varphi = -\frac{q}{2} : \sqrt{\frac{-p^3}{27}}$.

2°. Separating the real roots of the equation $f(x) = 0$. There is a unique root of the equation $f(x) = 0$ between a and b, if $f(a)$ and $f(b)$ have opposite signs and $f(x)$ is continuous and has a derivative $f'(x) \neq 0$ within the interval $[a, b]$. We suppose that also $f''(x) \neq 0$ within this interval.

3°. The method of chords applied to approximate solution of an equation $f(x) = 0$. Let α_0 be the end-point of the root isolating interval $[a, b]$ at which $f(\alpha_0) \cdot f''(\alpha_0) < 0$. Then the approximation of the root x will be the point α_1 at which the *chord AB* intersects the axis OX (Fig. 23):

$$\alpha_1 = \alpha_0 - \frac{f(\alpha_0)}{k},$$

where $k = \frac{f(b) - f(a)}{b - a}$.

4°. Method of tangents (Newton's method). Let β_0 be the end-point of the interval $[a, b]$ at which $f(\beta_0) \cdot f''(\beta_0) > 0$. Then the approximation of the root x will be the point β_1 of intersection of the axis OX and the *tangent line* to the curve $y=f(x)$ at the point $[\beta_0, f(\beta_0)]$ (Fig. 23):

$$\beta_1=\beta_0-\frac{f(\beta_0)}{k_1},$$

where $k_1=f'(\beta_0)$.

Applying the methods of chords and tangents once again, we obtain the following table:

α	β	$f(\alpha)$	$f(\beta)$	k	k_1	$\Delta\alpha$	$\Delta\beta$
..	..	..	..	..	..	..	..

, (2)

where k and k_1 are the slopes of the chords and tangents, and

$$\Delta\alpha=-\frac{f(\alpha)}{k} \text{ and } \Delta\beta=-\frac{f(\beta)}{k_1}.$$

Continuing the process we find successive values of α and β. The sequence has as its limit the required root.

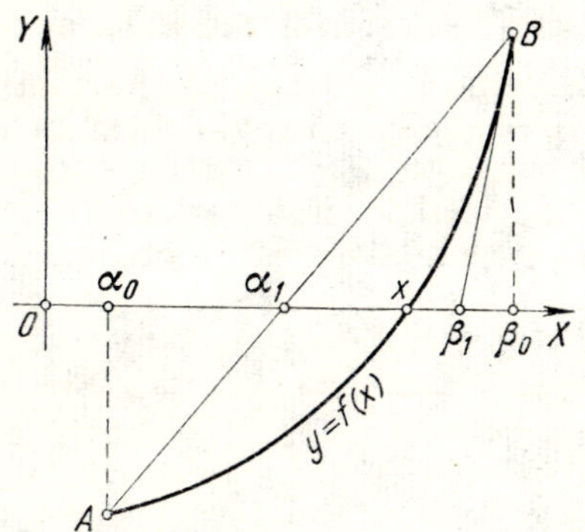

Fig. 23

5°. Method of iterations. If an equation $f(x)=0$ can be reduced to the form $x=\varphi(x)$ and in some neighbourhood of the root $|\varphi'(x)|<\theta\leqslant 1$, x_0 being any number in this neighbourhood, then the required sequence of approximate solutions will be:

$$x_1=\varphi(x_0), \quad x_2=\varphi(x_1), \quad x_3=\varphi(x_2), \text{ etc.}$$

In the equations of Problems 660 and 661 choose one root out of the integral factors of the constant term, then divide the left-hand member by $x-x_1$ and find the rest of the roots.

660. (1) $x^3-4x^2+x+6=0$; (2) $x^3-4x^2-4x-5=0$. Verify the solution by forming the expressions:

$$x_1+x_2+x_3, \quad x_1x_2+x_2x_3+x_1x_3, \quad x_1x_2x_3.$$

661. (1) $x^3-5x^2-2x+24=0$; (2) $x^4+x^3+2x-4=0$; (3) $9x^3+18x^2-x-2=0$; (4) $4x^3-4x^2+x-1=0$.

Solve the following equations, using Cardan's formula:

662. (1) $z^3-6z-9=0$; (2) $z^3-12z-16=0$.

663. (1) $z^3-12z-8=0$; (2) $z^3+6z-7=0$.

664. $x^3+9x^2+18x+9=0$.

665. Given the equation $f(x)=x^4-x-10=0$. Making a table of signs for $f(x)$ at $x=0, 1, 2, \ldots$, determine the boundaries of the positive root and compute it to two decimal places using the methods of chords and tangents.

666. Construct the graph of the function $y=\frac{x^3}{3}$, determine graphically the boundaries of the roots of the equation $x^3-6x+3=0$, and compute them to three decimal places.

667. Using the method of iterations (i.e. of successive approximations), find the real roots of the equations: (1) $x^3+60x-80=0$; (2) $2^x=4x$; (3) $x^3+l^2x+l^3=0$; (4) $x^4-2x-2=0$.

---

668. Solve the following equations, choosing one root among the integral factors of the constant term:

(1) $x^3+8x^2+15x+18=0$; (2) $x^3-3x^2+4=0$.

Check the solution by writing the expressions $\sum x_i$, $\sum x_ix_j$, and $x_1x_2x_3$.

669. Solve the following equations, using Cardan's formula:

(1) $z^3+18z-19=0$; (2) $z^3-6z-4=0$;
(3) $z^3-3z+2=0$; (4) $x^3+6x^2+9x+4=0$.

670. Constructing the graph of the function $y=\frac{x^4}{5}$, determine the boundaries of the roots of the equation $x^4+3x-15=0$ and compute the roots to two decimal places.

671. Find to two decimal places the positive roots of the equations: (1) $x^3+50x-60=0$; (2) $x^3+x-32=0$.

672. Using the method of iterations, find the real root of the equation $x^3+2x-8=0$ computing the successive approximations by the formula $x=\sqrt[3]{8-2x}$ (with the aid of a slide rule).

CHAPTER 5

INTRODUCTION TO MATHEMATICAL ANALYSIS

5.1. *Variable Quantities and Functions*

1°. Intervals. A set of numbers x satisfying the inequalities $a < x < b$, where a and b are fixed numbers, is called an *open interval*; it is usually denoted as (a, b). A set of numbers x satisfying the inequalities $a \leqslant x \leqslant b$ is called a *closed interval*; its notation is $[a, b]$. A set of numbers x satisfying the inequalities $a \leqslant x < b$ or $a < x \leqslant b$ is called a *half-open interval* ($[a, b)$ or $(a, b]$).

Open, *closed*, and *half-open intervals* are covered by a single term *interval*.

Equivalent inequalities (for $a > 0$):

$$x^2 < a^2, \quad |x| < a, \text{ and } -a < x < a$$

define an interval which is symmetrical with respect to zero.

2°. Variable quantities and functions. A quantity y is called a *function* of a variable quantity x if with every value assumed by x we can associate one or several definite values of y. Here, the variable x is called the *argument*.

We can put it otherwise: the quantity y depends on the quantity x; accordingly, the *argument* is called the *independent variable* and the *function* is termed the *dependent variable*. The collection of all values which the argument of a function can assume is called the *domain of definition* (or simply, domain) of the function.

If to every value of the argument there corresponds one value of the function, the function is termed *single-valued*; if there correspond two or more values, then it is called *multiple-valued* (double-valued, triple-valued, etc.).

The *symbol* $f(x)$ is an abbreviation of the phrase "a function of x". If two or more different functions of x are being considered, then, in addition to $f(x)$, we can use such notations as $f_1(x)$, $f_2(x)$, $F(x)$, $\varphi(x)$, $\Phi(x)$.

The notation $y=f(x)$ expresses the fact that the quantity y is equal to some function of x or that y is a function of the argument x. The letter f is called the function symbol.

The symbol $f(x)$ can be used to designate both an unknown function and a known function.

673. Construct the interval of a variable x satisfying the following inequalities:

(1) $|x|<4$; (2) $x^2 \leqslant 9$; (3) $|x-4|<1$;
(4) $-1<x-3 \leqslant 2$; (5) $x^2>9$; (6) $(x-2)^2 \leqslant 4$.

674. Write in the form of inequalities and construct the intervals of variables: $[-1, 3]$; $(0, 4)$; $[-2, 1]$.

675. Determine the interval of the variable $x=1-\frac{1}{t}$, where t takes on any value $\geqslant 1$.

In Problems 676 to 678 plot the graphs of the given functions over the interval $|x| \leqslant 3$:

676. (1) $y=2x$; (2) $y=2x+2$; (3) $y=2x-2$.

677. (1) $y=x^2$; (2) $y=x^2+1$; (3) $y=x^2-1$.

678. (1) $y=\frac{x^3}{3}$; (2) $y=\frac{x^3}{3}+1$; (3) $y=\frac{x^3}{3}-1$.

679. Construct the graphs of the functions: (1) $y=\frac{6}{x}$; (2) $y=2^x$; (3) $y=\log_2 x$. What feature can be noticed in the location of these curves with respect to the coordinate axes?

680. Construct two curves in the same drawing: (1) $y=\sin x$; (2) $y=\cos x$ making use of the points at which y has the maximum, minimum and zero values. By adding the ordinates of these curves, depict the function $y=\sin x+\cos x$ in the same drawing.

681. Find the roots x_1 and x_2 of the function $y=4x-x^2$ and plot its graph over the interval $[x_1-1, x_2+1]$.

682. Graph the following functions:

(1) $y=|x|$; (2) $y=-|x-2|$; (3) $y=|x|-x$.

In each of the following problems (683 to 686), find the domain of definition of real values of the given functions and draw their graphs.

683. (1) $y=\sqrt{x+2}$; (2) $y=\sqrt{9-x^2}$; (3) $y=\sqrt{4x-x^2}$.

684. (1) $y=\sqrt{-x}+\sqrt{4+x}$; (2) $y=\arcsin\frac{x-1}{2}$.

685. (1) $y=\frac{x(2\pm\sqrt{x})}{4}$; (2) $y=\pm x\sqrt{4-x}$.

686. (1) $y=-\sqrt{2\sin x}$; (2) $y=-\frac{x\sqrt{16-x^2}}{2}$.

687. (1) $f(x)=x^2-x+1$; evaluate $f(0)$, $f(1)$, $f(-1)$, $f(2)$, $f(a+1)$; (2) $\varphi(x)=\frac{2x-3}{x^2+1}$; evaluate $\varphi(0)$, $\varphi(-1)$, $\varphi\left(\frac{3}{2}\right)$, $\varphi\left(\frac{1}{x}\right)$, $\frac{1}{\varphi(x)}$.

688. $F(x)=x^2$; evaluate:

(1) $\frac{F(b)-F(a)}{b-a}$; (2) $F\left(\frac{a+h}{2}\right)-F\left(\frac{a-h}{2}\right)$.

689. $f(x)=x^2$, $\varphi(x)=x^3$; evaluate $\frac{f(b)-f(a)}{\varphi(b)-\varphi(a)}$.

690. $F(x, y)=x^3-3xy-y^2$; evaluate $F(4, 3)$ and $F(3, 4)$.

691. A function $f(x)$ is said to be *even* if $f(-x)=f(x)$, and *odd* if $f(-x)=-f(x)$. Which of the following functions are even and which are odd: (1) $f(x)=\frac{\sin x}{x}$; (2) $\varphi(x)=\frac{a^x-1}{a^x+1}$; (3) $F(x)=a^x+\frac{1}{a^x}$; (4) $\Phi(x)=a^x-\frac{1}{a^x}$; (5) $\Psi(x)=x\sin^2 x-x^3$; (6) $f_1(x)=x+x^2$?

692. The midpoint of any chord of a certain graphically represented function $f(x)$ lies above the graph of this function. Write this property of the function using an inequality. Check whether the function $f(x)=x^2$ possesses this property.

693. Which elementary function possesses the following properties:

$$f(1)=0;\quad f(a)=1;\quad f(xy)=f(x)+f(y)?$$

694. Which elementary function possesses the following properties:

$$f(0)=1, \quad f(1)=a, \quad f(x+y)=f(x)f(y)?$$

---

695. Construct the intervals of the variable x which satisfies the following inequalities:

(1) $|x|<3$; (2) $x^2\leqslant 4$; (3) $|x-2|<2$; (4) $(x-1)^2\leqslant 4$.

696. Determine the interval of the variable $x=2+\frac{1}{t}$, where t takes on any value $\geqslant 1$.

697. Graph the functions:

(1) $y=4-\frac{x^3}{2}$ over the interval $|x|\leqslant 2$;

(2) $y=3.5+3x-\frac{x^2}{2}$ between the points of intersection with the axis of abscissas.

698. Graph the functions:

(1) $y=x-4+|x-2|$ over the interval $[-2, 5]$;

(2) $y=1-\cos x$ over the interval $|x|\leqslant 2\pi$.

699. Construct the graphs of the following functions:

(1) $y=-\frac{4}{x}$; (2) $y=2^{-x}$.

700. Find the domains of definition of real values of the following functions:

(1) $y=\sqrt{4-x^2}$; (2) $y=\sqrt{x+1}-\sqrt{3-x}$;

(3) $y=1-\sqrt{2\cos 2x}$; (4) $y=\frac{4}{1+\sqrt{x^2-4}}$

and construct their graphs.

701. (1) $f(x)=\frac{2x+1}{x^2+1}$; find $f(0)$, $f(-2)$, $f\left(-\frac{1}{2}\right)$, $f(x-1)$, $f\left(\frac{1}{2}\right)$;

(2) $\varphi(x)=x^3$; find $\frac{\varphi(x+h)-\varphi(x-h)}{h}$;

(3) $f(x)=4x-x^2$; find $f(a+1)-f(a-1)$.

5.2. Number Sequences. Infinitesimals and Infinities. The Limit of a Variable. The Limit of a Function

1°. Number sequences. Let a variable x attain successively the values

$$x_1, x_2, x_3, \ldots, x_n, \ldots \tag{1}$$

Such an *ordered set of numbers is called an infinite sequence* or just a *sequence*. The sequence (1) is given by the formula of the nth term.

For example, let $x_n = n + (-1)^n$; putting $n = 1, 2, 3, \ldots$, we obtain the sequence

$$0, 3, 2, 5, 4, 7, \ldots \tag{2}$$

Suppose the variable x attains not only the values defined by sequence (2), but also all the intermediate values from 0 to 3 (increasing), then from 3 to 2 (de-

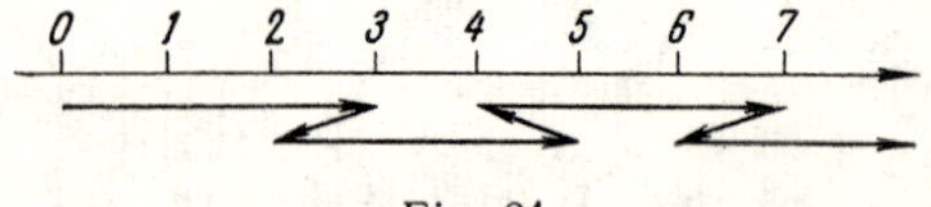

Fig. 24

creasing) and so on, then the variation of x can be represented by the path of a point $M(x)$ moving along the axis OX. Figure 24 illustrates the path covered by the variable x specified by sequence (2).

Let us assume here that a variable is given by the sequence $x = f(n)$, or in general by the function $x = f(t)$ defined on the interval $a \leqslant t \leqslant b$, provided $x = f(t)$ *follows* $x_0 = f(t_0)$, if $t > t_0$ (in particular, t may denote time).

2°. Infinitesimals. A variable α is called an *infinitesimal* if for any positive number ε there exists a value α_0 such that each subsequent value of α will be less than ε by its absolute value.

If α is an infinitesimal, then we say that α *tends* to zero which is written as $\alpha \to 0$. Or in other words: an infinitesimal is a quantity whose limit is equal to zero.

3°. An infinite quantity. A variable x is termed an *infinite quantity* if for any positive number c there exists a value x_0 such that each subsequent value of x will be greater than c by its absolute value. Notation: $x \to \infty$.

If all the values of the variable x which follow a certain x_0 retain the sign, the notation will be: $x \to +\infty$ (or $x \to -\infty$).

A quantity inverse to an infinite quantity is an infinitesimal quantity, and vice versa.

4°. The limit of a variable. A constant a is called the *limit* of a variable x if the difference between them is an infinitesimal, i.e. if $x = a + \alpha$, then $\lim x = a$, and conversely.

If a is the limit of the variable x, then it is also said that x *tends* to a, the corresponding notation being: $x \to a$, or $x \to a - 0$ (if x remains on the *left* of a), or $x \to a + 0$ (if x remains on the *right* of a).

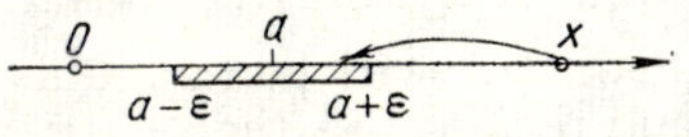

Fig. 25

The interval $(a - \varepsilon,\ a + \varepsilon)$ is called the *ε-neighbourhood* of the number a. We may say that x *tends* to a if for any positive number ε there exists a value x_0 such that all successive values of x will be found within the ε-neighbourhood of the number a (Fig. 25).

If $x \to +\infty$ (or $x \to -\infty$), then it is said that the limit of the variable x is $+\infty$ (or $-\infty$), the corresponding notation being:

$$\lim x = +\infty \text{ (or } \lim x = -\infty).$$

5°. The limit of a function. A number b is called the *limit of a function* $f(x)$ as x *tends* to a, if from the fact that x *tends* to a never attaining the value a it always follows that $f(x)$ *tends* to b; notation: $\lim\limits_{x \to a} f(x) = b$. The given definition also covers special cases, when the numbers

a or b will be replaced by the symbols $+\infty$ or $-\infty$: $\lim\limits_{x\to a} f(x)=+\infty$, $\lim\limits_{x\to -\infty} f(x)=b$, $\lim\limits_{x\to +\infty} f(x)=-\infty$, and so forth.

The limit $\lim\limits_{x\to a-0} f(x)=b$ $\left(\text{or} \lim\limits_{x\to a+0} f(x)=b\right)$ is called the *limit of the function* $f(x)$ *as* x *tends to* a *from the left* (or *from the right*).

702. Putting $n=0, 1, 2, 3$, etc. write the sequences:

$$\alpha=\frac{1}{2^n}, \quad \alpha=-\frac{1}{2^n}, \quad \alpha=\left(-\frac{1}{2}\right)^n$$

and represent graphically their variation. Beginning with what n will the modulus of each of the variables become and remain less than 0.001; less than a given positive ε?

703. Write the sequence of values of the variable $x=1+\frac{(-1)^n}{2n+1}$ and represent its variation graphically. Beginning with what n will the modulus of the difference $x-1$ become and remain less than 0.01; less than a given positive ε?

704. Adding to 3 (or subtracting from 3) first 1, then 0.1, then 0.01, etc. show in terms of "decimal" sequences the ways the variable tends to the limit: $x\to 3+0$, $x\to 3-0$.

705. Writing "decimal" sequences, show how the variables tend to the following limits: $x\to 5+0$, $x\to 5-0$; $x\to -2+0$, $x\to -2-0$; $x\to 1+0$, $x\to 1-0$; $x\to 1.2+0$, $x\to 1.2-0$.

706. Prove that $\lim\limits_{x\to 2} x^2=4$. Clarify this by making tables of values of x and x^2.

Hint. Putting $x=2+\alpha$, where α is an infinitesimal, form the difference x^2-4 and show that it equals an infinitesimal.

707. Prove that $\lim\limits_{x\to 3} (2x-1)=5$. Given the number $\varepsilon>0$, find a maximum number $\delta>0$ such that for any x from the δ-neighbourhood of the number 3 the corresponding value of the function $(2x-1)$ turns out to be within the ε-neighbourhood of the number 5. Explain this graphically.

708. Prove that $\lim\limits_{x \to -1} (3-2x-x^2)=4$. From what maximum δ-neighbourhood of the number -1 is it necessary to take a value of x so that the corresponding value of the function $(3-2x-x^2)$ differs from its limit by less than $\varepsilon=0.0001$?

709. Prove that $\sin\alpha$ is an infinitesimal if α is an infinitesimal.

Hint. Show graphically that $|\sin\alpha|<|\alpha|$.

710. Prove that $\lim\limits_{x \to a} \sin x=\sin a$.

Hint. Putting $x=a+\alpha$, make up the difference $\sin x - \sin a$.

711. Prove that $\lim\limits_{x \to \infty} \frac{3x+4}{x}=3$. Clarify this by making tables of values of x and $\frac{3x+4}{x}$ at $x=1, 10, 100, 1000, \ldots$.

Hint. Show that the difference $\frac{3x+4}{x}-3$ is an infinitesimal, as $x \to \infty$.

712. Prove that $\lim\limits_{x \to \infty} \frac{4x-3}{2x+1}=2$. For what values of x will the corresponding values of the function differ from its limit by less than 0.001?

713. Prove that $\lim\limits_{x \to \infty} \frac{1-2x^2}{2+4x^2}=-0.5$. For what values of x will the corresponding values of the function differ from its limit by less that 0.01?

714. Prove that $\lim\limits_{n \to \infty} \underbrace{0.333\ldots3}_{n \text{ digits}}=\frac{1}{3}$ by forming the differences: $\frac{1}{3}-0.3$; $\frac{1}{3}-0.33$; $\frac{1}{3}-0.333$; $\ldots$; $\frac{1}{3}-\underbrace{0.333\ldots3}_{n \text{ digits}}$.

715. Write the sequences of values of the following variables:

(1) $x=\frac{n}{n+1}$; (2) $x=-\frac{n}{n+1}$; (3) $x=\frac{(-1)^n n}{n+1}$;

(4) $x=\frac{8\cos n\frac{\pi}{2}}{n+4}$; (5) $x=\frac{2n+(-1)^n}{n}$; (6) $x=2^{-n} a\cos n\pi$

and represent their variation graphically. Does $\lim\limits_{n\to+\infty} x$ exist in each case and what is it equal to?

716. Find $\lim\limits_{x\to 2+0}\frac{3}{x-2}$ and $\lim\limits_{x\to 2-0}\frac{3}{x-2}$ and give the explanatory tables.

717. Find $\lim\limits_{x\to 0+0} 2^{\frac{1}{x}}$ and $\lim\limits_{x\to 0-0} 2^{\frac{1}{x}}$ and give the explanatory tables.

718. Find out the exact meaning of the following "conventional" notations:

(1) $\frac{2}{\infty}=0$; (2) $\frac{2}{0}=\pm\infty$; (3) $3^{\infty}=\infty$; (4) $3^{-\infty}=0$;
(5) $\log_{10} 0=-\infty$; (6) $\tan 90^\circ=\pm\infty$.

719. Show that $\lim\limits_{x\to\infty}\sin x$ does not exist by forming sequences of values of $\sin x$ at

(1) $x=n\pi$; (2) $x=\frac{\pi}{2}+2\pi n$; (3) $x=-\frac{\pi}{2}+2\pi n$ ($n=0$, 1, 2, 3, 4, ...).

720. Show that $\lim\limits_{x\to 0}\sin\frac{1}{x}$ does not exist.

721. Applying one of the theorems on infinitesimals, show that $\lim\limits_{x\to 0} x\sin\frac{1}{x}=0$ irrespective of the way in which x tends to 0.

722. Inscribed in a circle of radius R is a regular n-gon whose side is a_n. Circumscribing a square about the circle, show that $a_n<\varepsilon$ as soon as $n>\frac{8R}{\varepsilon}$, i.e. $a_n\to 0$ as $n\to\infty$.

723. Let r_n be the apothem of a regular n-gon inscribed in a circle. Prove that $\lim\limits_{n\to\infty} r_n=R$, where R is the radius of the circle.

724. The vertex B of a triangle ABC keeps displacing along a straight line $BE\parallel AC$ moving off infinitely to the right. How will the sides of the triangle, its area, its interior angles and the exterior angle BCD change?

725. Write "decimal" sequences to show how the variables tend to the following limits: $x \to 4+0$, $x \to 4-0$; $x \to -1.5+0$, $x \to -1.5-0$.

726. Prove that (1) $\lim\limits_{x \to 3} x^3 = 27$; (2) $\lim\limits_{x \to 1} (x^2+2x) = 3$ (see the hint to Problem 706).

727. Prove that $\lim\limits_{x \to \infty} \frac{5x+2}{2x} = 2.5$, showing that the difference $\frac{5x+2}{2x} - 2.5$ is an infinitesimal if x is an infinite value. Clarify this by a table, putting $x = 1, 10, 100, 1000, \ldots$.

728. Prove that $\lim\limits_{x \to a} \cos x = \cos a$ (see Problem 709).

729. Write the sequences of values of the following variables:

(1) $x = 1 + \left(-\frac{1}{2}\right)^n$; (2) $x = (-1)^n + \frac{1}{2^n}$;

(3) $x = (-1)^n (2n+1)$; (4) $x = \dfrac{2n \sin \frac{n\pi}{2}}{n+1}$

and represent their variation graphically. Which of the variables has a limit at $n \to +\infty$?

730. Find: (1) $\lim\limits_{x \to 1-0} 2^{\frac{1}{x-1}}$; (2) $\lim\limits_{x \to 1+0} 2^{\frac{1}{x-1}}$;

(3) $\lim\limits_{x \to \frac{\pi}{4}-0} 3^{\tan 2x}$; (4) $\lim\limits_{x \to \frac{\pi}{4}+0} 3^{\tan 2x}$; (5) $\lim\limits_{x \to \frac{\pi}{2}+0} \frac{2}{1+2^{\tan x}}$;

(6) $\lim\limits_{x \to \frac{\pi}{2}-0} \frac{2}{1+2^{\tan x}}$; (7) $\lim\limits_{x \to +\infty} \frac{a}{1+a^x}$.

731. Prove that $\lim\limits_{n \to \infty} \underbrace{0.666\ldots6}_{n \text{ digits}} = \frac{2}{3}$, by forming the differences $\frac{2}{3} - 0.6$; $\frac{2}{3} - 0.66$; $\ldots$; $\frac{2}{3} - \underbrace{0.66\ldots6}_{n \text{ digits}}$.

732. Let α_n be the interior angle of a reqular n-gon. Prove that $\lim\limits_{n \to \infty} \alpha_n = \pi$.

733. On the extension of the line segment $AB=a$ a point M is taken on its right at a distance $BM=x$. Find $\lim\limits_{x\to\infty}\frac{AM}{BM}$.

5.3. Basic Properties of Limits. Evaluating the Indeterminate Forms $\frac{0}{0}$ and $\frac{\infty}{\infty}$

1°. The limit of a constant quantity is the quantity itself.

2°. $\lim(u+v)=\lim u+\lim v$
3°. $\lim(uv)=\lim u\cdot\lim v$
} if $\lim u$ and $\lim v$ exist.

4°. $\lim\frac{u}{v}=\frac{\lim u}{\lim v}$, if $\lim u$ and $\lim v$ exist and $\lim v\neq 0$.

5°. If for all values of x within a certain neighbourhood of point a, except perhaps $x=a$, the functions $f(x)$ and $\varphi(x)$ are equal to each other and one of them has a limit as $x\to a$, then the second function has the same limit.

This property is applied to evaluating the indeterminate forms $\frac{0}{0}$ and $\frac{\infty}{\infty}$. For example, $\frac{x^2-a^2}{x-a}=x+a$ for any x, except for $x=a$. By property 5° $\lim\limits_{x\to a}\frac{x^2-a^2}{x-a}=\lim\limits_{x\to a}(x+a)=2a$.

Find the limits:

734. (1) $\lim\limits_{x\to 2}\frac{x^2-4x+1}{2x+1}$; (2) $\lim\limits_{x\to\frac{\pi}{4}}\frac{1+\sin 2x}{1-\cos 4x}$.

735. $\lim\limits_{x\to 2}\frac{x^2-4}{x-2}$ (clarify by a table).

736. $\lim\limits_{x\to 2}\frac{x-2}{x^2-3x+2}$. 737. $\lim\limits_{x\to 3}\frac{x^2-9}{x^2-2x-3}$.

Hint. Solve Problem 736 by two methods: (1) put $x=2+\alpha$; (2) factorize the denominator.

738. $\lim\limits_{x\to\pi}\frac{\tan x}{\sin 2x}$. 739. $\lim\limits_{x\to\frac{\pi}{4}}\frac{\sin x-\cos x}{\cos 2x}$.

740. $\lim\limits_{x\to 0}\frac{x}{\sqrt{1+3x}-1}$. 741. $\lim\limits_{x\to a}\frac{\sqrt{ax}-x}{x-a}$.

742. $\lim\limits_{x\to 1}\frac{\sqrt[3]{x}-1}{\sqrt{x}-1}$. 743. $\lim\limits_{x\to 0}\frac{\sqrt[3]{1+mx}-1}{x}$.

Hint. Put $x=t^6$ in Problem 742, and $1+mx=t^3$ in Problem 743.

744. $\lim\limits_{x\to 0}\dfrac{\sqrt{1+x}-\sqrt{1-x}}{x}$.

745. $\lim\limits_{x\to \pi}\dfrac{\sqrt{1-\tan x}-\sqrt{1+\tan x}}{\sin 2x}$.

746. (1) $\lim\limits_{x\to\infty}\dfrac{2x^2-1}{3x^2-4x}$; (2) $\lim\limits_{x\to\infty}\dfrac{5x^3-7x}{1-2x^3}$.

Hint. Two methods can be used: (1) divide both the numerator and the denominator by x in higher power; (2) put $x=\dfrac{1}{\alpha}$.

747. $\lim\limits_{x\to\infty}\dfrac{3x-1}{x^2+1}$.

748. $\lim\limits_{x\to\infty}\dfrac{x^3-1}{x^2+1}$.

749. $\lim\limits_{x\to\infty}\dfrac{\sqrt{x}-6x}{3x+1}$.

750. $\lim\limits_{n\to\infty}\dfrac{3n}{1-2n}$.

751. $\lim\limits_{n\to\infty}\dfrac{\sqrt{2n^2+1}}{2n-1}$.

752. $\lim\limits_{n\to\infty}\dfrac{1+2+3+\ldots+n}{\sqrt{9n^4+1}}$.

Find the limits:

753. $\lim\limits_{x\to -2}\dfrac{3x+6}{x^3+8}$.

754. $\lim\limits_{x\to 3}\dfrac{9-x^2}{\sqrt{3x}-3}$.

755. $\lim\limits_{x\to -1}\dfrac{x^2-x-2}{x^3+1}$.

756. $\lim\limits_{x\to \pi+0}\dfrac{\sqrt{1+\cos x}}{\sin x}$.

757. $\lim\limits_{x\to\infty}\dfrac{5x^2-3x+2}{2x^2+4x+1}$.

758. $\lim\limits_{n\to\infty}\dfrac{3n+1}{\sqrt{3n^2+1}}$.

759. $\lim\limits_{x\to\infty}\left(\dfrac{5x^2}{1-x^2}+2^{\frac{1}{x}}\right)$.

760. $\lim\limits_{n\to\infty}\dfrac{1+3+5+\ldots+(2n-1)}{1+2+3+\ldots+n}$.

761. $\lim\limits_{x\to 7}\dfrac{2-\sqrt{x-3}}{x^2-49}$.

762. $\lim\limits_{x\to\frac{\pi}{4}}\dfrac{\sin 2x-\cos 2x-1}{\cos x-\sin x}$.

5.4. *The Limit of the Ratio* $\frac{\sin\alpha}{\alpha}$ *as* $\alpha\to 0$

If an angle α is expressed in radians, then

$$\lim_{\alpha\to 0}\frac{\sin\alpha}{\alpha}=1;\quad \lim_{\alpha\to 0}\frac{\alpha}{\sin\alpha}=1.$$

Find the limits:

763. $\lim\limits_{x\to 0}\frac{\sin 4x}{x}$. **764.** $\lim\limits_{x\to 0}\frac{\sin\frac{x}{3}}{x}$.

Hint. In Problem 763 multiply both the numerator and the denominator by 4 (or put $4x=\alpha$).

765. $\lim\limits_{x\to 0}\frac{\tan x}{x}$. **766.** $\lim\limits_{x\to 0}\frac{\sin^2\frac{x}{2}}{x^2}$. **767.** $\lim\limits_{x\to 0}\frac{1-\cos 2x}{x\sin x}$.

768. $\lim\limits_{x\to 0}\frac{\sin 3x}{\sqrt{x+2}-\sqrt{2}}$. **769.** $\lim\limits_{h\to 0}\frac{\sin(x+h)-\sin(x-h)}{h}$.

770. (1) $\lim\limits_{x\to 0}\frac{\arctan x}{x}$; (2) $\lim\limits_{x\to\frac{1}{2}}\frac{\arcsin(1-2x)}{4x^2-1}$.

Hint. Put $\arctan x=\alpha$ in (1) and $\arcsin(1-2x)=\alpha$ in (2).

771. $\lim\limits_{x\to 0}\frac{1-\cos x}{x^2}$. **772.** $\lim\limits_{x\to 0}\frac{\tan x-\sin x}{x^3}$.

Find the limits:

773. $\lim\limits_{x\to 0}\frac{x}{\sin 3x}$. **774.** $\lim\limits_{x\to 0}\frac{\sin 4x}{\sqrt{x+1}-1}$.

775. $\lim\limits_{x\to -0}\frac{\sqrt{1-\cos 2x}}{x}$. **776.** $\lim\limits_{x\to 0}\frac{2x\sin x}{\sec x-1}$.

777. $\lim\limits_{x\to 0}\frac{1-\cos mx}{x^2}$. **778.** $\lim\limits_{x\to 0}\frac{1-\cos 2x+\tan^2 x}{x\sin x}$.

779. $\lim\limits_{x\to 2}\left[\frac{\sin(x-2)}{x^2-4}+2^{-\frac{1}{(x-2)^2}}\right]$ (put $x=2+\alpha$).

780. (1) $\lim\limits_{h\to 0}\frac{\cos(x+h)-\cos(x-h)}{h}$; (2) $\lim\limits_{x\to -2}\frac{\arcsin(x+2)}{x^2+2x}$.

781. $\lim\limits_{x\to 0}\frac{\sin^2 x}{\sqrt{1+x\sin x}-\cos x}$.

5.5. Indeterminate Expressions of the Form $\infty - \infty$ and $0 \cdot \infty$

Find the limits:

782. $\lim\limits_{x\to+\infty} (\sqrt{x^2+3x}-x)$.

783. $\lim\limits_{x\to1} \left(\frac{1}{x-1}-\frac{2}{x^2-1}\right)$.

784. $\lim\limits_{x\to+\infty} (\sqrt{x^2+x+1}-\sqrt{x^2-x})$.

785. $\lim\limits_{x\to2} \left(\frac{1}{x-2}-\frac{12}{x^3-8}\right)$. **786.** $\lim\limits_{x\to0} \left(\frac{1}{\sin^2 x}-\frac{1}{4\sin^2 \frac{x}{2}}\right)$.

787. $\lim\limits_{n\to\infty} \left[\frac{1+3+\ldots+(2n-1)}{n+3}-n\right]$.

788. $\lim\limits_{x\to1} (1-x)\tan\frac{\pi}{2}x$ (put $x=1-\alpha$).

789. $\lim\limits_{x\to-\infty} (\sqrt{x^2+1}-\sqrt{x^2-4x})$.

790. $\lim\limits_{x\to-2} \left(\frac{1}{x+2}+\frac{4}{x^2-4}\right)$.

Find the limits:

791. $\lim\limits_{x\to+\infty} (x-\sqrt{x^2-x+1})$.

792. $\lim\limits_{x\to+\infty} (x-\sqrt{x^2-a^2})$. **793.** $\lim\limits_{x\to\frac{\pi}{2}} \left(\frac{\sin x}{\cos^2 x}-\tan^2 x\right)$.

794. $\lim\limits_{n\to\infty} \left(\frac{1+2+3+\ldots+n}{n+2}-\frac{n}{2}\right)$.

795. $\lim\limits_{x\to\frac{\pi}{2}} \left(x-\frac{\pi}{2}\right)\tan x$ $\left(\text{put } x=\frac{\pi}{2}+\alpha\right)$.

5.6. Miscellaneous Problems on Limits

Find the limits:

796. (1) $\lim\limits_{x\to0} \frac{\sqrt{x+4}-2}{\sin 5x}$; (2) $\lim\limits_{x\to0} \frac{1+x\sin x-\cos 2x}{\sin^2 x}$.

797. (1) $\lim\limits_{x\to1} \frac{\sqrt[4]{x}-1}{\sqrt[3]{x}-1}$; (2) $\lim\limits_{x\to0} \frac{x}{\sqrt[4]{1+2x}-1}$.

798. $\lim\limits_{x\to-\infty}(\sqrt{x^2+ax}-\sqrt{x^2-ax})$.

799. (1) $\lim\limits_{x\to\infty}\left(\frac{1-2x}{\sqrt[3]{1+8x^3}}+2^{-x^2}\right)$; (2) $\lim\limits_{x\to\infty}\frac{x-\sin x}{1-5x}$.

800. (1) $\lim\limits_{x\to-1}\frac{x^3+1}{\sin(x+1)}$; (2) $\lim\limits_{x\to-2}\frac{x^2+x-2}{x^2+2x}$.

801. (1) $\lim\limits_{x\to0}\frac{1-\cos x}{x(\sqrt{1+x}-1)}$; (2) $\lim\limits_{x\to\pi}\frac{\cos\frac{x}{2}}{x-\pi}$.

802. (1) $\lim\limits_{x\to1}\frac{\sin(1-x)}{\sqrt{x}-1}$; (2) $\lim\limits_{n\to+\infty}\frac{1-10^n}{1+10^{n+1}}$.

803. (1) $\lim\limits_{x\to\infty}\left[\frac{3x^4}{1-2x^4}-2^{\frac{1}{x}}\right]$; (2) $\lim\limits_{n\to-\infty}\frac{3-10^n}{2+10^{n+1}}$.

804. (1) $\lim\limits_{x\to\frac{\pi}{2}+0}\frac{\sqrt{1+\cos 2x}}{\sqrt{\pi}-\sqrt{2x}}$; (2) $\lim\limits_{x\to-1}\cos\frac{\pi(x+1)}{\sqrt[3]{x}+1}$.

5.7. Comparison of Infinitesimals

1°. Definitions. Let the functions $\alpha(x)$ and $\beta(x)$ be infinitesimals as $x\to a$. Then:

I. If $\lim\limits_{x\to a}\frac{\beta}{\alpha}=0$, then β is termed an *infinitesimal quantity of higher order* relative to α; and α is a quantity of lower order with respect to β.

II. If $\lim\limits_{x\to a}\frac{\beta}{\alpha^n}=A$ (finite and not equal to zero), then β is called an *infinitesimal* of the nth *order* with respect to α.

III. If $\lim\limits_{x\to a}\frac{\beta}{\alpha}=1$, then β and α are termed the *equivalent infinitesimals.* The equivalence of infinitesimals is denoted by the same symbol $\approx$ as approximate equality. Thus $\beta\approx\alpha$.

2°. The properties of equivalent infinitesimals:

(a) The difference $\alpha-\beta$ of two equivalent infinitesimals α and β is an infinitesimal of higher order with respect to either α or β.

(b) If infinitesimals of the higher orders are rejected from a sum of several infinitesimals of different orders, then the remaining or *principal* summand of the lower order is equivalent to the entire sum.

It follows from the first property that equivalent infinitesimals can become approximately equal with an arbitrary small relative error. Therefore, we use the symbol $\approx$ to denote both the equivalence of infinitesimals and the approximate equality of their arbitrarily small values.

805. Determine the orders of the infinitesimals: (1) $1-\cos x$; (2) $\tan x-\sin x$ with respect to the infinitesimal x.

Show on the graph that a reduction of x to half its value results in decreasing $1-\cos x$ to approximately $\frac{1}{4}$ its value and $\tan x-\sin x$ to approximately $\frac{1}{8}$ its value.

806. Determine the orders of the following infinitesimals: (1) $2\sin^4 x-x^5$; (2) $\sqrt{\sin^2 x+x^4}$; (3) $\sqrt{1+x^3}-1$ with respect to x.

807. Determine the order of smallness of the sagitta of a circular segment relative to the infinitely small arc of the segment.

808. Prove that

$$(1)\ \sin mx \approx mx;\quad (2)\ \tan mx \approx mx;\quad (3)\ \sqrt[3]{1+x}-1 \approx \frac{1}{3}x,$$

as $x \longrightarrow 0$.

809. The volumetric expansion coefficient of a solid is assumed to be approximately equal to three times the linear expansion coefficient. On equivalence of what infinitesimals is this assumption based?

810. Using the theorem that $\lim \frac{\beta}{\alpha}=\lim \frac{\beta_1}{\alpha_1}$ if $\alpha \approx \alpha_1$, $\beta \approx \beta_1$, and that one of the limits exists, find the following limits:

$$(1)\ \lim_{x\to 0} \frac{\sin 5x}{\sin 2x};\quad (2)\ \lim_{x\to 0} \frac{\sin ax+x^2}{\tan bx};\quad (3)\ \lim_{x\to 0} \frac{3x+\sin^2 x}{\sin 2x-x^3}.$$

---

811. A water drop evaporates so that its radius tends to zero. Determine the orders of the infinitesimals expressing the surface and volume of the drop with respect to its radius.

812. Determine the orders of the infinitesimals:
(1) $\sqrt{1+x^2}-1$; (2) $\sin 2x-2\sin x$; (3) $1-2\cos\times$ $\times\left(x+\frac{\pi}{3}\right)$ with respect to the infinitesimal x.

813. Prove that as $x\to 0$ (1) $\arctan mx \approx mx$;
(2) $\sqrt{1+x}-1\approx\frac{1}{2}x$; (3) $1-\cos^3 x\approx 1.5\sin^2 x$.

5.8. The Continuity of a Function

1°. Definition. A function $f(x)$ is called *continuous* at a point $x=a$ if it is defined in some neighbourhood a and

$$\lim_{x\to a} f(x)=f(a)$$

This definition contains the following four conditions:
(1) $f(x)$ must be defined in some neighbourhood of a;
(2) there must exist finite limits $\lim\limits_{x\to a-0} f(x)$ and $\lim\limits_{x\to a+0} f(x)$;
(3) these limits (both from the left and from the right) must be equal to each other;
(4) these limits must be equal to $f(a)$.

A function is called *continuous on a closed interval* $[x_1, x_2]$ if it is continuous at every point of the interval, and at its end-points $\lim\limits_{x\to x_1+0} f(x)=f(x_1)$ and $\lim\limits_{x\to x_2-0} f(x)=f(x_2)$.

Elementary functions: power function $y=x^n$, exponential function $y=a^x$, logarithmic function $y=\log_a x$, trigonometric functions $y=\sin x$, $y=\cos x$, $y=\tan x$, $y=\cot x$, $y=\sec x$, $y=\operatorname{cosec} x$, circular or inverse trigonometric functions $y=\arcsin x$, $y=\arccos x$, $y=\arctan x$, $y=\operatorname{arccot} x$, $y=\operatorname{arcsec} x$, $y=\operatorname{arccosec} x$, as also their sum, product, quotient are continuous at any x at which they have a definite value.

2°. Discontinuities of a function. A function has a *discontinuity* at $x=a$ if it is defined both from the left and from the right of a, but at the point a at least one of the continuity conditions is not fulfilled. We usually distinguish between two basic kinds of discontinuity.

(1) *Discontinuity of the first kind*. Such a case occurs when there exist the limits on the right and on the left

and they are finite, i.e. when the second condition of continuity is fulfilled, and the rest of the conditions (or at least one of them) are not fulfilled.

For example, the function $y=\frac{x-a}{|x-a|}$, equal to -1 for $x<a$ and to $+1$ for $x>a$, has a discontinuity of the first kind at the point $x=a$ (Fig. 26), since there exist the limits $\lim\limits_{x\to a-0} y=-1$ and $\lim\limits_{x\to a+0} y=+1$, but they are not equal.

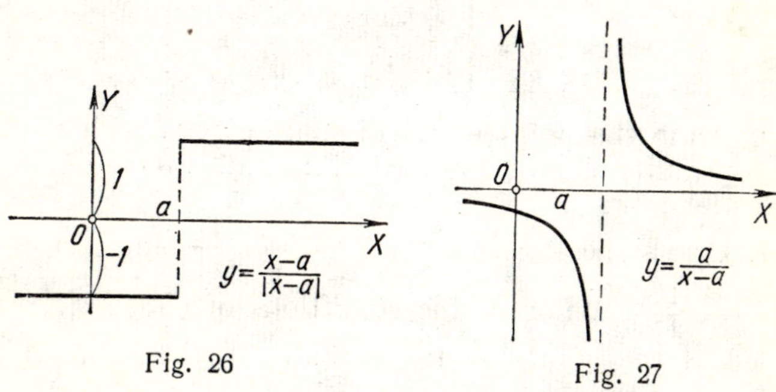

Fig. 26

Fig. 27

(2) *Discontinuity of the second kind.* This is the case, when $\lim\limits_{x\to a} f(x)$ either on the left or on the right is equal to $\pm\infty$.

For example, the function $y=f(x)=\frac{a}{x-a}$ (Fig. 27) has a discontinuity of the second kind at the point $x=a$. All the fractional functions whose denominator becomes zero at $x=a$, and the numerator is not equal to zero, have a discontinuity of the second kind at the point $x=a$. The function $f(x)=2^{\frac{1}{x}}$ (Problem 819, Fig. 42 on p. 322) also has a discontinuity of the second kind at $x=0$, since $\lim\limits_{x\to -0} f(x)=0$, but $\lim\limits_{x\to +0} f(x)=\infty$.

814. Indicate the point of discontinuity of the function $y=\frac{4}{x-2}$, find $\lim\limits_{x\to 2-0} y$, $\lim\limits_{x\to 2+0} y$, $\lim\limits_{x\to \pm\infty} y$, and plot the curve using the points

$$x=-2,\ 0,\ 1,\ 3,\ 4,\ \text{and}\ 6.$$

815. Find the points of discontinuity and graph the functions:

(1) $y=-\frac{6}{x}$; (2) $y=\tan x$; (3) $y=\frac{4}{4-x^2}$.

816. Graph the function

$$y=\begin{cases}\frac{x}{2} & \text{for } x\neq 2\\ 0 & \text{for } x=2\end{cases}$$

and indicate the point of its discontinuity. Which of the four continuity conditions are fulfilled at this point and which are not?

817. Graph the functions: (1) $y=\frac{x+1}{|x+1|}$ and (2) $y=x+\frac{x+1}{|x+1|}$. Which of the conditions of continuity are fulfilled at the points of discontinuity of these functions and which are not?

818. Graph the function

$$y=f(x)=\begin{cases}\frac{\sin x}{x} & \text{for } x\neq 0\\ 2 & \text{for } x=0\end{cases}$$

and indicate the point of its discontinuity. Which of the continuity conditions are fulfilled here and which are not?

819. Indicate the point of discontinuity of the function $y=2^{\frac{1}{x}}$, find $\lim\limits_{x\to-0} y$, $\lim\limits_{x\to+0} y$, $\lim\limits_{x\to\pm\infty} y$ and construct the graph of the function. Which conditions of continuity are not fulfilled at the point of discontinuity?

820. Graph the function

$$y=f(x)=\begin{cases}0.5x^2 & \text{for } |x|<2\\ 2.5 & \text{for } |x|=2\\ 3 & \text{for } |x|>2\end{cases}$$

and indicate the points of discontinuity.

821. Find the points of discontinuity and plot the graphs of the following functions:

$$(1)\ y=\frac{1}{1+2^{\frac{1}{x}}};\quad (2)\ y=\arctan\frac{a}{x-a};\quad (3)\ y=\frac{x^3-x^2}{2\,|x-1|}.$$

822. How many single-valued functions are given by the equation $x^2-y^2=0$? Among them define (1) an even function; (2) an odd function so that they have finite discontinuities (of the first kind) at $x=\pm 1, \pm 2, \pm 3, \ldots,$ and plot their graphs.

---

823. Indicate the point of discontinuity of the function $y=\frac{x}{x+2}$, find $\lim\limits_{x\to-2-0} y$, $\lim\limits_{x\to-2+0} y$, $\lim\limits_{x\to\pm\infty} y$ and plot its graph using the points $x=-6, -4, -3, -1, 0, 2$.

824. Graph the function

$$y=f(x)=\begin{cases} 2 & \text{for } x=0 \text{ and } x=\pm 2 \\ 4-x^2 & \text{for } 0<|x|<2 \\ 4 & \text{for } |x|>2 \end{cases}$$

and indicate the points of discontinuity. Which continuity conditions are fulfilled at these points and which are not?

825. Find the points of discontinuity and construct the graphs of the following functions:

$$(1)\ y=2-\frac{|x|}{x};\quad (2)\ y=2^{\frac{1}{x-2}};\quad (3)\ y=1-2^{\frac{1}{x}};$$

$$(4)\ y=\frac{x^3+x}{2\,|x|};\quad (5)\ y=\frac{4-x^2}{|4x-x^3|}.$$

826. How many single-valued functions are specified by the equation $x^2+y^2=4$? Out of them define (1) two continuous functions on the interval $|x|\leqslant 2$; (2) the one which is negative on the interval $|x|\leqslant 1$ and positive for the rest of permissible values of x. Graph the latter function and indicate its discontinuities.

5.9. Asymptotes

Definition. The straight line AB is called the *asymptote* of curve L if the distance MK from M (on L) to the straight line AB tends to zero as M recedes to infinity.

I. If $\lim_{x \to a} f(x) = \pm\infty$, then the straight line $x=a$ is an asymptote of the curve $y=f(x)$. For instance, the curve $y=\frac{a}{x-a}$ has an asymptote $x=a$ (Fig. 27).

II. If in the right-hand member of the equation of a curve $y=f(x)$ it is possible to single out a linear part $y=f(x)=kx+b+\alpha(x)$ so that the remaining part $\alpha(x) \to 0$ as $x \to \pm\infty$, then the straight line $y=kx+b$ is the asymptote of the curve. Examples: (1) the curve $y = \frac{x^3+x^2+1}{x^2} = x+1+\frac{1}{x^2}$ has two asymptotes: $y=x+1$ and $x=0$; (2) the curve $y=\frac{a}{x-a}=0+\frac{a}{x-a}$ has the asymptote $y=0$ (Fig. 27).

III. If there exist finite limits $\lim_{x \to +\infty \text{ or } -\infty} \frac{f(x)}{x} = k$ and $\lim_{x \to +\infty \text{ or } -\infty} [f(x)-kx]=b$, then the straight line $y=kx+b$ is an asymptote.

827. Determine the asymptotes of the curve $y=1-\frac{4}{x^2}$ and plot the curve given the points $x=\pm 1, \pm 2, \pm 4$.

In Problems 828 to 830 find the asymptotes of the given curves by singling out of the fractions a whole linear part; construct both the asymptotes and the curves.

828. (1) $y=\frac{x^2+1}{x}$; (2) $y=\frac{x^2}{x+1}$; (3) $y=\frac{x^2}{x^2+1}$.

829. (1) $y=\frac{2}{|x|}-1$; (2) $y=\frac{x^2-x-1}{x}$; (3) $y=\frac{ax+b}{mx+n}$.

830. (1) $y=\frac{1-4x}{1+2x}$; (2) $y=\frac{x^3}{x^2+1}$; (3) $y=\frac{4x-x^3}{x^2+4}$.

Find the asymptotes of the given curves and construct the curves:

831. (1) $x^2-y^2=a^2$; (2) $x^3+y^3=3axy$;
(3) $y=x-2\arctan x$; (4) $y=\arctan\frac{x}{a-x}$.

832. (1) $y=\sqrt{x^2+1}-\sqrt{x^2-1}$;

(2) $y=\sqrt{x^2+1}+\sqrt{x^2-1}$; (3) $y=x-\frac{1}{\sqrt{x}}$.

833. Construct the curves: (1) $y=\frac{x^4+1}{3x}$; (2) $y=\frac{x^3+x^2-2}{x+1}$ and the parabolas to which these curves approach asymptotically.

---

834. Find the asymptotes of the curves: (1) $y=\left(1-\frac{2}{x}\right)^2$; (2) $y=-x+\frac{1}{x^2}$ and plot the curves by the points $x=\pm\frac{1}{2}$, ± 1, ± 2.

835. Find the asymptotes of the given curves and construct the curves:

(1) $y=\frac{x-4}{2x+4}$; (2) $y=\frac{x^2}{2-2x}$; (3) $y=\frac{x^2}{x^2-4}$;

(4) $y=\frac{x^3}{1-x^2}$.

5.10. *The Number e*

The number e is defined as

$$\lim_{n\to\infty}\left(1+\frac{1}{n}\right)^n=\lim_{n\to-\infty}\left(1+\frac{1}{n}\right)^n=\lim_{\alpha\to 0}(1+\alpha)^{\frac{1}{\alpha}}=e.$$

Its value is 2.71828.... Since it is an irrational number, it cannot be expressed as a fraction, or as a decimal, or even as a recurring decimal. It is used as the base for *natural* or Napierian logarithms; notation: $\log_e x=\ln x$.

Common or Briggs' logarithm: $\log_{10}x=M\ln x$, where $M=0.43429\ldots$.

Find the limits:

836. $\lim_{n\to\infty}\left(1-\frac{5}{n}\right)^n$ $\left(\text{put } -\frac{5}{n}=\alpha\right)$.

837. (1) $\lim_{n\to\infty}\left(1-\frac{1}{3n}\right)^n$; (2) $\lim_{n\to-\infty}\left(1+\frac{4}{n}\right)^{n+3}$.

838. (1) $\lim_{x\to 0}(1+2x)^{\frac{1}{x}}$; (2) $\lim_{x\to 0}(1-4x)^{\frac{1-x}{x}}$.

839. (1) $\lim\limits_{n\to\infty}\left(\frac{n}{n+1}\right)^n$; (2) $\lim\limits_{x\to\infty}\left(\frac{2x-1}{2x+1}\right)^{2x}$.

840. (1) $\lim\limits_{n\to\infty} n[\ln(n+3)-\ln n]$; (2) $\lim\limits_{x\to 0}(1+3\tan^2 x)^{\cot^2 x}$.

841. $\lim\limits_{x\to 0}(\cos x)^{\cot^2 x}$ (put $\sin^2 x=\alpha$).

842. (1) $\lim\limits_{\alpha\to 0}\frac{\ln(1+\alpha)}{\alpha}$; (2) $\lim\limits_{x\to 0}\frac{e^{-x}-1}{x}$;

(3) $\lim\limits_{x\to 0}\frac{a^{2x}-1}{x}$.

Hint: In (2) put $e^{-x}-1=\alpha$.

843. Find two consecutive whole numbers between which the number $6(1-1.01^{-100})$ is contained.

Find the limits:

844. (1) $\lim\limits_{n\to\infty}\left(1+\frac{2}{n}\right)^{3n}$; (2) $\lim\limits_{n\to\infty}\left(\frac{n-3}{n}\right)^{\frac{n}{2}}$.

845. (1) $\lim\limits_{x\to\infty}\left(\frac{3x-2}{3x+1}\right)^{2x}$; (2) $\lim\limits_{x\to\infty}\frac{e^{-3x}-1}{x}$.

846. $\lim\limits_{x\to\frac{\pi}{4}}(\sin 2x)^{\tan^2 2x}$ (put $\cos^2 2x=\alpha$).

847. (1) $\lim\limits_{t\to 0}\frac{t}{\ln(1+xt)}$; (2) $\lim\limits_{n\to\infty} n[\ln n-\ln(n+2)]$.

CHAPTER 6

THE DERIVATIVE AND THE DIFFERENTIAL

6.1. The Derivatives of Algebraic and Trigonometric Functions

1°. Definitions. The *derivative* of the function $y=f(x)$ at a given point x is defined as the limit

$$\lim_{\Delta x \to 0} \frac{f(x+\Delta x)-f(x)}{\Delta x} = \lim_{\Delta x \to 0} \frac{\Delta y}{\Delta x}. \qquad (1)$$

If this limit is *finite*, then the function $f(x)$ is called *differentiable* at the point x; it is infallibly *continuous* at this point.

If limit (1) is equal to $+\infty$ (or $-\infty$), the function $f(x)$ is said to have an *infinite derivative* at the point x under an additional condition that the function is continuous at this point.

The derivative is denoted by y', or $f'(x)$, or $\frac{dy}{dx}$, or $\frac{df(x)}{dx}$. The process of finding the derivative is called the *differentiation* of a function.

2°. Basic differentiation formulas:

(1) $(c)'=0$; (2) $(x^n)'=nx^{n-1}$; (3) $(cu)'=cu'$;

(4) $(u+v)'=u'+v'$; (5) $(uv)'=u'v+uv'$;

(6) $\left(\frac{u}{v}\right)'=\frac{u'v-v'u}{v^2}$; (7) $(\sqrt{x})'=\frac{1}{2\sqrt{x}}$;

(8) $(\sin x)'=\cos x$; (9) $(\cos x)'=-\sin x$;

(10) $(\tan x)'=\frac{1}{\cos^2 x}$; (11) $(\cot x)'=-\frac{1}{\sin^2 x}$.

848. By computing $\lim\limits_{\Delta x \to 0} \frac{\Delta y}{\Delta x}$ find the derivatives of the

following functions:

(1) $y=x^3$; (2) $y=x^4$; (3) $y=\sqrt{x}$; (4) $y=\sin x$; (5) $y=\frac{1}{x}$; (6) $y=\frac{1}{\sqrt{x}}$; (7) $y=\frac{1}{x^2}$; (8) $y=\tan x$; (9) $y=\frac{1}{x^3}$; (10) $y=\sqrt{1+2x}$; (11) $y=\frac{1}{3x+2}$; (12) $y=\sqrt{1+x^2}$.

Taking advantage of the differentiation formulas, find the derivatives of the following functions:

849. (1) $y=\frac{x^3}{3}-2x^2+4x-5$; (2) $y=\frac{bx+c}{a}$.

850. (1) $y=\frac{x^5}{5}-\frac{2x^3}{3}+x$; (2) $y=\left(1-\frac{x^2}{2}\right)^2$.

851. (1) $y=x+2\sqrt{x}$; (2) $y=(\sqrt{a}-\sqrt{x})^2$.

852. (1) $y=\frac{10}{x^3}$; (2) $y=\frac{1}{x}+\frac{1}{x^2}+\frac{1}{x^3}$.

853. $y=x+\frac{1}{x^2}-\frac{1}{5x^5}$; (2) $y=3x-6\sqrt{x}$.

854. (1) $y=6\sqrt[3]{x}-4\sqrt[4]{x}$; (2) $y=\left(1-\frac{1}{\sqrt[3]{x}}\right)^2$.

855. (1) $y=\frac{1}{2x^2}-\frac{1}{3x^3}$; (2) $y=\frac{8}{\sqrt[4]{x}}-\frac{6}{\sqrt[3]{x}}$.

856. (1) $y=x-\sin x$; (2) $y=x-\tan x$.

857. (1) $y=x^2\cos x$; (2) $y=x^2\cot x$.

858. (1) $y=\frac{\cos x}{x^2}$; (2) $y=\frac{x^2}{x^2+1}$.

859. (1) $y=\frac{x}{1-4x}$; (2) $y=\frac{\tan x}{\sqrt{x}}$.

860. (1) $f(x)=\frac{\cos x}{1-\sin x}$; (2) $\varphi(x)=\frac{\sqrt{x}}{\sqrt{x}+1}$.

861. (1) $s=\frac{gt^2}{2}$; (2) $x=a(t-\sin t)$.

862. $f(x)=\frac{x^3}{3}-x^2+x$; evaluate $f'(0)$, $f'(1)$, $f'(-1)$.

863. $f(x)=x^2-\frac{1}{2x^2}$; evaluate $f'(2)-f'(-2)$.

864. $f(x)=\frac{(\sqrt{x}-1)^2}{x}$; evaluate $0.01\cdot f'(0.01)$.

Find the derivatives of the following functions:

865. (1) $y=(a-bx^2)^3$; (2) $y=(1+\sqrt[3]{x})^2$.

866. (1) $y=\frac{1}{10x^5}-\frac{1}{4x^4}$; (2) $y=\frac{3}{\sqrt[3]{x}}-\frac{2}{\sqrt{x}}$.

867. (1) $y=x+\sin x$; (2) $y=x+\cot x$.

868. (1) $y=x^2\sin x$; (2) $y=x^2\tan x$.

869. (1) $y=\sqrt{x}\cos x$; (2) $s=\frac{t}{2}-\frac{2}{t}$.

870. (1) $y=x-\frac{2}{x}-\frac{1}{3x^3}$; (2) $y=\frac{x^2-1}{x^2+1}$.

871. (1) $y=\left(1+\frac{1}{\sqrt[3]{x}}\right)^3$; (2) $y=\frac{\cos x}{1+2\sin x}$.

872. $f(x)=\sqrt[3]{x^2}$; find $f'(-8)$.

873. $f(x)=\frac{x}{2x-1}$; find $f'(0)$, $f'(2)$ and $f'(-2)$.

6.2. *The Derivative of a Composite Function*

If $y=f(u)$ and $u=\varphi(x)$, then y is called a *function of a function* or a *composite function* of x. Then

$$\frac{dy}{dx}=\frac{dy}{du}\cdot\frac{du}{dx} \quad \text{or} \quad y'=f'(u)\cdot u'. \tag{1}$$

Now the formulas of the previous section take the general form:

(1) $(u^n)'=nu^{n-1}u'$; (2) $(\sin u)'=\cos u\cdot u'$;

(3) $(\cos u)'=-\sin u\cdot u'$; (4) $(\sqrt{u})'=\frac{u'}{2\sqrt{u}}$;

(5) $(\tan u)'=\frac{u'}{\cos^2 u}$; (6) $(\cot u)'=-\frac{u'}{\sin^2 u}$.

Find the derivatives of the following functions:

874. (1) $y=\sin 6x$; (2) $y=\cos(a-bx)$.

875. (1) $y=\sin\frac{x}{2}+\cos\frac{x}{2}$; (2) $y=6\sin\frac{x}{3}$.

876. (1) $y=(1-5x)^4$; (2) $y=\sqrt[3]{(4+3x)^2}$.

877. (1) $y=\frac{1}{(1-x^2)^5}$; (2) $y=\sqrt{1-x^2}$; (3) $y=\sqrt{\cos 4x}$

878. $y=\sqrt{2x-\sin 2x}$. **879.** $y=\sin^4 x=(\sin x)^4$.
880. (1) $y=\sin^2 x$; (2) $y=\cos^2 x$; (3) $y=\sec^2 x$.
881. $y=\sin^3 x+\cos^3 x$. **882.** $y=\tan^3 x-3\tan x+3x$.
883. $y=\sqrt[4]{1+\cos^2 x}$. **884.** $y=\sin\sqrt{x}$.
885. $y=\sqrt{1+\sin 2x}-\sqrt{1-\sin 2x}$.
886. $y=\dfrac{1}{(1+\cos 4x)^5}$. **887.** $y=\cot^3\dfrac{x}{3}$.
888. $y=\dfrac{\sin^2 x}{\cos x}$. **889.** $y=x\sqrt{x^2-1}$.
890. $y=\dfrac{\sqrt{2x-1}}{x}$. **891.** $s=a\cos^2\dfrac{t}{a}$.
892. (1) $r=a\sqrt{\cos 2\varphi}$; (2) $r=\sqrt{2\varphi+\cos^2\left(2\varphi+\frac{\pi}{4}\right)}$.
893. $f(t)=\sqrt{a^2+b^2-2ab\cos t}$; find $f'\left(\frac{\pi}{2}\right)$, $f'(\pi)$, $f'\left(\frac{3\pi}{2}\right)$. **894.** $f(x)=\sqrt{x+2\sqrt{x}}$; find $f'(1)$.

Find the derivatives of the following functions:

895. $y=\sqrt{4x+\sin 4x}$. **896.** $y=x^2\sqrt{1-x^2}$.
897. $y=\sin^4 x+\cos^4 x$. **898.** $y=\sqrt[3]{1+\cos 6x}$.
899. (1) $y=\tan x+\frac{2}{3}\tan^3 x+\frac{1}{5}\tan^5 x$; (2) $y=\sin^2 x^3$.
900. $y=\dfrac{1+\sin 2x}{1-\sin 2x}$. **901.** $s=\sqrt{\dfrac{t}{2}-\sin\dfrac{t}{2}}$.
902. $r=\cos^2\left(\frac{\pi}{4}-\frac{\varphi}{2}\right)$. **903.** $y=\dfrac{\sqrt{4x+1}}{x^2}$.
904. $f(t)=\sqrt{1+\cos^2 t^2}$; find $f'\left(\frac{\sqrt{\pi}}{2}\right)$.

6.3. The Tangent Line and the Normal to a Plane Curve

The slope (k) of the tangent to the curve $y=f(x)$ at the point (x_0, y_0) is *equal to the value of the derivative* of $f(x)$ at the point x_0:

$$k=\tan\varphi=f'(x_0)=[y']_{x=x_0}. \qquad (1)$$

The equation of the *tangent* to the curve at the point $M(x_0, y_0)$ (Fig. 28):

$$y-y_0=k(x-x_0). \tag{2}$$

The equation of the *normal*:

$$y-y_0=-\frac{1}{k}(x-x_0), \tag{3}$$

where k is determined by formula (1).

The line segments $TA=y_0\cot\varphi$ and $AN=y_0\tan\varphi$ (Fig. 28) are called the *subtangent* and the *subnormal*

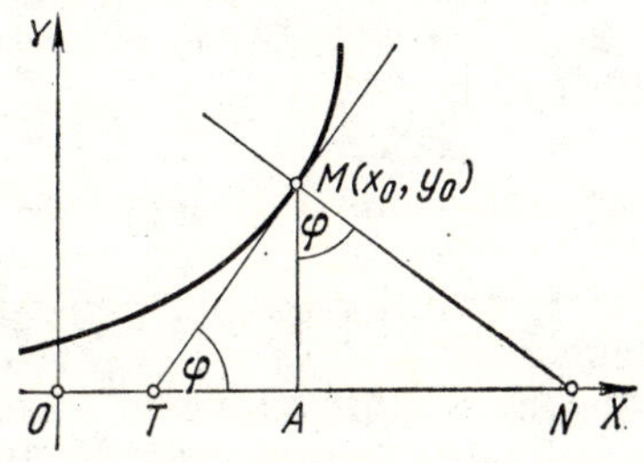

Fig. 28

respectively; the lengths of the segments MT and MN are termed the lengths of the tangent and the normal respectively.

905. Find the slopes of the parabola $y=x^2$ at the points $x=\pm 2$.

906. Write the equations of the tangent and the normal to the parabola $y=4-x^2$ at the point of its intersection with the axis OX (for $x>0$) and construct the parabola, the tangent, and the normal.

In Problems 907 to 910 write the equations of the tangent lines to the given curves and construct the curves and the tangent lines.

907. To the curve $y=\frac{x^3}{3}$ at the point $x=-1$.

908. To the curve $y^2=x^3$ at the points $x_1=0$ and $x_2=1$.

909. To the versiera $y=\frac{8}{4+x^2}$ at the point $x=2$.

910. To the sinusoid $y=\sin x$ at the point $x=\pi$.

911. At what angle does the curve $y=\sin x$ intersect the axis OX?

912. At what angle do the curves $2y=x^2$ and $2y=8-x^2$ intersect?

913. Find the length of the subtangent, the subnormal, the tangent, and the normal to the curve (1) $y=x^2$; (2) $y^2=x^3$ at the point $x=1$.

914. Prove that the subtangent of the parabola $y^2=2px$ is equal to twice the abscissa of the point of tangency, and the subnormal, to p.

915. In the equation of the parabola $y=x^2+bx+c$ determine b and c if the parabola contacts the straight line $y=x$ at the point $x=2$.

---

916. Write the equations of the tangent lines to the hyperbola $xy=4$ at the points $x_1=1$ and $x_2=-4$ and find the angle of their intersection. Construct the hyperbola and the tangents.

Write the equations of the tangent lines to the given curves and construct the curves and the tangents:

917. $y=4x-x^2$ at the points of intersection with the axis OX.

918. $y^2=4-x$ at the points of intersection with the axis OY.

919. $y^2=(4+x)^3$ at the points of intersection with the axes OX and OY.

920. Find the distance of the vertex of the parabola $y=x^2-4x+5$ from the straight line tangent to it at the point of intersection of the parabola and the axis OY.

921. At what angle does the straight line $y=0.5$ intersect the curve $y=\cos x$?

922. At what point is the tangent to the parabola $y=x^2+4x$ parallel to the axis OX?

923. At what point of the parabola $y=x^2-2x+5$ is the line tangent to it perpendicular to the bisector of the first quadrant?

924. Find the lengths of the subtangent, the subnormal, the tangent, and the normal to the curve $y=\frac{2}{1+x^2}$ at the point $x=1$.

925. What angles are formed by the parabola $y=\frac{x^2}{4}$ and its chord if the abscissas of the end-points of the chord are equal to 2 and 4?

6.4. Cases of Non-differentiability of a Continuous Function

1°. A corner point. The point $A(x_1, y_1)$ of the curve $y=f(x)$ (Fig. 29) is termed *corner* if the curve has no single derivative y' but has two different derivatives at this point—a *left-hand* derivative and a *right-hand* derivative: $\lim\limits_{\Delta x \to -0} \frac{\Delta y}{\Delta x}=k_1$ and $\lim\limits_{\Delta x \to +0} \frac{\Delta y}{\Delta x}=k_2$. Two tangent rays emanate from a corner point with slopes k_1 and k_2.

2°. A cuspidal point with a vertical tangent line. The point $B(x_2, y_2)$ (Fig. 29) is called the *cusp* with a verti-

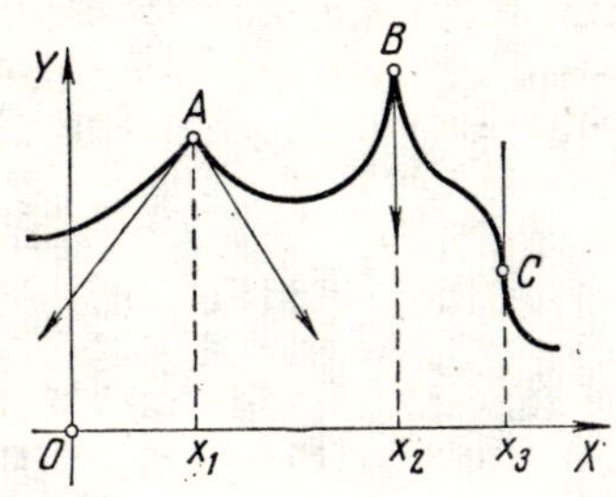

Fig. 29

cal tangent line if the curve has no derivative y' at this point, but it has a *left-hand* and a *right-hand infinite derivatives* of opposite signs ($+\infty$ and $-\infty$). The cusp is a particular case of the corner. One vertical tangent ray emanates from such a point, or it is better to say that two coincident tangent rays emanate from it.

3°. A point of inflection with a vertical tangent line. The point $C(x_3, y_3)$ (Fig. 29) is called the *point of inflection with a vertical tangent* if the curve has an infinite derivative at this point: $y'=\lim\limits_{\Delta x \to -0} \frac{\Delta y}{\Delta x}=\lim\limits_{\Delta x \to +0} \frac{\Delta y}{\Delta x}=+\infty$ (or $-\infty$). In such a point there exists a vertical tangent line.

At the points A and B the function $y=f(x)$ has no derivative, at the point C it has an infinite derivative. At all three points the function is continuous but *non-differentiable*.

926. Graph the function $y=\sqrt{x^2}$ (or $y=|x|$) and find the left-hand y'_- and the right-hand y'_+ derivatives at the corner point of the curve.

927. Graph the function $y=0.5\sqrt{(x-2)^2}$ on the interval $[0, 4]$ and find the left-hand y'_- and the right-hand y'_+ derivatives at the corner point of the curve.

928. Graph the function $y=\sqrt{\sin^2 x}$ on the interval $[-\pi, \pi]$ and write the equations of the tangent lines at the corner point of the curve.

929. Graph the function $y=\sqrt{1+\cos x}$ on the interval $[0, 2\pi]$ and write the equations of the tangent lines at the corner point of the curve and find the angle between them.

930. Graph the function $y=\sqrt[3]{x^2}$ on the interval $[-2, 2]$ and write the equation of the tangent line at the point $x=0$.

931. Graph the function $y=1-\sqrt[3]{(x-2)^2}$ on the interval $[0, 4]$ and write the equation of the tangent line at the point $x=2$.

932. Graph the function $y^3=4x$ on the interval $[-2, 2]$ and write the equation of the tangent line at the point $x=0$.

933. Graph the function $y^3=4(2-x)$ on the interval $[0, 4]$ and write the equation of the tangent line at the point $x=2$.

---

934. Graph the function $y=1-\sqrt{\cos^2 x}$ on the interval $[0, \pi]$ and write the equations of the tangent lines at the corner point of the curve.

935. Graph the function $y=\sqrt[3]{(x+1)^2}-1$ on the interval $[-2, 0]$ and write the equation of the tangent line at the point $x=-1$.

936. Graph the function $y=|4x-x^2|$ on the interval $[-1, 5]$ and write the equations of the tangent lines at the corner point $x=0$, and find the angle between them.

6.5. The Derivatives of Logarithmic and Exponential Functions

The basic formulas:

$$(\ln u)' = \frac{u'}{u}; \quad (e^u)' = e^u \cdot u'; \quad (a^u)' = a^u \ln a \cdot u'.$$

Find the derivatives of the following functions:

937. (1) $y = x \ln x$; (2) $y = \frac{1+\ln x}{x}$; $y = \log (5x)$.

938. (1) $y = \ln x - \frac{2}{x} - \frac{1}{2x^2}$; (2) $y = \ln (x^2 + 2x)$.

939. (1) $y = \ln (1 + \cos x)$; (2) $y = \ln \sin x - \frac{1}{2} \sin^2 x$.

940. $y = \ln (\sqrt{x} + \sqrt{x+1})$.

941. $y = \ln \frac{a^2 + x^2}{a^2 - x^2}$.

942. $y = \ln \frac{x^2}{1 - x^2}$.

943. $y = \ln \tan \left(\frac{\pi}{4} + \frac{x}{2} \right)$.

944. $y = \ln \sqrt{\frac{1+2x}{1-2x}}$.

945. $y = \ln (x + \sqrt{a^2 + x^2})$.

946. $y = 2\sqrt{x} - 4 \ln (2 + \sqrt{x})$.

947. (1) $y = \frac{\cos x}{\sin^2 x} + \ln \tan \frac{x}{2}$; (2) $y = \ln \frac{x^2}{\sqrt{1 - ax^4}}$.

948. Write the equation of the tangent line to the curve $y = \ln x$ at the point of its intersection with the axis OX. Construct the curve and the tangent line.

949. Show that the parabola $y = \frac{x^2}{2e}$ is tangent to the curve $y = \ln x$, and find the point of tangency. Construct the curves.

Find the derivatives of the functions:

950. (1) $y = x^2 + 3^x$; (2) $y = x^2 \cdot 2^x$; (3) $y = x^2 e^x$.

951. (1) $y = a^{\sin x}$; (2) $y = e^{-x^2}$; (3) $y = x^2 e^{-2x}$.

952. $y = 2\left(e^{\frac{x}{2}} - e^{-\frac{x}{2}}\right)$.

953. $y = \sqrt{x} e^{\sqrt{x}}$.

954. $y = \frac{1 + e^x}{1 - e^x}$.

955. $y = e^{\frac{x}{a}} \cos \frac{x}{a}$.

956. (1) $y=e^{-x}(\sin x+\cos x)$; (2) $y=\ln(e^{-x}+xe^{-x})$.

957. $y=\ln\frac{e^x}{x^2+1}$. 958. $y=(e^{ax}-e^{-ax})^2$.

959. $f(t)=\ln(1+a^{-2t})$; evaluate $f'(0)$.

960. At what angle does the curve $y=e^{2x}$ intersect the axis OY?

961. Prove that the length of the subtangent at any point of the curve $y=e^{\frac{x}{a}}$ is equal to a.

962. Find the derivatives of the following functions: (1) $y=x^x$; (2) $y=x^{\sin x}$.

Hint. First take logarithms of the given functions.

Find the derivatives of the following functions:

963. $y=\ln\cos x-\frac{1}{2}\cos^2 x$.

964. $y=\ln(\sqrt{x}-\sqrt{x-1})$. 965. $y=\ln\frac{1+\sqrt{x^2+1}}{x}$.

966. $y=\ln(\sin x+\sqrt{1+\sin^2 x})$.

967. $y=\ln\frac{x}{\sqrt{1-x^2}}$. 968. $y=\frac{1}{2}\ln\tan x+\ln\cos x$.

969. $y=\ln\sqrt{\frac{\sin 2x}{1-\sin 2x}}$. 970. $y=\ln(1+\sec x)$.

971. $y=a\ln(\sqrt{x+a}+\sqrt{x})-\sqrt{x^2+ax}$.

972. $y=ae^{-\frac{x}{a}}+xe^{-\frac{x}{a}}$. 973. $y=\frac{a}{2}\left(e^{\frac{x}{a}}+e^{-\frac{x}{a}}\right)$.

974. $y=\frac{e^x+e^{-x}}{e^x-e^{-x}}$. 975. $y=\ln(e^{2x}+\sqrt{e^{4x}+1})$.

976. $y=\ln\sqrt{\frac{e^{4x}}{e^{4x}+1}}$. 977. $y=x^{\frac{1}{x}}$.

978. $f(t)=\ln\frac{2+\tan t}{2-\tan t}$; evaluate $f'\left(\frac{\pi}{3}\right)$.

979. Write the equation of the tangent to the curve $y=1-e^{\frac{x}{2}}$ at the point of its intersection with the axis OY. Construct the curve, the tangent, and the asymptote of the curve.

6.6. The Derivatives of Inverse Trigonometric Functions

$$(\arcsin u)' = \frac{u'}{\sqrt{1-u^2}}; \quad (\arccos u)' = -\frac{u'}{\sqrt{1-u^2}};$$

$$(\arctan u)' = \frac{u'}{1+u^2}; \quad (\operatorname{arccot} u)' = -\frac{u'}{1+u^2}.$$

Find the derivatives of the following functions:

980. $y=\sqrt{1-x^2}+\arcsin x$.

981. $y=x-\arctan x$.

982. $y=\arcsin\sqrt{1-4x}$.

983. $y=\arcsin\frac{x}{a}$.

984. $y=\arctan\frac{x}{a}$.

985. $y=\arccos(1-2x)$.

986. $y=\operatorname{arccot}\frac{1+x}{1-x}$.

987. (1) $y=x\sqrt{1-x^2}+\arcsin x$; (2) $y=\arcsin(e^{3x})$.

988. $y=\arctan x+\ln\sqrt{\frac{1+x}{1-x}}$.

989. $y=\arccos\frac{1}{\sqrt{x}}$.

990. $y=x\arctan\frac{x}{a}-\frac{a}{2}\ln(x^2+a^2)$.

Find the derivatives of the following functions:

991. $y=\arcsin\sqrt{x}$.

992. $y=\arctan\sqrt{6x-1}$.

993. (1) $y=\arccos(1-x^2)$; (2) $y=\operatorname{arccot} x-\frac{1}{x}$.

994. $y=e^x\sqrt{1-e^{2x}}+\arcsin e^x$.

995. $y=x\arccos x-\sqrt{1-x^2}$.

996. $y=\arctan e^{2x}+\ln\sqrt{\frac{e^{2x}+1}{e^{2x}-1}}$.

997. $s=\sqrt{4t-t^2}+4\arcsin\frac{\sqrt{t}}{2}$.

998. $y=\arccos\sqrt{1-2x}+\sqrt{2x-4x^2}$.

999. $f(z)=(z+1)\arctan e^{-2z}$; evaluate $f'(0)$.

6.7. The Derivatives of Hyperbolic Functions

1°. Definitions. The expressions $\frac{e^x - e^{-x}}{2}$, $\frac{e^x + e^{-x}}{2}$ and their ratios are termed the *hyperbolic sine, cosine, tangent*, and *cotangent*, respectively. They are denoted:

$$\sinh x = \frac{e^x - e^{-x}}{2}, \quad \cosh x = \frac{e^x + e^{-x}}{2}, \quad \tanh x = \frac{\sinh x}{\cosh x},$$

$$\coth x = \frac{\cosh x}{\sinh x}.$$

2°. The properties of hyperbolic functions:
(1) $\cosh^2 x - \sinh^2 x = 1$;
(2) $\cosh^2 x + \sinh^2 x = \cosh 2x$;
(3) $\sinh 2x = 2 \sinh x \cosh x$;
(4) $\sinh 0 = 0$, $\cosh 0 = 1$;
(5) $(\sinh x)' = \cosh x$, $(\cosh x)' = \sinh x$;
(6) $(\tanh x)' = \frac{1}{\cosh^2 x}$, $(\coth x)' = -\frac{1}{\sinh^2 x}$.

Find the derivatives of the following functions:

1000. (1) $y = \sinh^2 x$; (2) $y = x - \tanh x$;
(3) $y = 2\sqrt{\cosh x - 1}$.

1001. $f(x) = \sinh \frac{x}{2} + \cosh \frac{x}{2}$; evaluate $f'(0) + f(0)$.

1002. (1) $y = \ln[\cosh x]$; (2) $y = \tanh x + \coth x$.

1003. (1) $y = x - \coth x$; (2) $y = \ln[\tanh x]$.

1004. (1) $y = \arcsin[\tanh x]$; (2) $y = \sqrt{1 + \sinh^2 4x}$.

1005. The line $y = \frac{a}{2}\left(e^{\frac{x}{a}} + e^{-\frac{x}{a}}\right) = a \cosh \frac{x}{a}$ is called the *catenary*. Write the equation of the normal to this line at the point $x = a$ (see the Tables of hyperbolic functions on p. 391). Construct the curve and the normal.

1006. Write the equation of the tangent to the curve $y = \sinh x$ at the point $x = -2$. Construct the curve and the tangent to it.

1007. Prove that the projection of the ordinate of any point of the catenary curve $y = a \cosh \frac{x}{a}$ on its normal is a constant quantity equal to a.

6.8. *Miscellaneous Problems on Differentiation*

Find the derivatives of the following functions:

1008. (1) $y=\frac{\sqrt{x^2-1}}{x}+\arcsin\frac{1}{x}$; (2) $y=\frac{\tan^2 x}{2}+\ln\cos x$.

1009. $y=\sqrt{4x-1}+\operatorname{arccot}\sqrt{4x-1}$.

1010. $x=\ln(e^{2t}+1)-2\arctan(e^t)$.

1011. $y=4\ln(\sqrt{x-4}+\sqrt{x})+\sqrt{x^2-4x}$.

1012. $s=\frac{1}{4}\tan^4 t-\frac{1}{2}\tan^2 t-\ln(\cos t)$.

1013. $f(x)=(x^2+a^2)\arctan\frac{x}{a}-ax$; evaluate $f'(a)$.

1014. (1) $y=\ln\left[x-\frac{a^2}{x}\right]$; (2) $y=x(\cos\ln x+\sin\ln x)$.

1015. $f(x)=\arcsin\frac{x-1}{x}$; evaluate $f'(5)$.

1016. $\varphi(u)=e^{-\frac{u}{a}}\cos\frac{u}{a}$; show that $\varphi(0)+a\varphi'(0)=0$.

1017. $f(y)=\arctan\frac{y}{a}-\ln\sqrt[4]{y^4-a^4}$; evaluate $f'(2a)$.

1018. $F(z)=\frac{\cos^2 z}{1+\sin^2 z}$; show that $F\left(\frac{\pi}{4}\right)-3F'\left(\frac{\pi}{4}\right)=3$.

1019. Show that the function $s=\frac{1}{t\ln ct}$ satisfies the differential equation $t\frac{ds}{dt}+s=-ts^2$.

1020. Show that the function $x=\frac{t-e^{-t^2}}{2t^2}$ satisfies the differential equation $t\frac{dx}{dt}+2x=e^{-t^2}$.

6.9. *Higher-Order Derivatives*

Let $y'=f'(x)$ be a derivative of the function $y=f(x)$; then the derivative of the function $f'(x)$ is called the *second derivative* of the function $f(x)$ and is denoted by y'', or $f''(x)$, or $\frac{d^2y}{dx^2}$.

The second derivative is also called a *second-order derivative*. In contrast, the function $f'(x)$ is called a *first-order derivative*, or the *first derivative*.

A derivative of the second derivative is called the *third derivative* of the function $f(x)$ (or the *third-order derivative*). It is denoted by $f'''(x)$.

In similar manner we denote the derivatives of the fourth order $f^{IV}(x)$, fifth order $f^{V}(x)$ and so forth (numbers are used instead of dashes to save space and Roman numerals are used to avoid confusion with exponents).

A derivative of the nth order is symbolized by $f^{(n)}(x)$. Thus,

the derivative of the third order $y''' = f'''(x) = \dfrac{d^3y}{dx^3}$,

the derivative of the fourth order $y^{IV} = f^{IV}(x) = \dfrac{d^4y}{dx^4}$,

and, in general,

the derivative of the nth order $y^{(n)} = f^{(n)}(x) = \dfrac{d^ny}{dx^n}$.

1021. Find the second-order derivative of the function:

(1) $y = \sin^2 x$; (2) $y = \tan x$; (3) $y = \sqrt{1+x^2}$.

1022. Find the third-order derivative of the function:

(1) $y = \cos^2 x$; (2) $y = \dfrac{1}{x^2}$; (3) $y = x \sin x$.

1023. Find the third-order derivative of the function:

(1) $y = x \ln x$; (2) $s = te^{-t}$; (3) $y = \arctan \dfrac{x}{a}$.

1024. $s = \dfrac{t}{2}\sqrt{2-t^2} + \arcsin \dfrac{t}{\sqrt{2}}$; find $\dfrac{d^3s}{dt^3}$.

Find the derivative of the nth order of the function:

1025. (1) $e^{-\frac{x}{a}}$; (2) $\ln x$; (3) $\sqrt{x}$.

1026. (1) x^n; (2) $\sin x$; (3) $\cos^2 x$.

1027. Deduce the Leibniz rule by means of successive differentiation:

$(uv)'' = u''v + 2u'v' + uv''$;

$(uv)''' = u'''v + 3u''v' + 3u'v'' + uv'''$;

$(uv)^{IV} = u^{IV}v + 4u'''v' + 6u''v'' + 4u'v''' + uv^{IV}$ and so on.

1028. Using the Leibniz rule find the second derivative of the function:

(1) $y=e^x \cos x$; (2) $y=a^x x^3$; (3) $y=x^2 \sin x$.

1029. Using the Leibniz rule find the third derivative of the function:

(1) $y=e^{-x}\sin x$; (2) $y=x^2 \ln x$; (3) $y=x\cos x$.

1030. $f(x)=xe^{\frac{x}{a}}$; find $f'''(x)$, $f^{(n)}(x)$, $f^{(n)}(0)$.

1031. $f(x)=(1+x)^m$; find $f(0)$, $f'(0)$, $f''(0)$, $f'''(0)$, ..., $f^{(n)}(0)$.

1032. $f(x)=\frac{x}{\sqrt{1+x}}$; show that for $n\geqslant 2$

$$f^{(n)}(0)=(-1)^{n-1}\frac{1\cdot 3\cdot 5\ldots(2n-3)}{2^{n-1}}n.$$

1033. $f(x)=\frac{1}{1-x^2}$; show that

$$f^{(n)}(0)=\begin{cases} n! & \text{at } n=2m, \\ 0 & \text{at } n=2m-1. \end{cases}$$

Hint. Take advantage of the identity

$$\frac{1}{1-x^2}=\frac{1}{2}\left(\frac{1}{1+x}+\frac{1}{1-x}\right).$$

1034. By differentiating the identity $(x-1)(x^2+x^3+ +\ldots+x^n)=x^{n+1}-x^2$ three times with respect to x and putting then $x=1$, find the sum $\sum\limits_{k=1}^{n} k(k-1)=\frac{(n+1)n(n-1)}{3}$ and then the sum of squared numbers of the natural series

$$\sum_{k=1}^{n} k^2=1^2+2^2+\ldots+n^2=\frac{n(n+1)(2n+1)}{6}.$$

1035. Find the second derivative of the function:

(1) $y=e^{-x^2}$; (2) $y=\cot x$; (3) $y=\arcsin\frac{x}{2}$.

1036. Find the nth derivative of the function:

(1) $y=a^x$; (2) $y=\frac{1}{1+2x}$; (3) $y=\sin^2 x$.

1037. $f(x)=\arcsin\frac{1}{x}$; find $f(2)$, $f'(2)$ and $f''(2)$.

1038. Using the Leibniz rule, find the third derivative of the function:

(1) $y=x^3e^x$; (2) $y=x^2\sin\frac{x}{a}$;
(3) $y=xf'(a-x)+3f(a-x)$.

1039. Show that the function $y=e^x\cos x$ satisfies the differential equation $y^{\mathrm{IV}}+4y=0$.

1040. Show that the function $y=xe^{-\frac{1}{x}}$ satisfies the equation $x^3y''-xy'+y=0$.

1041. $f(x)=x^2e^{-\frac{x}{a}}$; show that $f^{(n)}(0)=\frac{n(n-1)(-1)^n}{a^{n-2}}$.

1042. $f(x)=e^{-x^2}$; show that
$f^{(n)}(0)=-2(n-1)f^{(n-2)}(0)$, $f^{(2m-1)}(0)=0$,
$f^{2m}(0)=(-2)^m(2m-1)(2m-3)\ldots5\cdot3\cdot1$.

1043. $f(x)=x^n$; show that

$$f(1)+\frac{f'(1)}{1}+\frac{f''(1)}{2!}+\ldots+\frac{f^{(n)}(1)}{n!}=2^n.$$

6.10. *The Derivative of an Implicit Function*

If an equation $F(x, y)=0$, unsolved with respect to y, defines y as a single-valued function of x, then y is termed the *implicit* function of x. To find the derivative y' of this implicit function, we have to differentiate both members of the function $F(x, y)=0$ with respect to x, considering y as a function of x. From the equation thus obtained we find the required derivative y'. To find y'' we have to differentiate twice the equation $F(x, y)=0$ with respect to x, and so on.

Find y' from the equations:

1044. (1) $x^2+y^2=a^2$; (2) $y^2=2px$; (3) $\frac{x^2}{a^2}-\frac{y^2}{b^2}=1$.

1045. (1) $x^2+xy+y^2=6$; (2) $x^2+y^2-xy=0$.

1046. (1) $x^{\frac{2}{3}}+y^{\frac{2}{3}}=a^{\frac{2}{3}}$; (2) $e^y-e^{-x}+xy=0$.
1047. $e^x \sin y-e^{-y}\cos x=0$.
1048. $x=y+\operatorname{arccot} y$.
1049. $e^{xy}-x^2+y^3=0$; find $\frac{dy}{dx}$ at $x=0$.
1050. Find y'' from the equations:
(1) $x^2+y^2=a^2$; (2) $ax+by-xy=c$; (3) $x^my^n=1$.
1051. $\frac{x^2}{a^2}+\frac{y^2}{b^2}=1$; find y'' at the point $(0, b)$.
1052. Write the equations of the tangents to the curve $x^2+y^2+4x-2y-3=0$ at the points of its intersection with the axis OY.
1053. Find the points of intersection of the normal of the hyperbola $x^2-y^2=9$, drawn from the point $(5, 4)$, with the asymptotes.
1054. Write the equation of the tangent to the curve:

(1) $\frac{x^2}{a^2}+\frac{y^2}{b^2}=1$; (2) $y^2=2px$ at the point (x_0, y_0).

1055. Write the equations of the tangents to the astroid $x^{\frac{2}{3}}+y^{\frac{2}{3}}=a^{\frac{2}{3}}$ at the points of its intersection with the straight line $y=x$.
1056. At what angle do the curves $x^2+y^2=5$ and $y^2=4x$ intersect?

1057. Find y' from the equations:

(1) $\frac{x^2}{a^2}+\frac{y^2}{b^2}=1$; (2) $x^3+y^3-3axy=0$.

1058. Find y'' from the equations:

(1) $x^2-y^2=a^2$; (2) $(x-\alpha)^2+(y-\beta)^2=R^2$;
(3) $\arctan y=x+y$; (4) $x^2+xy+y^2=a^2$.

1059. Write the equations of the tangents to the circle $x^2+y^2+4x-4y+3=0$ at the points of its intersection with the axis OX. Construct the circle and the tangents.
1060. Write the equation of the tangent to the ellipse

$x^2+4y^2=16$ at the midpoint of the segment of a tangent line intercepted by the coordinate axes if the point lies in the first quadrant.

1061. $te^{-\frac{s}{2}}+se^{-\frac{t}{2}}=2$; find $\frac{ds}{dt}$ at $t=0$.

1062. $t\ln x-x\ln t=1$; find $\frac{dx}{dt}$ at $t=1$.

1063. $x^2\sin y-\cos y+\cos 2y=0$; find y' at $y=\frac{\pi}{2}$.

6.11. *The Differential of a Function*

If a function $y=f(x)$ is differentiable at the point x, i.e. it has a finite derivative y' at this point, then $\frac{\Delta y}{\Delta x}=y'+\alpha$, where $\alpha\longrightarrow 0$ as $\Delta x\longrightarrow 0$; hence

$$\Delta y=y'\Delta x+\alpha\Delta x. \tag{1}$$

The principal linear part $y'\Delta x$ of the increment Δy of the function, which is *proportional* to Δx, is called the *differential* of the function and is denoted by dy:

$$dy=y'\Delta x. \tag{2}$$

Putting $y=x$ in formula (2), we get $dx=x'\Delta x=1\cdot\Delta x=\Delta x$, and therefore

$$dy=y'dx. \tag{3}$$

Formula (3) also holds true if x is a function of a new variable t.

It follows from (1) that $\Delta y\approx dy$, i.e. for a sufficiently small $dx=\Delta x$ the *increment* of a function is approximately equal to its *differential*.

In particular, for a linear function $y=ax+b$, we have: $\Delta y=dy$.

Find the differentials of the following functions:

1064. (1) $y=x^n$; (2) $y=x^3-3x^2+3x$.

1065. (1) $y=\sqrt{1+x^2}$; (2) $s=\frac{gt^2}{2}$.

1066. (1) $r=2\varphi-\sin 2\varphi$; (2) $x=\frac{1}{t^2}$.

1067. (1) $d(\sin^2 t)$; (2) $d(1-\cos u)$.

1068. (1) $d\left(\frac{a}{x}+\arctan\frac{x}{a}\right)$; (2) $d(\alpha+\ln\alpha)$;

(3) $d\left(\cos\frac{\varphi}{2}\right)$; (4) $d\left(\arcsin\frac{1}{x}\right)$.

1069. By finding the differential of each term of the equation, find $\frac{dy}{dx}$ from the following equations:

(1) $x^2+y^2=a^2$; (2) $xy=a^2$; (3) $x^2-xy-y^2=0$.

1070. (1) $y=x^2$; find the approximate value of the increment of y $(\Delta y\approx dy)$ for x varying from 2 to 2.01;

(2) $y=\sqrt{x}$; find the approximate value of the increment of y for x varying from 100 to 101.

1071. (1) The edge of a cube $x=5$ m ± 0.01 m. Determine the absolute and the relative errors in computing the volume of the cube.

(2) The length of telegraph wire $s=2b\left(1+\frac{2f^2}{3b^2}\right)$, where $2b$ is the distance between two neighbouring poles, and f, the maximum deflection of the wire. By how much will the deflection f increase when the wire is elongated by ds as a result of heating?

1072. (1) What must be the accuracy in measuring the abscissas of the curve $y=x^2\sqrt{x}$ for $x\leqslant 4$ in order to compute its ordinates with an error not exceeding 0.1?

(2) With what relative accuracy must the radius of a sphere be measured in order to compute its volume with an error not exceeding 1 per cent?

1073. Find the approximate values of the: (1) area of a circular ring; (2) volume of a spherical shell. Compare them with the exact values.

Find the differentials of the functions:

1074. (1) $y=\frac{1}{x}-\frac{1}{x^2}$; (2) $r=\cos(a-b\varphi)$;

(3) $s=\sqrt{1-t^2}$.

1075. (1) $y=\ln\cos x$; (2) $z=\arctan\sqrt{4u-1}$; (3) $s=e^{-2t}$.

1076. (1) $d(\sqrt{x}+1)$; (2) $d(\tan\alpha-\alpha)$; (3) $d(bt-e^{-bt})$.

1077. (1) $y = x^3$; determine Δy and dy and calculate them for x varying from 2 to 1.98.

(2) The period of oscillation of a pendulum $T = 2\pi\sqrt{\frac{l}{980}}$ sec., where l is the length of the pendulum in centimetres. How must the length of the pendulum ($l = 20$ cm) be changed to reduce the period of oscillation by 0.1 sec?

(3) What must be the accuracy in measuring the abscissas of the curve $xy = 4$ for $x \geqslant 0.5$ in order to compute its ordinates with an error not exceeding 0.1?

6.12. Parametric Equations of a Curve

Let a curve be represented parametrically by the equations $x = f(t)$ and $y = \varphi(t)$. Denoting the derivatives with respect to the parameter by dots, we find:

$$\frac{dy}{dx} = \frac{\dot{y}}{\dot{x}}; \quad \frac{d^2y}{dx^2} = \frac{d\left(\frac{\dot{y}}{\dot{x}}\right)}{dx} = \frac{\ddot{y}\dot{x} - \ddot{x}\dot{y}}{\dot{x}^3}.$$

1078. Construct the curves specified parametrically:

$$(1) \begin{cases} x = t^2 \\ y = \frac{1}{2}t^3; \end{cases} \quad (2) \begin{cases} x = t^2 \\ y = \frac{t^3}{3} - t. \end{cases}$$

Eliminating t from the given equations, write the equation of each curve in the usual form $F(x, y) = 0$.

Reduce to the form $F(x, y) = 0$ (or $y = f(x)$) the equations of the curves represented parametrically:

1079. $$(1) \begin{cases} x = a\cos t \\ y = b\sin t; \end{cases} \quad (2) \begin{cases} x = a\cos^3 t \\ y = a\sin^3 t. \end{cases}$$

1080. $$(1) \begin{cases} x = \frac{e^t + e^{-t}}{2} \\ y = \frac{e^t - e^{-t}}{2}; \end{cases} \quad (2) \begin{cases} x = \tan t \\ y = \cos^2 t. \end{cases}$$

1081. Construct the involute of a circle (see Problem 368)

$$\begin{cases} x=a(\cos t+t\sin t) \\ y=a(\sin t-t\cos t), \end{cases}$$

putting $t=0,\ \frac{\pi}{2},\ \pi,\ \frac{3\pi}{2},\ 2\pi.$

1082. Putting $y=xt$, obtain the parametric equations of the folium of Descartes $x^3+y^3-3axy=0$ (see Problem 366) and investigate the motion of a current point along the curve with t varying monotonically (1) from 0 to $+\infty$; (2) from 0 to -1; (3) from $-\infty$ to -1.

1083. Write the equation of the tangent to the cycloid (see Problem 367) $x=a(t-\sin t)$, $y=a(1-\cos t)$ at the point $t=\frac{\pi}{2}$. Construct the curve and the tangent line.

1084. Write the equation of the tangent to the hypocycloid (astroid) $x=a\cos^3 t$, $y=a\sin^3 t$ at the point $t=\frac{\pi}{4}$. Construct the curve and the tangent line.

Hint. Prior to constructing the curve tabulate the values of x and y at $t=0;\ \frac{\pi}{4};\ \frac{\pi}{2};\ \frac{3\pi}{4}$ and so on.

1085. Find $\frac{d^2y}{dx^2}$ from the equations:

(1) $\begin{cases} x=a\cos t \\ y=a\sin t; \end{cases}$ (2) $\begin{cases} x=t^2 \\ y=\frac{t^3}{3}-t; \end{cases}$ (3) $\begin{cases} x=a(t-\sin t) \\ y=a(1-\cos t). \end{cases}$

1086. Construct the curves given by the parametric equations:

(1) $x=2t-1,\quad y=1-4t^2$; (2) $x=t^3,\ y=t^2-2$,

by finding the points of their intersection with the coordinate axes and taking into account that for the second curve $\frac{dy}{dx}=\infty$ at $t=0$. Write the equations of the curve in the form $F(x,\ y)=0$.

1087. Write the equation of the tangent to the cycloid $x=a(t-\sin t)$, $y=a(1-\cos t)$ at the point $t=\frac{3\pi}{2}$. Construct the curve and the tangent.

1088. Write the equation of the tangent to the involute of the circle $x=a(\cos t+t\sin t)$, $y=a(\sin t-t\cos t)$ at the point $t=\frac{\pi}{4}$.

1089. Find $\frac{d^2y}{dx^2}$ from the equations

(1) $\begin{cases} x=2\cos t \\ y=\sin t; \end{cases}$ (2) $\begin{cases} x=t^2 \\ y=t+t^3; \end{cases}$ (3) $\begin{cases} x=e^{2t} \\ y=e^{3t}. \end{cases}$

CHAPTER 7

APPLICATIONS OF THE DERIVATIVE

7.1. *Velocity and Acceleration*

Let a point move along the axis OX and at a moment t have the ordinate $x=f(t)$. Then at the moment t

the *velocity* $v=\lim\limits_{\Delta t\to 0}\frac{\Delta x}{\Delta t}=\frac{dx}{dt}$;

the *acceleration* $w=\lim\limits_{\Delta t\to 0}\frac{\Delta v}{\Delta t}=\frac{dv}{dt}=\frac{d^2x}{dt^2}$.

1090. An antiaircraft projectile is launched upwards at the initial velocity of a m/sec. At what height x will it be in t seconds? Determine the velocity and acceleration of its motion. When will the projectile reach the highest point, and at what distance from earth's surface will this point be?

1091. A body moves along a straight line OX according to the law: $x=\frac{t^3}{3}-2t^2+3t$. Determine the velocity and acceleration of its motion. At what moments does the body change the direction of motion?

1092. A material point is in oscillating motion obeying the law $x=a\cos\omega t$. Determine the velocity and acceleration at the points $x=\pm a$ and $x=0$. Show that the acceleration $\frac{d^2x}{dt^2}$ and displacement x are related by a differential equation $\frac{d^2x}{dt^2}=-\omega^2x$.

1093. A revolving flywheel, which is being hindered by a brake, in t seconds turns through an angle $\varphi=a+bt-ct^2$, a, b, and c are positive constants. Determine the angular velocity and angular acceleration. When will the flywheel stop?

1094. A wheel of radius a rolls along a straight line. The angle φ through which the wheel turns during t seconds is determined by the equation $\varphi = t + \frac{t^2}{2}$. Find the velocity and acceleration specifying the motion of the centre of the wheel.

1095. Let v be the velocity and w the acceleration of a point moving along the axis OX. Show that $w\,dx = v\,dv$.

1096. A point is in rectilinear motion characterized by the equation $v^2 = 2ax$, where v is the velocity and x is the path covered, a being a constant. Determine the acceleration.

1097. A body situated at a height of 10 m was thrown upwards with an initial velocity of 20 m/sec. At what height will it be in t seconds? Determine the velocity and acceleration of its motion. In how many seconds and at what height will the body reach the highest point?

1098. A hemispherical vessel of radius R cm is being filled with water at a constant rate of a litre/sec. Determine the rate of water level rise at the height of h cm and show that it is inversely proportional to the area of the free surface of the liquid.

Hint. The volume of a spherical segment $V = \pi h^2 \left(R - \frac{h}{3}\right)$. Differentiate both members of this equality with respect to t, $\frac{dV}{dt}$ being equal to a (by hypothesis).

1099. The relationship between the quantity x of a substance obtained in a chemical reaction and the time t is expressed by the equation $x = A(1 - e^{-kt})$. Determine the reaction rate.

1100. Let $\frac{d\varphi}{dt} = \omega$ (angular velocity) and $\frac{d\omega}{dt} = \varepsilon$ (angular acceleration). Show that $\frac{d(\omega^2)}{d\varphi} = 2\varepsilon$.

7.2. Mean-Value Theorems

1°. Rolle's theorem. If $f(x)$ (1) is continuous on a closed interval $[a, b]$; (2) has a derivative inside it; (3) $f(a)=f(b)$, then for some value of x (say c) between a and b

$$f'(c)=0. \tag{1}$$

2°. Lagrange's theorem. If $f(x)$ (1) is continuous on a closed interval $[a, b]$; (2) has a derivative inside it, then for some value of x (say c) between a and b

$$f(b)-f(a)=(b-a)f'(c). \tag{2}$$

3°. Cauchy's theorem. If $f(x)$ and $\varphi(x)$ (1) are continuous on a closed interval $[a, b]$; (2) have derivatives inside it, and $\varphi'(x)\neq 0$, then for some value of x (say c) between a and b

$$\frac{f(b)-f(a)}{\varphi(b)-\varphi(a)}=\frac{f'(c)}{\varphi'(c)}. \tag{3}$$

These theorems are called the mean-value theorems, since they treat some value of $x=c$ lying between a and b.

Geometrical interpretation: Rolle's and Lagrange's theorems assert that there is at least one point between A and B on the arc AB of a continuous curve $y=f(x)$ where the tangent is parallel to the chord AB, provided that there is a tangent at every point of the arc AB. It is obvious that on arcs having corners and cusps the conditions for the mean-value theorems are not fulfilled.

The following proposition is a special case of Rolle's theorem when $f(b)=f(a)=0$: if a and b are roots of a function $f(x)$, then between a and b there is at least one root of its derivative $f'(x)$, provided $f(x)$ is continuous on a closed interval $[a, b]$ and has a derivative inside it.

1101. Check to see that between the roots of the function $f(x)=x^2-4x+3$ there is a root of its derivative. Illustrate this graphically.

1102. Is Rolle's theorem applicable to the function

$f(x)=1-\sqrt[3]{x^2}$ on the closed interval $[-1, 1]$? Illustrate this graphically.

1103. Construct the arc $\breve{AB}$ of the curve $y=|\sin x|$ over the interval $\left[-\frac{\pi}{2}, \frac{\pi}{2}\right]$. Why does the arc have no tangent parallel to the chord AB? Which of the conditions of Rolle's theorem is not fulfilled here?

1104. At what point is the tangent to the parabola $y=x^2$ parallel to the chord connecting the points $A(-1, 1)$ and $B(3, 9)$? Illustrate this graphically.

1105. Write Lagrange's formula for the function $f(x)=x^2$ on the closed interval $[a, b]$ and find c. Illustrate this graphically.

1106. Write Lagrange's formula for the function $f(x)=\sqrt{x}$ on the closed interval $[1, 4]$ and find c.

1107. Show that on the interval $[-1, 2]$ Lagrange's theorem is not applicable to the functions $\frac{4}{x}$ and $1-\sqrt[3]{x^2}$. Illustrate this graphically.

1108. Construct $\breve{AB}$ of the curve $y=|\cos x|$ for the interval $\left[0, \frac{2\pi}{3}\right]$. Why does the arc have no tangent parallel to the chord AB? Which of the conditions of Lagrange's theorem is not fulfilled here?

1109. Construct the graph of the function $f(x)=\begin{cases} x \text{ for } |x|<2 \\ 1 \text{ for } |x|\geqslant 2. \end{cases}$ Having taken on it the points $O(0, 0)$ and $B(2, 1)$, show that between O and B the curve has no point at which the tangent is parallel to OB. Which conditions of Lagrange's theorem are fulfilled for this function on the interval $[0, 2]$ and which ones are not?

1110. A train covered the distance between two neighbouring stations with a mean (average) velocity $v_0=40$ km/h. Lagrange's theorem asserts that during motion there was a moment at which the instantaneous (but not mean) velocity of motion $\frac{ds}{dt}$ equaled 40 km/h. Show this.

1111. It is given that $f(x)$ is continuous on a closed interval $[a, b]$ and has a derivative at each point inside it. Applying Rolle's theorem to the function

$$\Phi(x)=\begin{vmatrix} x & f(x) & 1 \\ b & f(b) & 1 \\ a & f(a) & 1 \end{vmatrix},$$

obtain Lagrange's theorem. Find out the geometrical meaning of the function $\Phi(x)$.

1112. Write Cauchy's formula $\frac{f(b)-f(a)}{\varphi(b)-\varphi(a)}=\frac{f'(c)}{\varphi'(c)}$ for the functions $f(x)=x^3$ and $\varphi(x)=x^2$, and find c.

1113. Cauchy's theorem asserts geometrically that on an arc of a curve given by the parametric equations $x=\varphi(t)$, $y=f(t)$ corresponding to the interval $a\leqslant t\leqslant b$ there is an intermediate point at which the tangent is parallel to the chord if the functions $\varphi(t)$ and $f(t)$ on the closed interval $[a, b]$ satisfy the conditions of Cauchy's theorem. Prove this.

1114. Write Lagrange's formula in the form $f(x+\Delta x)-f(x)=\Delta x f'(x+\theta\Delta x)$, where $0<\theta<1$, for the functions: (1) $f(x)=x^2$; (2) $f(x)=x^3$, and show that for the first function θ is independent of x, and for the second it depends on x and Δx.

1115. Show that $\sqrt{101}=10+\frac{1}{2\sqrt{100+\theta}}\approx 10.05$.

1116. With the aid of Cauchy's formula prove that if

$$f(0)=f'(0)=f''(0)=\ldots=f^{(n-1)}(0)=0,$$

then

$$\frac{f(x)}{x^n}=\frac{f^{(n)}(\theta x)}{n!},$$

where

$$0<\theta<1.$$

1117. Write Lagrange's formula

$$f(b)-f(a)=(b-a)f'(c)$$

for the function $f(x)=x^3$ and find c.

1118. Write Lagrange's formula and find c for the functions:

(1) $f(x)=\arctan x$ on the interval $[0, 1]$;

(2) $f(x)=\arcsin x$ on the interval $[0, 1]$;
(3) $f(x)=\ln x$ on the interval $[1, 2]$.

1119. Write Cauchy's formula and find c for the functions:
(1) $\sin x$ and $\cos x$ on the interval $\left[0, \frac{\pi}{2}\right]$;
(2) x^2 and $\sqrt{x}$ on the interval $[1, 4]$.

1120. Graph the function $y=|x-1|$ on the interval $[0, 3]$. Why is it impossible here to draw a tangent parallel to the chord? Which of the conditions of Lagrange's theorem is not fulfilled here?

1121. At what point is the tangent to the curve $y=4-x^2$ parallel to the chord connecting the points $A(-2, 0)$ and $B(1, 3)$? Illustrate this graphically.

7.3. Evaluating Indeterminate Forms. L'Hospital's Rule

1°. The indeterminate form $\frac{0}{0}$. The first L'Hospital rule. If $\lim\limits_{x\to a} f(x) = \lim\limits_{x\to a} \varphi(x)=0$, then $\lim\limits_{x\to a} \frac{f(x)}{\varphi(x)} = \lim\limits_{x\to a} \frac{f'(x)}{\varphi'(x)}$, when the latter exists.

2°. The indeterminate form $\frac{\infty}{\infty}$. The second L'Hospital rule. If $\lim\limits_{x\to a} f(x) = \lim\limits_{x\to a} \varphi(x)=\infty$, then $\lim\limits_{x\to a} \frac{f(x)}{\varphi(x)} = \lim\limits_{x\to a} \frac{f'(x)}{\varphi'(x)}$, when the latter exists.

3°. The indeterminate forms $0\cdot\infty$, $\infty-\infty$, 1^∞ and 0^0 are reduced to the indeterminate forms $\frac{0}{0}$ and $\frac{\infty}{\infty}$ by means of algebraic transformations.

Find the limits:

1122. $\lim\limits_{x\to 0} \frac{\sin 3x}{x}$.

1123. $\lim\limits_{x\to 0} \frac{e^x-1}{\sin 2x}$.

1124. $\lim\limits_{x\to a} \frac{x-a}{x^n-a^n}$.

1125. $\lim\limits_{x\to 1} \frac{x-1}{\ln x}$.

1126. $\lim\limits_{x\to 0} \frac{1-\cos ax}{1-\cos bx}$.

1127. $\lim\limits_{x\to 0} \frac{1-\cos x}{x^2}$.

1128. $\lim\limits_{x\to 0} \frac{x-\sin x}{x^3}$.

1129. $\lim\limits_{x\to 0} \frac{\tan x-\sin x}{x-\sin x}$.

1130. (1) $\lim\limits_{x \to +\infty} \frac{e^x}{x^3}$; (2) $\lim\limits_{x \to -\infty} \frac{e^x}{x^3}$.

1131. $\lim\limits_{x \to \infty} \frac{\ln x}{x}$.

1132. $\lim\limits_{x \to 0} \frac{\ln x}{\cot x}$.

1133. $\lim\limits_{x \to \frac{\pi}{2}} \frac{\tan x}{\tan 3x}$.

1134. $\lim\limits_{x \to \pi} (\pi - x) \tan \frac{x}{2}$.

1135. $\lim\limits_{x \to 0} x \ln x$.

1136. $\lim\limits_{x \to +\infty} x^n \cdot e^{-x}$.

1137. $\lim\limits_{x \to 0} x^x$.

1138. $\lim\limits_{x \to 0} (\sin x)^{\tan x}$.

1139. $\lim\limits_{x \to \infty} \left(1 + \frac{3}{x}\right)^x$.

1140. Determine the order of the infinitesimal $xe^x - \sin x$ with respect to $x \to 0$.

1141. Prove that as $x \to 0$:

(1) $x - \arctan x \approx \frac{x^3}{3}$; (2) $a^x - b^x \approx x \ln \frac{a}{b}$;

(3) $e^{2x} - 1 - 2x \approx 2x^2$; (4) $2x - \ln(1 + 2x) \approx 2x^2$.

1142. Prove that (as $x \to 0$) $x - \sin x \approx \frac{x^3}{6}$ and hence $\sin x \approx x$ with an error approximately equal to $\frac{x^3}{6}$. Evaluate $\sin 1°$ and $\sin 6°$ and estimate the error.

1143. Prove that (as $\alpha \to 0$) $\sqrt[3]{1+\alpha} - 1 - \frac{1}{3}\alpha \approx -\frac{\alpha^2}{9}$ and hence $\sqrt[3]{1+\alpha} \approx 1 + \frac{1}{3}\alpha$ with an error $\approx \frac{\alpha^2}{9}$. Compute $\sqrt[3]{1.006}$, $\sqrt[3]{0.991}$, $\sqrt[3]{65}$, $\sqrt[3]{210}$ and estimate the error.

Find the limits:

1144. $\lim\limits_{x \to 0} \frac{e^{ax} - e^{bx}}{\sin x}$.

1145. $\lim\limits_{x \to 0} \frac{x - \arctan x}{x^3}$.

1146. $\lim\limits_{x \to \frac{\pi}{2a}} \frac{1 - \sin ax}{(2ax - \pi)^2}$.

1147. $\lim\limits_{x \to 0} \frac{a^x - l^x}{\tan x}$.

1148. $\lim\limits_{x \to \frac{\pi}{6}} \frac{1 - 2\sin x}{\cos 3x}$.

1149. $\lim\limits_{x \to \frac{\pi}{4}} \frac{1 - \tan x}{\cos 2x}$.

1150. $\lim\limits_{x \to 0} \frac{e^{2x} - 1}{\ln(1 + 2x)}$.

1151. $\lim\limits_{x \to 1} \frac{\ln x}{1 - x^3}$.

1152. $\lim\limits_{x\to 0}(1-e^{2x})\cot x$. **1153.** $\lim\limits_{x\to 1} x^{\frac{1}{1-x}}$.

1154. $\lim\limits_{x\to 0}\left(\frac{1}{x\sin x}-\frac{1}{x^2}\right)$. **1155.** $\lim\limits_{x\to 0}(e^{2x}+x)^{\frac{1}{x}}$.

1156. Prove that as $x\to 0$ $\arcsin x - x \approx \frac{x^3}{6}$.

1157. Prove that (as $\alpha\to 0$) $\sqrt{1+\alpha}-1-\frac{\alpha}{2}\approx -\frac{\alpha^2}{8}$ and hence $\sqrt{1+\alpha}\approx 1+\frac{\alpha}{2}$ with an error approximately equal to $\frac{\alpha^2}{8}$. Compute $\sqrt{1.006}$, $\sqrt{1.004}$, $\sqrt{0.998}$, $\sqrt{0.994}$, $\sqrt{65}$, $\sqrt{85}$ and estimate the error.

7.4. Increase and Decrease of a Function. Maxima and Minima

1°. Definitions. I. A function $f(x)$ is called an *increasing function at a point* x_0 if, in a sufficiently small ε-neighbourhood of this point,

$$f(x_0-h)<f(x_0)<f(x_0+h)$$

for any positive $h<\varepsilon$.

II. A function $f(x)$ is called *increasing in an interval* $[a, b]$ if for any x_1 and x_2 within this interval $f(x_1)<f(x_2)$ when $x_1<x_2$.

A function decreasing at a point and in an interval is similarly defined.

III. A function $f(x)$ has a maximum or minimum (extremum) at a point x_0 if $f(x_0)$ is less or greater, respectively, than all neighbouring values.

2°. Sufficiency tests for the increase and decrease of a function $y=f(x)$ (at a point and in an interval):

if $y'>0$, then the function *increases*;

if $y'<0$, then the function *decreases*.

3°. Necessary condition for an extremum. A function $y=f(x)$ has an extremum only at points where $y'=0$ or does not exist. Such points are called *critical*. At these points the tangent is either horizontal ($y'=0$), vertical (at a cuspidal point) or there is no definite tangent (for instance, at a corner point). In the latter two cases y' does not exist.

4°. Sufficient conditions for an extremum. If a function $f(x)$ is continuous at a point x_0 and has a finite derivative within some neighbourhood of x_0, except, perhaps, the point x_0, and if, when x passes through x_0,

y' changes $+$ for $-$, then $f(x_0)=y_{max}$,

y' changes $-$ for $+$, then $f(x_0)=y_{min}$,

y' does not change the sign, then there is no extremum.

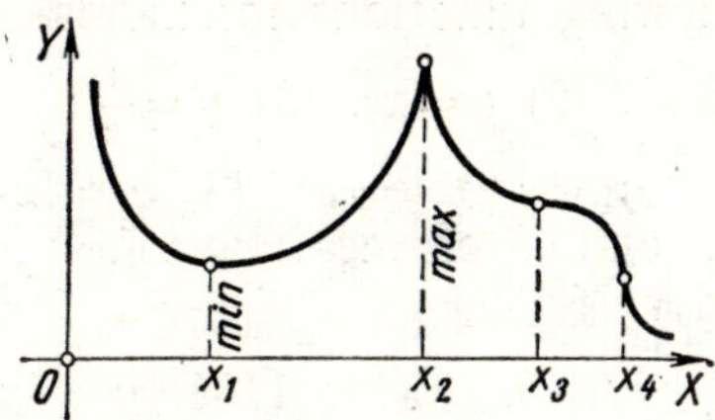

Fig. 30

The third case takes place at an ordinary point (for $y'>0$ or $y'<0$), and also at a point of inflection and at a corner.

Thus, to find an extremum of a function, it is necessary to:

(1) Find y' and the critical points at which $y'=0$ or does not exist.

(2) Determine the sign of y' on the left and on the right of each critical point, making a table of he form

x		x_1		x_2		x_3		x_4	
y'	$-$	0	$+$	does not exist	$-$	0	$-$	$-\infty$	$-$
y	decreases	∪ min	increases	∧ max	decreases	inflection	decreases	inflection	decreases

Then find y_{max} and y_{min} and plot the curve. Figure 30 shows a graph constructed by the points given in the table.

5°. Sufficient conditions for an extremum (a second method of investigation).

If at some point $x=x_0$:

(1) $y'=0$ and $y''<0$, then $f(x_0)=y_{max}$;
(2) $y'=0$ and $y''>0$, then $f(x_0)=y_{min}$;
(3) $y'=0$ and $y''=0$, then the problem remains unsolved and it is necessary to resort to the first method.

Test the following functions for increase and decrease:

1158. (1) $y=x^2$; (2) $y=x^3$; (3) $y=\frac{1}{x}$; (4) $y=\ln x$.

1159. (1) $y=\tan x$; (2) $y=e^x$; (3) $y=4x-x^2$.

Find the extremum of the function and construct its graph *.

1160. $y=x^2+4x+5$.

1161. $y=4x-\frac{x^3}{3}$.

1162. $y=\frac{x^3}{3}-x^2-3x$.

1163. $y=1+2x^2-\frac{x^4}{4}$.

1164. $y=\frac{x^4}{4}-x^3$.

1165. $y=\frac{x}{2}+\frac{2}{x}$.

1166. $y=\sqrt[3]{x^2}-1$.

1167. $y=\frac{1}{1+x^2}$.

1168. $y=\frac{x^2-6x+13}{x-3}$.

1169. $y=x^2(1-x)$.

1170. $y=1-\sqrt[3]{(x-4)^2}$.

1171. $y=e^{-x^2}$.

1172. $y=x+\cos 2x$ on the interval $(0, \pi)$.

1173. $y=4x-\tan x$ on the interval $\left(-\frac{\pi}{2}, \frac{\pi}{2}\right)$.

1174. $y=\frac{1+\ln x}{x}$.

1175. $y=x-\arctan 2x$.

1176. (1) $y=xe^{-\frac{x}{2}}$; (2) $y=x\ln x$.

1177. (1) $y=\sqrt{\sin x^2}$; (2) $y=\sqrt{e^{x^2}-1}$.

1178. $y=\sin^4 x+\cos^4 x$.

1179. $y=x\sqrt{1-x}$.

---

* In Problems 1165, 1168, 1173 and some others the curves are constructed by finding their asymptotes (see Sec. 5.9).

1180. $y=\frac{4\sqrt{x}}{x+2}$. **1181.** $y=\frac{x}{(x-1)(x-4)}$.

1182. $y=\frac{x^2}{2}+\frac{1}{x}$. **1183.** $y=x^{\frac{2}{3}}+(x-2)^{\frac{2}{3}}$.

1184. $y=\frac{x^5}{5}-x^4+x^3$. **1185.** $y=x^3(x+2)^2$.

1186. $y=2\left(\frac{1}{x}-\frac{1}{x^2}\right)$. **1187.** $y=\frac{x^3}{x^2-3}$.

1188. $y=2\tan x-\tan^2 x$. **1189.** $y=x+\ln(\cos x)$.

1190. (1) $y=\ln\sqrt{1+x^2}-\arctan x$; (2) $y=|x|(x+2)$.

1191. $y=x^2e^{-x}$. **1192.** $y=3\sqrt[3]{(x+1)^2}-2x$.

Find the extremum of the function and construct its graph:

1193. $y=4x-x^2$. **1194.** $y=x^2+2x-3$.

1195. $y=\frac{x^3}{3}+x^2$. **1196.** $y=x^3+6x^2+9x$.

1197. $y=\frac{x^2}{x-2}$. **1198.** $y=x^3+\frac{x^4}{4}$.

1199. $y=\frac{x^4}{4}-2x^2$. **1200.** $y=2x-3\sqrt[3]{x^2}$.

1201. $y=\frac{(x-1)^2}{x^2+1}$. **1202.** $y=xe^{-\frac{x^2}{2}}$.

1203. $y=x-2\ln x$. **1204.** $y=x^{\frac{2}{3}}(x-5)$.

1205. $y=\sin 2x-x$ on the interval $\left(-\frac{\pi}{2}, \frac{\pi}{2}\right)$.

1206. $y=2x+\cot x$ on the interval $(0, \pi)$.

1207. $y=x+\operatorname{arccot} 2x$. **1208.** $y=1+\sqrt[3]{(x-1)^2}$.

1209. $y=2\sin x+\cos 2x$ on the interval $(0, \pi)$.

1210. $y=3x^4-8x^3+6x^2$. **1211.** $y=\frac{\ln x}{x}$.

1212. $y=\frac{3-x^2}{x+2}$. **1213.** $y=x+\frac{1}{x}$.

1214. (1) $y=ae^{-x}\cos x$ (for $x>0$); (2) $y=3x^5-5x^3$.

1215. $y=\frac{(4-x)^3}{9(2-x)}$. **1216.** $y=\frac{12\sqrt[3]{(x+2)^2}}{x^2+8}$.

1217. $y=\frac{2x^2-1}{x^4}$. **1218.** $y=(1-x^2)(1-x^3)$.

1219. $y=\frac{1+x+x^2}{1-x+x^2}$. **1220.** $y=x+2\sqrt{-x}$.

1221. (1) $y=\frac{(x+3)^3}{(x+2)^2}$; (2) $y=\sqrt{1-\cos x}$.

7.5. *Finding Greatest and Least Values of a Function*

1222. A rectangular playground of the greatest possible area is to be enclosed by a fence 120 m long. Determine the dimensions of the playground.

1223. Break the number 10 into two addends so that, when multiplied by each other, they yield the greatest product.

1224. A rectangle of the greatest possible area is inscribed in a triangle whose base is a and altitude h. Determine the area of the rectangle.

1225. Equal squares are cut away from the corners of a square sheet of cardboard and then a rectangular box is made. What side must the cut-away square have to get a box of the maximum volume?

1226. Determine the most economical dimensions of an outdoor swimming pool of volume 32 m³ with a square bottom so that the facing of its walls and bottom requires the least quantity of material.

1227. The non-parallel sides and the smaller base of a trapezoid are equal to 10 cm each. Determine its greater base for which the area of the trapezoid attains the greatest value.

1228. Inscribed in a semicircle is a trapezoid whose base is equal to the diameter of the semicircle. Determine the angle at the base of the trapezoid at which the area of the trapezoid takes on the greatest value.

1229. The section of a tunnel has the form of a rectangle completed with a semicircle. The perimeter of the section equals 18 m. At what radius of the semicirle the section area will be maximum?

1230. A factory A is to be connected by a highway with a straight railway on which a town B is situated.

At what angle α should the highway be connected with the railway so as to ensure the least freight charges from factory to town, if freight charges on the highway are m times higher than on the railway?

1231. Two sources of light are situated 30 m apart. On the straight line connecting these sources find the least illuminated point if the ratio of candle powers of the light sources is 27:8.

1232. Two aircrafts are flying in a straight line and in the same plane at an angle of 120° to each other and with an equal speed of v km/h. At a certain moment one aircraft reaches the point of intersection of their routes, while the second is at a distance of a km from it. When will the distance between the aircraft be least and what is that distance?

1233. A freely supported rectangular beam is uniformly loaded over the entire length. Its bending deflection is inversely proportional to the moment of inertia of the beam section $I=\frac{xy^3}{12}$, where x and y are the dimensions of the beam. Determine the dimensions of the beam to ensure the least deflection if the beam is made from a log of diameter D.

1234. How many times does the volume of a sphere exceed the volume of the greatest cylinder inscribed in this sphere?

1235. Two corridors 2.4 m and 1.6 m wide intersect at a right angle. Determine the greatest length of a ladder which can be carried horizontally from one corridor into the other.

1236. A cylinder of the greatest volume is inscribed in a cone of radius 4 dm and height 6 dm. Find this volume.

1237. A rectangle of the greatest area is inscribed in a semicircle of radius R. Determine its dimensions.

1238. On the parabola $y=x^2$ find the point least distant from the straight line $y=2x-4$.

1239. A picture hangs on the wall. Its bottom is b cm, and its top is a cm higher than the eye of the observer. At what distance from the wall should the position of the observer be found to ensure the greatest angle of examining the picture?

1240. The total length of the walls of the house shown in Fig. 31 must be 90 m. What width x of the corridor ensures the greatest area of the rooms?

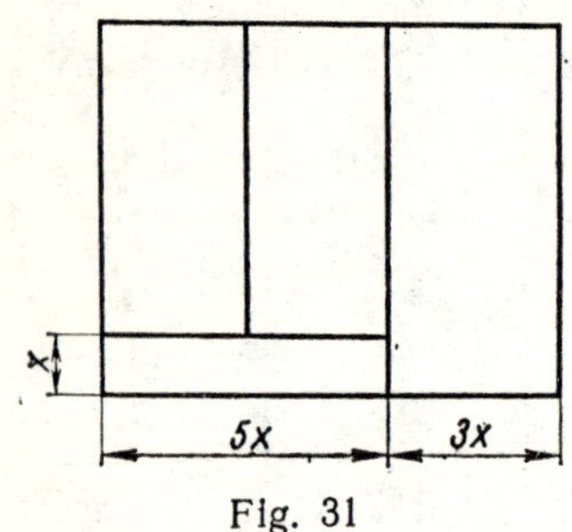

Fig. 31

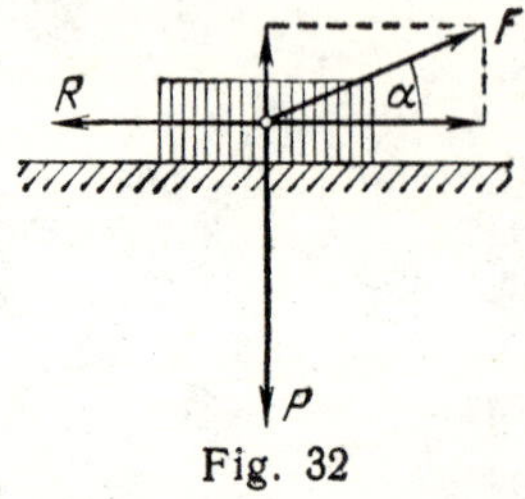

Fig. 32

1241. Inscribed in a right triangle with the hypotenuse 8 cm long and an angle of 60° is a rectangle whose base is situated on the hypotenuse. What must be the dimensions of the rectangle to yield the greatest area?

1242. Given the points $A(0, 3)$ and $B(4, 5)$. On the axis OX find the point M so that the distance $S=AM+MB$ is the least.

1243. The resistance of a beam to axial compression is proportional to the area of its cross-section. What must be the dimensions of the beam to ensure the greatest resistance to axial compression if it is made from a log of diameter D?

1244. A circular sector of angle α is convoluted to form a cone. At what α the volume of the cone thus obtained will be the greatest?

1245. A body of weight P lying on a horizontal plane must be displaced by a force F applied to it (Fig. 32). What angle α with the horizontal must the force F form to ensure its least value? The coefficient of friction $\mu=0.25$.

7.6. Direction of Convexity and Points of Inflection of a Curve. Construction of Graphs

1°. The convexity of a plane curve. A plane curve is called *convex up (down)* at a point $x=x_0$ if in a sufficiently small neighbourhood of this point the curve is situated below (above) the tangent at this point. If at the point $x=x_0$

(1) $y''>0$, then the curve is convex down;

(2) $y''<0$, then the curve is convex up.

2°. The point of inflection. If a curve near some point lies on both sides of the tangent then the point is called a point of inflection of the curve. The *necessary* condition for a point of inflection: at this point $y''=0$ or does not exist, and the *sufficient* condition: y'' changes sign.

3°. To construct a curve it is recommended to determine the following: (1) symmetry; (2) domain; (3) points of intersection with the axes OX and OY; (4) points of discontinuity of the function $y=\varphi(x)$ or $x=f(y)$ an asymptotes; (5) increase or decrease of y or x and extremum points; (6) direction of convexity and points of inflection.

1246. Investigate the direction of convexity and construct the following curves:

$$(1)\ y=x^2;\quad (2)\ y=x^3;\quad (3)\ y=e^x;\quad (4)\ y=\ln x;$$

$$(5)\ y=x^{\frac{5}{3}}.$$

1247. Determine the extrema and the points of inflection and plot the curves:

$$(1)\ y=\frac{x^3}{6}-x^2;\quad (2)\ y=e^{-x^2};\quad (3)\ y=\frac{2x}{1+x^2};\quad (4)\ y=2^{\frac{1}{x}}.$$

Applying some of the rules of Item 3°, graph the curves given in Problems 1248 to 1262 by the following equations:

1248. $y^2=2x+9$. **1249.** $y=-x^2-4x$.

Hint. In Problem 1248 determine the symmetry, domain, and points of intersection with the axes, and in Problem 1249 the point of extremum and the points of intersection with OX.

1250. $y=\sin x$, $y=\cos x$. **1251.** $y=\sinh x$, $y=\cosh x$.

Hint. In Problems 1250 and 1251 determine the points of extremum and inflection.

1252. $y=\ln(x+2)$. **1253.** $y=e^{-x}$.

Hint. In Problems 1252 and 1253 determine the domain, points of intersection with the axes, asymptote, and direction of convexity.

1254. (1) $y^2=x^3$; (2) $y^2=(x+3)^3$.

1255. (1) $y=2+\frac{12}{x^2-4}$; (2) $y=\frac{3}{x}-\frac{1}{x^3}$.

1256. (1) $y=\frac{e\ln x}{x}$; (2) $y=exe^{-x}$.

1257. (1) $y=x+\frac{4}{x+2}$; (2) $y=\frac{1}{x^4}-\frac{2}{x^2}$.

1258. (1) $y=x-\ln x$; (2) $y=\frac{a}{2}\left(e^{\frac{x}{a}}+e^{-\frac{x}{a}}\right)$.

1259. (1) $y=\frac{x^4}{x^3-1}$; (2) $y=\frac{4}{x}+\frac{1}{x^4}$.

1260. (1) $y^2=2x^2-x^4$; (2) $x(y-x)^2=4$.

1261. $y=(x+2)^{2/3}-(x-2)^{2/3}$. **1262.** $y^2=xe^{-x}$.

CHAPTER 8

THE INDEFINITE INTEGRAL

8.1. Indefinite Integral. Integration by Expansion

1°. By the indefinite integral $\int f(x)\,dx$ is meant a function $F(x)+C$, containing an arbitrary constant C, whose differential is equal to the *integrand expression* $f(x)\,dx$, i. e.

$$\int f(x)\,dx = F(x)+C$$

if

$$d[F(x)+C]=f(x)\,dx.$$

2°. Table of basic integrals:

1. $\int x^n dx = \frac{x^{n+1}}{n+1}+C$ $(n \neq -1)$.
2. $\int \frac{dx}{x} = \ln|x|+C$.
3. $\int a^x dx = \frac{a^x}{\ln a}+C$.
4. $\int e^x dx = e^x + C$.
5. $\int \cos x\,dx = \sin x + C$.
6. $\int \sin x\,dx = -\cos x + C$.
7. $\int \frac{dx}{\cos^2 x} = \tan x + C$.
8. $\int \frac{dx}{\sin^2 x} = -\cot x + C$.
9. $\int \frac{dx}{1+x^2} = \begin{cases} \arctan x + C \\ \text{or} \\ -\operatorname{arccot} x + C_1. \end{cases}$
10. $\int \frac{dx}{\sqrt{1-x^2}} = \begin{cases} \arcsin x + C \\ \text{or} \\ -\arccos x + \\ + C_1. \end{cases}$

3°. The properties of the indefinite integral:

I. $d\int u\,dx = u\,dx$. II. $\int du = u + C$.

III. $\int Au\,dx = A\int u\,dx$. IV. $\int (u+v)\,dx = \int u\,dx + \int v\,dx$.

Integration by *expansion* means the reduction of a given integral (by Property IV) to a sum of simpler integrals.

1263. Fill in the blanks in the following equalities:

(1) $d(\quad)=2x\,dx$; (2) $d(\quad)=x^3\,dx$;

(3) $d(\quad)=\cos x\,dx$; (4) $d(\quad)=\frac{dx}{x}$;

(5) $d(\quad)=\frac{dx}{\cos^2 x}$; (6) $d(\quad)=\frac{dx}{1+x^2}$.

Then find the integrals: $\int 2x\,dx$, $\int x^3\,dx$ and so forth.

Find the integrals:

1264. (1) $\int\left(x^2+2x+\frac{1}{x}\right)dx$; (2) $\int\frac{10x^8+3}{x^4}dx$.

1265. (1) $\int\frac{x-2}{x^3}dx$; (2) $\int\frac{(x^2+1)^2}{x^3}dx$.

1266. (1) $\int(\sqrt{x}+\sqrt[3]{x})\,dx$; (2) $\int\left(\frac{1}{\sqrt{x}}-\frac{1}{\sqrt[4]{x^3}}\right)dx$.

1267. (1) $\int\frac{(\sqrt{x}-1)^3}{x}dx$; (2) $\int\frac{x-1}{\sqrt[3]{x^2}}dx$.

1268. (1) $\int e^x\left(1-\frac{e^{-x}}{x^2}\right)dx$; (2) $\int a^x\left(1+\frac{a^{-x}}{\sqrt{x^3}}\right)dx$.

1269. (1) $\int\frac{\cos 2x}{\cos^2 x\sin^2 x}dx$; (2) $\int\cot^2 x\,dx$.

1270. (1) $\int\frac{dx}{\sin^2 x\cos^2 x}$; (2) $\int\frac{3-2\cot^2 x}{\cos^2 x}dx$.

1271. (1) $\int\sin^2\frac{x}{2}dx$; (2) $\int\cos^2\frac{x}{2}dx$.

1272. (1) $\int\left(\frac{2}{1+x^2}-\frac{3}{\sqrt{1-x^2}}\right)dx$; (2) $\int\frac{x^4}{1+x^2}dx$.

Find the integrals:

1273. (1) $\int\frac{(x^2-1)^2}{x^3}dx$; (2) $\int\left(\frac{1}{\sqrt[3]{x^2}}-\frac{1}{x\sqrt{x}}\right)dx$.

1274. (1) $\int\frac{x-2}{\sqrt{x^3}}dx$; (2) $\int\frac{(2\sqrt{x}+1)^2}{x^2}dx$.

1275. (1) $\int\left(\frac{1}{x}+\frac{1}{x^2}+\frac{1}{x^3}\right)dx$; (2) $\int\left(\sin\frac{x}{2}-\cos\frac{x}{2}\right)^2 dx$.

1276. (1) $\int e^x\left(1+\frac{e^{-x}}{\cos^2 x}\right)dx$; (2) $\int a^x\left(1+\frac{a^{-x}}{x^5}\right)dx$.

1277. $\int\frac{1-\sin^3 x}{\sin^2 x}dx$. **1278.** $\int \tan^2 x\,dx$.

8.2. Integration by Substitution and Direct Integration

Putting $x=\varphi(u)$, $dx=\varphi'(u)\,du$, we get

$$\int f(x)\,dx=\int f[\varphi(u)]\,\varphi'(u)\,du. \tag{1}$$

Such transformation of an integral is called *integration by substitution.*

In simple cases the new variable u is recommended to be introduced mentally, using the following transformations of the differential dx:

$$dx=\frac{1}{a}\,d(ax+b);\quad 2x\,dx=d(x^2);$$

$$\cos x\,dx=d(\sin x);\quad \frac{dx}{x}=d(\ln x)\ \text{and so on,}$$

and denoting mentally the bracketed expression by u. This method is called the *direct integration.*

Find the integrals:

1279. $\int\cos 3x\,dx$. **1280.** $\int\sin\frac{x}{2}\,dx$.

Hint. Problem 1279 can be solved by two methods: (1) putting $3x=u$, $x=\frac{u}{3}$, $dx=\frac{du}{3}$; (2) reducing the integral to the form $\frac{1}{3}\int\cos 3x\,d(3x)$.

1281. $\int e^{-3x}\,dx$. **1282.** $\int\frac{dx}{\cos^2 5x}$.

1283. $\int\left(e^{\frac{x}{2}}+e^{-\frac{x}{2}}\right)dx$. **1284.** $\int\sqrt{4x-1}\,dx$.

1285. $\int(3-2x)^4\,dx$. **1286.** $\int\sqrt[3]{5-6x}\,dx$.

1287. $\int \frac{dx}{\sqrt{3-2x}}$.

1288. $\int \sin(a-bx)\,dx$.

1289. $\int \frac{2x-5}{x^2-5x+7}\,dx$.

1290. $\int \frac{x\,dx}{x^2+1}$.

Hint. Problems 1289 to 1298 are solved by the formula

$$\int \frac{u'\,dx}{u} = \int \frac{du}{u} = \ln|u| + C,$$

i.e. if the numerator of the integrand is a derivative of the denominator then the integral is equal to the logarithm of the denominator.

1291. $\int \frac{dx}{1-10x}$.

1292. $\int \frac{e^{2x}\,dx}{1-3e^{2x}}$.

1293. $\int \cot x\,dx$.

1294. $\int \tan x\,dx$.

1295. $\int \frac{\cos 2x}{\sin x \cos x}\,dx$.

1296. $\int \frac{\sin x\,dx}{1+3\cos x}$.

1297. $\int \frac{\cos x}{1+2\sin x}\,dx$.

1298. $\int \frac{dx}{x(1+\ln x)}$.

1299. $\int \sin^2 x \cos x\,dx$.

1300. $\int \cos^3 x \sin x\,dx$.

Hint. Problem 1299 can be solved using the substitution $\sin x = u$ or directly replacing $\cos x\,dx$ by $d(\sin x)$.

1301. $\int \frac{\cos x\,dx}{\sin^4 x}$.

1302. $\int \frac{\sin x\,dx}{\cos^3 x}$.

1303. $\int \frac{1-2\cos x}{\sin^2 x}\,dx$.

1304. $\int \sin x \cos x\,dx$.

1305. $\int e^{\cos x} \sin x\,dx$.

1306. $\int e^{x^3} x^2\,dx$.

Hint. Problem 1306 can be solved using the substitution $x^3 = u$ or directly replacing $x^2\,dx$ by $\frac{1}{3}d(x^3)$.

1307. $\int e^{-x^2} x\,dx$.

1308. $\int \frac{e^{\sqrt{x}}\,dx}{\sqrt{x}}$.

1309. $\int \sqrt{x^2+1}\,x\,dx$.

1310. $\int \sqrt[3]{x^3-8}\,x^2\,dx$.

Hint. Problem 1309 can be solved using the substitution $x^2+1=u$ or directly by writing the integral in the form $\frac{1}{2}\int (x^2+1)^{\frac{1}{2}}\,d(x^2+1)$.

1311. $\int \frac{x^2\,dx}{\sqrt[3]{1+x^3}}$. **1312.** $\int \frac{x\,dx}{\sqrt{1-x^2}}$.

1313. $\int \frac{\sin x\,dx}{\sqrt{1+2\cos x}}$. **1314.** $\int \frac{\sqrt{1+\ln x}\,dx}{x}$.

1315. $\int \sqrt{1+4\sin x}\cos x\,dx$. **1316.** $\int \sqrt[3]{1-6x^5}\,x^4\,dx$.

Find the integrals:

1317. $\int (e^x+e^{-x})^2\,dx$. **1318.** $\int \sin^3 x\cos x\,dx$.

1319. $\int \frac{dx}{\sqrt{1-4x}}$. **1320.** $\int \cos(a-bx)\,dx$.

1321. $\int \sqrt[3]{1+3x}\,dx$. **1322.** $\int \sqrt[6]{1-2x^3}\,x^2\,dx$.

1323. $\int \frac{x\,dx}{\sqrt{1+x^2}}$. **1324.** $\int \frac{1-2\sin x}{\cos^2 x}\,dx$.

1325. $\int \frac{1+\sin 2x}{\sin^2 x}\,dx$. **1326.** $\int e^{\sin x}\cos x\,dx$.

1327. $\int \frac{x^2\,dx}{1-x^3}$. **1328.** $\int \frac{dx}{(a-bx)^3}$.

8.3. *Integrals of the form* $\int \frac{dx}{x^2 \pm a^2}, \int \frac{dx}{\sqrt{a^2-x^2}}, \int \frac{dx}{\sqrt{x^2+k}}$ *and Those Reduced to Them*

1329. Show that

(1) $\int \frac{dx}{a^2+x^2} = \frac{1}{a}\arctan\frac{x}{a}+C$, putting $x=a\tan t$;

(2) $\int \frac{dx}{\sqrt{a^2-x^2}} = \arcsin\frac{x}{a}+C$, putting $x=a\sin t$;

(3) $\int \frac{dx}{x^2-a^2} = \frac{1}{2a}\ln\left|\frac{x-a}{x+a}\right|+C$, expanding

$$\frac{1}{x^2-a^2} = \frac{1}{2a}\,\frac{a+x+a-x}{x^2-a^2} = \frac{1}{2a}\left(\frac{1}{x-a}-\frac{1}{x+a}\right);$$

(4) $\int \frac{dx}{\sqrt{x^2+k}} = \ln\left|x+\sqrt{x^2+k}\right|+C$,

putting $\sqrt{x^2+k}=t-x$.

1330. (1) $\int \frac{dx}{x^2-25}$; (2) $\int \frac{dx}{x^2+9}$.

1331. (1) $\int \frac{dx}{\sqrt{4-x^2}}$; (2) $\int \frac{dx}{\sqrt{x^2+5}}$.

1332. (1) $\int \frac{dx}{\sqrt{x^2-4}}$; (2) $\int \frac{dx}{x^2+3}$.

1333. (1) $\int \frac{dx}{\sqrt{5-x^2}}$; (2) $\int \frac{x^2\,dx}{4+x^6}$.

1334. (1) $\int \frac{x\,dx}{\sqrt{3-x^4}}$; (2) $\int \frac{dx}{b^2x^2-a^2}$.

1335. (1) $\int \frac{dx}{\sqrt{3-4x^2}}$; (2) $\int \frac{x^3\,dx}{\sqrt{x^8-1}}$.

1336. (1) $\int \frac{5x-2}{x^2+4}\,dx$; (2) $\int \frac{3x-4}{x^2-4}\,dx$.

1337. (1) $\int \frac{x+1}{\sqrt{x^2+1}}\,dx$; (2) $\int \frac{x+1}{\sqrt{1-x^2}}\,dx$.

1338. $\int \frac{x^2\,dx}{x^2+1}$. **1339.** $\int \frac{x^4\,dx}{x^2-3}$.

Hint. In Problems 1338 and 1339 eliminate a whole expression from the improper fraction.

1340. $\int \frac{dx}{x^2+4x+5}$. **1341.** $\int \frac{dx}{x^2-6x+13}$.

Hint. In Problems 1340-1347 separate a perfect square from the quadratic trinomial.

1342. $\int \frac{dx}{\sqrt{x^2+2x+3}}$. **1343.** $\int \frac{dx}{\sqrt{1-2x-x^2}}$.

1344. $\int \frac{dx}{\sqrt{4x-x^2}}$. **1345.** $\int \frac{dx}{x^2+3x+3}$.

1346. $\int \frac{dx}{\sqrt{2+3x-2x^2}}$. **1347.** $\int \frac{dx}{\sqrt{3x^2-2x-1}}$.

Find the integrals:

1348. $\int \left(\frac{3}{x^2+3}+\frac{6}{x^2-3}\right) dx$.

1349. $\int \left(\frac{1}{\sqrt{2-x^2}}+\frac{1}{\sqrt{2+x^2}}\right) dx$.

1350. $\int \frac{4x-5}{x^2+5}\,dx.$ **1351.** $\int \frac{x^2\,dx}{x^2-2}.$

1352. $\int \frac{x^4\,dx}{x^2+2}.$ **1353.** $\int \frac{e^x\,dx}{\sqrt{1-e^{2x}}}.$

1354. $\int \frac{x\,dx}{x^4+0.25}.$ **1355.** $\int \frac{dx}{x^2+4x+29}.$

1356. $\int \frac{dx}{x^2-2x+5}.$ **1357.** $\int \frac{dx}{\sqrt{5-4x-x^2}}.$

1358. $\int \frac{x\,dx}{x^2+x+1}.$ **1359.** $\int \frac{dx}{\sqrt{4x^2+4x+3}}.$

8.4. Integration by Parts

From the formula of the differential of a product $d(uv) = udv+vdu$ we obtain the formula for integration by parts:

$$\int udv = uv - \int vdu.$$

This formula is widely used when the integrand is a product of an algebraic function by a transcendental one, for instance $\int x^2e^x\,dx$ or $\int x^2 \ln x\,dx$. Here the role of u is played by the function to be simplified by differentiation, and the role of dv, the portion of the integrand which contains dx and whose integral is known or can be found.

In case of transcendental functions the role of u is usually played by $\ln x$, $\arctan x$ and $\arcsin x$.

For example, in the integral $\int x^2 \ln x\,dx$ take $u=\ln x$ (but not x^2), and in the integral $\int x^2e^x\,dx$, $u=x^2$ (but not e^x).

Find the integrals:

1360. $\int \ln x\,dx.$ **1361.** $\int x \ln (x-1)\,dx.$

1362. $\int xe^{2x}\,dx.$ **1363.** $\int x \arctan x\,dx.$

1364. $\int x^2 \cos x\,dx.$ **1365.** $\int e^x \sin x\,dx.$

1366. Show that

$$\int \sqrt{x^2+k}\,dx = \frac{1}{2}\left[x\sqrt{x^2+k} + k\ln\left(x+\sqrt{x^2+k}\right)\right]+C.$$

1367. $\int (\ln x)^2\,dx$.

1368. $\int \frac{x\,dx}{\sin^2 x}$.

1369. $\int \frac{\ln x\,dx}{x^2}$.

1370. $\int \frac{\arcsin x\,dx}{\sqrt{1+x}}$.

1371. $\int \arcsin x\,dx$.

1372. $\int x^3 e^{-x}\,dx$.

1373. $\int \ln(x^2+1)\,dx$.

1374. $\int \cos(\ln x)\,dx$.

Find the integrals:

1375. $\int \sqrt{x}\ln x\,dx$.

1376. $\int x^2 e^{-\frac{x}{2}}\,dx$.

1377. $\int \arctan x\,dx$.

1378. $\int \frac{x\,dx}{\cos^2 x}$.

1379. $\int e^x \cos x\,dx$.

1380. $\int \frac{\arcsin \frac{x}{2}\,dx}{\sqrt{2-x}}$.

1381. $\int \frac{x\cos x\,dx}{\sin^3 x}$.

1382. $\int \arctan\sqrt{2x-1}\,dx$.

8.5. *Integration of Some Trigonometric Functions*

1°. Integrals of the second and other even powers of sine and cosine are found by means of the following power reducing formulas:

$$\sin^2 x = \frac{1-\cos 2x}{2}; \quad \cos^2 x = \frac{1+\cos 2x}{2}; \quad \sin x\cos x = \frac{\sin 2x}{2}.$$

2°. ntegrals of the third and other odd powers of sine and cosine are found by separating one factor from the odd power and taking the *cofunction* equal to the new variable u.

The integral $\int \cos^m x \sin^n x\,dx$ is found by rule 1° if both m and n are even, and by rule 2° if either m or n is odd.

1383. $\int \sin^2 3x\,dx$.

1384. $\int (1+2\cos x)^2\,dx$.

1385. $\int (1-\sin 2x)^2\,dx$.

1386. $\int \cos^4 x\,dx$.

1387. $\int \sin^2 x\cos^2 x\,dx$.

1388. $\int \sin^4 x\cos^4 x\,dx$.

1389. $\int \sin^2 x \cos^4 x \, dx.$ **1390.** $\int \sin^5 x \, dx.$

1391. $\int \sin^2 x \cos^3 x \, dx.$ **1392.** $\int \sin^3 x \cos^3 x \, dx.$

1393. $\int \cos^7 x \, dx.$ **1394.** $\int (1+2\cos x)^3 \, dx.$

1395. $\int \frac{\cos^3 x \, dx}{\sin^2 x}.$ **1396.** $\int \frac{\sin^3 x \, dx}{\cos^2 x}.$

1397. $\int \frac{dx}{\sin 2x} = \int \frac{\sin^2 x + \cos^2 x}{2 \sin x \cos x} dx = ?$

1398. (1) $\int \frac{dx}{\sin x}$; (2) $\int \frac{dx}{\cos x}$.

1399. $\int \frac{\cos x + \sin x}{\sin 2x} dx.$ **1400.** $\int \frac{dx}{\sin x - \cos x}.$

1401. $\int \tan^3 x \, dx.$ **1402.** $\int \cot^3 x \, dx.$

Hint. In Problem 1401 put $\tan x = t$, $x = \arctan t$.

1403. $\int \sin 3x \cos x \, dx.$ **1404.** $\int \cos mx \cos nx \, dx.$

Hint. In Problems 1403 to 1406 make use of the formulas:

$$\sin \alpha \cos \beta = \frac{1}{2} [\sin (\alpha + \beta) + \sin (\alpha - \beta)],$$

$$\cos \alpha \cos \beta = \frac{1}{2} [\cos (\alpha + \beta) + \cos (\alpha - \beta)],$$

$$\sin \alpha \sin \beta = \frac{1}{2} [\cos (\alpha - \beta) - \cos (\alpha + \beta)].$$

1405. (1) $\int \sin 3x \sin 5x \, dx$; (2) $\int \sin mx \sin nx \, dx.$

1406. $\int \sin \left(5x - \frac{\pi}{4}\right) \cos \left(x + \frac{\pi}{4}\right) dx.$

1407. Integrating by parts, prove the "power reducing" formulas:

(1) $\int \sin^n x \, dx = -\frac{1}{n} \cos x \sin^{n-1} x + \frac{n-1}{n} \int \sin^{n-2} x \, dx$;

(2) $\int \cos^n x \, dx = \frac{1}{n} \sin x \cos^{n-1} x + \frac{n-1}{n} \int \cos^{n-2} x \, dx$

and using these formulas find: (1) $\int \sin^6 x \, dx$; (2) $\int \cos^6 x \, dx$.

1408. Find the integrals: (1) $\int \frac{dx}{\sin^3 x}$, (2) $\int \frac{dx}{\cos^3 x}$.

Hint. Apply the formulas given in the previous problem to the integrals $\int \frac{dx}{\sin x}$ and $\int \frac{dx}{\cos x}$.

1409. $\int (1+3\cos 2x)^2\,dx$.

1410. $\int \sin^4 x\,dx$.

1411. $\int \sin^4 x \cos^2 x\,dx$.

1412. $\int \cos^5 x\,dx$.

1413. $\int \sin^3 x \cos^2 x\,dx$.

1414. $\int (1+2\sin x)^3\,dx$.

1415. $\int \frac{(\sin x-\cos x)^2}{\sin 2x}\,dx$.

1416. $\int \sin 3x \sin x\,dx$.

1417. $\int \frac{\sin^3 x+1}{\cos^2 x}\,dx$.

1418. $\int \sin\left(x+\frac{\pi}{6}\right)\cos x\,dx$.

8.6. *Integration of Rational Algebraic Functions*

1°. If the integrand is an *improper* fraction, then it is necessary to take out the integral part.

2° The denominator of a proper fraction is factorized into factors of the kind $(x-a)^\alpha$ and $(x^2+px+q)^\beta$, and the proper fraction itself is expanded into a sum of elementary fractions in the following way:

$$\frac{P(x)}{(x-a)^\alpha (x^2+px+q)^\beta \ldots} = \frac{A_1}{x-a} + \frac{A_2}{(x-a)^2} + \ldots + \frac{A_\alpha}{(x-a)^\alpha} +$$
$$+ \frac{M_1 x+N_1}{x^2+px+q} + \frac{M_2 x+N_2}{(x^2+px+q)^2} + \ldots + \frac{M_\beta x+N_\beta}{(x^2+px+q)^\beta} + \ldots,$$

where $P(x)$ is a polynomial of the degree lower than that of the denominator.

Find the integrals:

1419. (1) $\int \frac{x^3}{x-2}\,dx$; (2) $\int \frac{x^4}{x^2+a^2}\,dx$; (3) $\int \frac{x^5}{x^3-a^3}\,dx$.

1420. $\int \frac{x-4}{(x-2)(x-3)}\,dx$.

1421. $\int \frac{2x+7}{x^2+x-2}\,dx$.

1422. $\int \frac{3x^2+2x-3}{x^3-x}\,dx$.

1423. $\int \frac{(x+1)^3}{x^2-x}\,dx$.

1424. $\int \frac{x+2}{x^3-2x^2}\,dx$.

1425. $\int \frac{3x-2a}{x^4-ax^3}\,dx$.

1426. $\int \frac{2x^2-5x+1}{x^3-2x^2+x}\,dx.$ **1427.** $\int \frac{5x-1}{x^3-3x-2}\,dx.$

1428. $\int \frac{5x+2}{x^2+2x+10}\,dx.$ **1429.** $\int \frac{4x-2.4}{x^2-0.2x+0.17}\,dx.$

Hint. In Problem 1428 single out a perfect square in the denominator and then put $x+1=t$.

1430. $\int \frac{2x^2+x+4}{x^3+x^2+4x+4}\,dx.$ **1431.** $\int \frac{7x-15}{x^3-2x^2+5x}\,dx.$

1432. $\int \frac{dx}{x^3+8}.$ **1433.** $\int \frac{3x^2+2x+1}{(x+1)^2(x^2+1)}\,dx.$

1434. (1) $\int \frac{dx}{(x^2+b^2)^2}.$ (2) $\int \frac{dx}{(x^2+b^2)^3}.$

Hint. Put $x=b\tan t$ and then (in the second case) use formula (2) of Problem 1407.

1435. (1) $\int \frac{(2x+1)\,dx}{(x^2+2x+5)^2}.$ (2) $\int \frac{dx}{(x^2-6x+10)^3}.$

1436. $\int \frac{4x\,dx}{(1+x)(1+x^2)^2}.$ **1437.** $\int \frac{x+1}{x^4+4x^2+4}\,dx.$

Find the integrals without applying the general method of indefinite coefficients.

1438. $\int \frac{dx}{x(x+a)}.$ **1439.** $\int \frac{dx}{(x+a)(x+b)}.$

Hint to Problems 1438 to 1442. In the nominator of the integrand fraction write the difference of the factors of the denominator dividing the integral by the corresponding number.

1440. $\int \frac{dx}{x^2-2x}.$ **1441.** $\int \frac{dx}{(x^2-3)(x^2+2)}.$

1442. $\int \frac{dx}{x^4-x^2}.$ **1443.** $\int \frac{dx}{x^3+4x}.$

Find the integrals:

1444. $\int \frac{2x-1}{(x-1)(x-2)}\,dx.$ **1445.** $\int \frac{3x+2}{2x^2+x-3}\,dx.$

1446. $\int \frac{5x-14}{x^3-x^2-4x+4}\,dx.$ **1447.** $\int \frac{11x+16}{(x-1)(x+2)^2}\,dx.$

1448. $\int \frac{5x-8}{x^3-4x^2+4x}\,dx.$ 1449. $\int \frac{x+2}{x^3-2x^2+2x}\,dx.$

1450. $\int \frac{x-a}{x^3+a^2x}\,dx.$ 1451. $\int \frac{dx}{x^3+x^2+2x+2}.$

1452. $\int \frac{dx}{x^3-8}.$ 1453. $\int \frac{x\,dx}{(x^2+2x+2)^2}.$

In Problems 1454 to 1457 integrate without using the method of indefinite coefficients.

1454. $\int \frac{dx}{x^2+5x}.$ 1455. $\int \frac{dx}{x^4+3x^2}.$

1456. $\int \frac{dx}{x^4-1}.$ 1457. $\int \frac{dx}{x^4-x^2-2}.$

8.7. Integration of Certain Irrational Algebraic Functions

1°. The integral $\int R(x, \sqrt[n]{ax+b})\,dx$, where $R(x, y)$ is a rational function, is found by the substitution $ax+b=t^n$, and the integral of a more general form $\int R(x^m, \sqrt[n]{ax^m+b})\,x^{m-1}\,dx$, by the substitution $ax^m+b=t^n$.

2°. The integral $\int \frac{Mx+N}{(x-\alpha)\sqrt{ax^2+bx+c}}\,dx$ is found by the substitution $x-\alpha=\frac{1}{t}$.

3°. Trigonometric substitutions. The following integrals are reduced to the rational trigonometric form:

$\int R(x, \sqrt{a^2-x^2})\,dx$ by making the substitution $x=a\sin t$,

$\int R(x, \sqrt{a^2+x^2})\,dx$ by making the substitution $x=a\tan t$.

4°. The algebraic part can be separated from the integral $\int \frac{a_0x^m+a_1x^{m-1}+\ldots+a_m}{\sqrt{ax^2+bx+c}}\,dx$ by the formula

$$\int \frac{a_0x^m+\ldots+a_m}{W}\,dx=(A_0x^{m-1}+\ldots+A_{m-1})\,W+A_m\int \frac{dx}{W},$$

where $W=\sqrt{ax^2+bx+c}$. The coefficients A are found on differentiating the equality and getting rid of the denominator by comparing the coefficients of equal powers of x on the left and on the right.

5°. The integral of a binomial differential $\int x^m (a+bx^n)^p\,dx$ is expressible in terms of elementary functions in the following three cases: (1) when p is an integer—by expansion; (2) when $\frac{m+1}{n}$ is an integer—by the substitution $a+bx^n=t^s$; (3) when $\frac{m+1}{n}+p$ is an integer—by the substitution $ax^{-n}+b=t^s$, where s is the denominator of the fraction p.

Using substitutions 1°, find the following integrals:

1458. $\int \frac{x+1}{\sqrt[3]{3x+1}}\,dx$.

1459. $\int \frac{x\,dx}{\sqrt{2x+1}+1}$.

1460. $\int \frac{dx}{\sqrt[3]{x}+\sqrt{x}}$.

1461. $\int x\sqrt{a-x}\,dx$.

1462. $\int \frac{x^3\,dx}{1+\sqrt[3]{x^4+1}}$.

1463. $\int \frac{x^3\,dx}{\sqrt{x^2+2}}$.

Using substitution 2°, find the following integrals:

1464. $\int \frac{dx}{x\sqrt{x^2-1}}$.

1465. $\int \frac{dx}{x\sqrt{2x^2+2x+1}}$.

1466. $\int \frac{dx}{x\sqrt{2ax-x^2}}$.

1467. $\int \frac{dx}{(x+1)\sqrt{x^2+2x+2}}$.

Using substitutions 3°, find the following integrals:

1468. $\int \sqrt{a^2-x^2}\,dx$.

1469. $\int \frac{dx}{\sqrt{(4+x^2)^3}}$.

1470. $\int x^2\sqrt{4-x^2}\,dx$.

1471. $\int \frac{x^2\,dx}{\sqrt{(a^2+x^2)^5}}$.

1472. $\int \sqrt{3+2x-x^2}\,dx$.

1473. $\int \frac{x^2\,dx}{\sqrt{(2-x^2)^3}}$.

Using rule 4°, find the following integrals:

1474. $\int \frac{x^2+4x}{\sqrt{x^2+2x+2}}\,dx$.

1475. $\int \frac{x\,dx}{\sqrt{3-2x-x^2}}$.

1476. $\int \sqrt{x^2+k}\,dx$.

1477. $\int \sqrt{2ax-x^2}\,dx$.

Find the integrals of binomial differentials:

1478. $\int \frac{dx}{x\sqrt[4]{1+x^3}}$.

1479. $\int \frac{dx}{x^3\sqrt[3]{2-x^3}}$.

1480. $\int \frac{dx}{x^2\sqrt{(1+x^2)^3}}$.

1481. $\int \frac{x^3\,dx}{(a-bx^2)^{3/2}}$.

Find the integrals:

1482. $\int \frac{x-1}{\sqrt{2x-1}}\,dx$.

1483. $\int \frac{dx}{\sqrt[3]{3x+1}-1}$.

1484. $\int \frac{\sqrt{x}\,dx}{\sqrt{x}+1}$.

1485. $\int \frac{x}{\sqrt[3]{a-x}}\,dx$.

1486. $\int \frac{x+1}{x\sqrt{x-2}}\,dx$.

1487. $\int \frac{x^3\,dx}{\sqrt[3]{x^2+1}-1}$.

1488. $\int \frac{x\,dx}{x^2+2+2\sqrt{1+x^2}}$.

1489. $\int \frac{x^3\,dx}{2+\sqrt{4-x^2}}$.

1490. $\int \frac{dx}{x\sqrt{x^2+2x}}$.

1491. $\int \frac{dx}{(x-1)\sqrt{x^2-2x}}$.

1492. $\int \frac{x^2\,dx}{\sqrt{4-x^2}}$.

1493. $\int \sqrt{\frac{x}{2-x}}\,dx$.

Hint. In Problem 1493 put $x=2\sin^2 t$.

1494. $\int \sqrt{4x+x^2}\,dx$.

1495. $\int \frac{x^2}{\sqrt{5+4x-x^2}}\,dx$.

1496. $\int \frac{dx}{x^3\sqrt{1+x^2}}$.

1497. $\int \frac{dx}{x^2\sqrt{1+x^2}}$.

1498. $\int \frac{dx}{x\sqrt{1-x^3}}$.

1499. $\int \frac{dx}{x\sqrt{3x^2-2x-1}}$.

8.8. Integration of Certain Transcendental Functions

The following integrals are reduced to the algebraic form:

$\int R(e^x)\,dx$ by the substitutions $e^x=t$, $x=\ln t$, $dx=\frac{dt}{t}$;

$\int R(\tan x)\,dx$ by the substitutions $\tan x=t$, $x=\arctan t$, $dx=\frac{dt}{1+t^2}$;

$\int R(\sin x, \cos x)\,dx$ by the substitutions $\tan\frac{x}{2}=t$, $\sin x=\frac{2t}{1+t^2}$, $\cos x=\frac{1-t^2}{1+t^2}$, $dx=\frac{2dt}{1+t^2}$.

Find the integrals:

1500. $\int \frac{e^{2x}-2e^x}{e^{2x}+1}\,dx$.

1501. $\int \tan^4 x\,dx$.

1502. $\int \frac{e^{3x}\,dx}{e^x+2}$.

1503. $\int \frac{dx}{\sin x}$.

1504. $\int \frac{dx}{5+3\cos x}$.

1505. $\int \frac{dx}{3\sin x+4\cos x}$.

1506. $\int \frac{dx}{\sin^4 x}$.

1507. $\int \frac{dx}{1+3\cos^2 x}$.

Hint. In Problems 1506, 1507, 1512, and 1513, where the integrand expressions contain only even powers of $\sin x$ and $\cos x$, it is better to apply the substitutions: $\tan x=t$, $\sin^2 x=\frac{t^2}{1+t^2}$, $\cos^2 x=\frac{1}{1+t^2}$, $dx=\frac{dt}{1+t^2}$.

Find the integrals:

1508. $\int \frac{e^{2x}\,dx}{e^x-1}$.

1509. $\int \tan^5 x\,dx$.

1510. $\int \frac{e^{3x}\,dx}{e^{2x}-1}$.

1511. $\int \frac{dx}{3+\cos x}$.

1512. $\int \frac{dx}{\cos^4 x}$.

1513. $\int \frac{dx}{1+3\sin^2 x}$.

1514. $\int \frac{dx}{2\sin x+\sin 2x}$.

1515. $\int \frac{1+\cos x}{\sin^3 x}\,dx$.

1516. $\int \frac{e^x+1}{e^x-1}\,dx$.

1517. $\int \frac{1+\tan x}{\sin 2x}\,dx$.

8.9. Integration of Hyperbolic Functions. Hyperbolic Substitutions

1. $\int \cosh x\,dx = \sinh x + C.$ 2. $\int \sinh x\,dx = \cosh x + C.$

3. $\int \frac{dx}{\cosh^2 x} = \tanh x + C.$ 4. $\int \frac{dx}{\sinh^2 x} = -\coth x + C.$

Integrals of the second and other even powers of $\cosh x$ and $\sinh x$ are found by the following formulas:

$$\cosh^2 x = \frac{\cosh 2x + 1}{2}, \quad \sinh^2 x = \frac{\cosh 2x - 1}{2},$$

$$\sinh x \cosh x = \frac{\sinh 2x}{2}.$$

Integrals of odd powers of $\sinh x$ and $\cosh x$ are found in the same way as integrals of odd powers of $\sin x$ and $\cos x$.

Hyperbolic substitutions are sometimes used for finding integrals of the form

$\int R(x, \sqrt{x^2 - a^2})\,dx$ by the substitution $x = a\cosh t$;

$\int R(x, \sqrt{x^2 + a^2})\,dx$ by the substitution $x = a\sinh t$.

In this case if $x = a \cosh t$, then $t = \ln\left|\frac{x + \sqrt{x^2 - a^2}}{a}\right|$,

and if $x = a \sinh t$, then $t = \ln\left|\frac{x + \sqrt{x^2 + a^2}}{a}\right|$.

Find the integrals:

1518. (1) $\int \sinh^2 3x\,dx$; (2) $\int (1 + \sinh 2x)^2\,dx$.

1519. $\int \cosh^3 x\,dx$. **1520.** $\int \tanh x\,dx$.

1521. $\int \frac{dx}{\cosh x + 1}$. **1522.** $\int \frac{dx}{\tanh x - 1}$.

1523. $\int \sqrt{x^2 + a^2}\,dx$. **1524.** $\int \sqrt{x^2 - a^2}\,dx$.

1525. $\int \frac{dx}{\sqrt{(x^2 + 4)^3}}$. **1526.** $\int \frac{dx}{\sqrt{(x^2 - 5)^3}}$.

Find the integrals:

1527. $\int \sinh^3 3x\,dx.$

1528. $\int \sinh^2 x \cosh^2 x\,dx.$

1529. $\int \sinh^4 x \cosh x\,dx.$

1530. $\int \coth^2 x\,dx.$

1531. $\int \sqrt{\cosh x+1}\,dx.$

1532. $\int \frac{1+2\sinh x}{\cosh^2 x}\,dx.$

1533. $\int \frac{x^2\,dx}{\sqrt{x^2-3}}.$

1534. $\int \frac{\sqrt{x^2+3}}{x^2}\,dx.$

8.10. Miscellaneous Problems on Integration

Find the integrals:

1535. $\int \frac{\sqrt{1+x}\,dx}{x}.$

1536. $\int \frac{\arctan x\,dx}{1+x^2}.$

1537. $\int \frac{dx}{x^3+ax^2}.$

1538. $\int \frac{dx}{1+\sin x}.$

1539. $\int \frac{dx}{\sqrt{x(1-x)}}.$

1540. $\int \frac{dx}{\frac{\sin^2 x}{a^2}+\frac{\cos^2 x}{b^2}}.$

1541. $\int x\cos^2 x\,dx.$

1542. $\int \frac{dx}{e^{2x}+e^x}.$

1543. $\int \sqrt{\frac{1-x}{1+x}}\,dx.$

1544. $\int \frac{\cos^2 x\,dx}{\sin^4 x}.$

1545. $\int x\tan^2 x\,dx.$

1546. $\int \frac{\cos^2 x\,dx}{\sin x}.$

1547. $\int \frac{\sin x\,dx}{b^2+\cos^2 x}.$

1548. $\int \frac{dx}{\sqrt[3]{x^2}+2\sqrt{x}}.$

1549. $\int \frac{ax-b}{(ax+b)^4}\,dx.$

1550. $\int \frac{dx}{x^4+x^2}.$

1551. $\int \frac{dx}{(\sin x+\cos x)^2}.$

1552. $\int \frac{dx}{x\sqrt{a+b\ln x}}.$

1553. $\int \frac{x^2\,dx}{(a-bx^3)^n}.$

1554. $\int \sqrt{1-2x-x^2}\,dx.$

1555. $\int \frac{dx}{(1+\sqrt{x})^3}.$

1556. $\int \frac{\arctan x\,dx}{x^2}.$

1557. $\int \frac{e^x-2}{e^{2x}+4}\,dx.$

1558. $\int \frac{dx}{(2x+1)(1+\sqrt{2x+1})}.$

7 —1895

1559. $\int \cot^4 x\,dx$.

1560. $\int \frac{\sqrt{4-x^2}}{x^2}\,dx$.

1561. (1) $\int \frac{\cos x}{\cos 3x}\,dx$; (2) $\int \frac{\sin x}{\sin 3x}\,dx$.

1562. (1) $\int \frac{dx}{\sqrt{x+a}+\sqrt{x}}$; (2) $\int \frac{dx}{\sqrt{x^2+1}-x}$.

1563. $\int \frac{x^4+1}{x^3-x^2}\,dx$.

1564. $\int \frac{\sqrt{x^2+2x}}{x^3}\,dx$.

1565. $\int \frac{dx}{x\sqrt{x^3-1}}$.

1566. $\int \frac{dx}{1+\tan x}$.

1567. $\int \frac{\arcsin \sqrt{x}}{\sqrt{x}}\,dx$.

1568. $\int \frac{\sin 2x}{\cos^4 x}\,dx$.

1569. $\int \frac{\cos 2x}{\sin^4 x}\,dx$.

1570. $\int \frac{\ln(\cos x)\,dx}{\sin^2 x}$.

1571. $\int \frac{dx}{e^{3x}-e^x}$.

1572. $\int \frac{\sin^3 x\,dx}{\cos^5 x}$.

1573. $\int \frac{\ln(x+1)\,dx}{x^2}$.

1574. $\int \sqrt{1-\sin x}\,dx$.

1575. $\int \frac{dx}{1+\sin^2 x}$.

1576. $\int \frac{x\,dx}{x^4-x^2-2}$.

1577. $\int e^{-\sqrt{x}}\,dx$.

1578. $\int \frac{\arctan \sqrt{x}\,dx}{\sqrt{x}}$.

1579. $\int \frac{\sqrt{\tan x}\,dx}{\sin 2x}$.

1580. $\int \frac{\ln(x^2+1)\,dx}{x^3}$.

1581. $\int \frac{a^x\,dx}{a^{2x}+1}$.

1582. $\int \frac{1-\sin \sqrt{x}}{\sqrt{x}}\,dx$.

1583. $\int \sqrt{\frac{(x+1)^3}{(x-1)^2}}\,dx$.

1584. $\int \frac{x \arcsin x\,dx}{\sqrt{1-x^2}}$.

1585. $\int \frac{dx}{x^2\sqrt{x^2-1}}$.

1586. $\int \frac{x^2\,dx}{(x+1)^4}$.

1587. $\int \frac{x-a}{\sqrt{2ax+x^2}}\,dx$.

1588. $\int \frac{4x+1}{2x^3+x^2-x}\,dx$.

1589. $\int \frac{\cos^3 x+1}{\sin^2 x}\,dx$.

1590. $\int \frac{dx}{x^4+4}$.

CHAPTER 9

THE DEFINITE INTEGRAL

9.1. Computing the Definite Integral

Let a function $f(x)$ be defined on a closed interval $[a, b]$. This interval is partitioned into n subintervals by points $a=x_0<x_1<x_2<\ldots<x_n=b$. In each of the subintervals (x_{i-1}, x_i) take an arbitrary point ξ_i and form the sum $\sum_{i=1}^{n} f(\xi_i)\,\Delta x_i$, where $\Delta x_i=x_i-x_{i-1}$. The sum of the form $\sum_{i=1}^{n} f(\xi_i)\,\Delta x_i$ is termed the *integral sum*, and the limit to which this sum tends as the largest subinterval approaches zero ($\max \Delta x_i \rightarrow 0$), if it exists and is finite, is called the *definite integral* of the function $f(x)$. The end-points a, b of the given interval (the interval of integration) are called the limits of integration: the lower limit (a) and the upper limit (b).

The definite integral is denoted by

$$\int_a^b f(x)\,dx=\lim_{\max \Delta x_i \rightarrow 0} \sum_{i=1}^{n} f(\xi_i)\,\Delta x_i. \qquad (1)$$

In this case the function $f(x)$ is called *integrable* over the interval $[a, b]$.

For a function to be *integrable* it is sufficient that it is either *continuous* on the interval $[a, b]$ or has a finite number of finite discontinuities.

Let $f(x)$ be continuous on $[a, b]$. Then on this interval there exists an indefinite integral

$$\int f(x)\,dx=F(x)+C \qquad (2)$$

and the following formula takes place:

$$\int_a^b f(x)\,dx = F(b) - F(a) = \left[\int f(x)\,dx\right]_a^b, \qquad (3)$$

i.e. the *definite integral* of a continuous functions *is equal to the difference of the values of the antiderivative* (or the indefinite integral) for the upper and lower limits. Formula (3) is called the *Newton-Leibnitz formula*.

1591. By forming integral sums and proceeding to the limit, find the following integrals:

(1) $\int_0^a x\,dx$; (2) $\int_0^a x^2\,dx$; (3) $\int_0^a e^x\,dx$; (4) $\int_0^\pi \sin x\,dx$.

Hint. When solving (2) and (4) make use of the results of Problems 1034 and 647.

1592. Compute the lower and the upper integral sums s_5 and S_5 for the integral $\int_1^2 \frac{dx}{x}$, dividing the closed interval [1, 2] into five equal subintervals. Compare the result thus obtained with the exact value of the integral.

Hint. $s_5 = \sum_{i=1}^{5} m_i \Delta x$, $S_5 = \sum_{i=1}^{5} M_i \Delta x$, where m_i is the least value, and M_i, the greatest value of the integrand function in *i*th subinterval.

Compute:

1593. $\int_1^3 x^3\,dx$.

1594. $\int_1^2 \left(x^2 + \frac{1}{x^4}\right) dx$.

1595. $\int_1^4 \sqrt{x}\,dx$.

1596. $\int_0^1 \frac{dx}{\sqrt{4-x^2}}$.

1597. $\int_a^{a\sqrt{3}} \frac{dx}{a^2+x^2}$.

1598. $\int_0^3 e^{\frac{x}{3}}\,dx$.

1599. $\int_0^1 \frac{dx}{\sqrt{x^2+1}}$.

1600. $\int_0^{\frac{\pi}{4}} \sin 4x\, dx$.

1601. $\int_4^9 \frac{dx}{\sqrt{x}-1}$.

1602. $\int_{\frac{\pi}{4}}^{\frac{\pi}{3}} \frac{1+\tan^2 x}{(1+\tan x)^2}\, dx$.

Hint. In Problem 1601 apply the substitution $x=t^2$; then the limits of the integral will change, which is written in the tabular form $\begin{array}{c|c|c} x & 4 & 9 \\ \hline t & 2 & 3 \end{array}$. Analogously, in Problem 1602, when integrating by the substitution $\tan x=t$, change the limits accordingly.

1603. $\int_0^4 \frac{dx}{1+\sqrt{2x+1}}$.

1604. $\int_0^1 \frac{x^2\, dx}{\sqrt{4-x^2}}$.

1605. $\int_0^1 \frac{dx}{e^x+1}$.

1606. $\int_0^{\frac{a}{2}} \sqrt{\frac{x}{a-x}}\, dx$.

1607. $\int_0^{\frac{\pi}{2}} \sin x \cos^2 x\, dx$.

1608. $\int_0^{\sqrt{a}} x^2\sqrt{a-x^2}\, dx$.

1609. $\int_0^1 \ln(x+1)\, dx$.

1610. $\int_0^1 \sqrt{1+x^2}\, dx$.

1611. $\int_1^{\sqrt{3}} \frac{dx}{\sqrt{(1+x^2)^3}}$.

1612. $\int_1^3 \frac{dx}{x+x^2}$.

1613. From the formula of Problems 1407 obtain that

$$\int_0^{\frac{\pi}{2}} \sin^n x\, dx = \frac{n-1}{n}\int_0^{\frac{\pi}{2}} \sin^{n-2} x\, dx,$$

and compute:

(1) $\int\limits_0^{\frac{\pi}{2}} \sin^2 x\,dx$; (2) $\int\limits_0^{\frac{\pi}{2}} \sin^4 x\,dx$; (3) $\int\limits_0^{\frac{\pi}{2}} \sin^6 x\,dx$.

Compute:

1614. $\int\limits_0^a (x^2 - ax)\,dx$.

1615. $\int\limits_2^3 \frac{dx}{x^2}$.

1616. $\int\limits_0^{\sqrt{3}} \frac{x\,dx}{\sqrt{4-x^2}}$.

1617. $\int\limits_{\frac{\pi}{8}}^{\frac{\pi}{6}} \frac{dx}{\cos^2 2x}$.

1618. $\int\limits_1^4 \frac{dx}{(1+\sqrt{x})^2}$.

1619. $\int\limits_0^1 \frac{e^x\,dx}{1+e^{2x}}$.

1620. $\int\limits_1^5 \frac{x\,dx}{\sqrt{4x+5}}$.

1621. $\int\limits_1^{\sqrt{2}} \sqrt{2-x^2}\,dx$.

1622. $\int\limits_0^{\frac{\pi}{2}} x\cos x\,dx$.

1623. $\int\limits_0^{\frac{\pi}{4}} \tan^3 x\,dx$.

1624. From the formula of Problem 1407 obtain that

$$\int\limits_0^{\frac{\pi}{2}} \cos^n x\,dx = \frac{n-1}{n} \int\limits_0^{\frac{\pi}{2}} \cos^{n-2} x\,dx,$$

and compute

(1) $\int\limits_0^{\frac{\pi}{2}} \cos^2 x\,dx$; (2) $\int\limits_0^{\frac{\pi}{2}} \cos^4 x\,dx$; (3) $\int\limits_0^{\frac{\pi}{2}} \cos^6 x\,dx$.

9.2. Computing Areas

1°. The area of curvilinear trapezoid A_1ABB_1 adjacent to the axis OX (Fig. 33):

$$S = \lim_{\Delta x \to 0} \sum y \, \Delta x = \int_{x_1}^{x_2} y \, dx. \tag{1}$$

The differential of a variable area A_1AMM_1 is $dS = y\,dx$.

If a curve is given by the equations $x = f(t)$ and $y = \varphi(t)$, then $dS = \varphi(t) \cdot f'(t)\,dt$.

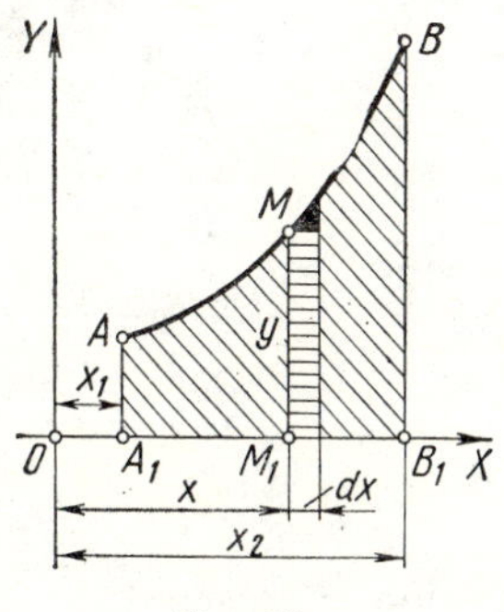

Fig. 33

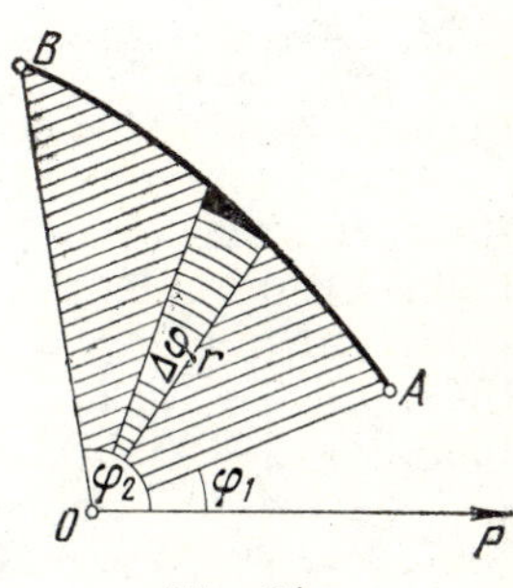

Fig. 34

2°. The area of the curvilinear trapezoid adjacent to the axis OY:

$$S = \lim_{\Delta y \to 0} \sum x \, \Delta y = \int_{y_1}^{y_2} x \, dy. \tag{2}$$

The differential of a variable area $dS = x\,dy$.

3°. The area of the sector OAB (Fig. 34) of a curve given in *polar* coordinates:

$$S = \lim_{\Delta\varphi \to 0} \sum \frac{1}{2} r^2 \, \Delta\varphi = \int_{\varphi_1}^{\varphi_2} \frac{1}{2} r^2 \, d\varphi. \tag{3}$$

The differential of the area variable $dS = \frac{1}{2} r^2 \, d\varphi$.

Compute the areas bounded by the following lines:

1625. $y=4-x^2$, $y=0$.

1626. $\frac{x^2}{a^2}+\frac{y^2}{b^2}=1$.

1627. $y^2=2px$, $x=h$.

1628. $y=3-2x-x^2$, $y=0$.

1629. $xy=4$, $x=1$, $x=4$, $y=0$.

1630. $y=\ln x$, $x=e$, $y=0$.

1631. $y^2=2x+4$, $x=0$.

1632. $y^2=x^3$, $y=8$, $x=0$.

1633. $y^2=(4-x)^3$, $x=0$.

1634. The loop of the curve $4(y^2-x^2)+x^3=0$.

1635. $y=x^2$, $y=2-x^2$.

1636. $y=x^2+4x$, $y=x+4$.

1637. $a^2y^2=x^3(2a-x)$.

1638. $(y-x)^2=x^3$, $x=1$.

1639. The loop of the strophoid $y^2(2a-x)=x(x-a)^2$.

1640. Catenary $y=\frac{a}{2}\left(e^{\frac{x}{a}}+e^{-\frac{x}{a}}\right)$, $x=\pm a$ and $y=0$.

1641. One arc of the cycloid $x=a(t-\sin t)$, $y=a\times$ $\times(1-\cos t)$ and the axis OX.

1642. Astroid $x=a\cos^3 t$, $y=a\sin^3 t$.

1643. Lemniscate $r^2=a^2\cos 2\varphi$.

1644. Cardioid $r=a(1-\cos\varphi)$.

1645. $r=3+\sin 2\varphi$ \
1646. $r=2-\cos 3\varphi$ } find the area enclosed between the adjacent maximum and minimum radius vectors of each curve.

1647. $r=a\cos 2\varphi$.

1648. $r=a\sin 3\varphi$.

1649. $r=a(\sin\varphi+\cos\varphi)$.

1650. $r=\frac{a}{\varphi}$, $\frac{\pi}{4}\leqslant\varphi\leqslant 2\pi$.

1651. $r=a\sin^3\frac{\varphi}{3}$, located below the polar axis.

1652. The loop of the folium of Descartes $x^3+y^3-3axy=0$ (see Fig. 83 on p. 386) (pass to polar coordinates).

Hint. In the integral $\int\frac{\sin^2\varphi\cos^2\varphi\,d\varphi}{(\sin^3\varphi+\cos^3\varphi)^2}$ put $\tan\varphi=u$, first dividing both the numerator and denominator by $\cos^6\varphi$.

Compute the areas bounded by the following lines:

1653. $y=6x-x^2$, $y=0$.

1654. $y=x^3$, $y=8$, $x=0$.

1655. $y^2=1-x$ and $x=-3$.

1656. $y^2+x^4=x^2$.

1657. $y=x^2+4x+5$, $x=0$, $y=0$ and the minimum ordinate.

1658. A half-wave of the sinusoid $y=\sin x$ and $y=0$.

1659. $4y=x^2$ and $y^2=4x$. **1660.** $xy=6$ and $x+y-7=0$.

1661. The loop of the curve $x^3+x^2-y^2=0$.

1662. $r=3-\cos 2\varphi$

1663. $r=2+\sin 3\varphi$

} find the area enclosed between the adjacent maximum and minimum radius vectors of each curve.

1664. $r=a\sin 2\varphi$. **1665.** $r=a\cos 3\varphi$.

1666. $r=ae^{\varphi}$ from $\varphi=-\pi$ to $\varphi=\pi$.

1667. Find the area of the common portion of the ellipses $\frac{x^2}{a^2}+\frac{y^2}{b^2}=1$ and $\frac{x^2}{b^2}+\frac{y^2}{a^2}=1$ (pass to polar coordinates).

1668. $r=a(1+\sin^2 2\varphi)$ and $r=a$.

9.3. The Volume of a Solid of Revolution

1°. The volume of a solid generated by revolving a curvilinear trapezoid A_1ABB_1 about the axis OX (Fig. 35),

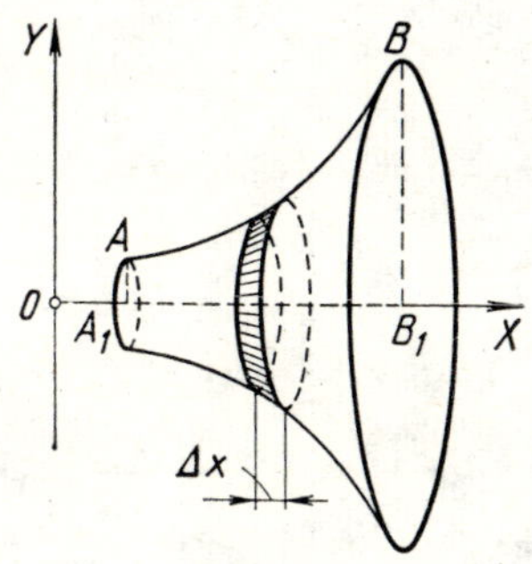

Fig. 35

where $\breve{AB}$ is the arc of a curve $y=f(x)$, is determined by the formula

$$V=\lim_{\Delta x\to 0}\sum \pi y^2\Delta x=\int_{x_1}^{x_2}\pi y^2\,dx. \qquad (1)$$

The differential of a variable volume $dV=\pi y^2\,dx$.

2°. The volume of a solid generated by revolving about the axis OY a curvilinear trapezoid adjacent to the axis

OY is determined by the formula

$$V=\lim_{\Delta y\to 0}\sum \pi x^2\Delta y=\int_{y_1}^{y_2}\pi x^2\,dy. \qquad (2)$$

The differential of a variable volume $dV=\pi x^2\,dy$.

Determine the volume of the solid generated by revolving a figure bounded by the following lines:

1669. $y^2=2px$ and $x=h$ about the axis OX.

1670. $\frac{x^2}{a^2}-\frac{y^2}{b^2}=1$ and $y=\pm b$ about the axis OY.

1671. $xy=4$, $x=1$, $x=4$, $y=0$ about the axis OX.

1672. $y^2=(x+4)^3$ and $x=0$ about the axis OY.

1673. $x^2+y^2=a^2$ about the straight line $x=b>a$.

Hint. $dV=\pi(b+x)^2\,dy-\pi(b-x)^2\,dy=4\pi bx\,dy$.

1674. $y=a\cosh\frac{x}{a}$, $x=\pm a$, $y=0$ about the axis OX.

1675. $y^2=4-x$, $x=0$ about the axis OY.

1676. $(y-a)^2=ax$, $x=0$, $y=2a$ about the axis OX.

1677. $y=\cos x$ and $y=-1$ about the straight line $y=-1$ for $-\pi\leqslant x\leqslant\pi$.

1678. $y=x\sqrt{-x}$, $x=-4$ and $y=0$ about the axis OY.

1679. $y=\cos\left(x-\frac{\pi}{3}\right)$, $x=0$, $y=0$ (for $x>0$) about the axis OX.

1680. $y=a-\frac{x^2}{a}$ and $x+y=a$ about the axis OY.

Determine the volumes of the solids generated by revolving the figures bounded by the following lines:

1681. $y=\sin x$ (a half-wave), $y=0$ about the axis OX.

1682. $x^2-y^2=4$, $y=\pm 2$ about the axis OY.

1683. $y=\frac{1}{1+x^2}$, $x=\pm 1$, $y=0$ about the axis OX.

1684. $\frac{x^2}{a^2}+\frac{y^2}{b^2}=1$ about the axis OY.

1685. $x^{2/3}+y^{2/3}=a^{2/3}$ about the axis OX.

1686. $y=x^3$, $x=0$, $y=8$ about the axis OY.

1687. $x^2-y^2=a^2$, $x=\pm 2a$ about the axis OX.

1688. $y=x^2$, $y=4$, about the straight line $x=2$.
Hint. $dV=\pi(2+x)^2\,dy-\pi(2-x)^2\,dy$.
1689. One arc of the cycloid

$x=a(t-\sin t)$, $y=a(1-\cos t)$ about the axis OX.

1690. $(y-3)^2+3x=0$, $x=-3$ about the axis OX.

9.4. The Arc Length of a Plane Curve

1°. The length of an arc $\breve{AB}$ of the curve $y=f(x)$ is given by the integral

$$s=\int_{x_A}^{x_B}\sqrt{1+y'^2}\,dx. \tag{1}$$

Differential of arc length: $ds=\sqrt{1+y'^2}\,dx=\sqrt{dx^2+dy^2}$.
2°. The length of an arc $\breve{AB}$ of the curve $x=f(t)$, $y=\varphi(t)$:

$$s=\int_{t_A}^{t_B}\sqrt{\dot{x}^2+\dot{y}^2}\,dt. \tag{2}$$

3°. The length of an arc $\breve{AB}$ of the curve $r=f(\varphi)$:

$$s=\int_{\varphi_A}^{\varphi_B}\sqrt{r^2+r'^2}\,d\varphi. \tag{3}$$

Determine the length of the arc of the curve:
1691. $y^2=x^3$ cut off by the straight line $x=\frac{4}{3}$.
1692. Of the entire curve $x^2+y^2=a^2$.
1693. Of the entire curve $x^{\frac{2}{3}}+y^{\frac{2}{3}}=a^{\frac{2}{3}}$.
1694. $y^2=(x+1)^3$ cut off by the straight line $x=4$.
1695. Of one arc of the cycloid

$$x=a(t-\sin t),\quad y=a(1-\cos t).$$

1696. $x=\frac{t^6}{6}$, $y=2-\frac{t^4}{4}$ between the points of intersection with the coordinate axes.

1697. $y=\frac{x^2}{2}-1$ cut off by the axis OX.

Hint. $\int\sqrt{1+x^2}\,dx$ can be found by parts, or written by the formula of Problem 1366.

1698. $y=\frac{a}{2}\left(e^{\frac{x}{a}}+e^{-\frac{x}{a}}\right)=a\cosh\frac{x}{a}$ between the straight lines $x=\pm a$.

1699. $y=\ln x$ from $x=\frac{3}{4}$ to $x=\frac{12}{5}$.

Hint. The integral $\int\frac{\sqrt{1+x^2}\,dx}{x}$ is found by the substitution $1+x^2=t^2$.

1700. $y=\ln(2\cos x)$ between the adjacent points of intersection with the coordinate axes OY and OX.

1701. (1) $9y^2=x(x-3)^2$ between the points of intersection with the axis OX.

(2) $e^{2y}\tanh x=1$ between the points $x=1$ and $x=2$.

1702. (1) The cardioid $r=a(1-\cos\varphi)$.

(2) The first turn of the spiral $r=a\varphi$.

1703. The entire curve $r=a\sin^3\frac{\varphi}{3}$.

1704. A flexible thread is suspended from the points A and B situated at the same height; $AB=2b$, the sag is f. Taking the suspended thread as a parabola, show that its length $s\approx 2b\left(1+\frac{2}{3}\frac{f^2}{b^2}\right)$ for a sufficiently small $\frac{f}{b}$.

Hint. Apply the approximate formula $\sqrt{1+\alpha}\approx 1+\frac{1}{2}\alpha$ from Problem 1157.

Find the length of the arc of the curve:

1705. $y^2=\frac{4}{9}(2-x)^3$ cut off by the straight line $x=-1$.

1706. $y=\ln(\sin x)$ from $x=\frac{\pi}{3}$ to $x=\frac{2\pi}{3}$.

1707. $y=\ln(1-x^2)$ from $x=-\frac{1}{2}$ to $x=\frac{1}{2}$.

1708. $y^2=2px$ cut off by the straight line $x=\frac{p}{2}$.

1709. $\left.\begin{aligned}x&=t^2,\\ y&=\frac{t}{3}(t^2-3)\end{aligned}\right\}$ between the points of intersection with the axis OX.

9.5. The Area of a Surface of Revolution

1°. The area of a surface formed by the revolution of an arc $\breve{AB}$ of the curve $y=f(x)$ about the x-axis is

$$P_x=2\pi\int_{\breve{AB}} y\,ds, \quad \text{where } ds=\sqrt{dx^2+dy^2}.$$

2°. The area of a surface formed by the revolution of an arc $\breve{AB}$ of the curve $x=\varphi(y)$ about the y-axis is

$$P_y=2\pi\int_{\breve{AB}} x\,ds, \quad \text{where } ds=\sqrt{dx^2+dy^2}.$$

Determine the area of the surface formed by revolving the curve:

1710. $x^2+y^2=R^2$ about the x-axis.

1711. $y=\frac{x^2}{2}$ cut by the straight line $y=1.5$, about the y-axis.

1712. $y=a\cosh\frac{x}{a}$ between $x=\pm a$ about the x-axis.

1713. $4x^2+y^2=4$ about the axis OY.

Hint. Taking y for an independent variable, we get the required area $P=\pi\int_0^2\sqrt{16-3y^2}\,dy$. Then make use of the substitution $y=\frac{4}{\sqrt{3}}\sin t$.

1714. One half-wave of the curve $y=\sin x$ about the axis OX.

1715. One arc of the cycloid $\begin{cases} x=a(t-\sin t) \\ y=a(1-\cos t) \end{cases}$ about the x-axis.

1716. The loop of the curve $x=t^2$, $p=\frac{t}{3}(t^2-3)$ about the x-axis.

1717. $x^2+y^2=a^2$ about the straight line $x=b>a$.

Hint. $dP=2\pi(b+x)\,ds+2\pi(b-x)\,ds$.

Determine the area of a surface formed by rotating about the axis OX:

1718. The arc of the curve $y=\frac{x^3}{3}$ from $x=-2$ to $x=2$.

1719. The arc of the curve $y^2=4+x$ cut by the straight line $x=2$.

1720. The entire curve $x=a\cos^3 t$, $y=a\sin^3 t$.

1721. The arc of the curve $x=\frac{t^3}{3}$, $y=4-\frac{t^2}{2}$ between the points of intersection with the coordinate axes.

9.6. Problems in Physics

1722. Determine the force of pressure acting on a vertical rectangular water lock with base 8 m and height 6 m. Find also the force of pressure experienced by the lower half of the lock.

1723. Compute the force of pressure acting on a vertical triangle whose base a is flush with the water surface and altitude is equal to h.

1724. Find the force of pressure acting on a semicircle of radius R submerged vertically in water so that its diameter is flush with the water surface.

1725. A vertical dam has the form of a trapezoid whose upper base is 20 m, the lower one 10 m and the altitude 6 m. Find the force of water pressure experienced by the dam.

1726. Find the moments of inertia about the x- and y-axis of the rectangle bounded by the straight lines $x=a$, $y=0$, $y=b$, and $x=0$.

Hint. Subdividing the rectangle into horizontal strips, multiply each strip by its squared distance from the axis OX, i.e. by y^2. Summing and passing to the limit, we get

$$J_x=\lim_{\Delta y\to 0}\sum a\Delta y\, y^2=\int_0^b ay^2\,dy.$$

Similarly $J_y=\int_0^a bx^2\,dx$.

1727. Find the moment of inertia about the x- and y-axis of the triangle bounded by the lines $x=0$, $y=0$, and $\frac{x}{a}+\frac{y}{b}=1$.

1728. Find the moment of inertia about the y-axis of the figure bounded by the lines $x=2$, $y=x^2$, and $y=0$.

1729. Find the static moments about the x- and y-axis and the coordinates of the centre of gravity of the triangle formed by the lines $x=0$, $y=0$, and $x+y=a$.

Hint. The static moments: $M_x=\int\limits_0^a xy\,dy$, $M_y=\int\limits_0^a xy\,dx$. The coordinates of the centre of gravity: $x_c=\frac{M_y}{S}$, $y_c=\frac{M_x}{S}$, where S is the area of the figure.

1730. Find the centre of gravity of the figure bounded by the lines $a^2y=bx^2$, $x=a$, and $y=0$.

1731. Find the centre of gravity of the semicircle $x^2+y^2=a^2$ cut off by the axis OX.

1732. (1) Calculate the work needed to overcome the force of gravity in pumping the water out of a cylindrical vessel with the radius of the base circle 0.5 m if at the starting moment the water level in the vessel reaches 2.8 m and is 0.2 m lower that the outlet hole.

(2) Calculate the work needed to overcome the force of gravity in pumping the water out of a hemispherical boiler of radius R m.

1733. Compute the work needed to overcome the force of gravity in lifting a mass m from the earth surface to a height h.

Hint. The force F of gravity at a distance x from the centre of the earth is determined from the proportion $F:mg=R^2:x^2$, where R is the radius of the earth.

1734. A cauldron has the shape of a paraboloid of revolution; its depth is $H=0.5$ m and the radius of the circle base $R=0.4$ m. Calculate the work needed to overcome the force of gravity in pumping the water out of a brim-full cauldron.

1735. There is air of volume $V_0=0.1$ m^3 and pressure $p_0=103{,}300$ N/m^2 under a piston in a cylinder. Determine the work done by an isothermal compression of the air to a volume $V_1 = 0.03\ \text{m}^3$.

1736. Compute the work done by a 0.001 m stretching of a 1 m copper wire whose cross-sectional radius is 2 mm.

Hint. The force F required to stretch a wire of length l and cross-sectional area s by x is determined by the formula $F = E\frac{sx}{l}$, where E is Young's modulus. We may take $E \approx 12 \cdot 10^{10}\ \text{N/m}^2$ for copper.

1737. How long would it take the water in a full cylindrical vessel of base area $S = 420\ \text{cm}^2$ and height $H = 40$ cm to flow through an orifice on the bottom of area $s = 2\ \text{cm}^2$?

Hint. The velocity of discharge of a liquid at level x is determined by the formula $v = \mu\sqrt{2gx}$, where μ is a coefficient which depends on the liquid viscosity and the shapes of the vessel and the orifice. We assume here, as we shall in Problem 1738, that $\mu = 0.6$.

1738. How long would it take the water to flow out of a conical funnel of height $H = 40$ cm, lower base radius $r = 0.3$ cm and the upper base radius $R = 6$ cm (see hint to Problem 1737)?

1739. Determine the pressure exerted by water on a vertical triangle of height h, whose base a is parallel to, and whose opposite vertex is on, the surface of the water.

1740. Determine the pressure exerted by water on a vertical parabolic segment whose base is equal to 4 m and situated on the surface of the water, and whose vertex is at a depth of 4 m.

1741. Find the depth x at which a rectangular water lock of height h may be divided horizontally into two parts on each of which the water pressure is identical.

1742. A cylindrical cistern with horizontal axis is half filled with oil (specific gravity 0.9). Determine the pressure exerted by the oil on each of the cylinder plane walls, if its radius is equal to 2 m.

1743. Determine the moment of inertia of the quadrant $x = a\cos t$, $y = a\sin t$ about the x-axis.

1744. Find the coordinates of the centre of gravity of the area bounded by the curves $y = 4 - x^2$ and $y = 0$.

1745. Compute the work necessary for pumping the water out of an (inverted, circular) cone-shaped hole, whose height $H=2$ m and base radius $R=0.3$ m.

1746. Determine the work done by adiabatically compressing air of volume $V_0=0.1$ m³ under pressure $p_0=$ $=103{,}300$ N/m² to a volume $V_1=0.03$ m³. (Adiabatic compression obeys Poisson's law: $pV^k=p_0V_0^k$, where $k\approx 1.4$.)

1747. How long would it take the water in a full hemispherical bowl of radius 40 cm to flow through an orifice on the bottom of area 2 cm²? (See hint to Problem 1737; set coefficient of viscosity $\mu=0.8$.)

9.7. Improper Integrals

1°. Definitions.

I. The integral $\int\limits_a^{+\infty} f(x)\,dx$ is defined as $\lim\limits_{b\to+\infty}\int\limits_a^b f(x)\,dx$ if this limit exists and is finite. The integrals $\int\limits_{-\infty}^{b} f(x)\,dx$ and $\int\limits_{-\infty}^{+\infty} f(x)\,dx$ are determined analogously.

II. If $f(x)$ is continuous at all points of the closed interval $[a, b]$ except the point c at which $f(x)$ has a discontinuity of the second kind, then the integral of the function $f(x)$ from a to b is defined as the sum

$$\lim_{\varepsilon\to 0}\int\limits_a^{c-\varepsilon} f(x)\,dx+\lim_{\delta\to 0}\int\limits_{c+\delta}^{b} f(x)\,dx,$$

if these limits exist and are finite.

Integrals with *infinite limits* and those of *discontinuous (unlimited)* functions are called *improper integrals*.

If the above-mentioned limits are finite, we say that the improper integrals *converge*, if they are infinite, then we say that the improper integrals *diverge*.

2°. An improper integral is often tested for convergence by the method of comparison: if for $x>a\ |f(x)|\leqslant\varphi(x)$ and $\int\limits_a^{+\infty}\varphi(x)\,dx$ converges, then $\int\limits_a^{+\infty} f(x)\,dx$ also converges.

An analogous convergence test can also be formulated for the integral of a function with a discontinuity.

Compute the integrals:

1748. (1) $\int\limits_1^\infty \frac{dx}{x^2}$; (2) $\int\limits_1^\infty \frac{dx}{x}$; (3) $\int\limits_1^\infty \frac{dx}{\sqrt{x}}$; (4) $\int\limits_1^\infty \frac{dx}{x^n}$.

1749. (1) $\int\limits_0^\infty e^{-x}\,dx$; (2) $\int\limits_0^\infty xe^{-x^2}\,dx$; (3) $\int\limits_1^\infty \frac{dx}{1+x^2}$;

(4) $\int\limits_1^\infty \frac{dx}{x^2\sqrt{x^2-1}}$; (5) $\int\limits_1^\infty \frac{dx}{x^2+x}$; (6) $\int\limits_0^\infty x^2 e^{-\frac{x}{2}}\,dx$.

1750. (1) $\int\limits_2^\infty \frac{dx}{x\sqrt{x^2-1}}$; (2) $\int\limits_1^\infty \frac{\arctan x\,dx}{x^2}$; (3) $\int\limits_1^\infty \frac{dx}{(x^2+1)^2}$.

1751. (1) $\int\limits_2^6 \frac{dx}{\sqrt[3]{(4-x)^2}}$; (2) $\int\limits_0^2 \frac{dx}{(x-1)^2}$; (3) $\int\limits_0^2 \frac{dx}{\sqrt[3]{(x-1)^2}}$.

1752. Test the following integrals for convergence:

(1) $\int\limits_0^\infty \frac{dx}{\sqrt{1+x^3}}$; (2) $\int\limits_2^\infty \frac{dx}{\sqrt[3]{x^3-1}}$; (3) $\int\limits_1^\infty \frac{e^{-x}\,dx}{x}$;

(4) $\int\limits_1^\infty \frac{\sin x\,dx}{x^2}$; (5) $\int\limits_2^\infty \frac{x\,dx}{\sqrt{x^4+1}}$; (6) $\int\limits_0^\infty e^{-x^2}\,dx$.

1753. (1) $\int\limits_0^1 \frac{dx}{x^n}$; (2) $\int\limits_a^b \frac{dx}{(b-x)^n}$ (for $b>a$).

Hint. Consider three cases: $n=1-\alpha<1$, $n=1$ and $n=1+\alpha>1$.

1754. Compute the area bounded by the versiera $y=\frac{1}{1+x^2}$ and the asymptote of this curve.

1755. Compute the area bounded by the curve $y=xe^{-\frac{x^2}{2}}$ and its asymptote (for $x>0$).

1756. Compute the area contained between the cissoid $y^2 = \frac{x^3}{2a-x}$ and its asymptote.

Hint. Putting $x = 2a\sin^2 t$, pass over to parametric equations.

1757. Find the volume of the solid formed by revolving the cissoid $y^2 = \frac{x^3}{2a-x}$ about its asymptote (see Problem 1756).

1758. Determine the area of the surface formed by revolving about the x-axis an infinite arc of the curve $y = e^{-x}$ for positive x.

1759. Find the volume of the solid formed by revolving about the x-axis an infinite branch of the curve $y = 2\left(\frac{1}{x} - \frac{1}{x^2}\right)$ for $x \geqslant 1$.

1760. Show that

$$\left.\begin{aligned} &(1)\ \int_0^\infty e^{-x}x^m\,dx = m!; \\ &(2)\ \int_0^\infty e^{-x^2}x^{2m+1}dx = \frac{m!}{2} \end{aligned}\right\}\ \text{if } m \text{ is a positive integer}^*.$$

1761. Compute the following integrals:

(1) $\int_2^\infty \frac{dx}{x^2}$; (2) $\int_0^\infty x^2 e^{-x^3}\,dx$; (3) $\int_1^\infty \frac{\ln x\,dx}{x^2}$; (4) $\int_1^e \frac{dx}{x\ln x}$.

Hint. In case (3) use L'Hospital's rule for finding $\lim\limits_{x\to\infty} \frac{\ln x}{x}$.

---

* The function $\int_0^\infty e^{-x}x^{t-1}\,dx = \Gamma(t)$ is termed the gamma function of t. For integral $t > 1$, as it follows from Problem 1760 (1), $\Gamma(t) = (t-1)!$ Putting here $t = 1$, we get conventionally $0! = \Gamma(1) = \int_0^\infty e^{-x}x^0\,dx = 1$. Therefore, by convention, $0! = 1$.

1762. (1) $\int\limits_1^\infty \frac{dx}{x\sqrt{1+x^2}}$; (2) $\int\limits_0^\infty \frac{dx}{\sqrt{(1+x)^3}}$; (3) $\int\limits_1^\infty \frac{dx}{x^2+x^4}$.

1763. Compute the area contained between the curve $y=e^{-2x}$ and the coordinate axes (for $x>0$).

1764. Find the volume of the solid generated by revolving about the y-axis an area of infinite length contained between the lines $xy=4$, $y=1$, $x=0$.

1765. Determine the volume of the solid formed by revolving the curve $y=xe^{-\frac{x}{2}}$ (for $x>0$) about its asymptote.

9.8. The Mean Value of a Function

The mean-value theorem. If on a closed interval $[a, b]$ a function $f(x)$ is continuous, then for some value of x $(x=c)$ between the limits of the integral $\int\limits_a^b f(x)\,dx$

$$\int\limits_a^b f(x)\,dx=(b-a)\,f(c). \tag{1}$$

The value of the function

$$y_m=f(c)=\frac{\int\limits_a^b f(x)\,dx}{b-a} \tag{2}$$

is called the *mean* value of the function $f(x)$ on the interval $[a, b]$.

1766. Determine the mean value of the following functions on the given intervals:

(1) $y=\sin x$ on $[0, \pi]$;
(2) $y=\tan x$ on $\left[0, \frac{\pi}{3}\right]$;
(3) $y=\ln x$ on $[1, e]$;
(4) $y=x^2$ on $[a, b]$;
(5) $y=\frac{1}{1+x^2}$ on $[-1, 1]$.

Indicate the mean value of each function on its graph.

9.9. Trapezoid Rule and Simpson's Formula

1°. The trapezoid formula:

$$\int_a^b f(x)\,dx \approx h\left[\frac{y_0+y_n}{2}+\sum_{i=1}^{n-1} y_i\right], \qquad \text{(I)}$$

where $h=(b-a)/n$, and $y_0, y_1, y_2, \ldots y_n$ are equidistant of the curve $y=f(x)$ on the interval $[a, b]$. The limiting error formula (I):

$$\varepsilon(h) \leqslant \frac{(b-a)h^2}{12}|y''|_{\max}. \qquad (1)$$

2°. Simpson's formula (for parabolic trapezoids) for two subintervals:

$$\int_a^b f(x)\,dx \approx \frac{h}{3}(y_0+4y_1+y_2), \qquad \text{(II)}$$

where $h=(b-a)/2$.

3°. Simpson's formula for $2n$ equal subintervals:

$$\int_a^b f(x)\,dx \approx \frac{h}{3}\left[y_0+y_{2n}+4\sum_{i=1}^{n} y_{2i-1}+2\sum_{i=1}^{n-1} y_{2i}\right], \qquad \text{(III)}$$

where $h=(b-a)/2n$. The limiting error of formulas (II) and (III)

$$\varepsilon(h) \leqslant \frac{(b-a)h^4}{180}|y^{\mathrm{IV}}|_{\max}, \qquad (2)$$

i.e. formula (II) is accurate for parabolas of second and third powers: $y=a+bx+cx^2+dx^3$.

1767. Using the trapezoid rule, compute $\ln 2=\int_1^2 \frac{dx}{x}$ and estimate the error by formula (1).

1768. Using Simpson's formula (III), compute the integrals $\int_1^5 x^3\,dx$ and $\int_0^2 x^4\,dx$, estimate the error by formula (2), and compare the results with exact values of the integrals.

1769. Compute the following integrals by Simpson's formula (III):

(1) $\int\limits_0^2 \sqrt{1+x^3}\,dx\ (2n=4)$; (2) $\int\limits_0^{\frac{\pi}{2}} \sqrt{3-\cos 2x}\,dx\ (2n=6)$;

(3) $\int\limits_0^4 \frac{dx}{1+x^4}\ (2n=4)$, and estimate the error, putting in formula (2) $h^4 |y^{IV}|_{max} \approx |\Delta^4 y|_{max}$.

1770. Using Simpson's formula (II), find the volume of a barrel 50 cm high, the diameter of the bottoms being equal to 20 cm, and the diameter of the midsection to 30 cm.

1771. Deduce the formulas for the volume of a pyramid and a sphere from Simpson's formula (II).

1772. Compute $\ln 2 = \int\limits_1^2 \frac{dx}{x}$ by means of Simpson's formula (III) (at $2n=10$) and estimate the error by formula (2).

1773. Find the length of the arc of the ellipse $x = 5\cos t$, $y = 3\sin t$, applying Simpson's formula (II) to the integral determining the first quarter of the entire arc.

1774. Compute approximately $\pi = 6\int\limits_0^1 \frac{dx}{\sqrt{4-x^2}}$, applying Simpson's formula (II) to the integral.

1775. Compute $\frac{\pi}{4} = \int\limits_0^1 \frac{dx}{1+x^2}$ by means of Simpson's formula (III) (at $2n=10$), and estimale the error, putting approximately in formula (2) $h^4 |y^{IV}|_{max} \approx |\Delta^4 y|_{max}$.

1776. Considering the area of the portion of a circle bounded by the curve $x^2+y^2=32$, show that $\int_0^4 \sqrt{32-x^2}\,dx = 4\pi+8$; find π computing the integral by Simpson's formula (at $2n=4$).

1777. Using Simpson's formula (III), compute the length of the arc of a half-wave of the sinusoid $y=\sin x$ dividing the interval $|0, \pi|$ into six equal subintervals.

CHAPTER 10

CURVATURE OF PLANE AND SPACE CURVES

10.1. Curvature of a Plane Curve. The Centre and Radius of Curvature. The Evolute of a Plane Curve

1°. Curvature

$$k=\frac{d\varphi}{ds}=\frac{y''}{(1+y'^2)^{3/2}}. \qquad (1)$$

2°. The radius of curvature

$$R=\frac{(1+y'^2)^{3/2}}{|y''|}=\frac{(\dot{x}^2+\dot{y}^2)^{3/2}}{|\ddot{y}\dot{x}-\ddot{x}\dot{y}|}. \qquad (2)$$

3°. The coordinates of the centre of curvature

$$\left.\begin{aligned} X&=x-\frac{1+y'^2}{y''}y'=x+\frac{\dot{x}^2+\dot{y}^2}{\ddot{x}\dot{y}-\ddot{y}\dot{x}}\dot{y};\\ Y&=y+\frac{1+y'^2}{y''}=y+\frac{\dot{x}^2+\dot{y}^2}{\ddot{y}\dot{x}-\ddot{x}\dot{y}}\dot{x}. \end{aligned}\right\} \qquad (3)$$

The locus of the centres of curvature $C(X, Y)$ is called the *evolute*. Equations (3) are the *parametric equations* of the evolute.

4°. The radius of curvature of the curve $r=f(\varphi)$, where r and φ are polar coordinates

$$R=\frac{(r^2+r'^2)^{3/2}}{|r^2+2r'^2-rr''|}. \qquad (4)$$

Determine the radius of curvature and construct the curve and the circle of curvature of the given curve at its vertex:

1778. $y=4x-x^2$. **1779.** $y=e^{-x^2}$.

1780. $x^2+4y^2=4$. **1781.** $\begin{cases} x=a(t-\sin t), \\ y=a(1-\cos t). \end{cases}$

1782. $y=xe^{-x}$.

Determine the coordinates of the centre of curvature and construct the curve and its circle of curvature:

1783. $xy=4$ at the point $x=2$.

1784. $y=\ln x$ at the point of intersection with OX.

1785. $y=-\frac{x^3+1}{3}$ at the point of intersection with OX.

Write the equation of the evolute of the given curve and construct the curve and its evolute:

1786. $y=1-\frac{x^2}{2}$. **1787.** $\begin{cases} x=2\cos t \\ y=\sin t. \end{cases}$

1788. $x^2-y^2=a^2$ (or $x=a\cosh t$ and $y=a\sinh t$).

1789. $\begin{cases} x=a(\cos t+t\sin t) \\ y=a(\sin t-t\cos t). \end{cases}$

1790. Find the maximum curvature of the curve $y=e^x$.

1791. Prove that the radius of curvature of the catenary $y=a\cosh\frac{x}{a}$ is $\frac{y^2}{a}$ at any point and is equal to the segment of the normal between the curve and the x-axis.

1792. Determine the radius of curvature at an arbitrary point of the curve (1) $r=a(1-\cos\varphi)$; (2) $r^2=a^2\cos 2\varphi$; (3) $r^2=\frac{a^2}{\cos 2\varphi}$.

Determine the radius of curvature and construct the given curve and the circle of curvature of the curve at its vertex:

1793. $y=\frac{1}{1+x^2}$. **1794.** $x^2-y^2=4$.

1795. $y=\sin x$. **1796.** $2y=x^2+4x$.

Determine the coordinates of the centre of curvature and construct the curve and the circle of its curvature:

1797. $y=e^x$ at the point of its intersection with OY.

1798. $y=\frac{x^3}{3}$ at the point $\left(-1, -\frac{1}{3}\right)$.

1799. $y^2=x^3$ at the point $(1, 1)$.

1800. $y=\cos x$ at the point $x=\frac{\pi}{4}$.

Write the equation of the evolute of the given curve and construct the curve and its evolute:

1801. $y^2=2(x+1)$. **1802.** $x=t^2$, $y=\frac{t^3}{3}$.

1803. $xy=4$. **1804.** $x=a\cos^3 t$, $y=a\sin^3 t$.

1805. Show that at any point of the astroid $x^{\frac{2}{3}}+y^{\frac{2}{3}}=a^{\frac{2}{3}}$ the radius of curvature is equal to $3\sqrt[3]{a|xy|}$.

10.2. The Arc Length of a Space Curve

The differential of the arc $ds=\sqrt{dx^2+dy^2+dz^2}$ or

$$ds=\sqrt{\dot{x}^2+\dot{y}^2+\dot{z}^2}\,dt.$$

The length of the arc $s=\int\limits_{t_1}^{t_2}\sqrt{\dot{x}^2+\dot{y}^2+\dot{z}^2}\,dt.$

Find the length of the arc of the given curve:

1806. $x=t$, $y=t^2$, $z=\frac{2}{3}t^3$ from $t=0$ to $t=3$.

1807. $x=3\cos t$, $y=3\sin t$, $z=4t$ from $t=0$ to an arbitrary t.

1808. $y=\frac{x^2}{2}$, $z=\frac{x^3}{6}$ from $x=0$ to $x=3$.

Find the length of the arc of the given curve:

1809. $x=t-\sin t$, $y=1-\cos t$, $z=4\sin\frac{t}{2}$ from $t=0$ to $t=\pi$.

1810. $x=e^t$, $y=e^{-t}$, $z=t\sqrt{2}$ from $t=0$ to $t=1$.

1811. $y=\frac{1}{2}\ln x$, $z=\frac{x^2}{2}$ from $x=1$ to $x=2$.

10.3. The Derivative of a Vector Function of a Scalar Argument and Its Mechanical and Geometrical Interpretations. The Natural Trihedron of a Curve

The radius vector $\boldsymbol{r}=x\boldsymbol{i}+y\boldsymbol{j}+z\boldsymbol{k}$ of a point of the curve $x=x(t)$, $y=y(t)$, $z=z(t)$ is a *vector function* of the scalar t. The derivative $\dot{\boldsymbol{r}}=\dot{x}\boldsymbol{i}+\dot{y}\boldsymbol{j}+\dot{z}\boldsymbol{k}$ is a tangential vector and has the modulus $|\dot{\boldsymbol{r}}|=\sqrt{\dot{x}^2+\dot{y}^2+\dot{z}^2}=\dot{s}=$ $=\frac{ds}{dt}$. Therefore, if t is time, and the curve is the path of motion, then $\dot{\boldsymbol{r}}=\boldsymbol{v}$ is the vector of velocity, and $\ddot{\boldsymbol{r}}=\boldsymbol{w}$, the vector of acceleration.

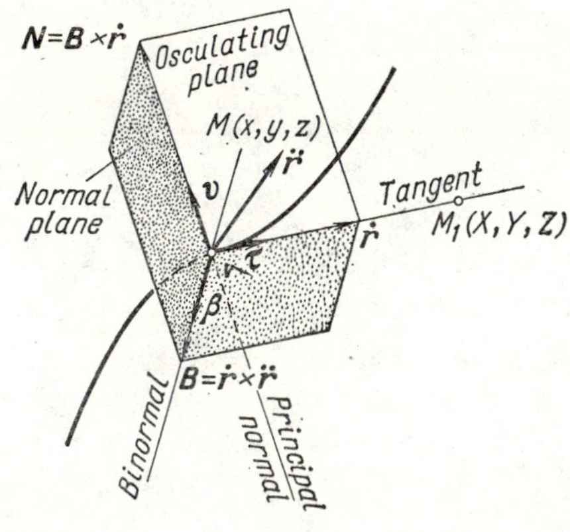

Fig. 36

Through the point $M(x, y, z)$ of the curve (Fig. 36) draw three planes:

(1) perpendicular to $\dot{\boldsymbol{r}}$, which is called the *normal* plane;

(2) containing $\dot{\boldsymbol{r}}$ and $\ddot{\boldsymbol{r}}$, which is called the *osculating* plane;

(3) perpendicular to the normal and osculating planes.

The three planes form a *natural trihedron* of a curve. They intersect along three straight lines: the *tangent*, the *binormal* and the *principal normal* determined by the vectors:

(1) $\dot{\boldsymbol{r}}$ which is termed the *tangential vector*,

(2) $\boldsymbol{B}=\dot{\boldsymbol{r}}\times\ddot{\boldsymbol{r}}$ which is called the *binormal vector*,

(3) $\boldsymbol{N}=\boldsymbol{B}\times\dot{\boldsymbol{r}}$ which is termed the *principal normal vector*.

Let us denote the unit vectors of these directions by $\boldsymbol{\tau}$, $\boldsymbol{\beta}$, $\boldsymbol{\nu}$; they are related in the following way: $\frac{d\boldsymbol{\tau}}{ds}=\left|\frac{d\boldsymbol{\tau}}{ds}\right|\boldsymbol{\nu}$ and $\boldsymbol{\beta}=\boldsymbol{\tau}\times\boldsymbol{\nu}$.

Let $M_1(X, Y, Z)$ be a point on the tangent (Fig. 36). Then $\overrightarrow{MM_1} \parallel \dot{\boldsymbol{r}}$, and from the condition of parallelism of vectors we get the equations of the tangent:

$$\frac{X-x}{\dot{x}} = \frac{Y-y}{\dot{y}} = \frac{Z-z}{\dot{z}}. \qquad \text{(I)}$$

Let $M_2(X, Y, Z)$ be a point in the normal plane. Then $\overrightarrow{MM_2} \perp \dot{\boldsymbol{r}}$, and from the condition of perpendicularity of vectors we get the equation of the normal plane:

$$\dot{x}(X-x)+\dot{y}(Y-y)+\dot{z}(Z-z)=0. \qquad \text{(II)}$$

The equations of the binormal and the principal normal are obtained by replacing $\dot{x}$, $\dot{y}$, $\dot{z}$ in equations (I) by B_x, B_y, B_z or N_x, N_y, N_z respectively. The equation of the osculating plane is obtained by replacing $\dot{x}$, $\dot{y}$, $\dot{z}$ in equation (II) by B_x, B_y, B_z.

1812. The radius vector of a moving point at the moment t is given by the equation $\boldsymbol{r}=4t\boldsymbol{i}-3t\boldsymbol{j}$. Determine the path, velocity, and acceleration of motion.

1813. The equation of motion is $\boldsymbol{r}=3t\boldsymbol{i}+(4t-t^2)\boldsymbol{j}$. Determine the path and velocity. Construct the path and the velocity vectors for the moments $t=0$, 1, 2, and 3 sec.

1814. In Problem 1813 determine the acceleration $\boldsymbol{w}$ and its tangential $w_\tau=\frac{dv}{dt}$ and normal $w_n=\sqrt{w^2-w_\tau^2}$ components at any moment t and at $t=0$.

1815. The equation of motion is $\boldsymbol{r}=a\cos t\cdot\boldsymbol{i}+b\sin t\cdot\boldsymbol{j}$. Determine the path, velocity and acceleration and construct the vectors of velocity and acceleration at the points $t=0, \frac{\pi}{4}, \frac{\pi}{2}$.

In Problem 1816 through 1818 write the equations of the tangent line and the normal plane of the curve:

1816. $x=t$, $y=t^2$, $z=t^3$ for any point and for $t=1$.

1817. $y=x^2$, $z^2=x$ for any point $(x \geqslant 0)$ and for $x=4$.

1818. $\begin{cases} x^2+y^2=10 \\ y^2+z^2=25 \end{cases}$ for the point (1, 3, 4).

Hint. Take the differentials of both the left-hand and right-hand members of each equation, and then find the ratios $dx:dy:dz$.

1819. Find the vectors $\dot{\boldsymbol{r}}$, $\boldsymbol{B}$, and $\boldsymbol{N}$ of the curve $x = 1-\sin t$, $y=\cos t$, $z=t$ at the point $t=0$. Find also $\boldsymbol{\tau}$, $\boldsymbol{\beta}$, and $\boldsymbol{\nu}$ at the same point.

1820. Write the equations of the principal normal, the binormal and the osculating plane of the curve $x=t$, $y=t^2$, $z=t^3$ at the point $t=1$.

1821. Write the equations of the principal normal and binormal to the curve $x=e^t$, $y=e^{-t}$, $z=t$ at the point $t=0$.

1822. Show that the equations $x=t\cos t$, $y=t\sin t$, $z=t$ determine a *conical* helix, and write the equations of the principal normal, the binormal, and the tangent to it at the origin.

1823. Write the equations of the tangent to the helix $x=a\cos t$, $y=a\sin t$, $z=bt$ for any point and at $t=\frac{\pi}{2}$. Show that the helix intersects the elements of the cylinder $x^2+y^2=a^2$ at one and the same angle $\gamma=\arccos\frac{b}{\sqrt{a^2+b^2}}$.

1824. Find the angles formed by the tangential vector of the curve $x^2=2az$ and $y^2=2bz$ with the coordinate axes at the point $z=\sqrt{ab}$.

1825. The plane $y=0$ containing the curve $2z=x^2$, $y=0$ is wound onto the cylinder $x^2+y^2=2y$. Write the parametric equations of the helix formed by the given curve and determine the binormal vector of the curve at any point and at the point $t=\frac{\pi}{2}$, where t is the angle through which the plane is turned.

1826. The radius vector of a moving point at the moment t is given by the equation $\boldsymbol{r}=a(t-\sin t)\boldsymbol{i}+a(1-\cos t)\boldsymbol{j}$. Determine and construct the velocity and acceleration vectors at $t=\frac{\pi}{2}$ and $t=\pi$.

In Problems 1827 through 1829 write the equations of the tangent to the curve:

1827. $y=x$, $z=2x^2$ at the point $x=2$.

1828. $\begin{cases} x^2+y^2+z^2=14 \\ x+2y-z=2 \end{cases}$ at the point (1, 2, 3) (see Problem 1818).

1829. $x=2t$, $y=\ln t$, $z=t^2$ at the point $t=1$.

1830. $\boldsymbol{r}=e^t\boldsymbol{i}+e^{-t}\boldsymbol{j}+t\sqrt{2}\boldsymbol{k}$. Find the angles formed by the binormal vector $\boldsymbol{b}$ with the coordinate axes at the point $t=0$.

1831. Write the equations of the principal normal and binormal to the curve $y=x^2$, $z=y^2$ at the point $x=1$.

1832. Write the equations of the principal normal and binormal of the curve $x=t-\sin t$, $y=1-\cos t$, $z=4\sin\frac{t}{2}$ at the point $t=\pi$.

10.4. Curvature and Torsion of a Space Curve

The *curvature* $\frac{1}{R}$ is the limit of the ratio of the angle φ (through which the *tangent* is turned) to the length of the arc Δs as $\Delta s\to 0$. The *torsion* $\frac{1}{\rho}$ is the limit of the ratio of the angle θ (through which the *binormal* is turned) to Δs as $\Delta s\to 0$. Since $\varphi\approx|\Delta\tau|$ and $\theta\approx\pm|\Delta\beta|$, $\frac{1}{R}$ and $\frac{1}{\rho}$ turn out to be equal to the moduli of the vectors:

$$\frac{d\tau}{ds}=\frac{1}{R}\nu,\qquad \frac{d\beta}{ds}=-\frac{1}{\rho}\nu. \tag{1}$$

If a curve is specified by the equation $\boldsymbol{r}=\boldsymbol{r}(t)$, then

$$\frac{1}{R}=\frac{|\dot{\boldsymbol{r}}\times\ddot{\boldsymbol{r}}|}{|\dot{\boldsymbol{r}}|^3},\qquad \frac{1}{\rho}=\frac{\dot{\boldsymbol{r}}\ddot{\boldsymbol{r}}\dddot{\boldsymbol{r}}}{|\dot{\boldsymbol{r}}\times\ddot{\boldsymbol{r}}|^2}. \tag{2}$$

1833. Differentiate the equality $\boldsymbol{v}=v\tau$ with respect to t, and with the aid of the first formula of (1) resolve the acceleration $\boldsymbol{w}$ into the tangential and normal components:

$$\boldsymbol{w}=\dot{v}\tau+\frac{v^2}{R}\nu.$$

1834. A point is moving along the parabola $x=t$, $y=t-t^2$, where t is the time of motion. Determine the curvature $\frac{1}{R}$ of the path and the tangential and normal accelerations at the moment t and at $t=0$.

1835. A point is moving along the ellipse $x=4\cos t$, $y=3\sin t$, where t is the time of motion. Determine the curvature $\frac{1}{R}$ of the path, and also the tangential and normal accelerations at $t=\frac{\pi}{4}$.

1836. For the motion specified by the equation $\boldsymbol{r}=t\boldsymbol{i}+t^2\boldsymbol{j}+\frac{2}{3}t^3\boldsymbol{k}$ determine the curvature $\frac{1}{R}$ of the path and the tangential and normal accelerations at any moment t and at $t=1$.

Determine the curvature $\frac{1}{R}$ and the torsion $\frac{1}{\rho}$ of the curve:

1837. $x=t$, $y=t^2$, $z=t^3$ at any point and at $t=0$.

1838. $x=e^t$, $y=e^{-t}$, $z=t\sqrt{2}$ at any point and at $t=0$.

1839. $y=\frac{x^2}{2}$, $z=\frac{x^3}{3}$ at any point and at $x=1$.

1840. Show that the torsion of the right-handed helix ($x=a\cos t$, $y=a\sin t$, $z=bt$) is positive; that of the left-handed helix ($x=a\cos t$, $y=-a\sin t$, $z=bt$) is negative.

Determine the curvature $\frac{1}{R}$ and the torsion $\frac{1}{\rho}$ of the curve:

1841. $x=2t$, $y=\ln t$, $z=t^2$ at any point and at $t=1$.

1842. $x=\frac{y^2}{2}$, $z=x^2$ at any point and at $y=1$.

1843. $x=e^t\sin t$, $y=e^t\cos t$, $z=e^t$ at the point $t=0$.

CHAPTER 11

PARTIAL DERIVATIVES, TOTAL DIFFERENTIALS AND THEIR APPLICATIONS

11.1. Functions of Two Variables and Their Geometrical Representation

1°. Definition. A variable quantity z is called a single-valued function of two variable quantities x and y if every pair of numbers that may (by the conditions of the problem) be the values of the variables x and y is associated with one definite value of z. The functional dependence of z on x and y (which are called arguments) is written in the form

$$z = F(x, y). \tag{1}$$

2°. Geometrical interpretation. Geometrically equation (1) defines some surface. A pair of values of x and y defines a point $P(x, y)$ in the plane XOY, and $z = F(x, y)$ the z-coordinate of the corresponding point $M(x, y, z)$ on the surface. Therefore, we say that z is a function of the point $P(x, y)$, and we write $z = F(P)$.

3°. The limit of the function $F(P)$: $\lim\limits_{P \to P_0} F(P) = A$ if the difference $F(P) - A$ is an infinitesimal as $\rho = P_0P \to 0$, where P approaches P_0 in an arbitrary fashion (for instance, along any line).

4°. Continuity of a function. A function $F(x, y)$ is called *continuous* at point P_0 if $\lim\limits_{P \to P_0} F(P) = F(P_0)$. In other words, a function $F(x, y)$ is continuous at some point (x, y) if

$$\lim_{\substack{\Delta x \to 0 \\ \Delta y \to 0}} F(x + \Delta x, y + \Delta y) = F(x, y).$$

1844. Indicate the ranges of x and y for which the following functions have real values:

(1) $z=x^2+y^2$; (2) $az=a^2-x^2-y^2$; (3) $z=\frac{4}{x^2+y^2}$;

(4) $z=\sqrt{a^2-x^2-y^2}$; (5) $z=\sqrt{xy}$; (6) $z=\frac{1}{\sqrt{1-x^2-y^2}}$;

(7) $z=\frac{xy}{y-x}$,

and depict the functions geometrically, cutting the surface by the planes $x=0$, $y=0$, $z=0$, and $z=h$.

1845. Given the perimeter $2p$ of a triangle. Express the area S of the triangle as a function of its two sides x and y. Define and construct the domain of possible values of x and y.

1846. $F(x, y)=\frac{x-2y}{2x-y}$; evaluate $F(3, 1)$, $F(1, 3)$, $F(1, 2)$, $F(2, 1)$, $F(a, a)$, $F(a, -a)$.

1847. $F(x, y)=\sqrt{x^4+y^4}-2xy$; prove that $F(tx, ty)=$ $=t^2F(x, y)$.

1848. $z=x^2-xy=y^2$; determine $\Delta_x z$, $\Delta_y z$, and Δz.

Compute $\Delta_x z$, $\Delta_y z$, Δz if x varies from 2 to 2.1 and y varies from 2 to 1.9.

1849. Show that the equation $x^2-y^2-z^2=0$ defines an infinite number of single-valued functions z of x and y, two of which are continuous. Indicate the domain of definition of all these functions and represent geometrically the positive continuous function. Give an example of a single-valued but discontinuous function $z=F(x, y)$, defined by the same equation $x^2-y^2=z^2$.

1850. Construct the level lines ($z=0$, 1, 2, etc.) for the following functions:

(1) $z=\sqrt{1-\frac{x^2}{4}-y^2}$; (2) $z=x^2-y$;

(3) $z=x^2-y^2$; (4) $z=xy$.

1851. Show that the expression $u=\frac{y}{x-y}$ tends to any limit as $x\to 0$ and $y\to 0$. Find the routes along which (x, y) approaches $(0, 0)$, for which $\lim u=3$, $\lim u=2$, $\lim u=1$, $\lim u=0$, $\lim u=-2$.

Hint. Consider the variation of x and y along straight lines $y=kx$.

1852. Show that

$$(1)\ \lim_{\substack{x\to 0\\ y\to 0}} \frac{2-\sqrt{xy+4}}{xy}=-\frac{1}{4};\quad (2)\ \lim_{\substack{x\to 0\\ y\to 0}} \frac{\sin(xy)}{xy}=1;$$

$$(3)\ \lim_{\substack{x\to 0\\ y\to 0}} \frac{\sin(xy)}{x}=0$$

irrespective to the way (x, y) approaches $(0, 0)$.

Hint. Put $xy=\alpha$.

1853. Represent geometrically the function

$$z=F(x, y)=\begin{cases} 1 \text{ for } xy>0\\ 0 \text{ for } xy=0\\ -1 \text{ for } xy<0\end{cases}$$

and indicate the lines of its discontinuity.

1854. Indicate the domains of definition of the following functions:

$$(1)\ z=x+y;\quad (2)\ z=\frac{4}{x+y};\quad (3)\ \frac{z}{c}=\sqrt{1-\frac{x^2}{a^2}-\frac{y^2}{b^2}};$$

$$(4)\ \frac{z}{c}=1-\frac{x^2}{a^2}-\frac{y^2}{b^2};\quad (5)\ z=x+\sqrt{x^2-y^2};$$

$$(6)\ \sqrt{z}=\sqrt{x}+\sqrt{y}$$

and depict geometrically these functions.

1855. $F(x, y)=\frac{x}{x-y}$; show that

$$F(a, b)+F(b, a)=1.$$

1856. Show that the equation $z^2=\frac{4}{4-x^2-y^2}$ defines an infinite number of single-valued functions z of x and y, of which two are continuous. Indicate the domain of definition of all these functions and give the geometrical representation of the function which is positive within the domain $x^2+y^2\leqslant 1$ and negative outside it.

1857. Depict geometrically the single-valued function $z=F(x, y)$ defined by the equation $x^2+y^2+z^2=a^2$, positive within the domain $x^2+y^2\leqslant\frac{a^2}{4}$ and negative outside it. Indicate the line of its discontinuity.

11.2. Partial Derivatives of the First Order

The derivative of a function $z=F(x, y)$ with respect to the argument x, found proceeding from the assumption that y remains constant, is called a *partial derivative* of z with respect to x and is denoted $\frac{\partial z}{\partial x}$ or $F'_x(x, y)$. Analogously, a partial derivative of z with respect to y: $\frac{\partial z}{\partial y}=F'_y(x, y)$.

Find the partial derivatives of the following functions:

1858. $z=x^3+3x^2y-y^3$. **1859.** $z=\ln(x^2+y^2)$.

1860. $z=\frac{y}{x}$. **1861.** $z=\arctan\frac{y}{x}$.

1862. $z=\frac{xy}{x-y}$. **1863.** $u=\ln\left(\frac{1}{\sqrt[3]{x}}-\frac{1}{\sqrt[3]{t}}\right)$.

1864. $c=\sqrt{a^2+b^2-2ab\cos\alpha}$.

1865. $u=\frac{y}{x}+\frac{z}{y}-\frac{x}{z}$. **1866.** $u=xe^{-yx}$.

1867. $u=\frac{2x-t}{x+2t}$. **1868.** $\alpha=\arcsin(t\sqrt{x})$.

1869. $z=\ln(\sqrt{x}+\sqrt{y})$; prove that

$$x\frac{\partial z}{\partial x}+y\frac{\partial z}{\partial y}=\frac{1}{2}.$$

1870. $z=\sqrt{x}\sin\frac{y}{x}$; prove that $x\frac{\partial z}{\partial x}+y\frac{\partial z}{\partial y}=\frac{z}{2}$.

1871. $u=e^{\frac{x}{t^2}}$; prove that $2x\frac{\partial u}{\partial x}+t\frac{\partial u}{\partial t}=0$.

1872. $u=x^y$; prove that $\frac{x}{y}\frac{\partial u}{\partial x}+\frac{1}{\ln x}\frac{\partial u}{\partial y}=2u$.

1873. In Problem 1898 we shall prove Euler's theorem:

If $z=F(x, y)$ is a homogeneous function of degree n, then $x\frac{\partial z}{\partial x}+y\frac{\partial z}{\partial y}=nz$.

Verify this theorem for the following functions:

(1) $z=x^3+xy^2-2y^3$; (2) $z=\sqrt{x^2+xy+y^2}$;

(3) $z=\frac{1}{x^3-y^3}$; (4) $z=e^{\frac{x}{y}}$.

Find the partial derivatives of the following functions:

1874. $z=\cos(ax-by)$. **1875.** $z=\arcsin\frac{y}{x}$.

1876. $z=\frac{x}{3y-2x}$. **1877.** $u=\ln\sin(x-2t)$.

1878. $u=\sin^2(x+y)-\sin^2 x-\sin^2 y$.

1879. $u=\sqrt{x^2+y^2+z^2}$; prove that

$$\left(\frac{\partial u}{\partial x}\right)^2+\left(\frac{\partial u}{\partial y}\right)^2+\left(\frac{\partial u}{\partial z}\right)^2=1.$$

1880. $z=e^{\frac{x}{y}}\ln y$; prove that $x\frac{\partial z}{\partial x}+y\frac{\partial z}{\partial y}=\frac{z}{\ln y}$.

1881. $T=\pi\sqrt{\frac{l}{g}}$; prove that $l\frac{\partial T}{\partial l}+g\frac{\partial T}{\partial g}=0$.

1882. $z=e^{\frac{x}{2}}\sin\left(\frac{\pi}{4}-\frac{y}{2}\right)$; prove that

$$\left(\frac{\partial z}{\partial x}+\frac{\partial z}{\partial y}\right)^2=\frac{1}{2}e^x\sin^2\frac{y}{2}.$$

1883. Verify Euler's theorem on homogeneous functions (see Problem 1873) for the following functions:

(1) $z=\frac{x^3}{x-y}$; (2) $z=\frac{1}{x^2+y^2}$; (3) $z=\arctan\frac{y}{x}$.

11.3. Total Differential of the First Order

If a function $z=F(x, y)$ has continuous partial derivatives at point (x, y), then its total increment may be represented in the form

$$\Delta z=\frac{\partial z}{\partial x}\Delta x+\frac{\partial z}{\partial y}\Delta y+\varepsilon\cdot\rho, \tag{1}$$

where $\varepsilon \to 0$ as $\rho=\sqrt{|\Delta x|^2+|\Delta y|^2} \to 0$. Then the expression $\frac{\partial z}{\partial x}\Delta x+\frac{\partial z}{\partial y}\Delta y$ is the *principal part of the total increment* Δz; it is called the *total differential* of the function and is denoted dz:

$$dz=\frac{\partial z}{\partial x}\Delta x+\frac{\partial z}{\partial y}\Delta y. \tag{2}$$

Putting in formula (2) z equal to (1) x; (2) y, we find: $dx=\Delta x$, $dy=\Delta y$. Therefore

$$dz=\frac{\partial z}{\partial x}dx+\frac{\partial z}{\partial y}dy. \tag{3}$$

From (1) it follows that

$$\Delta z \approx dz, \tag{4}$$

i. e. for sufficiently small Δx and Δy the total increment of a function approximately equals its total differential (see Sec. 5.7).

A function $F(x, y)$ is called *differentiable* at (x, y) if it has a total differential at this point.

1884. Find the total differentials of the following functions:

(1) $z=x^2y$; (2) $z=\frac{xy}{x-y}$; (3) $u=e^{\frac{s}{t}}$; (4) $z=\sqrt{x^2+y^2}$.

1885. Evaluate the total differentials of the following functions:

(1) $z=\frac{y}{x}$ for $x=2$, $y=1$, $dx=0.1$, $dy=0.2$;

(2) $u=e^{xy}$ for $x=1$, $y=2$, $dx=-0.1$, $dy=0.1$.

1886. Compute dz and Δz for the function $z=xy$ at $x=5$, $y=4$, $\Delta x=0.1$, $\Delta y=-0.2$.

1887. Calculate approximately the change of the function $\varphi=\arctan\frac{y}{x}$, when x varies from 2 to 2.1 and y from 3 to 2.5.

1888. As a result of deformation the radius R of a cylinder increased from 2 dm to 2.05 dm, and its height H

decreased from 10 dm to 9.8 dm. Find approximately the change in its volume V using the formula $\Delta V \approx dV$.

1889. When measured, the legs of a right triangle turned out to be equal to 7.5 cm and 18 cm (an accuracy of 0.1 cm). Determine the absolute error in computing the hypotenuse.

1890. Find the total differentials of the following functions:

(1) $z=\frac{y}{x}-\frac{x}{y}$; (2) $s=x\ln t$; (3) $u=\sqrt{x^2+y^2+z^2}$.

1891. Find the values of dz and Δz for the function $z=\ln(x^2+y^2)$ if x varies from 2 to 2.1 and y from 1 to 0.9.

1892. Compute approximately the increment of the function $z=\arcsin\frac{y}{x}$ when x varies from 5 to 4.5 and y from 3 to 3.3.

1893. As a result of deformation the radius of a cone R increases from 30 cm to 30.1 cm and its height H decreases from 60 cm to 59.5 cm. Find approximately the change in the volume of the cone using the formula $\Delta V \approx dV$.

11.4. The Derivative of a Composite Function

1°. If $z=F(x, y)$, $x=f(t)$, $y=\varphi(t)$, then z is called a *composite function* with respect to t. In this case

$$\frac{dz}{dt}=\frac{\partial z}{\partial x}\frac{dx}{dt}+\frac{\partial z}{\partial y}\frac{dy}{dt} \tag{1}$$

if the functions F, f, and φ are *differentiable.*

2°. If $z=F(x, y)$, where $x=f(u, v)$, $y=\varphi(u, v)$, and if the functions F, f, and φ are differentiable, then

$$\frac{\partial z}{\partial u}=\frac{\partial z}{\partial x}\frac{\partial x}{\partial u}+\frac{\partial z}{\partial y}\frac{\partial y}{\partial u}; \quad \frac{\partial z}{\partial v}=\frac{\partial z}{\partial x}\frac{\partial x}{\partial v}+\frac{\partial z}{\partial y}\frac{\partial y}{\partial v}. \tag{2}$$

1894. Using formula (1), find $\frac{dz}{dt}$ from the equations:

(1) $z=x^2+xy+y^2$, $x=t^2$, $y=t$;
(2) $z=\sqrt{x^2+y^2}$, $x=\sin t$, $y=\cos t$.

Check the result by preliminary substitution of the values of x and y into the expression for the function z.

1895. $z=\frac{y}{x}$, $x=e^t$, $y=1-e^{2t}$; find $\frac{dz}{dt}$.

1896. $z=u^v$, where u and v are functions of x. Find $\frac{dz}{dx}$.

1897. $z=xe^y$, where y is a function of x. Find $\frac{dz}{dx}$.

1898. The function $z=F(x, y)$ is called *homogeneous* if $F(xt, yt)=t^n\cdot F(x, y)$. Differentiating both members of this equality with respect to t and putting in the result $t=1$, prove Euler's theorem on homogeneous functions: $x\frac{\partial z}{\partial x}+y\frac{\partial z}{\partial y}=nz$.

1899. $z=\frac{x^2}{y}$, where $x=u-2v$, $y=v+2u$. Find $\frac{\partial z}{\partial u}$ and $\frac{\partial z}{\partial v}$.

1900. $z=F(x, y)$. Express $\frac{\partial z}{\partial x}$ and $\frac{\partial z}{\partial y}$ in terms of $\frac{\partial z}{\partial u}$ and $\frac{\partial z}{\partial v}$ if:

(1) $u=mx+ny$, $v=px+qy$;

(2) $u=xy$, $v=\frac{y}{x}$.

1901. $u=F(x, y)$; $x=r\cos\varphi$, $y=r\sin\varphi$. Express $\frac{\partial u}{\partial r}$ and $\frac{\partial u}{\partial \varphi}$ in terms of $\frac{\partial u}{\partial x}$ and $\frac{\partial u}{\partial y}$ and show that

$$\left(\frac{\partial u}{\partial r}\right)^2+\left(\frac{1}{r}\frac{\partial u}{\partial \varphi}\right)^2=\left(\frac{\partial u}{\partial x}\right)^2+\left(\frac{\partial u}{\partial y}\right)^2.$$

1902. $z=y+F(u)$, where $u=x^2-y^2$. Prove that $y\frac{\partial z}{\partial x}+x\frac{\partial z}{\partial y}=x$ for any differentiable function $F(u)$.

1903. Find $\frac{\partial z}{\partial t}$ from the equations:

(1) $z=Ax^2+2Bxy+Cy^2$, $x=\sin t$, $y=\cos t$;

(2) $z=\arctan\frac{y}{x}$, $x=e^{2t}+1$, $y=e^{2t}-1$.

1904. $z=xy+xF(u)$, where $u=\frac{y}{x}$. Prove that

$$x\frac{\partial z}{\partial x}+y\frac{\partial z}{\partial y}=z+xy.$$

1905. $z=y\varphi(u)$, where $u=x^2-y^2$. Prove that

$$\frac{1}{x}\frac{\partial z}{\partial x}+\frac{1}{y}\frac{\partial z}{\partial y}=\frac{z}{y^2}.$$

1906. $z=F(x, y)$. Express $\frac{\partial z}{\partial x}$ and $\frac{\partial z}{\partial y}$ in terms of $\frac{\partial z}{\partial u}$ and $\frac{\partial z}{\partial v}$ if:

(1) $u=x+2y, \quad v=x-y;$
(2) $u=\sqrt{xy}, \quad v=x+y.$

11.5. Derivatives of Implicit Functions

1°. The equation $F(x, y)=0$, having a solution (x_0, y_0), defines the variable y in the neighbourhood of x_0 as a continuous function of x, provided the derivative $\frac{\partial F}{\partial y}\neq 0$ and is continuous in some neighbourhood of the point (x_0, y_0).

If, in addition, in the neighbourhood of the point (x_0, y_0) there also exists a continuous derivative $\frac{\partial F}{\partial x}$, then an *implicit function* has a derivative $\frac{dy}{dx}$ defined by the formula

$$\frac{dy}{dx}=-\frac{\frac{\partial F}{\partial x}}{\frac{\partial F}{\partial y}}. \qquad (1)$$

2°. Under analogous conditions the equation $F(x, y, z)=0$ defines z as an implicit function of x and y which has the partial derivatives

$$\frac{\partial z}{\partial x}=-\frac{\frac{\partial F}{\partial x}}{\frac{\partial F}{\partial z}}; \quad \frac{\partial z}{\partial y}=-\frac{\frac{\partial F}{\partial y}}{\frac{\partial F}{\partial z}}. \qquad (2)$$

Find $\frac{dy}{dx}$ from the equations:

1907. $x^2+y^2-4x+6y=0$.

1908. (1) $x^{\frac{2}{3}}+y^{\frac{2}{3}}=a^{\frac{2}{3}}$; (2) $xe^{2y}-ye^{2x}=0$.

1909. $Ax^2+2Bxy+Cy^2+2Dx+2Ey+F=0$.

Find the slope of the tangent line to the given curve:

1910. $x^2+y^2=10y$ at the point of intersection with the straight line $x=3$.

1911. $x^3+y^3-2axy=0$ at the point $x=y=a$.

1912. Find the points at which the tangent line to the curve $x^2+y^2+2x-2y=2$ is parallel to (1) OX; (2) OY.

Find $\frac{\partial z}{\partial x}$ and $\frac{\partial z}{\partial y}$ from the equations:

1913. $x^2+y^2+z^2-6x=0$. **1914.** $z^2=xy$.

1915. $\cos(ax+by-cz)=k(ax+by-cz)$.

1916. $xyz=a^3$; prove that $x\frac{\partial z}{\partial x}+y\frac{\partial z}{\partial y}=-2z$.

1917. Prove that the differential equation $x\frac{\partial z}{\partial x}+y\frac{\partial z}{\partial y}=z$ is satisfied by the implicit function z defined by the equation (of conical surfaces) $\frac{z}{x}=\varphi\left(\frac{y}{x}\right)$.

Find $\frac{dy}{dx}$ from the equations:

1918. $x^2-4y^2=4$. **1919.** $xy+\ln y+\ln x=0$.

1920. $y+x=e^{\frac{y}{x}}$. **1921.** $2\cos(x-2y)=2y-x$.

1922. Find the slope of the tangent line to the curve $y^2-xy=4$ at the points of intersection with the straight line $x=3$.

1923. $x^2+y^2+z^2-2zx=a^2$. Find $\frac{\partial z}{\partial x}$ and $\frac{\partial z}{\partial y}$.

1924. $2\sin(x+2y-3z)=x+2y-3z$. Show that $\frac{\partial z}{\partial x}+\frac{\partial z}{\partial y}=1$.

1925. Show that the differential equation $m\frac{\partial z}{\partial x}+n\frac{\partial z}{\partial y}=1$ is satisfied by the implicit function z defined by the equation (of cylindrical surfaces) $x-mz=\varphi(y-nz)$.

11.6. Higher-Order Partial Derivatives and Total Differentials

Let there be given a function $z=F(x, y)$ having partial derivatives $\frac{\partial F}{\partial x}$ and $\frac{\partial F}{\partial y}$. The partial derivatives of these derivatives are called partial derivatives of the second order (or second partial derivatives). They are designated as follows:

$$\frac{\partial\left(\frac{\partial F}{\partial x}\right)}{\partial x}=\frac{\partial^2 F}{\partial x^2}; \quad \frac{\partial\left(\frac{\partial F}{\partial x}\right)}{\partial y}=\frac{\partial^2 F}{\partial x\,\partial y};$$

$$\frac{\partial\left(\frac{\partial F}{\partial y}\right)}{\partial x}=\frac{\partial^2 F}{\partial y\,\partial x}; \quad \frac{\partial\left(\frac{\partial F}{\partial y}\right)}{\partial y}=\frac{\partial^2 F}{\partial y^2}.$$

Partial derivatives of the third and still higher orders are defined and designated in a similar way.

Mixed derivatives, differing only in the order of differentiation, are equal if they are continuous:

$$\frac{\partial^2 F}{\partial x\,\partial y}=\frac{\partial^2 F}{\partial y\,\partial x}; \quad \frac{\partial^3 F}{\partial x^2\,\partial y}=\frac{\partial^3 F}{\partial x\,\partial y\,\partial x}=\frac{\partial^3 F}{\partial y\,\partial x^2} \text{ and so on.}$$

We get the following table of derivatives of higher orders:

of the second order $\frac{\partial^2 F}{\partial x^2}$; $\frac{\partial^2 F}{\partial x\,\partial y}$; $\frac{\partial^2 F}{\partial y^2}$;

of the third order $\frac{\partial^3 F}{\partial x^3}$; $\frac{\partial^3 F}{\partial x^2\,\partial y}$; $\frac{\partial^3 F}{\partial x\,\partial y^2}$; $\frac{\partial^3 F}{\partial y^3}$ and so forth.

Total differentials of higher orders are determined in the following way: $d^2z=\frac{\partial^2 z}{\partial x^2}dx^2+2\frac{\partial^2 z}{\partial x\,\partial y}dx\,dy+\frac{\partial^2 z}{\partial y^2}dy^2$. This equality can be rewritten symbolically as $d^2z=\left(\frac{\partial}{\partial x}dx+\frac{\partial}{\partial y}dy\right)^2 z$. Analogously, $d^3z=\left(\frac{\partial}{\partial x}dx+\frac{\partial}{\partial y}dy\right)^3 z$ and so on.

1926. $z=x^3+x^2y+y^3$. Find the partial derivatives of the third order.

1927. Check that $\frac{\partial^2 z}{\partial x\,\partial y}=\frac{\partial^2 z}{\partial y\,\partial x}$ for the following functions: (1) $z=\sin(ax-by)$; (2) $z=\frac{x^2}{y^2}$; (3) $z=\ln(x-2y)$.

1928. $u=x^4+3x^2y^2-2y^4$. Find the partial derivatives of the fourth order.

1929. $u=\frac{y}{x}$. Find the partial derivatives of the third order.

1930. $s=\ln\left(\frac{1}{x}-\frac{1}{t}\right)$; check that $\frac{\partial^2 s}{\partial x\,\partial t}+\frac{\partial^2 s}{\partial x^2}=\frac{1}{x^2}$.

1931. $z=\arctan\frac{y}{x}$. Find the second-order derivatives.

1932. $z=\sin\left(\frac{x}{a}-\frac{y}{b}\right)$; prove that

$$\left(\frac{\partial}{\partial x}+\frac{\partial}{\partial y}\right)^2 z=-\left(\frac{1}{a}-\frac{1}{b}\right)^2 z.$$

1933. $u=\arctan(2x-t)$; prove that $\frac{\partial^2 u}{\partial x^2}+2\frac{\partial^2 u}{\partial x\,\partial t}=0$.

1934. $s=\sqrt[3]{ax+bt}$; prove that

$$\left(x\frac{\partial}{\partial x}+t\frac{\partial}{\partial t}\right)^2 s=-\frac{2s}{9}.$$

1935. Show that the function $u=xe^{-\frac{y}{x}}$ satisfies the differential equation

$$x\frac{\partial^2 u}{\partial x\,\partial y}+2\left(\frac{\partial u}{\partial x}+\frac{\partial u}{\partial y}\right)=y\frac{\partial^2 u}{\partial y^2}.$$

1936. Prove that if $z=F(x, y)$ is a homogeneous function of degree n, then

$$x^2\frac{\partial^2 z}{\partial x^2}+2xy\frac{\partial^2 z}{\partial x\,\partial y}+y^2\frac{\partial^2 z}{\partial y^2}=n(n-1)z$$

or symbolically

$$\left(x\frac{\partial}{\partial x}+y\frac{\partial}{\partial y}\right)^2 z=n(n-1)z.$$

Hint. Differentiate the equality $x\frac{\partial z}{\partial x}+y\frac{\partial z}{\partial y}=nz$ (see Problem 1898) (1) with respect to x; (2) with respect to y and add termwise the results multiplied by x and by y respectively.

1937. Check the equality $\left(x\frac{\partial}{\partial x}+y\frac{\partial}{\partial y}\right)^2 z=n(n-1)z$ for the homogeneous functions: (1) $z=x^2+xy+y^2$; (2) $z=\frac{y}{x^2}$; (3) $z=\frac{1}{x^2-y^2}$; (4) $z=\ln\left(\frac{y}{x}-1\right)$.

1938. Find d^2u if (1) $u=\frac{y^2}{x^2}$; (2) $u=x\ln\frac{y}{x}$.

1939. $z=\cos(mx+ny)$. Prove that

$$d^2z=-z\,(m\,dx+n\,dy)^2.$$

1940. $z=\ln(ax+by)$. Prove that: (1) $d^3z=2dz^3$; (2) $d^nz=(-1)^{n-1}(n-1)!\,dz^n$.

1941. Prove that if $z=F(u, v)$ where $u=mx+ny$ and $v=px+qy$, then $\frac{\partial^2 z}{\partial x^2}=\left(m\frac{\partial}{\partial u}+p\frac{\partial}{\partial v}\right)^2 z$, $\frac{\partial^2 z}{\partial x\,\partial y}=\left(m\frac{\partial}{\partial u}+p\frac{\partial}{\partial v}\right)\left(n\frac{\partial}{\partial u}+q\frac{\partial}{\partial v}\right)z$; $\frac{\partial^2 z}{\partial y^2}=\left(n\frac{\partial}{\partial u}+q\frac{\partial}{\partial v}\right)^2 z$.

1942. Express $\frac{\partial^2 z}{\partial x^2}-4\frac{\partial^2 z}{\partial x\,\partial y}+3\frac{\partial^2 z}{\partial y^2}$ as a function of the new variables $u=3x+y$ and $v=x+y$ (see Problem 1941).

1943. Express $\frac{\partial^2 z}{\partial x^2}-4\frac{\partial^2 z}{\partial x\,\partial y}+4\frac{\partial^2 z}{\partial y^2}$ as a function of the new variables $u=2x+y$ and $v=y$ (see Problem 1941).

1944. Prove that if $z=F(u, v)$, where u and v are functions of x and y, then $\frac{\partial^2 z}{\partial x^2}=\left(u'_x\frac{\partial}{\partial u}+v'_x\frac{\partial}{\partial v}\right)^2 z+u''_{xx}\frac{\partial z}{\partial u}+v''_{xx}\frac{\partial z}{\partial v}$. Determine analogously $\frac{\partial^2 z}{\partial x\,\partial y}$ and $\frac{\partial^2 z}{\partial y^2}$.

1945. Express $x^2\frac{\partial^2 z}{\partial x^2}-y^2\frac{\partial^2 z}{\partial y^2}$ as a function of the new variables $u=xy$ and $v=\frac{y}{x}$ (see Problem 1944).

1946. Express $\frac{\partial^2 z}{\partial r^2}+\frac{1}{r^2}\frac{\partial^2 z}{\partial \varphi^2}+\frac{1}{r}\frac{\partial z}{\partial r}$ as a function of the new variables $x=r\cos\varphi$ and $y=r\sin\varphi$ (see Problem 1944).

1947. $z=\frac{x^2}{1-2y}$. Find the partial derivatives of the second order.

1948. $u=\frac{x}{\sqrt[3]{t}}$. Find the partial derivatives of the third order.

1949. $z=\frac{xy}{x-y}$. Prove that $\frac{\partial^2 z}{\partial x^2}+2\frac{\partial^2 z}{\partial x\,\partial y}+\frac{\partial^2 z}{\partial y^2}=\frac{2}{x-y}$.

1950. $s=\ln(ax-bt)$; prove that $\left(x\frac{\partial}{\partial x}+t\frac{\partial}{\partial t}\right)^3 s=2$.

1951. $z=2\cos^2\left(x-\frac{t}{2}\right)$; prove that $2\frac{\partial^2 z}{\partial t^2}+\frac{\partial^2 z}{\partial x\,\partial t}=0$.

1952. $z=e^{\frac{x}{y}}$; prove that $y\frac{\partial^2 z}{\partial x\,\partial y}=\frac{\partial z}{\partial y}-\frac{\partial z}{\partial x}$.

1953. $u=y\ln x$. Find d^2u and d^3u.

1954. Express $\frac{\partial^2 z}{\partial x^2}-a^2\frac{\partial^2 z}{\partial y^2}$ as a function of the new variables $u=ax+y$ and $v=ax-y$ (see Problem 1941).

1955. Express $x\frac{\partial^2 z}{\partial x^2}+y\frac{\partial^2 z}{\partial x\,\partial y}$ as a function of the new variables $u=y$ and $v=\frac{y}{x}$ (see Problem 1944).

1956. Show that the function $u=\frac{xf(x)}{y}+\varphi\left(\frac{y}{x}\right)$ satisfies the differential equation

$$xy\frac{\partial^2 u}{\partial x\,\partial y}+y^2\frac{\partial^2 u}{\partial y^2}+x\frac{\partial u}{\partial x}+2y\frac{\partial u}{\partial y}=0$$

for any twice differentiable functions f and φ.

11.7. Integration of Total Differentials

1° For an expression $P\,dx+Q\,dy$, where P and Q are differentiable functions of x and y, to be a total differential du, it is necessary and sufficient that the condition $\frac{\partial P}{\partial y}=\frac{\partial Q}{\partial x}$ is fulfilled.

To find u from the conditions $\frac{\partial u}{\partial x}=P$ and $\frac{\partial u}{\partial y}=Q$ we have two expressions: $u=\int P\,dx+\varphi_1(y)$, $u=\int Q\,dy+\varphi_2(x)$. Writing out all known terms from the first expression and the terms containing y and missing the first one from the second, we get the function u.

2°. For an expression $P\,dx+Q\,dy+R\,dz$, where P, Q, and R are differentiable functions of x, y, and z, to be a total differential du, it is necessary and sufficient that the following conditions are fulfilled:

$$\frac{\partial P}{\partial y}=\frac{\partial Q}{\partial x};\quad \frac{\partial P}{\partial z}=\frac{\partial R}{\partial x};\quad \frac{\partial Q}{\partial z}=\frac{\partial R}{\partial y}.$$

For finding u we have:

$$u=\int P\,dx+\varphi_1(y, z),\quad u=\int Q\,dy+\varphi_2(x, z),$$
$$u=\int R\,dz+\varphi_3(x, y).$$

Taking all known terms from the first expression and the missing terms with y and z from the second and third expressions, we get the function u.

Finding a function from its total differential is called the *integration of the total differential.*

Check to make sure that the following expression is a total differential du and find u:

1957. $(2x+y)\,dx+(x-2y-3)\,dy$.

1958. $x\sin 2y\,dx+x^2\cos 2y\,dy$.

1959. $(x+\ln y)\,dx+\left(\frac{x}{y}+\sin y\right)dy$.

1960. $\frac{x\,dy-y\,dx}{x^2+y^2}$.

1961. $(yz-2x)\,dx+(xz+y)\,dy+(xy-z)\,dz$.

1962. $\left(\frac{1}{z}-\frac{1}{x^2}\right)dx+\frac{dy}{y}-\left(\frac{x}{z^2}+\frac{1}{1+z^2}\right)dz$.

Check to make sure that the following expression is a total differential du and find u:

1963. $(y^2-1)\,dx+(2xy+3y)\,dy$.

1964. $(\sin 2y-y\tan x)\,dx+(2x\cos 2y+\ln\cos x+2y)\,dy$.

1965. $\left(y-\frac{\sin^2 y}{x^2}\right)dx+\left(x+\frac{\sin 2y}{x}+1\right)dy$.

1966. $t\sqrt{\frac{x}{t^2+1}}\,dt+\frac{1+\sqrt{t^2+1}}{2\sqrt{x}}\,dx$.

1967. $(\ln y-\cos 2z)\,dx+\left(\frac{x}{y}+z\right)dy+(y+2x\sin 2z)\,dz$.

1968. $\frac{dx-3dy}{z}+\frac{3y-z}{z^2}\,dz$.

11.8. Singular Points of a Plane Curve

A point of a curve $F(x, y)=0$ is called a *singular* one if at this point $\frac{\partial F}{\partial x}=0$ and $\frac{\partial F}{\partial y}=0$.

The slope $k=y'$ of the tangent at such a point is found from the equation $A+2Bk+Ck^2=0$, where A, B, and C are the values of the derivatives $\frac{\partial^2 F}{\partial x^2}$, $\frac{\partial^2 F}{\partial x \partial y}$, and $\frac{\partial^2 F}{\partial y^2}$, respectively, at this singular point. Three cases are possible here:

(1) if $B^2-AC>0$ (two tangents), then the point is a *node*.

(2) if $B^2-AC<0$ (no tangent), then the point is an *isolated* point.

(3) if $B^2-AC=0$, then the point is either an *isolated point*, or a *cuspidal point* (a *cusp*), or a point of osculation; at cusps and points of osculation there exists one common tangent to two branches of the curve.

To arrive at a final decision in the third, doubtful, case one has to find out whether there are points of the curve in an arbitrarily small neighbourhood of the point under investigation.

Determine the domains, points of intersection with the coordinate axes, and singular points of the given curves; construct the curves:

1969. $x^3+x^2-y^2=0$. **1970.** $y^2=(x+2)^3$.
1971. $x^3-x^2-y^2=0$. **1972.** $y^2+x^4-x^2=0$.
1973. $(y-x)^2=x^3$. **1974.** $y^2=x(x-2)^2$.

Determine the domains, singular points, and asymptotes of the given curves; construct the curves:

1975. $(x+2a)^3+xy^2=0$. **1976.** $x^3-y^3-3y^2=0$.
1977. $x^3+y^3-3axy=0$. **1978.** $y^2(x^2-a^2)=x^4$.

Determine the domains, points of intersection with the coordinate axes, and singular points of the given curves; construct the curves:

1979. $y^2+x^3-2x^2=0$. **1980.** $a^2y^2=x^2(2ax-x^2)$.
1981. $y^2=x(x+2)^2$. **1982.** $xy^2=(x+a)^3$.
1983. $4y^2=x^5+5x^4$. **1984.** $y^2-x^4+x^2=0$.

1985. Find the points of intersection with the coordinate axes, y_{max}, singular point, and asymptote of the curve $4x^2-y^2+x^3-y^3=0$; construct the curve.

Determine the domains, singular points, and asymptotes of the following curves:

1986. (1) $y^2(2a-x)=x(x-a)^2$ (strophoid);
(2) $a^2(x^2+y^2)=x^2y^2$.

1987. (1) $x(x^2+y^2)=a(x^2-y^2)$;
(2) $a(x^2+y^2)=x(x^2-y^2)$.

11.9. The Envelope of a Family of Plane Curves

A curve is called the *envelope* of a one-parameter family of curves $F(x, y, \alpha)=0$ if (1) it is tangent to each curve of the family; (2) different lines of the given family touch it at different points.

The envelope of a family of curves $F(x, y, \alpha)=0$ (if it exists) is found by eliminating the parameter α from the equations

$$F(x, y, \alpha)=0 \text{ and } F'_\alpha(x, y, \alpha)=0.$$

It may, however, happen that the curve thus obtained is not an envelope but a locus of singular points of the curves belonging to the family [see the answer to Problem 1990, (2)].

Find the envelope of the family of curves and construct the envelope and the curves belonging to the family:

1988. (1) $y=ax+a^2$; (2) $y=ax^2+\frac{1}{a}$.

1989. (1) $(x-a)^2+y^2=R^2$; (2) $4ay=(x-a)^2$.

1990. (1) $y-1=(x-a)^2$; (2) $(y-1)^3=(x-a)^2$;
(3) $(y-1)^2=(x-a)^3$; (4) $9(y-a)^2=(x-a)^3$.

1991. A line segment of a constant length a slides with its end-points along the coordinate axes. Find the envelope of the family of such segments.

1992. Find the envelope of the family of circles passing through the origin with centre on the parabola $y^2=4x$.

1993. Find the envelope of the family of circles whose diameters are radius vectors of the points belonging to the hyperbola $xy=a^2$.

1994. A projectile is launched from the origin with initial velocity b at an angle α to the axis OX. Find the envelope of a family of trajectories for different α.

1995. Find the envelope of the family of (1) straight lines $x\cos\alpha+y\sin\alpha-p=0$ with p constant; (2) straight lines $y=ax+\frac{1}{a}$; (3) cubic parabolas $y-1=(x-a)^3$.

1996. Find the envelope of the family of circles with centres on the x-axis, whose radii are the corresponding ordinates of the parabola $y^2=4x$.

1997. Find the envelope of the family of ellipses $\frac{x^2}{a^2}+\frac{y^2}{b^2}=1$ if the sum of the semi-axes has a constant length l.

1998. Find the envelope of the family of parabolas having an axis of symmetry parallel to the y-axis and passing through the points $(-a,\ 0)$, $(3a,\ 0)$, and $(0,\ 3a^2)$ for different a.

11.10. The Tangent Plane and the Normal to a Surface

Let a surface be given by an equation $F(x,\ y,\ z)=0$ and let us take a point $M(x,\ y,\ z)$ on it.

The equations of the normal to the surface at this point:

$$\frac{X-x}{\frac{\partial F}{\partial x}}=\frac{Y-y}{\frac{\partial F}{\partial y}}=\frac{Z-z}{\frac{\partial F}{\partial z}}. \qquad (1)$$

The equation of the tangent plane to the surface:

$$\frac{\partial F}{\partial x}(X-x)+\frac{\partial F}{\partial y}(Y-y)+\frac{\partial F}{\partial z}(Z-z)=0. \qquad (2)$$

In equations (1) and (2) X, Y, Z are the current coordinates of the normal and of the tangent plane respectively.

Vector $\mathbf{N}\left\{\frac{\partial F}{\partial x},\ \frac{\partial F}{\partial y},\ \frac{\partial F}{\partial z}\right\}$ is called the *normal* vector of the surface.

If there is a point on the surface at which $\frac{\partial F}{\partial x}=0$, $\frac{\partial F}{\partial y}=0$, and $\frac{\partial F}{\partial z}=0$, then it is called a *singular* point. At such a point there is neither a tangent plane nor a normal to the surface.

Write the equations of the tangent planes to the surfaces:

1999. $z=x^2+2y^2$ at the point (1, 1, 3).

2000. $xy=z^2$ at the point (x_0, y_0, z_0).

2001. $xyz=a^3$ at the point (x_0, y_0, z_0).

2002. $\frac{x^2}{a^2}+\frac{y^2}{b^2}-\frac{z^2}{c^2}=1$ at the points (x_0, y_0, z_0) and (a, b, c).

2003. Determine the plane tangent to the surface $x^2+4y^2+z^2=36$ and parallel to the plane $x+y-z=0$.

2004. Write the equations of the normal at the point (3, 4, 5) to the conical surface $x^2+y^2=z^2$. At what point of the cone is the normal indeterminate?

2005. Find the angles between the coordinate axes and the normal to the surface $x^2+y^2-zx-yz=0$ at the point (0, 2, 2).

2006. Write the equations of the normal to the surface $x^2z+y^2z=4$ at the point $(-2, 0, 1)$. Construct the normal and the surface.

2007. Show that the tangent planes to the surface $xyz=a^3$ form pyramids of a constant volume with the coordinate planes.

2008. Show that the sum of the squares of the intercepts cut off on the coordinate axes by a plane tangent to the surface $x^{\frac{2}{3}}+y^{\frac{2}{3}}+z^{\frac{2}{3}}=a^{\frac{2}{3}}$ is equal to a constant quantity a^2.

2009. Find the distance from the origin to the plane tangent to the helicoid $y=x\tan\frac{z}{a}$ at the point $\left(a, a, \frac{\pi a}{4}\right)$. Construct the surface using the sections: $z=0$; $\frac{\pi a}{4}$; $\frac{\pi a}{2}$; πa.

2010. Write the equation of the tangent plane to the surface $az=x^2+y^2$ at the points of its intersection with the straight line $x=y=z$.

2011. Show that the tangent plane to the surface $\frac{x^2}{a^2}+\frac{y^2}{b^2}+\frac{z^2}{c^2}=1$ at the point (x_0, y_0, z_0) on it is determined by the equation

$$\frac{xx_0}{a^2}+\frac{yy_0}{b^2}+\frac{zz_0}{c^2}=1.$$

2012. Write the equations of the normal to the surface $x^2+y^2-(z-5)^2=0$ at the point (4, 3, 0). Construct the surface and the normal in the first octant.

2013. Find the angles formed by the normal to the surface $2z=x^2-y^2$ with the coordinate axes at the point (2, 2, 0).

2014. Find the distance from the origin to the plane tangent to the conoid $(2a^2-z^2)x^2-a^2y^2=0$ at the point (a, a, a).

2015. Show that the sum of the intercepts cut off on the coordinate axes by a plane tangent to the surface $x^{\frac{1}{2}}+y^{\frac{1}{2}}+z^{\frac{1}{2}}=a^{\frac{1}{2}}$ is equal to a constant quantity a.

2016. At what point the tangent plane to the surface $z=4-x^2-y^2$ is parallel to the (1) plane XOY; (2) plane $2x+2y+z=0$? Write the equations of these tangent planes.

11.11. Scalar Field. Level Lines and Level Surfaces. A Derivative along a Given Direction. Gradient.

The equation $u=F(x, y)$ defines u at each point (x, y) of some domain which is called the *scalar field* of u. Along each of the lines $F(x, y)=u_1$, $F(x, y)=u_2$, ..., where u_1, u_2, ... are constants, the scalar u remains constant and changes only when the point (x, y) passes from one line to another. These lines are termed *isolines* (isotherms, isobars, etc.), or *level lines*.

The equation $u=F(x, y, z)$ defines the scalar field u in some part of three-dimensional space. *Isosurfaces, or level surfaces* are given by the equations:

$$F(x, y, z)=u_1, \quad F(x, y, z)=u_2, \quad \ldots .$$

Let a point (x, y, z) displace along the straight line $x=x_0+l\cos\alpha$, $y=y_0+l\cos\beta$, $z=z_0+l\cos\gamma$ with the velocity $\frac{dl}{dt}=1$. Then the scalar $u=F(x, y, z)$ will change at the rate

$$v=\frac{du}{dt}=\frac{du}{dl}=\frac{\partial F}{\partial x}\cos\alpha+\frac{\partial F}{\partial y}\cos\beta+\frac{\partial F}{\partial z}\cos\gamma=\boldsymbol{N}\cdot\boldsymbol{l}_0,$$

where $\boldsymbol{N}\left\{\frac{\partial F}{\partial x}, \frac{\partial F}{\partial y}, \frac{\partial F}{\partial z}\right\}$ is the *normal* vector of a *level surface* and $\boldsymbol{l}_0\{\cos\alpha, \cos\beta, \cos\gamma\}$ is the unit vector of direction $\boldsymbol{l}$.

The derivative

$$\frac{du}{dl}=\frac{\partial F}{\partial x}\cos\alpha+\frac{\partial F}{\partial y}\cos\beta+\frac{\partial F}{\partial z}\cos\gamma=\boldsymbol{N}\cdot\boldsymbol{l}_0$$

is called a *derivative of the function* $u=F(x, y, z)$ *along the given direction* $\boldsymbol{l}_0\{\cos\alpha, \cos\beta, \cos\gamma\}$.

The *gradient* of the scalar $u=F(x, y, z)$ is defined as the *vector* $\operatorname{grad} u=\frac{\partial u}{\partial x}\boldsymbol{i}+\frac{\partial u}{\partial y}\boldsymbol{j}+\frac{\partial u}{\partial z}\boldsymbol{k}$. The gradient is the vector of the rate of the *quickest* change of the scalar u.

2017. $z=4-x^2-y^2$. Construct the level lines and $\operatorname{grad} z$ at the point $A(1, 2)$.

2018. $z=\arctan\frac{y}{x}$. Construct the level lines and $\operatorname{grad} z$: (1) at any point of the straight line $y=x$; (2) at any point of the straight line $y=-x$, and in particular at the points $\left(\frac{1}{2}, \pm\frac{1}{2}\right)$ and $(1, \pm 1)$.

2019. The contours of a hill are determined by the equation $h=20-\frac{x^2}{4}-y^2$. Construct the contours corresponding to the height marks $h=20$, 19, 18, 16, and 11 m. Here the direction of $\operatorname{grad} h$ determines the direction of the line of the steepest slope, and its magnitude the steepness of this slope. Construct $\operatorname{grad} h$ at the point $x=2$ and $y=1$.

2020. Find the greatest steepness of the surface $z^2=xy$ at the point $(4, 2)$.

2021. Find the derivative of the function $u=\ln(e^x+e^y)$ in the direction parallel to the bisector of the first quadrant.

2022. Find the derivative of the function $u=x^2+y^2+z^2$ at the point (1, 1, 1) in the direction $l\{\cos 45°, \cos 60°, \cos 60°\}$; find grad u and its length at the same point. Construct the level surfaces.

2023. Construct the level surfaces of the scalar $u=x^2+y^2-2z$; find and construct grad u at the points of intersection of the axis OX with the surface $u=4$.

2024. Find the derivative of the function $u=\frac{x^2}{a^2}+\frac{y^2}{b^2}+\frac{z^2}{c^2}$ at the point (a, b, c) in the direction of the radius vector of this point.

2025. $z=\frac{4}{x^2+y^2}$. Construct the level lines and grad z at the point (—1, 2), and find $|\text{grad}\, z|$.

2026. $u=xyz$. At any point and at the point (1, 2, 1) find derivative $\frac{du}{dl}$ in the direction forming equal angles with the coordinate axes.

2027. Construct the level surfaces of the scalar $u=x^2+y^2-z^2$, determine grad u on the surface passing through the origin, and construct it at the points of this surface at which $y=0$ and $z=2$.

2028. $u=\sqrt{x^2+y^2+z^2}$. Find grad u and its length.

2029. Construct the level surfaces of the function $u=\frac{z}{c}-\frac{x^2}{a^2}-\frac{y^2}{b^2}$ and find the derivative of u at the point (a, b, c) in the direction of the radius vector of this point.

11.12. The Extremum of a Function of Two Variables

1°. Necessary conditions. A function $z=F(x, y)$ can have an *extremum* only at the points where $\frac{\partial F}{\partial x}=0$ and $\frac{\partial F}{\partial y}=0$. These points are called *critical*.

2°. Sufficient conditions. Let A, B, and C denote the values of the derivatives $\frac{\partial^2 F}{\partial x^2}$, $\frac{\partial^2 F}{\partial x\, \partial y}$, and $\frac{\partial^2 F}{\partial y^2}$ at the critical point (x_0, y_0).

If

(1) $\begin{vmatrix} A & B \\ B & C \end{vmatrix} > 0$, then $\begin{cases} F(x_0, y_0) = z_{\max} \text{ for } A < 0 \\ F(x_0, y_0) = z_{\min} \text{ for } A > 0; \end{cases}$

(2) $\begin{vmatrix} A & B \\ B & C \end{vmatrix} < 0$, then we have no extremum;

(3) $\begin{vmatrix} A & B \\ B & C \end{vmatrix} = 0$, then the existence of an extremum is doubtful (it may exist, and it may not).

3°. Conditional extremum. To find the extremum of the function $z = F(x, y)$, provided x and y are related by the equation $\varphi(x, y) = 0$, form an auxiliary function $u = F(x, y) + \lambda\varphi(x, y)$.

The coordinates (x, y) of the extremum must satisfy three equations: $\varphi(x, y) = 0$, $\frac{\partial u}{\partial x} = 0$, $\frac{\partial u}{\partial y} = 0$, wherefrom λ, x, and y are found.

Find the extrema of the following functions:

2030. $z = x^2 - xy + y^2 + 9x - 6y + 20$.

2031. $z = y\sqrt{x} - y^2 - x + 6y$.

2032. $z = x^3 + 8y^3 - 6xy + 1$.

2033. $z = 2xy - 4x - 2y$. **2034.** $z = e^{\frac{x}{2}}(x + y^2)$.

2035. $z = \sin x + \sin y + \sin(x + y)$ for $0 \leqslant x \leqslant \frac{\pi}{2}$ and $0 \leqslant y \leqslant \frac{\pi}{2}$.

2036. $z = \frac{1}{x} + \frac{1}{y}$ if $x + y = 2$.

2037. $z = x + y$ if $\frac{1}{x^2} + \frac{1}{y^2} = \frac{1}{2}$.

2038. Determine the dimensions of a rectangular outdoor pool having the least surface if its volume is equal to V.

2039. Construct the ellipse $x^2 + 4y^2 = 4$ and the straight line $2x + 3y - 6 = 0$ and find the points on the ellipse whose distances from the line are the greatest and the least.

2040. On the hyperbola $x^2 - y^2 = 4$ find the point nearest to the point $(0, 2)$.

2041. Determine the dimensions of a cylinder of the greatest volume if its total surface $S=6\pi$ dm^2.

2042. (1) In the ellipse $x^2+3y^2=12$ inscribe an isosceles triangle with its base parallel to the major axis so that its area is the greatest.

(2) The axis OX is situated on the boundary line of two media. Along what path must a beam of light pass from the point $A(0, a)$ to the point $B(c, -b)$ in order to spend minimum time to cover this distance ($a>0$, $b>0$, $c>0$)?

Hint. Find the minimum of the function $T=\frac{a}{v_1 \cos \alpha}+$ $+\frac{b}{v_2 \cos \beta}$, if $a \tan \alpha+b \tan \beta=c$, where v_1 and v_2 are the velocities of light in the two media, and α and β are the angles of incidence and refraction respectively.

Find the extrema of the following functions:

2043. $z=3x+6y-x^2-xy-y^2$.

2044. $z=x^2+y^2-2x-4\sqrt{xy}-2y+8$.

2045. $z=2x^3-xy^2+5x^2+y^2$.

2046. $z=3x^2-2x\sqrt{y}+y-8x+8$.

2047. $z=xy$ if $x^2+y^2=2$.

2048. Find the greatest volume of a right parallelepiped if the length of its diagonal is equal to $2\sqrt{3}$.

2049. (1) On the parabola $y^2=4x$ find the point nearest to the straight line $x-y+4=0$.

(2) A rectangle of he greatest area is inscribed in the ellipse $\frac{x^2}{a^2}+\frac{y^2}{b^2}=1$. Find this area.

2050. Determine the dimensions of a cone of the greatest volume, provided its lateral area is S.

CHAPTER 12

DIFFERENTIAL EQUATIONS

12.1. Fundamentals

1°. An equation of the form

$$F(x, y, y', y'', \ldots, y^{(n)}) = 0 \qquad (1)$$

is called an *ordinary differential equation of the* n*th order.*

A function $\varphi(x)$ which when substituted into equation (1) instead of y turns it into an identity is called its *solution.* The equation $y = \varphi(x)$ or $\Phi(x, y) = 0$ is called the *integral* of the differential equation. Each integral defines in the plane XOY a curve which is called an *integral curve* of the differential equation.

The equation

$$\Phi(x, y, C_1, C_2, \ldots, C_n) = 0, \qquad (2)$$

containing x, y, and n arbitrary constants, is called the *general integral* of equation (1) in the domain of existence and uniqueness of solution if, giving different values to the arbitrary constants in equation (2), we get the integral curves passing inside this domain and only these curves.

Integrals obtained from the general integral for certain values of the arbitrary constants are called *particular* integrals.

Differentiating general integral (2) n times with respect to x and eliminating n arbitrary constants from the obtained n equations and equation (2), we get the given differential equation (1).

2°. A differential equation of the first order has the form

$$F\left(x, y, \frac{dy}{dx}\right) = 0. \qquad (3)$$

Solving equation (3) with respect to $\frac{dy}{dx}$ (if it is possible) we obtain:

$$\frac{dy}{dx}=f(x, y). \tag{4}$$

Equation (4) defines the *slope* $k=\tan\alpha=\frac{dy}{dx}=f(x, y)$ of the integral curve at a point (x, y), i.e. defines the *directions* of field of integral curves.

If in some domain a function $f(x, y)$ is continuous and has a limited partial derivative $f'_y(x, y)$, then it turns out that only one integral curve passes through each interior point (x_0, y_0) of this domain.

In such a domain equation (4) has a general integral $y=\varphi(x, C)$ or $\Phi(x, y, C)=0$ from which we can find the only partial integral satisfying the initial conditions: $y=y_0$ at $x=x_0$.

2051. Check by substitution that $y=Cx^3$ is the solution of the differential equation $3y-xy=0$. Construct the integral curves passing through the points:

(1) $\left(1, \frac{1}{3}\right)$; (2) $(1, 1)$; (3) $\left(1, -\frac{1}{3}\right)$.

2052. Check by substitution that the differential equations (1) $y''+4y=0$ and (2) $y'''-9y'=0$ have the general integrals (1) $y=C_1\cos 2x+C_2\sin 2x$ and (2) $y=C_1+$ $+C_2e^{3x}+C_3e^{-3x}$ respectively.

2053. Construct the parabolas $y=Cx^2$ for $C=0$; ±1; ±2 and derive a differential equation of a family of such parabolas.

2054. Represent graphically a family of (1) circles $x^2+y^2=2Cx$; (2) parabolas $y=x^2+2Cx$ and derive their differential equations.

2055. Represent graphically the direction fields defined by each of the following equations:

(1) $\frac{dy}{dx}=\frac{y}{x}$; (2) $\frac{dy}{dx}=y-x$; (3) $\frac{dy}{dx}=y+x^2$.

2056. Represent graphically the direction field defined by the equation $\frac{dy}{dx}=\sqrt{x^2+y^2}$ with the aid of circles along which $\frac{dy}{dx}=\frac{1}{2}$; 1; 2; 3; .... Draw approximately the integral curve passing through the origin.

12.2. First-Order Differential Equation with Variables Separable. Orthogonal Trajectories

1°. The first-order differential equation

$$P\,dx+Q\,dy=0, \tag{1}$$

where P and Q are functions of x and y, is termed the equation with *separable variables* if the coefficients P and Q of the differentials are factorized into multipliers which depend only on x, or only on y, i.e. if it has the form

$$f(x)\,\varphi(y)\,dx+f_1(x)\,\varphi_1(y)\,dy=0. \tag{2}$$

Dividing both terms of equation (2) by $\varphi(y)\,f_1(x)$, we get

$$\frac{f(x)\,dx}{f_1(x)}+\frac{\varphi_1(y)\,dy}{\varphi(y)}=0. \tag{3}$$

The total integral of equation (3) and, consequently, of (2) will be:

$$\int\frac{f(x)\,dx}{f_1(x)}+\int\frac{\varphi_1(y)\,dy}{\varphi(y)}=C. \tag{4}$$

2°. Orthogonal trajectories of a family of lines $F(x, y, a)=0$ are defined as lines intersecting the lines of the given family at right angles. Differentiating the equation $F(x, y, a)=0$ with respect to x and eliminating a from the obtained and given equations, we get the differential equation of the lines of the given family $y'=f(x, y)$. Then the *differential equation of the orthogonal trajectories* will be $y'=-\frac{1}{f(x, y)}$.

In each of the following differential equations: (1) find the general integral; (2) construct several integral curves; (3) find the particular integral for the given initial conditions: $x=-2$, $y=4$.

2057. $xy'-y=0$. **2058.** $xy'+y=0$.
2059. $yy'+x=0$. **2060.** $y'=y$.

Find the total integrals of the following equations:

2061. $x^2y' + y = 0$. **2062.** $x + xy + y'(y + xy) = 0$.
2063. $\varphi^2\,dr + (r - a)\,d\varphi = 0$. **2064.** $2st^2\,ds = (1 + t^2)\,dt$.

In the following equations find the total and particular integrals for the given initial conditions:

2065. $2y'\sqrt{x} = y$, $y = 1$ at $x = 4$.

2066. $y' = (2y + 1)\cot x$, $y = \frac{1}{2}$ at $x = \frac{\pi}{4}$.

2067. $x^2y' + y^2 = 0$, $y = 1$ at $x = -1$.

2068. Construct the integral curves of each of the equations: (1) $y'(x^2 - 4) = 2xy$, (2) $y' + y\tan x = 0$ passing through the points:

(1) $(0, 1)$; (2) $\left(0, \frac{1}{2}\right)$; (3) $\left(0, -\frac{1}{2}\right)$; (4) $(0, -1)$.

2069. Find the curve passing through the point $\left(1, \frac{1}{3}\right)$ if the slope of the tangent to it at any point of the curve is three times the slope of the radius vector of the point of tangency.

2070. A curve passes through the point $A(0, a)$; MN is an arbitrary ordinate of the curve. Determine the curve from the condition that the area of $OAMN = as$, where s is the length of the arc AM.

2071. Find the curve passing through the point (a, a) if its subtangent at any point is twice the length of the abscissa of the point of tangency.

2072. Find the curve passing through the point $(-1, -2)$ if its subnormal at any point is equal to 2.

2073. In what time a body heated to 100° C will cool to 25° C in a room with ambient temperature of 20° C if in 10 minutes it cools to 60° C? (According to Newton's law, the rate of cooling is proportional to the difference of temperatures.)

2074. The load carried by a cable of a suspension bridge (see Fig. 6 on p. 39) from each unit length of the horizontal beam amounts to p N. Neglecting the weight of the cable, find its shape if the tension of the cable at the lowest point is taken to be equal to H N.

Hint. Take an arbitrary point M on the arc $\breve{OC}$ (Fig. 6). Three forces will act on the sector OM: a horizontal force H (to the left of the point M), a vertical one, i.e. the weight px, and a tangential force of tension T (to the right of the point M). For equilibrium to exist the sum of the projections of the forces on the axes OX and OY must be zero.

2075. Determine and construct the curve passing through the point $P(-a, a)$ if the segment AB of any tangent to it contained between the coordinate axes is bisected by the point of tangency M.

2076. Find the orthogonal trajectories of a family of parabolas $ay = x^2$. Construct them.

2077. Find the orthogonal trajectories of a family of parabolas $xy = c$.

2078. Find the orthogonal trajectories of a family of semicubic parabolas $ay^2 = x^3$.

2079. Find the orthogonal trajectories of a family of ellipses $x^2 + 4y^2 = a^2$.

Solve the equations:

2080. $y'x^3 = 2y$. **2081.** $(x^2 + x)y' = 2y + 1$.

2082. $y'\sqrt{a^2 + x^2} = y$. **2083.** $(1 + x^2)y' + 1 + y^2 = 0$.

2084. $dr + r\tan\varphi\,d\varphi = 0$; $r = 2$ at $\varphi = \pi$.

2085. $y' = 2\sqrt{y}\ln x$; $y = 1$ at $x = e$.

2086. $(1 + x^2)y' + y\sqrt{1 + x^2} = xy$; $y = 1$ at $x = 0$.

2087. Determine the curve passing through the point A $(-1, 1)$ if the slope of the tangent at any point of the curve is equal to the squared ordinate of the point of tangency.

2088. A curve passes through the point $A(0, a)$, MN is an arbitrary ordinate of the curve. Determine the curve if the area of $OAMN = a(MN - a)$.

2089. Determine and construct the curve passing through the point $(-1, -1)$, for which the line segment OT cut off on the x-axis by the tangent to the curve at any point is equal to the squared abscissa of the point of tangency.

2090. Find the orthogonal trajectories of a family of hyperbolas $x^2 - 2y^2 = a^2$.

2091. Determine the curve the radius vector of any point of which is equal to the segment of the normal between the curve and the x-axis.

2092. Determine the line if the area bounded by the coordinate axes, this line, and its arbitrary ordinate is equal to one third the area of a rectangle constructed on the coordinates of the end-point of the line.

12.3. First-Order Differential Equations: (1) Homogeneous, (2) Linear, (3) Bernoulli's

1°. Homogeneous. The equation $P\,dx+Q\,dy=0$ is called *homogeneous* if P and Q are homogeneous functions of x and y of the same order. It is reduced to the form $\frac{dy}{dx}=\varphi\left(\frac{y}{x}\right)$ and is solved by the substitution $\frac{y}{x}=u$ or $y=ux$.

2°. Linear. A differential equation is called *linear* if it is of the first degree with respect to the required function y and all of its derivatives. A linear equation of the first order has the form $y'+Py=Q$. It is reduced to two equations with separable variables by the substitution $y=uv$. Another method of solution (*variation of constants*) consists in that first we solve the equation $y'+Py=0$; we get $y=-Ae^{-\int P\,dx}$. Substituting this solution into the given equation (taking A as a function of x), we then find A' and A.

3°. *Bernoulli's equation* $y'+Py=Qy^n$ is solved in the same way as a linear one, i.e. either by the substitution $y=uv$ or by variation of the arbitrary constant. Bernoulli's equation is reduced to the linear one by means of the substitution $z=y^{1-n}$.

Integrate the following differential equations:

2093. $yy'=2y-x$. **2094.** $x^2+y^2-2xyy'=0$.

2095. $\frac{ds}{dt}=\frac{s}{t}-\frac{t}{s}$. **2096.** $y'-\frac{3y}{x}=x$.

2097. $y'+\frac{2y}{x}=\frac{e^{-x^2}}{x}$. **2098.** $y'\cos x-y\sin x=\sin 2x$.

2099. $y'x+y=-xy^2$. **2100.** $y'-xy=-y^3e^{-x^2}$.

2101. $xy'\cos\frac{y}{x}=y\cos\frac{y}{x}-x$.

2102. $x^2y'=y^2+xy$. **2103.** $xy'+y=\ln x+1$.

2104. $x^2y^2y' + yx^3 = 1$.

In Problems 2105 to 2107 find the particular integrals for the given initial conditions:

2105. $y + \sqrt{x^2+y^2} - xy' = 0$; $y = 0$ at $x = 1$.

2106. $t^2 \frac{ds}{dt} = 2ts - 3$; $s = 1$ at $t = -1$.

2107. $xy' = y\left(1 + \ln\frac{y}{x}\right)$; $y = \frac{1}{\sqrt{e}}$ at $x = 1$.

2108. Find the family of curves, the subtangent at any point of which is the arithmetic mean of the coordinates of the point of tangency.

2109. Find the orthogonal trajectories of the family of circles $x^2 + y^2 = 2ax$.

2110. Current intensity i in a circuit with resistance R, inductance L, and electromotive force E satisfy the differential equation $L\frac{di}{dt} + Ri = E$. Solve this equation taking R and L for constants and the electromotive force E for a linearly increasing quantity: $E = kt$. The initial conditions are: $i = 0$ at $t = 0$.

2111. Find the shape of a mirror that will reflect all incident rays from a point source parallel to a given direction.

Hint. Considering the plane section of the mirror, take a given source as the origin, and a given direction for the y-axis. The tangent to the required curve at the point M forms equal angles with OM and the y-axis, i.e. cuts off on the y-axis an intercept $ON = OM$.

Solve the following differential equations:

2112. $xy + y^2 = (2x^2 + xy)\, y'$.

2113. $(a^2 + x^2)\, y' + xy = 1$.

2114. $xy' + 2\sqrt{xy} = y$.

2115. $(2x + 1)\, y' + y = x$.

2116. $y' - y \tan x = \cot x$.

2117. $t\, ds - 2s\, dt = t^3 \ln t\, dt$.

2118. $y' + xy = xy^3$.

2119. $y' + y \cos x = \sin 2x$.

2120. $y' = \frac{y^2}{x^2} - \frac{y}{x}$; for $x = -1$ $y = 1$.

2121. $3y^2y' + y^3 = x + 1$; for $x = 1$ $y = -1$.

2122. $(1-x^2)\,y'-xy=xy^2$; for $x=0$ $y=0.5$.

2123. Determine the curve passing through the point $A(a, a)$ if the distance of the origin from the tangent at any point of the curve is equal to the abscissa of this point.

12.4. Differential Equations Containing Differentials of a Product or a Quotient

$$d(xy)=x\,dy+y\,dx;\quad d\left(\frac{y}{x}\right)=\frac{x\,dy-y\,dx}{x^2};$$

$$d\left(\frac{x}{y}\right)=\frac{y\,dx-x\,dy}{y^2}.$$

Such equations are sometimes solved easily if we put $xy=u$, $y=\frac{u}{x}$ or $\frac{y}{x}=u$, $y=ux$ respectively.

2124. $x^2\,dy+xy\,dx=dx$. **2125.** $y^2x\,dy-y^3\,dx=x^2\,dy$.

Hint. In Problem 2125 the equation is reduced to the form

$$y^2d\left(\frac{y}{x}\right)=dy \quad \text{or} \quad y^2du=dy.$$

2126. $y\,dx+(x-y^3)\,dy=0$. **2127.** $y\,dx-(x-y^3)\,dy=0$.

2128. $y\cos x\,dx+\sin x\,dy=\cos 2x\,dx$.

2129. $t\frac{ds}{dt}-s=s^2\ln t$. **2130.** $x^2y^2+1+x^3yy'=0$.

2131. $t^2s\,dt+t^3\,ds=dt$. **2132.** $x\,dy-y\,dx=x^2\,dx$.

2133. $xy'+\tan y=2x\sec y$. **2134.** $y\left(ye^{-\frac{x}{2}}+1\right)=xy'$.

12.5. First-Order Differential Equations in Total Differentials. Integrating Factor

1°. If in the differential equation

$$P\,dx+Q\,dy=0,$$

$\frac{\partial P}{\partial y}=\frac{\partial Q}{\partial x}$, then it has the form $du=0$ and its general integral will be $u=C$.

2°. If $\frac{\partial P}{\partial y} \neq \frac{\partial Q}{\partial x}$, then for certain conditions there exists a function $\mu(x, y)$ such that $\mu P\,dx + \mu Q\,dy = du$. This function $\mu(x, y)$ is called the *integrating factor*.

The integrating factor is readily found in the following cases:

(1) if $\dfrac{\frac{\partial P}{\partial y} - \frac{\partial Q}{\partial x}}{Q} = \Phi(x)$, then $\ln \mu = \int \Phi(x)\,dx$;

(2) if $\dfrac{\frac{\partial Q}{\partial x} - \frac{\partial P}{\partial y}}{P} = \Phi_1(y)$, then $\ln \mu = \int \Phi_1(y)\,dy$.

The differential equations considered in Sec. 12.4 are particular cases of the equations treated in the present section.

Solve the following differential equations "in total differentials":

2135. $\left(4 - \frac{y^2}{x^2}\right) dx + \frac{2y}{x}\,dy = 0$.

2136. $3x^2 e^y\,dx + (x^3 e^y - 1)\,dy = 0$.

2137. $e^{-y}\,dx + (1 - xe^{-y})\,dy = 0$.

2138. $2x \cos^2 y\,dx + (2y - x^2 \sin 2y)\,dy = 0$.

Find the integrating factors and solve the following differential equations:

2139. $(x^2 - y)\,dx + x\,dy = 0$.

2140. $2x \tan y\,dx + (x^2 - 2\sin y)\,dy = 0$.

2141. $(e^{2x} - y^2)\,dx + y\,dy = 0$.

2142. $(1 + 3x^2 \sin y)\,dx - x \cot y\,dy = 0$.

Show that the left-hand members of the following differential equations are total differentials, and solve the equations:

2143. $(3x^2 + 2y)\,dx + (2x - 3)\,dy = 0$.

2144. $(3x^2 y - 4xy^2)\,dx + (x^3 - 4x^2 y + 12y^3)\,dy = 0$.

2145. $(x \cos 2y + 1)\,dx - x^2 \sin 2y\,dy = 0$.

Find the integrating factors and solve the equations:

2146. $y^2\,dx+(yx-1)\,dy=0$.
2147. $(x^2-3y^2)\,dx+2xy\,dy=0$.
2148. $(\sin x+e^y)\,dx+\cos x\,dy=0$.
2149. $(x\sin y+y)\,dx+(x^2\cos y+x\ln x)\,dy=0$.

12.6. First-Order Differential Equations Not Solved for the Derivative. Lagrange's and Clairaut's Equations

1°. If $F(x, y, y')=0$ is a second-degree equation with respect to y', then it has two solutions with respect to y': $y'=f_1(x, y)$ and $y'=f_2(x, y)$, continuous with respect to x and y in some domain, and, geometrically, determines two directions of integral curves at any point (x_0, y_0) of this domain.

Such differential equations $F(x, y, y')=0$, in addition to the total integral $\Phi(x,y,C)=0$ and particular integrals, sometimes also have a *singular* integral which does not contain an arbitrary constant and at the same time is not obtained from the total integral whatever is the value of the constant.

A singular integral, if it exists, can be obtained by eliminating $p=y'$ from the equations $F(x, y, p)=0$ and $F'_p(x, y, p)=0$ or by eliminating C from the total integral $\Phi(x, y, C)=0$ and $\Phi'_C=0$. Geometrically, a *singular integral* determines the *envelope of a family of integral curves**.

2°. *Lagrange's equation*

$$y=xf(p)+\varphi(p), \tag{1}$$

where $p=y'$, is integrated in the following way.

Differentiating (1) with respect to x, we find:

$$p=f(p)+[xf'(p)+\varphi'(p)]\frac{dp}{dx}.$$

This equation is a linear one with respect to x and $\frac{dx}{dp}$. We get the following solution:

$$x=CA(p)+B(p). \tag{2}$$

* For the definition of the envelope see Sec. 11.9.

Equations (1) and (2) parametrically determine the general integral. Eliminating from them the parameter p (if it is possible), we get the general integral in the form $\Phi(x, y, C)=0$.

3°. *Clairaut's equation*

$$y=px+\varphi(p) \tag{3}$$

is a particular case of Lagrange's equations. It has a general integral $y=Cx+\varphi(C)$ and a singular one obtained by eliminating the parameter p from the equations $y=px+\varphi(p)$ and $x=-\varphi'(p)$.

2150. Construct several integral curves of the equation $y'^2=4y$. Find two integral curves passing through the point $M(1, 4)$.

2151. Construct two integral curves of the equation $y'^2+y^2-1=0$. Determine the two integral curves passing through the point $M\left(\frac{\pi}{2}, \frac{1}{\sqrt{2}}\right)$.

2152. Show that the integral curves of the equation $xy'^2-2yy'+4x=0$ are contained inside the acute angle between the straight lines $y=\pm 2x$. Construct the integral curves, putting in the total integral $C=\pm\frac{1}{2}, \pm 1, \pm 2$, etc.

2153. Solve the equations:

$$(1)\quad yy'^2+y'(x-y)-x=0; \qquad (2)\quad xy'^2+2xy'-y=0$$

and construct the integral curves.

2154. Solve the equations with one of the variables expressed implicitly:

$$(1)\ y=1+y'^2; \quad (2)\ x=2y'-\frac{1}{y'^2}.$$

Hint. Denoting y' by p, differentiate the first equation with respect to x, and the second one with respect to y.

2155. Find the general and singular integrals of Lagrange's equations:

$$(1)\ y=xy'^2+y'^2; \quad (2)\ y=2xy'+\frac{1}{y'^2}; \quad (3)\ 2y=\frac{xy'^2}{y'+2}.$$

2156. Find the general and singular integrals of Clairaut's equation and construct the integral curves:

$$(1)\ y=xy'-y'^2;\ (2)\ y=xy'-a\sqrt{1+y'^2};$$

$$(3)\ y=xy'+\frac{1}{2y'^2}.$$

2157. Construct the integral curves of the equation $y'^2+y=1$. Determine two integral curves passing through the point $M\left(1, \frac{3}{4}\right)$.

2158. Solve the equations with one of the variables expressed implicitly: (1) $y=y'^2+y'^3$; (2) $x=\frac{ay'}{\sqrt{1+y'^2}}$.

2159. $y=2y'x+\frac{x^2}{2}+y'^2$.

2160. Find the total and singular integrals of Clairaut's equation and construct the integral curves:

$$(1)\ y=y'x+\frac{1}{y'};\quad (2)\ y=xy'+y'+y'^2.$$

2161. Find the curve whose tangents form with the coordinate axes a triangle of constant area equal to $2a^2$.

2162. Find the curve whose tangent cuts off intercepts on the coordinate axes the sum of which is a.

12.7. Differential Equations of Higher Orders Allowing for Reduction of the Order

1°. An equation of the form $y^{(n)}=f(x)$ is solved by successive n-fold integration of the right-hand member. Each integration yields one arbitrary constant, with the final result containing n arbitrary constants.

2°. The equation $F(x, y', y'')=0$, not containing y in an explicit form, by means of the substitution $y'=p$ $y''=\frac{dp}{dx}$ is reduced to the form

$$F\left(x, p, \frac{dp}{dx}\right)=0.$$

3°. The equation $F(y, y', y'')=0$, not containing x in an explicit form, by means of the substitution $y'=p$ $y''=\frac{dp}{dx}=p\frac{dp}{dy}$ is reduced to the form

$$F\left(y, p, p\frac{dp}{dy}\right)=0.$$

Solve the equations:

2163. (1) $y'''=\frac{6}{x^3}$; the initial conditions: for $x=1$ $y=2$, $y'=1$, $y''=1$; (2) $y''=4\cos 2x$; for $x=0$ $y=0$, $y'=0$; (3) $y''=\frac{1}{1+x^2}$.

2164. $x^3y''+x^2y'=1$.

2165. $yy''+y'^2=0$.

2166. $y''+y'\tan x=\sin 2x$.

2167. $y''+2y(y')^3=0$.

2168. $y''x\ln x=y'$.

2169. $y''\tan y=2(y')^2$.

2170. (1) $xy''-y'=e^x x^2$; (2) $y''+2xy'^2=0$.

2171. Determine the bending curve for a horizontal beam whose one end is fixed and the other is acted upon by a concentrated force P (the weight of the beam should be neglected and the bend considered small enough so that $1+y'^2\approx 1$).

2172. Determine the curves whose radius of curvature is twice the length of the normal.

2173. Determine the curves whose radius of curvature is equal to the length of the normal.

2174. On the closed interval $[0, 1]$ determine the curve tangent to the axis OX at the origin if its curvature $k=x$, i.e. increases uniformly along the x-axis (the *transition* curve). Put $1+y'^2\approx 1$.

Solve the equations:

2175. $y''=\frac{1}{\cos^2 x}$; for $x=\frac{\pi}{4}$ $y=\frac{\ln 2}{2}$, $y'=1$.

2176. $(1+x^2)y''+2xy'=x^3$.

2177. $y''y^3=1$.

2178. $2yy''=(y')^2$.

2179. $t\frac{d^2s}{dt^2}+\frac{ds}{dt}+t=0$.

2180. $2yy''=1+y'^2$.

2181. $y''\tan x=y'+1$.

2182. Determine the curves whose radius of curvature is equal to the cubed length of the normal.

2183. In the interval $\left(-\frac{\pi}{2}, \frac{\pi}{2}\right)$ determine the curve tangent to the axis OX at the origin if at any point its curvature $k=\cos x$.

12.8. Linear Homogeneous Differential Equations with Constant Coefficients

The homogeneous linear differential equation

$$y^{(n)}+p_1y^{(n-1)}+\ldots+p_ny=0, \tag{1}$$

where p_i is a function of x, has a general solution of the form

$$y=C_1y_1+C_2y_2+\ldots+C_ny_n, \tag{2}$$

where $y_1, y_2, \ldots, y_n$ are linearly independent particular solutions of equation (1) and $C_1, C_2, \ldots, C_n$ are arbitrary constants.

If the coefficients $p_1, p_2, \ldots, p_n$ of equation (1) are constant, then the particular solutions $y_1, y_2, \ldots, y_n$ are found with the aid of the characteristic equation

$$r^n+p_1r^{n-1}+\ldots+p_n=0. \tag{3}$$

(1) To each real root $r=a$ of equation (3) of multiplicity m there correspond m particular solutions $e^{\alpha x}$, $xe^{\alpha x}$, ..., $x^{m-1}e^{\alpha x}$.

(2) To each pair of imaginary roots $r=\alpha\pm\beta i$ of multiplicity m there correspond m pairs of particular solutions

$$\begin{cases} e^{\alpha x}\cos\beta x, & xe^{\alpha x}\cos\beta x, \ \ldots, \ x^{m-1}e^{\alpha x}\cos\beta x, \\ e^{\alpha x}\sin\beta x, & xe^{\alpha x}\sin\beta x, \ \ldots, \ x^{m-1}e^{\alpha x}\sin\beta x. \end{cases}$$

Solve the equations:

2184. $y''-4y'+3y=0.$

2185. $y''-4y'+4y=0.$

2186. $y''-4y'+13y=0.$

2187. $y''-4y=0.$

2188. $y''+4y=0.$

2189. $y''+4y'=0.$

2190. $\frac{d^2x}{dt^2}+3\frac{dx}{dt}-4x=0.$

2191. $4\frac{d^2\rho}{d\varphi^2}+\rho=0.$

2192. $\frac{d^2s}{dt^2}+2\frac{ds}{dt}+2s=0$; for $t=0$ $s=1$, $s'=1$.

2193. $y''' - 5y'' + 8y' - 4y = 0.$
2194. $y^{\text{IV}} - 16y = 0.$ **2195.** $y''' - 8y = 0.$
2196. $y''' + 3ay'' + 3a^2y' + a^3y = 0.$
2197. $y^{\text{IV}} + 4y = 0.$ **2198.** $4y^{\text{IV}} - 3y'' - y = 0.$
2199. Determine the equation of oscillations of a pendulum of mass m suspended from a thread of length l (neglect the resistance and put $\sin\alpha \approx \alpha$ for small α). Determine the period of oscillation.

2200. Two equal weights are suspended from the end of a spring. Under the action of one weight the spring is elongated by a cm. Determine the motion of the first weight if the second one drops (resistance should be neglected). Determine the period of oscillation.

2201. Solve Problem 2200 taking into consideration the resistance which is proportional to the speed of motion.

Solve the equations:

2202. $y'' + 3y' + 2y = 0.$ **2203.** $y'' + 2ay' + a^2y = 0.$
2204. $y'' + 2y' + 5y = 0.$ **2205.** $\frac{d^2x}{dt^2} - 2\frac{dx}{dt} - 3x = 0.$
2206. $\frac{d^2x}{dt^2} + \omega^2 x = 0.$ **2207.** $\frac{d^2s}{dt^2} + a\frac{ds}{dt} = 0.$
2208. $\ddot{x}_{tt} + 2\dot{x}_t + 3x = 0.$ **2209.** $y''' - 3y'' + 4y = 0.$
2210. $y^{\text{IV}} - 3y'' - 4y = 0.$ **2211.** $y^{\text{IV}} + 8y'' + 16y = 0.$
2212. Find the integral curve of the equation $y'' - y = 0$ tangent to the straight line $y = x$ at the point $(0, 0)$.

12.9. Linear Non-homogeneous Differential Equations with Constant Coefficients

1°. Basic property. Let there be given the equations:

$$y^{(n)} + p_1y^{(n-1)} + \ldots + p_ny = f(x) \text{—non-homogeneous,} \quad (1)$$

$$y^{(n)} + p_1y^{(n-1)} + \ldots + p_ny = 0 \text{—homogeneous,} \quad (2)$$

and let u be the *general* solution of equation (2), and y_1 a *particular* solution of equation (1). The *general* solution y of equation (1) will be:

$$y = u + y_1. \quad (3)$$

2°. The method of undetermined coefficients. With constant $p_1, p_2, \ldots, p_n$ the particular solution y_1 is found by the *method of undetermined coefficients* in the following cases:

(1) $f(x)$ is a polynomial,

(2) $f(x) = e^{mx}(a\cos nx + b\sin nx)$,

(3) $f(x)$ is a sum or a product of the previous functions.

In these cases the particular solution y_1 has the same form as $f(x)$, differing from the latter only by coefficients.

Exceptions are the cases when: (1) $f(x)$ is a polynomial but $r=0$ is the root of a characteristic equation of multiplicity k; (2) $f(x) = e^{mx}(a\cos nx + b\sin nx)$ but $r = m \pm ni$ is the root of a characteristic equation of multiplicity k. In these special cases y_1 differs from $f(x)$ not only by coefficients, but also by the factor x^k.

3°. The method of variation of constants. The most common method of solving a non-homogeneous linear equation is Lagrange's method, or the *method of variation of constants*.

If y_1 and y_2 are independent particular solutions of the equation $y'' + py' + qy = 0$, then the solution of the equation $y'' + py' + qy = f(x)$ by Lagrange's method is found in the form $y = Ay_1 + By_2$, where A and B are functions of x satisfying the system of equations

$$\begin{cases} A'y_1 + B'y_2 = 0, \\ A'y_1' + B'y_2' = f(x). \end{cases}$$

Hence

$$A' = -\frac{y_2 f(x)}{w}, \quad B' = \frac{y_1 f(x)}{w} \quad \text{and } w = \begin{vmatrix} y_1 & y_2 \\ y_1' & y_2' \end{vmatrix}.$$

Solve the equations:

2213. $y'' - 2y' + y = e^{2x}$. **2214.** $y'' - 4y = 8x^3$.

2215. $y'' + 3y' + 2y = \sin 2x + 2\cos 2x$.

2216. $y'' + y = x + 2e^x$. **2217.** $y'' + 3y' = 9x$.

2218. $y'' + 4y' + 5y = 5x^2 - 32x + 5$.

2219. $y'' - 3y' + 2y = e^x$. **2220.** $\frac{d^2x}{dt^2} + k^2x = 2k\sin kt$.

2221. $y''-2y=xe^{-x}$. **2222.** $y''-2y'=x^2-x$.

2223. $y''+5y'+6y=e^{-x}+e^{-2x}$.

2224. $\ddot{x}+2k\dot{x}+2k^2x=5k^2\sin kt$.

2225. $y'''+y''=6x+e^{-x}$. **2226.** $y^{IV}-81y=27e^{-3x}$.

2227. $\dddot{x}+\dot{x}=3t^2$. **2228.** $y'''+8y=e^{-2x}$.

2229. (1) $\ddot{x}+4\dot{x}+4x=e^{-2t}$; (2) $a^3\ddot{x}+ax=1$.

2230. $y''+4y=\frac{1}{\sin 2x}$. **2231.** $y''-4y'+5y=\frac{e^{2x}}{\cos x}$.

2232. $y''-2y'+y=x^{-2}e^x$. **2233.** $y''+y=\tan x$.

2234. (1) $y''+y'+\frac{1}{1+e^x}$; (2) $y''+4y'+4y=\frac{e^{-2x}}{x^3}$.

2235. A unit mass moves along the axis OX under the action of a constant force a directed along the axis with tractive resistance numerically equal to the velocity of motion. Find the equation of motion if at $t=0$ $x=0$ and velocity $v=0$.

Solve the equations:

2236. $y''+y'-2y=6x^2$. **2237.** $y''-5y'+6y=13\sin 3x$.

2238. $y''+2y'+y=e^x$. **2239.** $y''+y'+2.5y=25\cos 2x$.

2240. $4y''-y=x^3-24x$. **2241.** $y''-y=e^{-x}$.

2242. $\frac{d^2s}{dt^2}+2\frac{ds}{dt}+2s=2t^3-2$.

2243. (1) $y''-2my'+m^2y=\sin mx$; (2) $n^3y''-4ny=8$.

2244. $y^{IV}+5y''+4y=3\sin x$.

2245. $y'''-3y''+3y'-y=e^x$.

Solve the following equations using the method of variation of constants:

2246. $y''+4y'+4y=e^{-2x}\ln x$.

2247. (1) $y''+y=\frac{1}{\cos^3 x}$; (2) $y''+4y=\frac{1}{\sin^2 x}$.

2248. $y''-2y'+y=\frac{e^x}{\sqrt{4-x^2}}$.

12.10. Differential Equations of Various Types

Determine the type of the following differential equations and solve them:

2249. $y' + \frac{y}{1+x} = e^{-x}$. **2250.** $y' + y\tan x = \tan x$.

2251. $(x - x^3)\, y' + (2x^2 - 1)\, y = x^3$.

2252. $(1 + x^2)\, y' + y\left(x - \sqrt{1 + x^2}\right) = 0$.

2253. $t^2\, ds + 2ts\, dt = e^t\, dt$. **2254.** $xy' = 4\left(y + \sqrt{y}\right)$.

2255. $2xyy' = 2y^2 + \sqrt{y^4 + x^4}$.

2256. $xy'' + y' = \ln x$. **2257.** $yy'' - 2y'^2 = 0$.

2258. $y'' - m^2 y = e^{-mx}$. **2259.** $y'x\ln x + y = 2\ln x$.

2260. $xy' + y\ln\frac{y}{x} = 0$. **2261.** $2y' + y = y^3(x - 1)$.

2262. $y''' - 2y'' + y' = x^2$. **2263.** $y'' = y' + y'^2$.

2264. $\frac{d^3s}{dt^3} - 3\frac{ds}{dt} - 2s = \sin t + 2\cos t$.

2265. (1) $\sin t\, ds = \left(4t\sin^2\frac{t}{2} + s\right)dt$; (2) $yy'x - y^2 = 1$.

2266. (1) $xy' + y\,(x\tan x + 1) = \sec x$; (2) $y''' + y = e^{-x}$.

2267. (1) $y'' - 3y' + 2y = \frac{e^{3x}}{1 + e^{2x}}$; (2) $y'''y = y''y'$.

2268. A cylinder of radius a m and weight $P = a^3$ N floats on water with its axis in the vertical position. Find the period of oscillation which is caused when the cylinder is a bit dipped into the water and then is left free. Tractive resistance should be taken approximately equal to zero.

2269. A hollow iron sphere has the radii of the surfaces a and $2a$. Its interior surface is kept at a constant temperature of 100° C, its exterior surface at 20° C. Determine the temperature inside the wall at any distance r from the centre ($a \leqslant r \leqslant 2a$) and at $r = 1.6a$.

Hint. The rate of temperature drop $\frac{dT}{dr}$ in a conductor with stationary distribution of temperature is inversely proportional to the area of its cross section.

12.11. Euler's Linear Differential Equation

$$x^n y^{(n)} + a_1 x^{n-1} y^{(n-1)} + \ldots + a_{n-1} x y' + a_n y = f(x)$$

A particular solution of a homogeneous equation (for $f(x)=0$) can be found in the form $y=x^r$, where r is a constant number. To find r we have to substitute $y=x^r$ into a homogeneous differential equation and to solve the obtained *characteristic* equation with respect to r. In this case:

(1) To each real root $r=a$ of multiplicity m there correspond m particular solutions x^a, $x^a \ln x$, $x^a (\ln x)^2$, ...

(2) To each pair of imaginary roots $r=\alpha \pm \beta i$ of multiplicity m there correspond m pairs of particular solutions:

$$\begin{cases} x^\alpha \cos(\beta \ln x), & x^\alpha \cos(\beta \ln x) \ln x, \ \ldots, \\ x^\alpha \sin(\beta \ln x), & x^\alpha \sin(\beta \ln x) \ln x, \ \ldots. \end{cases}$$

Euler's non-homogeneous differential equation is solved by the method of variation of constants.

Solve the equations:

2270. (1) $x^3 y''' - 3xy' + 3y = 0$; (2) $x^2 y'' - 2y = 0$;
(3) $x^2 y'' + 2xy' - n(n+1) y = 0$.

2271. (1) $x^2 y'' + 5xy' + 4y = 0$; (2) $x^2 y'' + xy' + y = 0$.

2272. (1) $xy'' + 2y' = 10x$; (2) $x^2 y'' - 6y = 12 \ln x$.

2273. (1) $x^2 y'' - 2xy' + 2y = 4x$;
(2) $x^3 y'' + 3x^2 y' + xy = 6 \ln x$.

2274. (1) $x^2 y'' - 4xy' + 6y = x^5$; (2) $x^2 y'' + xy' + y = x$.

12.12. Systems of Linear Differential Equations with Constant Coefficients

Solve the equations:

2275. $\begin{cases} \dfrac{dx}{dt} + y = 0 \\ \dfrac{dx}{dt} - \dfrac{dy}{dt} = 3x + y. \end{cases}$ **2276.** $\begin{cases} \dfrac{dx}{dt} + x - y = e^t \\ \dfrac{dy}{dt} - x + y = e^t. \end{cases}$

Hint to Problem 2275. By differentiating the first equation with respect to t, eliminate y and $\frac{dy}{dt}$ from three equations.

2277. $\begin{cases} 5\frac{dx}{dt}-2\frac{dy}{dt}+4x-y=e^{-t} \\ \frac{dx}{dt}+8x-3y=5e^{-t}. \end{cases}$

2278. $\begin{cases} \ddot{x}-4\dot{x}+4x-y=0 \\ \ddot{y}+4\dot{y}+4y-24x=16e^{t}. \end{cases}$

Solve the equations:

2279. $\begin{cases} \dot{x}+3x+y=0 \\ \dot{y}-x+y=0, \end{cases}$ for $t=0$ $x=1$, $y=1$.

2280. $\begin{cases} \dot{x}=y \\ \dot{y}=x+2\sinh t. \end{cases}$

12.13. Partial Differential Equations of the Second Order (the Method of Characteristics)

2281. Find the general solution (containing two arbitrary functions) of the equations:

(1) $\frac{\partial^2 u}{\partial x\,\partial y}=0$; (2) $\frac{\partial^2 u}{\partial y^2}=0$; (3) $\frac{\partial^2 u}{\partial x\,\partial y}-\frac{1}{x}\frac{\partial u}{\partial y}=0$;

(4) $\frac{\partial^2 u}{\partial x\,\partial y}=2a\frac{x}{y}+b$.

Hint. Put $\frac{\partial u}{\partial y}=z$.

2282. Find the particular solution of the equation $\frac{\partial^2 z}{\partial x^2}=0$ for the initial conditions: for $x=1$ $z=y^3$, $\frac{\partial z}{\partial x}=y^2$.

2283. Reduce the equation $\frac{\partial^2 u}{\partial x^2}-4\frac{\partial^2 u}{\partial x\,\partial y}+3\frac{\partial^2 u}{\partial y^2}=0$ to the canonical form and find its general solution.

2284. Reduce the equation

$$x^2\frac{\partial^2 u}{\partial x^2}+2xy\frac{\partial^2 u}{\partial x\,\partial y}+y^2\frac{\partial^2 u}{\partial y^2}=0$$

to the canonical form and find its general solution.

For the following differential equations find the general solutions, and, if given the initial conditions, also the particular solutions:

2285. $\frac{\partial^2 u}{\partial x^2} - 4\frac{\partial^2 u}{\partial x\,\partial y} + 4\frac{\partial^2 u}{\partial y^2} = 0.$

2286. $\frac{\partial^2 u}{\partial x^2} - \frac{\partial^2 u}{\partial y^2} = 0$; for $x=0$ $u=\sin y$, $\frac{\partial u}{\partial x} = y$.

2287. $x\frac{\partial^2 u}{\partial x^2} + y\frac{\partial^2 u}{\partial x\,\partial y} = 0$;

$$\text{for } x=1 \quad u=2y+1, \ \frac{\partial u}{\partial x} = y.$$

2288. $t^2\frac{\partial^2 u}{\partial t^2} - x^2\frac{\partial^2 u}{\partial x^2} = 0$; for $t=1$ $u=2x^2$, $\frac{\partial u}{\partial t} = x^2$.

Find the particular solutions of the following differential equations:

2289. $\frac{\partial^2 u}{\partial t^2} + \frac{\partial^2 u}{\partial x\,\partial t} + \frac{\partial u}{\partial t} = 0$;

$$\text{for } t=0 \quad u=0, \ \frac{\partial u}{\partial t} = -x-1.$$

2290. $4a^2x\frac{\partial^2 u}{\partial x^2} - \frac{\partial^2 u}{\partial t^2} + 2a^2\frac{\partial u}{\partial x} = 0$;

$$\text{for } t=0 \quad u=0, \ \frac{\partial u}{\partial t} = ax.$$

2291. $a^2\frac{\partial^2 u}{\partial x^2} = \frac{\partial^2 u}{\partial t^2}$; for $t=0$ $u=f(x)$, $\frac{\partial u}{\partial t} = F(x)$.

CHAPTER 13

DOUBLE, TRIPLE, AND LINE INTEGRALS

13.1. Computing Areas By Means of Double Integrals

1°. If a domain (*S*) is defined by the inequalities

$$a \leqslant x \leqslant b, \quad y_1(x) \leqslant y \leqslant y_2(x),$$

then the area of this domain

$$S = \lim_{\substack{\Delta x \to 0 \\ \Delta y \to 0}} \sum\sum \Delta x \, \Delta y = \iint\limits_{(S)} dx\, dy = \int\limits_a^b dx \int\limits_{y_1(x)}^{y_2(x)} dy.$$

2°. If a domain (*S*) is determined by the inequalities

$$h \leqslant y \leqslant l, \quad x_1(y) \leqslant x \leqslant x_2(y),$$

then

$$S = \iint\limits_{(S)} dx\, dy = \int\limits_h^l dy \int\limits_{x_1(y)}^{x_2(y)} dx.$$

3°. If a domain (*S*) is defined in polar coordinates by the inequalities $\varphi_1 \leqslant \varphi \leqslant \varphi_2$, $r_1(\varphi) \leqslant r \leqslant r_2(\varphi)$, then the area of this domain

$$S = \iint\limits_{(S)} r\, dr\, d\varphi = \int\limits_{\varphi_1}^{\varphi_2} d\varphi \int\limits_{r_1(\varphi)}^{r_2(\varphi)} r\, dr.$$

Express by double integrals and compute the areas bounded by the following lines:

2292. $xy = 4$, $y = x$, $x = 4$.

2293. (1) $y = x^2$, $4y = x^2$, $y = 4$;

(2) $y = x^2$, $4y = x^2$, $x = \pm 2$.

2294. $y^2=4+x,\ x+3y=0.$

2295. $ay=x^2-2ax,\ \ y=x.$

2296. $y=\ln x,\ \ x-y=1$ and $y=-1.$

2297. Construct the domains whose areas are expressed by the following integrals:

$$(1)\ \int_0^a dx\int_0^x dy;\quad (2)\ \int_0^a dy\int_{a-y}^{\sqrt{a^2-y^2}} dx;\quad (3)\ \int_0^a dx\int_x^{\sqrt{2a^2-x^2}} dy.$$

Change the order of integration.

Hint. To get the equations of the lines bounding the domain equate the limits of the integral with respect to dx to x, and those with respect to dy to y.

2298. Construct the domains whose areas are expressed by the integrals: (1) $\int_0^1 dx\int_x^{2-x^2} dy$; (2) $\int_{-2}^0 dy\int_{y^2-4}^0 dx$. Change the order of integration and compute the areas.

2299. Compute the area bounded by the lines $r=a(1-\cos\varphi)$ and $r=a$ and situated outside the circle.

2300. Compute the area bounded by the straight line $r\cos\alpha=a$ and the circle $r=2a$.

Compute the areas bounded by the lines:

2301. $xy=\frac{a^2}{2},\ \ xy=2a^2,\ \ y=\frac{x}{2},\ \ y=2x.$

Hint. In this problem it is advantageous to pass over to the new coordinates $xy=u$ and $y=vx$; then the area is determined by the formula $\iint |J|\,du\,dv$, where $J=$

$$=\begin{vmatrix}\frac{\partial x}{\partial u} & \frac{\partial y}{\partial u}\\ \frac{\partial x}{\partial v} & \frac{\partial y}{\partial v}\end{vmatrix}$$

and is called the *Jacobian*. In Problem 2302 put $y^2=ux$, $vy^2=x^3$, and in Problem 2303 pass over to generalized polar coordinates $x=r\cos^3\varphi$ and $y=r\sin^3\varphi$.

2302. $y^2=ax,\ \ y^2=16ax,\ \ ay^2=x^3,\ \ 16ay^2=x^3.$

2303. $x^{\frac{2}{3}}+y^{\frac{2}{3}}=a^{\frac{2}{3}}.$

Compute the areas bounded by the following lines:

2304. $y=x^2$, $y=x+2$.

2305. $ax=y^2-2ay$ and $y+x=0$.

2306. $y=\sin x$, $y=\cos x$, and $x=0$.

2307. $y^2=a^2-ax$, $y=a+x$.

2308. $r=4(1+\cos\varphi)$, $r\cos\varphi=3$ (to the right of the straight line).

2309. $r=a(1-\cos\varphi)$, $r=a$ and situated outside the cardioid.

2310. $xy=1$, $xy=8$, $y^2=x$, $y^2=8x$.

2311. Construct the domain whose areas are expressed by the integrals:

$$(1)\ \int_a^b dx\int_a^x dy;\quad (2)\ \int_0^a dy\int_{\sqrt{ay}}^{\sqrt{2a^2-y^2}} dx;\quad (3)\ \int_0^4 dx\int_{2\sqrt{x}}^{8-x} dy.$$

Change the order of integration and compute the areas.

13.2. The Centre of Gravity and the Moment of Inertia of an Area with Uniformly Distributed Mass (for Density $\mu=1$)

The coordinates of the centre of gravity of an area S with uniformly distributed mass:

$$x_c=\frac{\iint x\,dx\,dy}{S},\quad y_c=\frac{\iint y\,dx\,dy}{S}. \tag{1}$$

The moments of inertia of the area S

$$J_x=\iint_{(S)} y^2\,dx\,dy,\quad J_y=\iint_{(S)} x^2\,dx\,dy,\quad J_0=\iint_{(S)} r^2\,dx\,dy. \tag{2}$$

Determine the centre of gravity of an area bounded by the given lines:

2312. $y=0$ and a half-wave of the sinusoid $y=\sin x$.

2313. $y=x^2$, $x=4$, $y=0$. **2314.** $y^2=ax$ and $y=x$.

2315. $x^2+y^2=a^2$ and $y=0$.

2316. The astroid $x^{\frac{2}{3}}+y^{\frac{2}{3}}=a^{\frac{2}{3}}$ and the axis OX.

Hint. Pass over to generalized polar coordinates

$$x = r\cos^3\varphi \quad \text{and} \quad y = r\sin^3\varphi.$$

2317. Determine the moments of inertia J_x, J_y and J_0 of the area of a rectangle bounded by the lines $x=0$, $x=a$, $y=0$, and $y=b$.

2318. Determine the moment of inertia about the axis OX of the area bounded by the lines $y=\frac{x}{2}$, $x=a$, $y=a$.

2319. Determine the moment of inertia about the axis OY of the area of a triangle with the vertices $A(0, 2a)$, $B(a, 0)$, and $C(a, a)$.

In Problems 2320 through 2323 determine the polar moment of inertia of an area bounded by the lines:

2320. $x+y=a$, $x=0$, $y=0$.

2321. $r^2=a^2\cos 2\varphi$.

2322. A circle $r=a$.

2323. $y^2=ax$, $x=a$.

Determine the centre of gravity of:

2324. The half-segment of the parabola $y^2=ax$, $x=a$, $y=0$ (for $y>0$).

2325. The semi-ellipse $\frac{x^2}{a^2}+\frac{y^2}{b^2}=1$ cut off by the x-axis.

2326. Determine the moment of inertia about the y-axis of the area bounded by the lines $y=a+\frac{x^2}{a}$, $y=2x$, and $x=0$.

2327. Determine the moment of inertia about the x-axis of the area of a triangle with the vertices $A(1, 1)$, $B(2, 1)$, $C(3, 3)$.

Determine the polar moment of inertia of the area bounded by the lines:

2328. $\frac{x}{a}+\frac{y}{b}=1$, $x=0$, $y=0$.

2329. $y=4-x^2$ and $y=0$. **2330.** $r=a(1-\cos\varphi)$.

13.3. Computing Volumes by Means of Double Integrals

The volume of a solid bounded from the top by a surface $z=F(x, y)$, from the bottom by a plane $z=0$, and from the sides by a cylindrical surface cutting off a domain (S) on the plane XOY, is equal to

$$V=\iint\limits_{(S)} z\,dx\,dy=\iint\limits_{(S)} F(x, y)\,dx\,dy.$$

Compute the volumes of solids bounded by the following surfaces:

2331. $z=x^2+y^2$, $x+y=4$, $x=0$, $y=0$, $z=0$.

2332. $z=x+y+a$, $y^2=ax$, $x=a$, $z=0$, $y=0$ (for $y>0$).

2333. $(x+y)^2+az=a^2$, $x=0$, $y=0$, $z=0$ (construct the surface using the sections: $x=0$, $y=0$, $z=0$, $z=h\leqslant a$; see Problem 546).

2334. $x^2+y^2=a^2$, $x^2+z^2=a^2$ (see Problem 552).

2335. $z^2=xy$, $x=a$, $x=0$, $y=a$, $y=0$.

2336. $az=x^2-y^2$, $z=0$, $x=a$.

2337. $z^2=xy$, $x+y=a$.

2338. $x+y+z=3a$, $x^2+y^2=a^2$, $z=0$.

Hint. In Problems 2338 to 2344 pass to polar coordinates.

2339. $z=mx$, $x^2+y^2=a^2$, $z=0$.

2340. $az=a^2-x^2-y^2$, $z=0$.

2341. $x^2+y^2+z^2=4a^2$, $x^2+y^2=a^2$ (outside the cylinder).

2342. $x^2+y^2+z^2=a^2$, $x^2+y^2\pm ax=0$ (inside the cylinders).

2343. The first turn of the helicoid $y=x\tan\frac{z}{a}$ inside the cylinder $x^2+y^2=a^2$ and the plane $z=0$.

2344. $z^2=2ax$, $x^2+y^2=ax$.

2345. $\frac{z}{c}=1-\frac{x^2}{a^2}-\frac{y^2}{b^2}$, $z=0$.

Hint. In Problems 2345 and 2346 pass to elliptic polar coordinates: $x=ar\cos\varphi$, $y=br\sin\varphi$.

2346. $z=ce^{-\frac{x^2}{a^2}-\frac{y^2}{b^2}}$ and $\frac{x^2}{a^2}+\frac{y^2}{b^2}=1$.

2347. $x^{\frac{2}{3}}+y^{\frac{2}{3}}+z^{\frac{2}{3}}=a^{\frac{2}{3}}$ (put $x=r\cos^3\varphi$, $y=r\sin^3\varphi$).

Compute the volumes of solids bounded by the following surfaces:

2348. $z=a-x$, $y^2=ax$ and $z=0$.

2349. $z=x^2+y^2$, $y=x^2$, $y=1$, $z=0$.

2350. $y^2+z^2=4ax$, $y^2=ax$, $x=3a$ (outside the cylinder).

2351. $\frac{x^2}{a^2}+\frac{z^2}{b^2}=1$, $\frac{x^2}{a^2}+\frac{y^2}{b^2}=1$.

2352. Conoid $x^2y^2+h^2z^2=a^2y^2$ for $0\leqslant y\leqslant h$ (see Problem 559).

2353. $x^{\frac{2}{3}}+z^{\frac{2}{3}}=a^{\frac{2}{3}}$, $x^{\frac{2}{3}}+y^{\frac{2}{3}}=a^{\frac{2}{3}}$.

2354. $4z=16-x^2-y^2$, $z=0$, $x^2+y^2=4$ (outside the cylinder).

Hint. In Problems 2354 to 2358 pass to polar coordinates.

2355. $z^2=(x+a)^2$, $x^2+y^2=a^2$.

2356. $z=\frac{4}{x^2+y^2}$, $z=0$, $x^2+y^2=1$, $x^2+y^2=4$.

2357. $az=x^2+y^2$, $z=0$, $x^2+y^2\pm ax=0$.

2358. $az=a^2-x^2-y^2$, $z=0$, $x^2+y^2\pm ax=0$ (inside the cylinders).

2359. $\frac{x^2}{a^2}+\frac{y^2}{b^2}+\frac{z^2}{c^2}=1$.

Hint. Put $x=ar\cos\varphi$, $y=br\sin\varphi$.

13.4. Areas of Curved Surfaces

The area σ of a portion of the surface $F(x, y, z)=0$ whose projection on the plane $z=0$ defines the domain (σ_z), is

$$\sigma=\iint\limits_{(\sigma_z)}\frac{\sqrt{\left(\frac{\partial F}{\partial x}\right)^2+\left(\frac{\partial F}{\partial y}\right)^2+\left(\frac{\partial F}{\partial z}\right)^2}}{\left|\frac{\partial F}{\partial z}\right|}\,dx\,dy=\iint\limits_{(\sigma_z)}\frac{N}{\left|\frac{\partial F}{\partial z}\right|}\,dx\,dy.$$

Analogously, when projecting on the two other coordinate planes we get

$$\sigma=\iint\limits_{(\sigma_y)}\frac{N}{\left|\frac{\partial F}{\partial y}\right|}\,dx\,dz,\quad \sigma=\iint\limits_{(\sigma_x)}\frac{N}{\left|\frac{\partial F}{\partial x}\right|}\,dy\,dz.$$

Compute the area of:

2360. The surface of the cylinder $2z=x^2$ cut off by the planes $y=\frac{x}{2}$, $y=2x$, $x=2\sqrt{2}$.

2361. The surface of the cone $z^2=2xy$ cut off by the planes $x=a$ and $y=a$ for $x\geqslant 0$ and $y\geqslant 0$.

2362. The surface of the cone $y^2+z^2=x^2$ located inside the cylinder $x^2+y^2=a^2$.

2363. The surface $az=xy$ situated inside the cylinder $x^2+y^2=a^2$.

2364. The surface of the cone $x^2+y^2=z^2$ situated inside the cylinder $z^2=2px$.

Compute the area of:

2365. The surface of the cylinder $x^2+z^2=a^2$ situated inside the cylinder $x^2+y^2=a^2$.

2366. The surface of the sphere $x^2+y^2+z^2=a^2$ situated inside the cylinders $x^2+y^2\pm ax=0$.

2367. The surface of the paraboloid $x^2+y^2=2az$ located inside the cylinder $x^2+y^2=3a^2$.

2368. Using the double integral, determine the area of the portion of the earth surface bounded by the meridians 0° and β°, the equator, and the parallel of latitude α°. Consider the particular case: $\alpha=30°$; $\beta=60°$.

13.5. The Triple Integral and Its Applications

If a domain (V) is defined by the inequalities

$$a\leqslant x\leqslant b,\quad y_1(x)\leqslant y\leqslant y_2(x),\quad z_1(x,\,y)\leqslant z\leqslant z_2(x,\,y),$$

then

$$\iiint\limits_{(V)}F(x,\,y,\,z)\,dx\,dy\,dz=\int\limits_a^b dx\int\limits_{y_1(x)}^{y_2(x)}dy\int\limits_{z_1(x,\,y)}^{z_2(x,\,y)}F(x,\,y,\,z)\,dz.$$

For $F(x, y, z)=1$ we get the volume V. The coordinates of the centre of gravity of a homogeneous body of the volume V are computed by the formulas:

$$x_c=\frac{1}{V}\iiint\limits_{(V)} x\,dx\,dy\,dz,\quad y_c=\frac{1}{V}\iiint\limits_{(V)} y\,dx\,dy\,dz \text{ and so on.}$$

2369. Determine the volume of a solid bounded by the surfaces $az=x^2+y^2$, $2az=a^2-x^2-y^2$.

2370. Determine the volume of a solid bounded by the surfaces $x^2+y^2-z^2=0$, $x^2+y^2+z^2=a^2$ inside the cone.

2371. Show that the cone $x^2+y^2-z^2=0$ divides the volume of the sphere $x^2+y^2+z^2=2az$ in the ratio 3:1.

2372. Determine the mass of a pyramid formed by the planes $x+y+z=a$, $x=0$, $y=0$, $z=0$ if the density at each of its points is equal to the z-coordinate of this point.

Determine the centre of gravity of a uniform solid bounded by the surfaces:

2373. $x+y+z=a$, $x=0$, $y=0$, $z=0$.

2374. $az=a^2-x^2-y^2$, $z=0$.

Determine the moment of inertia about the axis OZ of a body bounded by the surfaces (density $\mu=1$):

2375. $x=0$, $y=0$, $y=a$, $z=0$, and $x+z=a$.

2376. $x+y+z=a\sqrt{2}$, $x^2+y^2=a^2$, $z=0$.

2377. Determine the volume of a body bounded by a closed surface:

(1) $(x^2+y^2+z^2)^2=a^3x$; (2) $(x^2+y^2+z^2)^2=az(x^2+y^2)$.

Hint. Pass to spherical coordinates using the formulas: $x=r\sin\theta\cos\varphi$, $y=r\sin\theta\sin\varphi$, $z=r\cos\varphi$; the element of volume $dV=r^2\sin\theta\,dr\,d\varphi\,d\theta$.

Determine the volume of a body bounded by the given surfaces:

2378. $az=x^2+y^2$, $x^2+y^2+z^2=2a^2$.

2379. $x^2+y^2-z^2=0$, $z=6-x^2-y^2$.

2380. $az=x^2+y^2$, $z^2=x^2+y^2$.

2381. Determine the mass of a solid bounded by the surfaces $x^2+y^2-z^2=0$ and $z=h$ if the density at each of its points is equal to the z-coordinate of this point.

2382. Determine the mass of a solid bounded by the surfaces $2x+z=2a$, $x+z=a$, $y^2=ax$, $y=0$ (for $y>0$) if the density at each of its points is equal to the ordinate y of this point.

2383. Determine the centre of gravity of a uniform hemisphere $x^2+y^2+z^2=a^2$, $z=0$.

2384. Determine the moment of inertia about the axis OZ of a solid bounded by the surfaces $z^2=2ax$, $z=0$, $x^2+y^2=ax$.

2385. Determine the volume of a solid bounded by the surface $(x^2+y^2+z^2)^2=axyz$ (pass to spherical coordinates; see Problems 2377).

2386. Determine the mass of a spherical layer between the surfaces $x^2+y^2+z^2=a^2$ and $x^2+y^2+z^2=4a^2$ if the density at each of its points is inversely proportional to the distance of a point from the origin (pass to spherical coordinates).

13.6. The Line Integral. Green's Formula

1°. Definition of a line integral. Let a continuous function $P(x, y, z)$ be defined on an arc $\breve{AB}$ of a rectifiable curve. Partition $\breve{AB}$ into elementary arcs by points $A(x_0, y_0, z_0)$, $M_1(x_1, y_1, z_1)$, $\ldots$, $M_{n-1}(x_{n-1}, y_{n-1}, z_{n-1})$, and $B(x_n, y_n, z_n)$; let $x_i-x_{i-1}=\Delta x_i$. Then $\lim\limits_{\Delta x_i \to 0} \sum\limits_{i=1}^{n} P(x_i, y_i, z_i)\Delta x_i$ is called the *line integral* taken along the arc $\breve{AB}$, and is denoted $\int\limits_{\breve{AB}} P(x, y, z)\,dx$. The integrals $\int\limits_{\breve{AB}} Q(x, y, z)\,dy$ and $\int\limits_{\breve{AB}} R(x, y, z)\,dz$ are defined similarly: the sum of the previous integrals is $\int\limits_{\breve{AB}} (P\,dx+Q\,dy+R\,dz)$. Finally, there also exists a line integral of the form: $\int\limits_{\breve{AB}} P(x, y, z)\, ds = \lim\limits_{\Delta s_i \to 0} \sum\limits_{i=1}^{n} P(x_i, y_i, z_i)\, \Delta s_i$, where $\Delta s_i = \breve{M_{i-1}M_i}$.

2°. Computing a line integral. Let a curve $\breve{AB}$ be given by the equations $x = f(t)$, $y = \varphi(t)$, $z = \psi(t)$, and the parameter t changes monotonically when a point $M(t)$ moves along the arc $\breve{AB}$ in one direction; then

$$\int\limits_{\breve{AB}} P(x, y, z)\, dx = \int\limits_{t_A}^{t_B} P[f(t), \varphi(t), \psi(t)]\, f'(t)\, dt,$$

i. e. *all the variables and differentials* of the integrand *must be expressed in terms of one variable* (t) *and its differential* (dt) *from the equations of the curve.*

3°. Mechanical meaning of a line integral. An integral of the form $\int\limits_{\breve{AB}} (P\,dx + Q\,dy + R\,dz)$ expresses the *work* performed during the displacement of unit mass along an arc $\breve{AB}$ in a field of a force $\boldsymbol{F}\{P, Q, R\}$.

4°. The case of a total differential. If in a certain domain (V) $P\,dx + Q\,dy + R\,dz = du$, then $\int\limits_{\breve{AB}} (P\,dx + Q\,dy + R\,dz) = u_B - u_A$, i. e. equal to the difference between the values of the function $u(x, y, z)$ at the points B and A and is *independent of the path of integration* $\breve{AB}$ taken in the domain (V).

5°. Green's formula

$$\oint\limits_{(C)} (P\,dx + Q\,dy) = \iint\limits_{(S)} \left(\frac{\partial Q}{\partial x} - \frac{\partial P}{\partial y} \right) dx\, dy$$

transforms a line integral of the expression $P\,dx + Q\,dy$ taken counterclockwise along a contour (C) into a double integral over the domain (S) bounded by this contour.

6°. The area bounded by the contour (C):

$$S = \frac{1}{2} \oint\limits_{(C)} (x\,dy - y\,dx).$$

2387. Given the points $A(2, 2)$ and $B(2, 0)$. Compute $\int\limits_{(C)} (x+y)\,dx$ along (1) the straight line OA; (2) the arc $\overset{\frown}{OA}$ of the parabola $y=\frac{x^2}{2}$; (3) the polygonal line OBA.

2388. Given the points $A(4, 2)$ and $B(2, 0)$. Compute $\int\limits_{(C)} [(x+y)\,dx-x\,dy]$ along (1) the straight line OA; (2) the polygonal line OBA.

2389. Solve Problem 2388 for the integral $\int\limits_{(C)} (y\,dx+x\,dy)$. Why is the value of the integral here independent of the choice of the path of integration?

2390. Given the points $A(a, 0, 0)$, $B(a, a, 0)$, and $C(a, a, a)$. Compute the integral $\int (y\,dx+z\,dy+x\,dz)$ along (1) the straight line OC; (2) the polygonal line $OABC$.

2391. A field is formed by a force $\boldsymbol{F}\{P, Q\}$, where $P=x-y$, $Q=x$. Construct the force $\boldsymbol{F}$ at each vertex of a square with sides $x=\pm a$ and $y=\pm a$, and compute the work performed by this force acting on unit mass which is in motion along the contour of the square.

2392. A field is formed by a force $\boldsymbol{F}\{P, Q\}$, where $P=x+y$, $Q=2x$. Construct the force $\boldsymbol{F}$ at the beginning of each quarter of the circle $x=a\cos t$, $y=a\sin t$ and compute the work performed by this force acting on unit mass which is in motion along the circle.

Solve the same problem if $P=x+y$, $Q=x$. Why is the work equal to zero here?

2393. A field is formed by a force $\boldsymbol{F}\{y, a\}$. Determine the work performed by this force acting on mass m moving along the contour made up of the coordinate semi-axes and the first quarter of the ellipse $x=a\cos t$, $y=b\sin t$.

2394. A field is formed by a force $\boldsymbol{F}\{x, y, z\}$. Compute the work performed by this force acting on unit mass moving along the polygonal line $OABCO$ joining the points $O(0, 0, 0)$, $A(0, a, 0)$, $B(a, a, 0)$, $C(a, a, a)$.

2395. Write and check Green's formula for $\oint\limits_{(C)} [(x+y)\,dx -$

$-2x\,dy]$ along the perimeter of a triangle with the sides $x=0$, $y=0$, $x+y=a$.

2396. Compute the integrals: (1) $\int\limits_{AB}[2xy\,dx+x^2dy]$; (2) $\int\limits_{AB}[\cos 2y\,dx-2x\sin 2y\,dy]$; (3) $\int\limits_{AB}[\tan y\,dx+x\sec^2 y\,dy]$ along any line from $A\left(1, \frac{\pi}{6}\right)$ to $B\left(2, \frac{\pi}{4}\right)$.

2397. Applying Green's formula, compute the integral $\oint\limits_{(C)}[y^2dx+(x+y)^2\,dy]$ along the contour of $\triangle ABC$ with the vertices $A(a, 0)$, $B(a, a)$ and $C(0, a)$.

2398. Determine the area of the ellipse $x=a\cos t$, $y=b\sin t$ by means of the line integral.

2399. Determine the area enclosed by the loop of the curve $x^3+x^2-y^2=0$ using the line integral (see Fig. 53 on p. 357).

Hint. Pass to parametric equations putting $y=xt$.

2400. Determine the area enclosed by the loop of the folium of Descartes $x^3+y^3-3axy=0$ using the line integral (see the hint to Problem 2399 and Fig. 83 on p. 386).

2401. With what force does the mass M uniformly distributed over the upper semicircle $x^2+y^2=a^2$ attract the mass m concentrated at the origin?

Hint. Let μ be the line density; ds, the element of the length of the semicircle; θ, the angle formed by the radius vector with the axis OX; X and Y, the projections of the attractive force. Then $X=\int\limits_{(C)}\frac{km\mu\cos\theta\,ds}{r^2}$, $Y=\int\limits_{(C)}\frac{km\mu\sin\theta\,ds}{r^2}$, where k is the gravity constant.

2402. Given the points $A(-a, a)$ and $B(a, a)$. What is the force with which a mass M uniformly distributed along the line segment AB attracts the mass m concentrated at the point $(0, 0)$?

2403. Given the points $A(a, 0)$, $B(0, a)$, and $C(-a, 0)$. What is the force with which a mass M uniformly distributed along the polygonal line ABC attracts the mass m concentrated at the origin?

2404. Given the points $A(0, 1)$, $B(2, 5)$, and $C(0, 5)$. Compute $\int\limits_{(C)} [(x+y)\,dx - 2y\,dy]$ along (1) the straight line AB; (2) the arc $\overset{\frown}{AB}$ of the parabola $y = x^2 + 1$; (3) the polygonal line ABC.

2405. Given the points $A(-a, 0)$ and $B(0, a)$. Compute the work performed by the force $\mathbf{F}\{P, Q\}$, where $P = y$ and $Q = y - x$, acting on unit mass moving along (1) the straight line AB; (2) the polygonal line AOB; (3) the arc $\overset{\frown}{AB}$ of the parabola $y = a - \frac{x^2}{a}$.

2406. Show that $\oint\limits_{(C)} [y\,dx + (x+y)\,dy]$ taken along any contour is equal to zero. Check this by computing the integral along the contour of a figure bounded by the lines $y = x^2$ and $y = 4$.

2407. Write and verify Green's formula for the integral $\oint\limits_{(C)} \left(\frac{dx}{y} - \frac{dy}{x}\right)$ taken along the contour of a triangle ABC with the vertices $A(1, 1)$, $B(2, 1)$, and $C(2, 2)$.

2408. Determine the area of the astroid $x = a\cos^3 t$, $y = a\sin^3 t$ by means of the line integral.

2409. Determine the area bounded by the curve $y^2 + x^4 - x^2 = 0$ using the line integral. (Pass to parametric equations putting $y = xt$.)

13.7. Surface Integrals. Ostrogradsky's and Stokes' Formulas

1°. Ostrogradsky's formula:

$$\iint\limits_{(S)} (P\cos\alpha + Q\cos\beta + R\cos\gamma)\,ds = \iiint\limits_{(V)} \left(\frac{\partial P}{\partial x} + \frac{\partial Q}{\partial y} + \frac{\partial R}{\partial z}\right) dx\,dy\,dz,$$

where α, β, and γ are the angles of the external normal to the closed surface S, and V is the volume bounded by this surface. The first integral can be written in the form $\pm \iint\limits_{(S_z)} \left[P \frac{\partial F}{\partial x} + Q \frac{\partial F}{\partial y} + R \frac{\partial F}{\partial z}\right] \frac{dx\,dy}{\frac{\partial F}{\partial z}}$, where $F(x, y, z)=0$ is an equation of a surface, and S_z is the projection of S on the plane $z=0$.

2°. Stokes' formula:

$$\oint\limits_{(C)} (P\,dx + Q\,dy + R\,dz) = \iint\limits_{(S)} \begin{vmatrix} \cos\alpha & \cos\beta & \cos\gamma \\ \frac{\partial}{\partial x} & \frac{\partial}{\partial y} & \frac{\partial}{\partial z} \\ P & Q & R \end{vmatrix} ds,$$

where α, β, and γ are the angles of the normal to the surface S directed in such a way that the traverse of the contour C is counterclockwise.

2410. Compute $\iint\limits_{(S)} [x\cos\alpha + y\cos\beta + z\cos\gamma]\,ds$ over the upper surface of the plane $x+y+z=a$ situated in the first octant.

2411. Compute

$$\iint\limits_{(S)} [x^2\cos(\widehat{\boldsymbol{n}, \boldsymbol{i}}) + y^2\cos(\widehat{\boldsymbol{n}, \boldsymbol{j}}) + z^2\cos(\widehat{\boldsymbol{n}, \boldsymbol{k}})]\,ds$$

over the upper surface of the paraboloid $x^2+y^2+2az=a^2$ situated in the second octant (where $x<0$, $y>0$, $z>0$).

Hint. Reducing the integral to the form

$$\iint\limits_{(S_z)} (x^3+y^3+az^2)\frac{dx\,dy}{a},$$

pass to polar coordinates. The angle φ will vary from $\frac{\pi}{2}$ to π.

2412. Write and check Ostrogradsky's formula for the integral $\iint\limits_{(S)} [x\cos(\widehat{\boldsymbol{n}, \boldsymbol{i}}) + y\cos(\widehat{\boldsymbol{n}, \boldsymbol{j}}) + z\cos(\widehat{\boldsymbol{n}, \boldsymbol{k}})]\,ds$, taken over the surface of the sphere $x^2+y^2+z^2=a^2$.

2413. Write and check Ostrogradsky's formula for the integral

$$\iint\limits_{(S)} [x^2 \cos(\widehat{\boldsymbol{n}, \boldsymbol{i}}) + y^2 \cos(\widehat{\boldsymbol{n}, \boldsymbol{j}}) + z^2 \cos(\widehat{\boldsymbol{n}, \boldsymbol{k}})]\, ds,$$

taken over the outside surface of a solid bounded by the surfaces $x^2+y^2+2az=a^2$, $x=0$, $y=0$, $z=0$ inside the first octant.

Hint. The double integral over plane faces of the solid is equal to zero since, for instance, on the plane $z=0$ both $\cos(\widehat{\boldsymbol{n}, \boldsymbol{i}})=0$ and $\cos(\widehat{\boldsymbol{n}, \boldsymbol{j}})=0$.

2414. Putting in Ostrogradsky's formula $P=x$, $Q=y$, $R=z$, obtain the formula for the volume:

$$V = \frac{1}{3} \iint\limits_{(S)} [x \cos\alpha + y \cos\beta + z \cos\gamma]\, ds.$$

Using this formula, compute the volume of the ellipsoid

$$\frac{x^2}{a^2}+\frac{y^2}{b^2}+\frac{z^2}{c^2}=1.$$

2415. Putting in Ostrogradsky's formula $P=\frac{\partial u}{\partial x}$, $Q=\frac{\partial u}{\partial y}$ and $R=\frac{\partial u}{\partial z}$ (i.e. putting the vector $\{P, Q, R\}$ to be equal to grad u), prove that

$$\iiint\limits_{(V)} \Delta u\, dx\, dy\, dz = \iint\limits_{(S)} \frac{du}{dn}\, ds,$$

where $\Delta u = \frac{\partial^2 u}{\partial x^2}+\frac{\partial^2 u}{\partial y^2}+\frac{\partial^2 u}{\partial z^2}$ is the Laplacian operator.

2416. Check the formula obtained in the previous problem for the function $u=x^2+y^2+z^2$ on the surface $x^2+y^2+z^2=a^2$.

2417. Show with the aid of Stokes' formula that $\int\limits_{(C)} (yz\, dx + xz\, dy + xy\, dz)$ taken along any contour is equal to zero. Check this by computing the integral along the contour of a triangle OAB with the vertices $O(0, 0, 0)$, $A(1, 1, 0)$, and $B(1, 1, 1)$.

2418. Write and check Stokes' formula for the integral $\oint\limits_{(C)} [(z-y)\,dx+(x-z)\,dy+(y-x)\,dz]$ taken along the contour of a triangle ABC with the vertices $A(a, 0, 0)$, $B(0, a, 0)$, and $C(0, 0, a)$.

Hint. The double integral can be taken over any surface passing through the perimeter of the triangle ABC, for instance, over the plane $x+y+z=a$.

2419. Write and check Ostrogradsky's formula for the integral $\iint\limits_{(S)} [x^3 \cos(\widehat{\boldsymbol{n}, \boldsymbol{i}})+y^3 \cos(\widehat{\boldsymbol{n}, \boldsymbol{j}})+z^3 \cos(\widehat{\boldsymbol{n}, \boldsymbol{k}})]\,ds$ taken over the surface of the sphere $x^2+y^2+z^2=a^2$.

Hint. Transform the triple integral to spherical coordinates.

2420. Write and check Stokes' formula for the integral $\oint\limits_{(C)} [x(z-y)\,dx+y(x-z)\,dy+z(y-x)\,dz]$ taken along the contour of a triangle with the vertices $A(a, 0, 0)$, $B(0, a, 0)$, and $C(0, 0, a)$. (See the hint to Problem 2418.)

2421. With the aid of Ostrogradsky's formula compute the integral $\iint\limits_{(S)} (x^3\,dy\,dz+y^3\,dx\,dz+z^3\,dx\,dy)$ taken over the outside surface of a pyramid formed by the planes $x+y+z=a$, $x=0$, $y=0$, $z=0$.

CHAPTER 14

SERIES

14.1 Numerical Series

1°. A series $u_1+u_2+u_3+\ldots+u_n+\ldots$ is called *convergent* if the sum S_n of its first n terms (as $n\to\infty$) tends to a finite limit S: $\lim\limits_{n\to\infty} S_n=S$. The number S is termed the *sum* of the convergent series. If the sum S_n has no finite limit, then the series is called *divergent*.

For a series to be convergent it is necessary but not sufficient that $u_n\to 0$ as $n\to\infty$.

2°. The *integral test* for convergence of a positive series with decreasing terms:

if $u_n=f(n)$, where $f(n)$ is a decreasing function, and

$$\int_1^\infty f(n)\,dn=\begin{cases} A, & \text{then a series converges,}\\ \infty, & \text{then a series diverges.}\end{cases}$$

3°. *D'Alembert's test* for a positive series: if

$$\lim_{n\to\infty}\frac{u_{n+1}}{u_n}=r\begin{cases} <1, & \text{then a series converges,}\\ >1, & \text{then a series diverges,}\\ =1, & \text{then the problem remains unsolved.}\end{cases}$$

4°. Comparing positive series:

$$u_1+u_2+u_3+\ldots+u_n+\ldots, \qquad (1)$$
$$v_1+v_2+v_3+\ldots+v_n+\ldots. \qquad (2)$$

(1) If $u_n\leqslant v_n$ and series (2) *converges*, then series (1) *converges* too.

(2) If $u_n\geqslant v_n$ and series (2) *diverges*, then series (1) *diverges* too.

5°. The alternating series $u_1 - u_2 + u_3 - u_4 + \ldots$ converges if $u_1 > u_2 > u_3 > \ldots$ and $\lim\limits_{n \to \infty} u_n = 0$.

6°. Absolute and conditional convergence. The series

$$u_1 + u_2 + u_3 + \ldots + u_n + \ldots \tag{3}$$

definitely converges if the positive series

$$|u_1| + |u_2| + |u_3| + \ldots + |u_n| + \ldots \tag{4}$$

composed of the absolute values of the terms of the given series converges. In this case series (3) is called *absolutely* convergent. But if series (3) converges and series (4) diverges, then series (3) is termed *conditionally* convergent.

Check whether the necessary condition for convergence is fulfilled:

2422. $\frac{1}{2} + \frac{3}{4} + \frac{5}{6} + \frac{7}{8} + \ldots$

2423. $\frac{1}{1} + \frac{1}{3} + \frac{1}{5} + \frac{1}{7} + \ldots$

2424. $\frac{2}{3} + \frac{4}{9} + \frac{6}{27} + \frac{8}{81} + \ldots$

Test the series for convergence by means of the integral test:

2425. $1 + \frac{1}{3} + \frac{1}{5} + \frac{1}{7} + \ldots$

2426. $1 + \frac{1}{\sqrt{4}} + \frac{1}{\sqrt{7}} + \frac{1}{\sqrt{10}} + \ldots$

2427. $\frac{1}{2^3} + \frac{2}{3^3} + \frac{3}{4^3} + \ldots$

2428. $\frac{1}{1+1^2} + \frac{1}{1+2^2} + \frac{1}{1+3^2} + \ldots$

2429. $\frac{1}{1+1^2} + \frac{2}{1+2^2} + \frac{3}{1+3^2} + \ldots$

2430. $\frac{1}{3^2-1} + \frac{1}{5^2-1} + \frac{1}{7^2-1} + \ldots$

2431. $\frac{1}{2\ln^2 2} + \frac{1}{3\ln^2 3} + \frac{1}{4\ln^2 4} + \ldots$

Test the series for convergence using d'Alembert's test:

2432. $\frac{2}{3} + \frac{4}{9} + \frac{6}{27} + \frac{8}{81} + \ldots$

2433. $1+\frac{2}{2!}+\frac{4}{3!}+\frac{8}{4!}+\ldots$

2434. $1+\frac{1\cdot 2}{1\cdot 3}+\frac{1\cdot 2\cdot 3}{1\cdot 3\cdot 5}+\ldots$

2435. $1+\frac{3}{2\cdot 3}+\frac{3^2}{2^2\cdot 5}+\frac{3^3}{2^3\cdot 7}+\ldots$

2436. $\frac{1}{2}+\frac{3!}{2\cdot 4}+\frac{5!}{2\cdot 4\cdot 6}+\frac{7!}{2\cdot 4\cdot 6\cdot 8}+\ldots$

2437. $\frac{1}{\sqrt{3}}+\frac{5}{\sqrt{2\cdot 3^2}}+\frac{9}{\sqrt{3\cdot 3^3}}+\frac{13}{\sqrt{4\cdot 3^4}}+\ldots$

By comparing with a harmonic series or a decreasing progression, test the series for convergence:

2438. $1+\frac{1}{\sqrt{2}}+\frac{1}{\sqrt{3}}+\frac{1}{\sqrt{4}}+\ldots$

2439. $1+\frac{1}{2\cdot 5}+\frac{1}{3\cdot 5^2}+\frac{1}{4\cdot 5^3}+\ldots$

2440. $\frac{1}{\ln 2}+\frac{1}{\ln 3}+\frac{1}{\ln 4}+\frac{1}{\ln 5}+\ldots$

2441. Using the method of comparison, show that the series $\frac{1}{1+x^2}+\frac{1}{1+x^4}+\frac{1}{1+x^6}+\ldots$ is divergent for $|x|\leqslant 1$, and convergent for $|x|>1$.

Hint. In the first case replace x^2, x^4, x^6, ... by unities, in the second case delete the unities from the denominators.

Find the sum of the series:

2442. $\frac{1}{1\cdot 2}+\frac{1}{2\cdot 3}+\frac{1}{3\cdot 4}+\ldots$

Hint. Expand u_n into partial fractions.

2443. $\frac{1}{1\cdot 4}+\frac{1}{4\cdot 7}+\frac{1}{7\cdot 10}+\ldots$

Test the series for convergence:

2444. $1-\frac{1}{\sqrt{2}}+\frac{1}{\sqrt{3}}-\frac{1}{\sqrt{4}}+\ldots$

2445. $1-\frac{1}{3^2}+\frac{1}{5^2}-\frac{1}{7^2}+\ldots$

2446. $\frac{1}{2\ln 2}-\frac{1}{3\ln 3}+\frac{1}{4\ln 4}-\ldots$

2447. $\frac{\sin\alpha}{1}+\frac{\sin 2\alpha}{2^2}+\frac{\sin 3\alpha}{3^2}+\ldots$

2448. Show that the sum S of the conditionally convergent series $1-\frac{1}{2}+\frac{1}{3}-\frac{1}{4}+\ldots$ will decrease by one half if two successive negative terms are placed after each positive term, and will increase by one and a half times if one negative term is placed after each two positive ones.

Test the series for convergence:

2449. $1+\frac{1}{3\sqrt{3}}+\frac{1}{5\sqrt{5}}+\ldots$

2450. $1+\frac{1}{101}+\frac{1}{201}+\frac{1}{301}+\ldots$

2451. $\frac{1}{1+1^4}+\frac{2}{1+2^4}+\frac{3}{1+3^4}+\ldots$

2452. $1+\frac{3}{4}+\frac{5}{9}+\frac{7}{16}+\ldots$

2453. $1+\frac{1}{4^2}+\frac{1}{7^2}+\frac{1}{10^2}+\ldots$

2454. $\frac{1}{2}+\frac{3}{2^2}+\frac{5}{2^3}+\frac{7}{2^4}+\ldots$ **2455.** $\frac{21}{3}+\frac{41}{9}+\frac{61}{27}+\ldots$

2456. $\frac{2}{1}+\frac{4}{3!}+\frac{6}{5!}+\ldots$ **2457.** $1-\frac{1}{\sqrt{3}}+\frac{1}{\sqrt{5}}-\ldots$

2458. $1-\frac{1}{2^3}+\frac{1}{3^3}-\frac{1}{4^3}+\ldots$

2459. $1-\frac{1}{2a^2}+\frac{1}{3a^4}-\frac{1}{4a^6}+\ldots$

Find the sum of the series:

2460. $\frac{1}{1\cdot 3}+\frac{1}{3\cdot 5}+\frac{1}{5\cdot 7}+\ldots$

2461. $\frac{1}{1\cdot 2\cdot 3}+\frac{1}{2\cdot 3\cdot 4}+\frac{1}{3\cdot 4\cdot 5}+\ldots$

14.2. Uniform Convergence of a Functional Series

1°. The totality of values of x for which the *functional* series $u_1(x)+u_2(x)+\ldots+u_n(x)+\ldots$ converges is called the *domain of convergence* of this series.

The function $S(x) = \lim_{n\to\infty} S_n(x)$ is called its *sum*, and the difference $R_n(x) = S(x) - S_n(x)$ the *remainder* of the series.

2° Functional series (1) convergent in an interval $[a, b]$ is called *uniformly convergent* in that interval if the remainder $R_n(x)$ beginning with some number N, which is the same for all values of x considered, remains less in absolute value than any preassigned positive number ε:

$$|R_n(x)| < \varepsilon \text{ for } n \geqslant N(\varepsilon).$$

3°. A test for uniform convergence. Series (1) converges absolutely and uniformly in an interval $[a, b]$ if there exists a convergent positive series

$$C_1 + C_2 + C_3 + \ldots C_n + \ldots$$

such that $|u_n(x)| \leqslant C_n$ for $a \leqslant x \leqslant b$.

2462. Determine the sum and the remainder of the series $1 + x + x^2 + x^3 + \ldots$ for $|x| < 1$ and show that it converges uniformly in the interval $\left[0, \frac{1}{2}\right]$. At what n is the remainder $|R_n(x)|$ less than 0.001 for any x on this interval?

2463. Show that the series

$$x + x(1-x) + x(1-x)^2 + x(1-x)^3 + \ldots$$

converges *nonuniformly* in the interval $[0, 1]$ and *uniformly* in the interval $\left[\frac{1}{2}, 1\right]$. At what n the remainder $|R_n(x)| < 0.01$ for any x on the interval $\left[\frac{1}{2}, 1\right]$?

2464. Show that the series $\frac{x}{1} - \frac{x^2}{2} + \frac{x^3}{3} - \ldots$ converges uniformly in the interval $[0, 1]$. At what values of n and any x on this interval $|R_n(x)| < 0.1$?

2465. Show that the series $x^3 + \frac{x^3}{1+x^3} + \frac{x^3}{(1+x^3)^2} + \ldots$ converges *nonuniformly* for $x > 0$ and *uniformly* for $x \geqslant 1$. At what n the remainder $|R_n| < 0.001$ for any $x \geqslant 1$?

2466. Show that the series $\frac{1}{\sqrt{1+x}} + \frac{1}{3\sqrt{1+3x}} + \frac{1}{3^2\sqrt{1+5x}} + \frac{1}{3^3\sqrt{1+7x}} + \ldots$ converges uniformly in the interval $0 \leqslant x < \infty$. At what n (and any $x \geqslant 0$) the remainder of the series $|R_n(x)| < 0.01$?

Hint. Compare the given series with a convergent numerical series.

2467. Show that the series $\frac{1}{x^2+1} - \frac{1}{x^2+4} + \frac{1}{x^2+9} - \frac{1}{x^2+16} + \ldots$ converges uniformly over the entire number line. At what n (and any x) the remainder of the series $|R_n(x)| < 0.0001$?

2468. Show that the series $\frac{1}{x(x+1)} + \frac{1}{(x+1)(x+2)} + \frac{1}{(x+2)(x+3)} + \ldots$ uniformly converges to $\frac{1}{x}$ in the interval $0 < x < \infty$. At what n (and any $x > 0$) the remainder of the series $|R_n(x)| < 0.1$?

2469. Show that the series $\frac{1}{\sqrt{1+x}} + \frac{1}{\sqrt{2^2+2x}} + \frac{1}{\sqrt{2^4+3x}} + \frac{1}{\sqrt{2^6+4x}} + \ldots$ converges uniformly in the interval $0 \leqslant x < \infty$. At what n the remainder $|R_n(x)| < 0.01$?

14.3. Power Series

Let there be given a power series

$$a_0 + a_1x + a_2x^2 + \ldots + a_nx^n + \ldots \quad (1)$$

The number R is called the *radius of convergence* of series (1) if for $|x| < R$ the series converges, and for $|x| > R$ it diverges. R can be found either by investigating series (1) for absolute convergence using d'Alembert's test, or by the formula $R = \lim\limits_{n \to \infty} \left| \frac{a_n}{a_{n+1}} \right|$ when all a_i are different from zero. In particular, if this limit equals ∞, then series (1) converges absolutely along the entire axis OX.

A power series converges not only *absolutely*, but also *uniformly* on any interval $[a, b]$ lying inside the *interval of convergence* $(-R, R)$.

Determine the interval of convergence of the series and test it for convergence at the extremities:

2470. $1+\frac{x}{3\cdot 2}+\frac{x^2}{3^2\cdot 3}+\frac{x^3}{3^3\cdot 4}+\ldots$

2471. $1-\frac{x}{5\sqrt{2}}+\frac{x^3}{5^2\sqrt{3}}-\frac{x^5}{5^3\sqrt{4}}+\ldots$

2472. $1+\frac{2x}{3^2\sqrt{3}}+\frac{4x^2}{5^2\sqrt{3^2}}+\frac{8x^3}{7^2\sqrt{3^3}}+\ldots$

2473. $\sum\limits_{n=1}^{\infty}\frac{x^n}{n!}$. **2474.** $\sum\limits_{n=1}^{\infty}\frac{(-x)^{n-1}}{n}$.

2475. $\sum\limits_{n=1}^{\infty}\frac{3^n x^n}{\sqrt{(3n-2)\,2^n}}$.

2476. (1) $\sum\limits_{n=1}^{\infty}x^{n-1}\cdot n!$; (2) $\sum\limits_{n=1}^{\infty}\frac{n!\,x^n}{(n+1)^n}$.

2477. $(x+1)+\frac{(x+1)^2}{2\cdot 4}+\frac{(x+1)^3}{3\cdot 4^2}+\frac{(x+1)^4}{4\cdot 4^3}+\ldots$

2478. $\frac{2x-3}{1}-\frac{(2x-3)^2}{3}+\frac{(2x-3)^3}{5}-\ldots$

Determine the interval of convergence and the expression for sum of the series:

2479. $1+2x+3x^2+4x^3+\ldots$

Hint. In finding the sum S first determine $\int\limits_0^x S\,dx$.

2480. $x-\frac{x^3}{3}+\frac{x^5}{5}-\frac{x^7}{7}+\ldots$

Hint. First find $\frac{dS}{dx}$.

2481. $1+3x+5x^2+7x^3+\ldots$

Hint. Denoting the sum of the series by S write the expression $S-Sx$ in the form of a summable series.

2482. $1+\frac{m}{1}x+\frac{m(m-1)}{1\cdot 2}x^2+\frac{m(m-1)(m-2)}{1\cdot 2\cdot 3}x^3+\ldots$

Hint. Show that $\frac{S'}{m}+\frac{S'x}{m}=S$, and solve this differential equation.

Determine the interval of convergence and test the series for convergence at the extremities:

2483. $1+\frac{2x}{\sqrt{5\cdot 5}}+\frac{4x^2}{\sqrt{9\cdot 5^2}}+\frac{8x^3}{\sqrt{13\cdot 5^3}}+\ldots$

2484. $1-\frac{x^2}{3\cdot 2\sqrt{2}}+\frac{x^4}{3^2\cdot 3\sqrt{3}}-\frac{x^6}{3^3\cdot 4\sqrt{4}}+\ldots$

2485. $\sum_{n=1}^{\infty}\frac{10^n x^n}{\sqrt{n}}$. 2486. $\sum_{n=1}^{\infty}(-1)^{n-1}\frac{x^{2n-1}}{2n-1}$.

2487. $\frac{x-1}{1\cdot 2}+\frac{(x-1)^2}{3\cdot 2^2}+\frac{(x-1)^3}{5\cdot 2^3}+\ldots$

2488. $\frac{2x+1}{1}+\frac{(2x+1)^2}{4}+\frac{(2x+1)^3}{7}+\ldots$

Find the interval of convergence and the sum of the series:

2489. $1-3x^2+5x^4-7x^6+\ldots$

Hint. To find the sum S first find $\int_0^x S\,dx$.

2490. $x+\frac{x^2}{2}+\frac{x^3}{3}+\ldots$ *Hint*. First find $\frac{dS}{dx}$.

2491. $1-4x+7x^2-10x^3+\ldots$

Hint. Form the expression $S+Sx$.

14.4. Taylor's and Maclaurin's Series

1°. Maclaurin's formula:

$$f(x)=f(0)+\frac{f'(0)}{1!}x+\frac{f''(0)}{2!}x^2+\ldots+R_n(x), \qquad (1)$$

where $R_n(x)=\frac{x^n}{n!}f^n(\theta x)$, $0\leqslant\theta<1$.

2°. Taylor's formula:

$$f(x)=f(a)+\frac{f'(a)}{1!}(x-a)+\frac{f''(a)}{2!}(x-a)^2+\ldots+R_n(x), \qquad (2)$$

where $R_n(x)=\frac{(x-a)^n}{n!}f^{(n)}[a+\theta(x-a)]$.

3°. Maclaurin's and Taylor's series. If as $n \to \infty$ in formulas (1) and (2) $R_n(x) \to 0$, then they yield infinite series:

$$f(x) = f(0) + \frac{f'(0)}{1!}x + \frac{f''(0)}{2!}x^2 + \ldots, \tag{3}$$

$$f(x) = f(a) + \frac{f'(a)}{1!}(x-a) + \frac{f''(a)}{2!}(x-a)^2 + \ldots, \tag{4}$$

converging to $f(x)$ for the values of x at which $\lim\limits_{n\to\infty} R_n(x) = 0$.

4°. Series expansions of elementary functions:

$$\left.\begin{aligned} e^x &= 1 + \frac{x}{1!} + \frac{x^2}{2!} + \frac{x^3}{3!} + \ldots, \\ \sin x &= x - \frac{x^3}{3!} + \frac{x^5}{5!} - \ldots, \\ \cos x &= 1 - \frac{x^2}{2!} + \frac{x^4}{4!} - \ldots \end{aligned}\right\} \text{converge to the function for all values of } x;$$

$(1+x)^m = 1 + \frac{m}{1}x + \frac{m(m-1)}{1\cdot 2}x^2 + \ldots$ the *binomial series;* it converges to the *binomial* $(1+x)^m$ for $|x| < 1$;

$\ln(1+x) = x - \frac{x^2}{2} + \frac{x^3}{3} - \ldots$ converges to $\ln(1+x)$ for $-1 < x \leqslant 1$;

$\arctan x = x - \frac{x^3}{3} + \frac{x^5}{5} - \ldots$ converges to $\arctan x$ for $|x| \leqslant 1$.

2492. Expand the following functions in series of powers of x: (1) $\cos(x-\alpha)$; (2) $\sin^2 x$; (3) xe^x; (4) $\sin\left(mx + \frac{\pi}{3}\right)$; write and analyse the formula of the remainder term.

2493. Write the first three terms of the expansion of the function $f(x) = \ln(1+e^{kx})$ in a series.

2494. Using Maclaurin's formula, write the expansion of the binomial $\left(1+\frac{x}{a}\right)^m$ in a series of powers of x, and show that the obtained series converges for $|x| < a$.

2495. With the aid of the binomial series show that for $|x|<1$

$$\frac{1}{(1+x)^3}=1-3x+6x^2-10x^3+\ldots=$$

$$=\sum_{n=1}^{\infty}\frac{n(n+1)}{2}(-x)^{n-1}.$$

2496. With the aid of the binomial series obtain the expansion of the function in a series

$$\frac{1}{\sqrt{1+x^2}}=1-\frac{1}{2}x^2+\frac{1\cdot 3}{2^2\cdot 2!}x^4-\frac{1\cdot 3\cdot 5}{2^3\cdot 3!}x^6+\ldots \text{ for } |x|<1.$$

2497. Expand the function in a series of powers of x:

(1) $\ln\frac{1+x}{1-x}$; (2) $\ln(2-3x+x^2)$; (3) $\ln(1-x+x^2)$.

2498. By integrating the series obtained in Problem 2496, write a series for $\ln(x+\sqrt{1+x^2})$.

2499. Expand $e^{\frac{x}{a}}$ in a series of powers of $x-a$; write and analyse the formula of the remainder term of the series.

2500. Expand the function $f(x)=x^3-3x$ in a series of powers of $x-1$.

2501. Expand x^4 in powers of $x+1$.

2502. Expand the function $f(x)=\frac{1}{x}$ in a series of powers of $x+2$ and test the series for convergence by means of d'Alembert's test.

2503. Expand the following functions: (1) $f(x)=\cos\frac{x}{2}$ in powers of $x-\frac{\pi}{2}$; (2) $f(x)=\sin 3x$ in powers of $x+\frac{\pi}{3}$.

2504. Expand the function $f(x)=\sqrt[3]{x}$ in a series of powers of $x+1$; test the obtained series for convergence by means of d'Alembert's test.

2505. Expand the following functions in series of powers of x: (1) 2^x; (2) $\cos\left(mx+\frac{\pi}{4}\right)$; write and analyse the formulas of the remainder terms of the expansions.

2506. Expand the function $f(x)=x^4-4x^2$ in a series of powers of $x+2$.

2507. Expand the function $f(x)=\cos^2 x$ in a series of powers of $x-\frac{\pi}{3}$; write and analyse the formula of the remainder term.

2508. Expand the function $f(x)=\sin\frac{\pi x}{3}$ in a series of powers of $x-1$.

2509. Expand the function $f(x)=\sqrt{x}$ in a series of powers of $x-4$ and test the obtained series for convergence by means of d'Alembert's test.

2510. With the aid of a binomial series show that
$\frac{1}{\sqrt{1-x^2}}=1+\frac{1}{2}x^2+\frac{1\cdot 3}{2^2\cdot 2!}x^4+\frac{1\cdot 3\cdot 5}{2^3\cdot 3!}x^6+\ldots$ for $|x|<1$.

2411. Integrating termwise the series obtained in Problem 2510, write a series for $\arcsin x$.

14.5. The Use of Series for Approximate Calculations

2512. Write the binomial series for $\sqrt{1+x}$ and calculate $\sqrt{1.004}$, $\sqrt{0.992}$, $\sqrt{90}$ by taking only the first two terms of the series. Estimate the error.

2513. Write a binomial series for $\sqrt[3]{1+x}$ and compute $\sqrt[3]{1.006}$, $\sqrt[3]{0.991}$, $\sqrt[3]{130}$ by taking only the first two terms of the series. Estimate the error.

2514. Compute $\sin 12°$ by taking only two terms of the series for $\sin x$, and estimate the error.

Hint. $x=12°$, or in radian measure $x=\frac{\pi}{15}=0.2094$. Determine the upper limit of the error from the condition $x<0.3$.

2515. Dividing the numerator of the fraction by its denominator, obtain the expansion $\frac{1}{1+x^2}=\sum_{n=1}^{\infty}(-1)^{n-1}x^{2n-2}$; integrating the obtained series termwise, write an expansion for $\arctan x$.

2516. Putting $x=\frac{1}{\sqrt{3}}$ in the expansion $\arctan x = \sum_{n=1}^{\infty}\frac{(-1)^{n-1}x^{2n-1}}{2n-1}$, obtain a series for computing π:

$$\pi = 2\sqrt{3}\sum_{n=1}^{\infty}\frac{(-1)^{n-1}}{(2n-1)\,3^{n-1}}.$$

2517. Compute π by taking the first five terms from the series of Problem 2516.

2518. With the aid of the series obtained in Problem 2497:

$$\ln\frac{1+x}{1-x} = 2\left[x+\frac{x^3}{3}+\frac{x^5}{5}+\ldots\right]$$

compute $\ln 2$; $\ln 3$; $\ln 4$; $\ln 6$.

Hint. Putting $\frac{1+x}{1-x}=2$, find x and so on.

2519. Express the integrals $\int\frac{\sin x}{x}dx$ and $\int\frac{e^x}{x}dx$ in the form of series.

2520. Write the function $\Phi(x)=\int_0^x e^{-x^2}dx$ in the form of a series and evaluate $\Phi\left(\frac{1}{3}\right)$ taking as many terms as is necessary to reduce the error to less than 0.001.

2521. Write the function $\Phi(x)=\int_0^x \sqrt[3]{1+x^2}\,dx$ in the form of series and evaluate $\Phi\left(\frac{1}{5}\right)$ taking as many terms as is necessary to reduce the error to less than 0.00001.

2522. Find the solution (in the form of a series) of the equation $y''=x^2y$ for the initial conditions: for $x=0$ $y=1$, $y'=1$.

2523. Find the first four terms of the series determining the solution of the Riccati equation $y'=1+x-y^2$ for the initial conditions: $y=1$ at $x=0$.

2524. Write the solution (in the form of a series) of the Bessel equation $xy''+y'+xy=0$ for the initial conditions: for $x=0$ $y=1$ and $y'=0$.

2525. Compute $\sqrt{1.005}$; $\sqrt[3]{1.0012}$; $\sqrt{0.993}$; $\sqrt[3]{0.997}$; $\sqrt{110}$; $\sqrt[3]{70}$; $\sqrt[5]{40}$ taking the first two terms of the binomial series $(1+x)^m=1+mx+\frac{m(m-1)x^2}{2!}+\ldots$, and estimate the error.

2526. Compute $\cos 12°$ by taking the first two terms of the expansion of $\cos x$. Estimate the error.

2527. Putting $x=\frac{1}{2}$ in the expansion of $\arcsin x$ (Problem 2511), compute π by taking the first three terms of the series.

Hint. First compute the first of the rejected terms, and then express each of the first three terms of the series as a decimal fraction with the error not exceeding the first rejected term.

2528. Using the identity $\frac{\pi}{4}=\arctan\frac{1}{2}+\arctan\frac{1}{3}$, write the expression for π as the sum of two infinite series.

2529. Putting $x=\frac{1}{N}$ in the expansion of $\ln(1+x)$, obtain the formulas:

(1) $\ln(N+1)=\ln N+\left[\frac{1}{N}-\frac{1}{2N^2}+\frac{1}{3N^3}-\ldots\right]$;

(2) $\log_{10}(N+1)=\log_{10}N+0.4343\left[\frac{1}{N}-\frac{1}{2N^2}+\frac{1}{3N^3}-\ldots\right]$.

2530. Knowing $\ln 2=0.6931$, compute $\ln 5$ and $\ln 10$ and show that the modulus $M=\frac{1}{\ln 10}\approx 0.4343$.

2531. Compute $\log_{10}101$ and $\log_{10}102$.

2532. Determine the length of an elliptic arc in the form of a series.

2533. Compute $\int_0^{0.5}\sqrt{1+x^3}\,dx$ taking as many terms as is necessary to reduce the error to 0.001.

2534. Determine the function $\Phi(x)=\int\limits_0^x \cos\frac{x^2}{4}\,dx$ in the form of a series and evaluate $\Phi\left(\frac{1}{2}\right)$ to six decimals.

2535. Write the first three terms of the series determining the solution of the equation $y'=x^2+y^2$, the equation satisfying the condition: $y=0$ at $x=0$.

2536. Write the solution (in the form of a series) of the equation $y''+xy=0$ for the initial conditions: for $x=0$ $y=1$ and $y'=0$.

2537. Write (in the form of a series) the equations of a transition line along which the curvature k increases in proportion to the length of the arc s.

Hint. Find φ from the condition $\frac{d\varphi}{ds}=\frac{s}{C}$, where C is a constant, and then solve the equations: $dx=ds\cos\varphi$ and $dy=ds\sin\varphi$.

14.6. Taylor's Series for a Function of Two Variables

The Taylor series for a function of two variables can be written in three forms:

$$F(x+h,\ y+l)=F(x,\ y)+\frac{1}{1!}\left[h\frac{\partial}{\partial x}+l\frac{\partial}{\partial y}\right]F(x,\ y)+\frac{1}{2!}\left[h\frac{\partial}{\partial x}+l\frac{\partial}{\partial y}\right]^2 F(x,\ y)+\ldots, \qquad \text{(I)}$$

$$F(x,\ y)=F(a,\ b)+\frac{1}{1!}\left[(x-a)\frac{\partial}{\partial x}+(y-b)\frac{\partial}{\partial y}\right]F(a,\ b)+\frac{1}{2!}\left[(x-a)\frac{\partial}{\partial x}+(y-b)\frac{\partial}{\partial y}\right]^2 F(a,\ b)+\ldots \qquad \text{(II)}$$

$$\Delta z=\frac{dz}{1!}+\frac{d^2z}{2!}+\ldots+\frac{d^nz}{n!}\Bigg|_{\substack{x=x_0+\theta\,\Delta x\\ y=y_0+\theta\,\Delta y}}. \qquad \text{(III)}$$

2538. Construct the expansion of the function $F(x+h,\ y+l)$ using the Taylor formula (I) if $F(x,\ y)=x^2+xy+y^2$.

2539. Expand the function $F(x,\ y)=x^3+2xy^2$ in powers of $(x-1)$ and $(y-2)$ [formula (II)].

2540. Expand the function $F(x, y) = \ln(x-y)$ in powers of x and $(y+1)$ keeping the terms of the first and second orders and the remainder term [formula (II)].

2541. Expand the function $F(x, y) = \sin(mx+ny)$ in powers of x and y keeping the terms of the first, second, and third order and the remainder term [formula (II) at $a=b=0$].

2542. Expand the function $e^{-x^2-y^2}$ in powers of x and y [formula (II) at $a=b=0$].

2543. Determine the increment Δz of the function $z = x^2-xy+y^2$ [formula (III)] and compute it if x varies from 2 to 2.1 and y from 3 to 2.8.

2544. Determine the increment Δz of the function $z = \cos(ax-by)$ keeping the first two terms of formula (III) and the remainder term.

2545. Expand the function $F(x, y) = x^2y$ in powers of $(x-1)$ and $(y+1)$ [formula (II)].

2546. Expand the function $F(x, y) = \arctan\frac{y}{x}$ in powers of $(x-1)$ and y keeping the terms of the first and second orders.

2547. Expand the function $z = y^x$ in powers of $(x-2)$ and $(y-1)$ keeping the terms of the first and second orders, and compute $1.1^{2.1}$.

2548. Determine the increment Δz for the function $z = x^2y-y^2$ and compute it to the fourth decimal if x varies from 2 to 1.99 and y from 5 to 5.02.

14.7. Fourier Series. Fourier Integral

1°. Definition. A *function* $f(x)$ is considered to *satisfy Dirichlet's conditions in an interval* $[a, b]$ if, inside this interval,

(1) it has a finite number of discontinuities, all of them being of the first kind;

(2) it has a finite number of extrema;

(3) for all points of (a, b) $f(x) = \frac{f(x-0)+f(x+0)}{2}$.

2°. A function $f(x)$, satisfying the Dirichlet conditions on an interval $[-l, l]$, can be defined for all points of this interval by the *Fourier series*:

$$f(x)=\frac{a_0}{2}+\sum_{n=1}^{\infty}\left[a_n\cos\frac{n\pi x}{l}+b_n\sin\frac{n\pi x}{l}\right], \quad (1)$$

where

$$a_n=\frac{1}{l}\int_{-l}^{l} f(x)\cos\frac{n\pi x}{l}\,dx; \quad b_n=\frac{1}{l}\int_{-l}^{l} f(x)\sin\frac{n\pi x}{l}\,dx. \quad (2)$$

If $f(x)=f(-x)$, i.e. if $f(x)$ is an *even* function, then $b_n=0$ and

$$f(x)=\frac{a_0}{2}+\sum_{n=1}^{\infty} a_n\cos\frac{n\pi x}{l}. \quad (3)$$

If $f(x)=-f(-x)$, i.e. if $f(x)$ is an *odd* function, then $a_n=0$ and

$$f(x)=\sum_{n=1}^{\infty} b_n\sin\frac{n\pi x}{l}. \quad (4)$$

If a function $f(x)$ defined by series (1) in a closed interval $[-l, l]$ is continued according to a periodic law with period $2l$ and it is required that $f(l)=\frac{f(l-0)+f(l+0)}{2}$, then this function will be determined by series (1) throughout its entire length.

3°. If a function $f(x)$ is *absolutely integrable* in the interval $(-\infty, \infty)$ $\left(\text{i. e. if } \int_{-\infty}^{+\infty}|f(x)|\,dx \text{ converges}\right)$ and satisfies the Dirichlet conditions in any finite interval, then it can be represented by the Fourier integral:

$$f(x)=\frac{1}{\pi}\int_{0}^{\infty}d\alpha\int_{-\infty}^{\infty}f(t)\cos\alpha(x-t)\,dt=\int_{0}^{\infty}[a(\alpha)\cos\alpha x+ +b(\alpha)\sin\alpha x]\,d\alpha, \quad (5)$$

where

$$a(\alpha)=\frac{1}{\pi}\int_{-\infty}^{+\infty} f(t)\cos\alpha t\,dt \text{ and } b(\alpha)=\frac{1}{\pi}\int_{-\infty}^{+\infty} f(t)\sin\alpha t\,dt. \quad (6)$$

Construct a Fourier series for the following periodic functions with period 2π.

2549. $f(x)=1$ for $0<x<\pi$ and $f(-x)=-f(x)$. With the aid of the obtained series show that

$$1-\frac{1}{3}+\frac{1}{5}-\frac{1}{7}+\ldots=\frac{\pi}{4}.$$

2550. $f(x)=x$ for $0\leqslant x\leqslant\pi$ and $f(-x)=f(x)$. With the aid of the obtained series show that

$$1+\frac{1}{3^2}+\frac{1}{5^2}+\frac{1}{7^2}+\ldots=\frac{\pi^2}{8}.$$

2551. $f(x)=x^2$ for $-\pi\leqslant x\leqslant\pi$. With the aid of the obtained series show that

(1) $1-\frac{1}{2^2}+\frac{1}{3^2}-\frac{1}{4^2}+\ldots=\frac{\pi^2}{12}$;

(2) $1+\frac{1}{2^2}+\frac{1}{3^2}+\frac{1}{4^2}+\ldots=\frac{\pi^2}{6}$.

2552. $f(x)=\begin{cases}\pi & \text{for } -\pi<x<0,\\ \pi-x & \text{for } 0\leqslant x\leqslant\pi.\end{cases}$

Expand in a Fourier series the following periodic functions with period $2l$:

2553. $f(x)=1$ for $0<x<l$ and $f(-x)=-f(x)$.

2554. $f(x)=1-x$ for $0\leqslant x\leqslant 1$, $f(-x)=f(x)$, $l=1$.

2555. $f(x)=\begin{cases}0 & \text{for } -l<x\leqslant 0,\\ x & \text{for } 0\leqslant x<l.\end{cases}$

2556. A function $f(x)$ is represented graphically (Fig. 37) and continued according to (1) an even; (2) an odd periodic law with period $2l=4$. Expand each of these functions in a Fourier series.

2557. Heat propagation in a bar of length l is determined by the equation $\frac{1}{a^2}\frac{\partial u}{\partial t}=\frac{\partial^2 u}{\partial x^2}$, where $u(x, t)$ is the temperature, and the following conditions:

(1) boundary: $u=0$ for $x=0$ and for $x=l$;

(2) initial: $u=\begin{cases} x \text{ for } x<\frac{l}{2}, \\ l-x \text{ for } x>\frac{l}{2} \end{cases}$ at $t=0$.

Determine the function $u(x, t)$ using the Fourier method.

2558. Longitudinal oscillations of a bar of length l, whose one end (at $x=0$) is fixed and the other (at $x=l$)

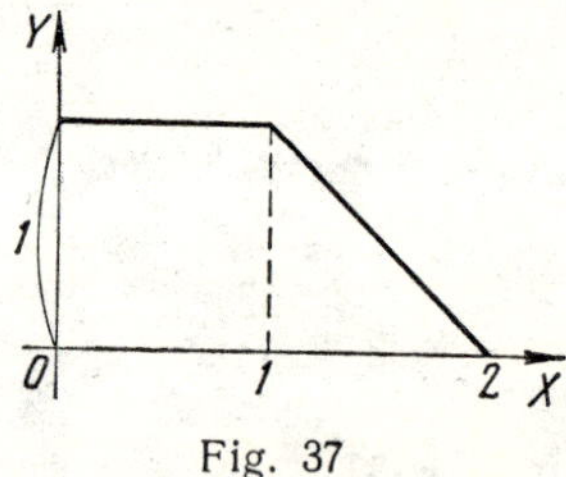

Fig. 37

is free, are determined by the equation $\frac{1}{a^2}\frac{\partial^2 u}{\partial t^2}=\frac{\partial^2 u}{\partial x^2}$, where $u(x, t)$ is longitudinal displacement, and the following conditions:

(1) boundary: $u=0$ for $x=0$; $\frac{\partial u}{\partial x}=0$ for $x=l$;

(2) initial: $u=f(x)$, $\frac{\partial u}{\partial t}=0$ for $t=0$.

Determine the function $u(x, t)$ using the Fourier method.

2559. Transverse oscillations of a bar of length l resting on supports at both ends are determined by the equation

$$\frac{1}{a^2}\frac{\partial^2 u}{\partial t^2}+\frac{\partial^4 u}{\partial x^4}=0$$

and the following conditions:

(1) boundary: $u=0$ and $\frac{\partial^2 u}{\partial x^2}=0$ for $x=0$ and $x=l$;

(2) initial: $u=f(x)$ and $\frac{\partial u}{\partial t}=0$ for $t=0$.

Determine the function $u(x, t)$ using the Fourier method.

In Problems 2560 to 2562 write the Fourier integral for the given functions:

2560. $f(x)=\begin{cases} 1 \text{ for } 0<x<1, \\ 0 \text{ for } \quad x>1 \end{cases}$ and $f(-x)=-f(x)$.

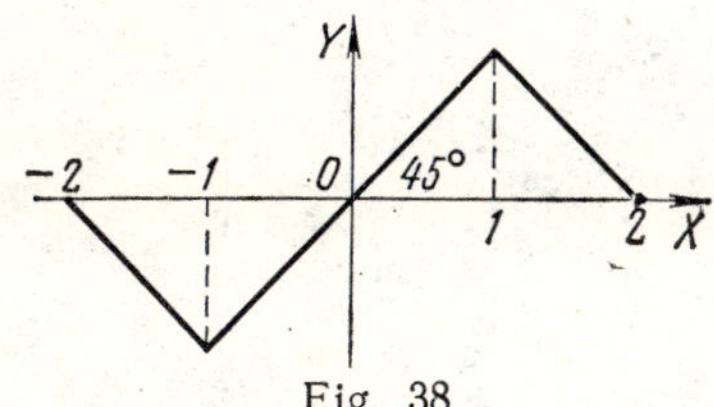

Fig. 38

2561. $f(x)=e^{-\beta x}$ for $x \geqslant 0$ and $f(-x)=f(x)$.

2562. $f(x)$ represented graphically on the closed interval $[-2, 2]$ (Fig. 38) and equal to zero outside this interval.

Expand the following functions in Fourier series:

2563. $f(x)=\frac{\pi-x}{2}$ for $0<x \leqslant \pi$;

$$f(-x)=f(x), \quad f(x+2\pi)=f(x).$$

2564. $f(x)=|\sin x|$; with the aid of the series obtained show that $\frac{1}{1\cdot 3}+\frac{1}{3\cdot 5}+\frac{1}{5\cdot 7}+\ldots=\frac{1}{2}$.

2565. $f(x)=\begin{cases} x \text{ for } 0 \leqslant x \leqslant \frac{\pi}{2}, \\ \pi-x \text{ for } \frac{\pi}{2} \leqslant x \leqslant \pi \end{cases}$ and $f(-x)=-f(x)$.

2566. $f(x)=x$ for $0 \leqslant x \leqslant l$;

$$f(-x)=f(x), \; f(x+2l)=f(x).$$

2567. $f(x)=\begin{cases} 1 \text{ for } -1 \leqslant x \leqslant 0, \\ x \text{ for } \quad 0<x \leqslant 1 \end{cases}$ and $f(x+2)=f(x)$.

2568. $f(x)=e^x$ for $-l<x<l$ and $f(x+2l)=f(x)$.

2569. Using the Fourier method, solve the equation $\frac{\partial^2 u}{\partial t^2}=\frac{\partial^2 u}{\partial x^2}$ that satisfies the following conditions:

$$\begin{cases} \text{for } x=0\ u=0, \text{ for } x=\pi\ \frac{\partial u}{\partial x}=0; \\ \text{for } t=0\ u=f(x) \text{ and } \frac{\partial u}{\partial t}=0. \end{cases}$$

2570. Write the Fourier integral for the function

$$f(x)=\begin{cases} 1 \text{ for } -1<x<1, \\ 0 \text{ for } |x|>1. \end{cases}$$

ANSWERS

1. $AB=9$, $BC=-6$, $AC=3$, $9-6=3$. **3.** $5(2+\sqrt{2})$, $90°$, $45°$. **5.** 20. **6.** $5\sqrt{2}$. **7.** (5 5), (5, —3). **8.** $B(0, 2)$ and $B(0, -4)$. **9.** $x=a\pm\sqrt{c^2-b^2}$; for $c>|b|$ two points, at $c=|b|$ one, for $c<|b|$ none. **10.** $M(5, 0)$. **11.** Centre (1, —1), $R=5$. **12.** $\text{pr}_{OX}\overrightarrow{AB}=-2$, $\text{pr}_{OY}\overrightarrow{AB}=-4$, $|\overrightarrow{AB}|=2\sqrt{5}$. **13.** $B(5, 8)$, $|\overrightarrow{AB}|=3\sqrt{2}$. **14.** $B(4, -3)$. **15.** —4, 1, 3. **16.** $18\sqrt{2}$. **17.** (0, 2.9). **18.** $B(4, 0)$, $B_1(-8, 0)$. **19.** Centre (2, —1), $R=5$. **21.** $X=7$, $Y=-1$; $5\sqrt{2}$. **22.** $M(1, 4)$. **23.** $M(13, 16)$. **24.** $x=\dfrac{m_1x_1+m_2x_2}{m_1+m_2}$. **26.** 26 cm from the centre of 100-g ball. **27.** (1, 2.5). **29.** $OC=5$, $OD=\dfrac{24\sqrt{2}}{7}$. **30.** (3, 3). **31.** 9 sq. units. **33.** 13 sq. units. **34.** (1, 3) if the forces are in one direction, and (25, 27) if in different ones. **35.** (1, —1). **36.** $\dfrac{10\sqrt{2}}{3}$. **37.** $x=\dfrac{x_1+x_2+x_3}{3}$; $y=\dfrac{y_1+y_2+y_3}{3}$. **38.** $\left(\dfrac{37}{27}, \dfrac{13}{27}\right)$. **39.** $C_1(3, 0)$, $C_2(-7, 0)$. **40.** $M(2, -6)$, $N(5, 8)$, $P(-4, 1)$, $k=\dfrac{7}{3}$. **42.** $x^2+y^2-6x-8y=0$, A and O lie on the circle. **43.** $x-y-2=0$, D and E lie on the line. **45.** $x^2+y^2=8$. **46.** $y=\pm x$. **47.** $\dfrac{x^2}{5}+y^2=1$. **48.** $y=\dfrac{x^2}{4}-x+2$. **49.** $y=\pm 2x$. **51.** (1, 0), (3, 0), (0, 3). **53.** $y^2=8(x-2)$. **54.** $2x-y+5=0$. B and D lie on the line. **55.** $x^2+y^2=4$. **57.** $y=\dfrac{x^2}{4}+1$. **58.** $\sqrt{(x+2)^2+(y+2)^2}-\sqrt{(x-2)^2+(y-2)^2}=4$ or $xy=2$; at $x=\pm\dfrac{1}{2}$, ± 1, ± 2, ± 4, $y=\pm 4$, ± 2, ± 1, $\pm\dfrac{1}{2}$; the curve can be plotted by these points. **59.** $y=x+3$, $y=-x+3$. **60.** $y=x\sqrt{3}-3$, $y=-x\sqrt{3}-3$. **62.** $y=-1.5x$. **63.** (1) $k=\dfrac{2}{3}$, $b=-2$; (2) $k=-\dfrac{2}{3}$, $b=0$; (3) $k=0$,

$b=-3$; (4) $k=-\frac{3}{4}$, $b=3$. **65.** $k=1$, $b=1$, $y=x+1$. **66.** (1) $\frac{x}{3}+\frac{y}{-2}=1$; (2) $\frac{x}{-4/3}+\frac{y}{2}=1$. **67.** $y=0$; $4x-3y=0$; $y=4$; $4x-3y+12=0$. **68.** $\frac{x}{2}-\frac{y}{3}=1$ or $-\frac{x}{4}+\frac{2y}{3}=1$. **69.** $\text{pr}_{OX}\overrightarrow{AB}=8$, $\text{pr}_{OY}\overrightarrow{AB}=6$, $|\overrightarrow{AB}|=10$. **70.** A and C are on the straight line, B is above and D below the straight line. **71.** The inequalities define: (1) all points lying above the straight line $y=3x+1$ (a half-plane); (2) all points situated below the straight line $y=3x+1$; (3) all points located both above and on the straight line $y=4-2x$; (4) the points lying below the straight line $y=4-2x$. **73.** $x-y=\pm a$. **74.** In t seconds the coordinates of the point M will be: $x=a+mt$, $y=b+nt$. Eliminating t, we get the equation of the path: $\frac{x-a}{m}=\frac{y-b}{n}$. **75.** (1) $y=x\sqrt{3}-2$; (2) $y=-x\sqrt{3}-2$. **76.** $k=1$, $b=5$. **77.** $x+y-4=0$; $x-y+4=0$; $y=3$, $y=0$. **78.** $\frac{x}{5}\pm\frac{y}{3}=\pm 1$. **79.** $\frac{x}{4}+\frac{y}{3}=1$ and $\frac{x}{-2}+\frac{y}{-6}=1$. **80.** $y=\pm 2(x+3)$. **81.** $AB+4\sqrt{5}$, $\text{pr}_{OX}\overrightarrow{AB}=4$, $\text{pr}_{OY}\overrightarrow{AB}=8$. **82.** (1) $\arctan\frac{3}{4}$; (2) 45°; (3) 45°; (4) 0°; (5) 90°; (6) $\arctan\frac{a^2-b^2}{2ab}$. **86.** $5x+2y+4=0$; $5x+2y=25$. **88.** $x-3y+2=0$; $5x-y=4$; $3x+y=12$. **89.** 28°, 12°30′ and 139°30′. **90.** $y=3x$ and $y=-\frac{1}{3}x$. **91.** $x-5y+6=0$; $5x+y=-4$. **92.** $y=2x-6$; $y=-2x+6$. **93.** $(3, -1)$, $(3, 3)$; $\left(-\frac{9}{5}, \frac{3}{5}\right)$, 45°, 71°34′, 63°26′. **94.** $\left(\frac{5}{2}, \frac{5}{2}\right)$. **95.** AE: $2x-5y=-4$; AD: $x-2y=-2$; $\sqrt{29}$. **96.** $A=18°26'$; $B=26°34'$; $C=135'$. **97.** $x+2y-11=0$. **98.** $\tan A=\frac{4}{3}$; $\tan B=\tan C=2$; $S=16$. **99.** $(1, -1)$, $\left(\frac{8}{3}, -2\right)$. **100.** $2x+y=-4$; $2x-y=-4$; $2x+y=4$. **103.** 2.8; 0; 1.4. **105.** $\frac{\sqrt{13}}{2}$. **106.** $k=\pm 2$. **107.** Two straight lines parallel to the given one: $4x-3y\pm 20=0$. **108.** $8x-15y+6=0$; $8x-15y=130$. **109.** $x-y=0$ and $x+y-4=0$. **110.** $3x-y=12$ and $x+3y=4$. **111.** $x+y=2$ or $4x+y-8=0$. **112.** $31x+26y=-21$. **113.** $x+3y=2$. **114.** $\sqrt{10}$. **115.** $3x-4y+10=0$; $x=2$. **116.** $h=\frac{18}{\sqrt{34}}$. **117.** Straight lines: $x+y=0$ and $x-3y=0$; distances: $d_1=2\sqrt{2}$, $d_2=0.4\sqrt{10}$. **118.** A pair of straight lines $x+2y=0$ and $x+2y=10$. **119.** $x+3y=0$ and $3x+y=0$. **120.** $11x+22y=74$. **121.** $y=-\frac{x}{2}$ and

$y=-\frac{3}{2}x$. **122.** $x+2y=4$. **123.** $y=0$; $2x+3y=-4$; $y=-4$; $2x+3y=0$; $x+2y=-2$; $y=-x$; $\tan\alpha=\frac{1}{8}$. **124.** 18°26′, 108°27′; $S_{\triangle}=\frac{2b^2}{3}$. **125.** $\frac{a^2}{5}$ sq. units. **126.** $A=36°52'$; $B=127°52'$. **127.** $4(\sqrt{10}+\sqrt{5})$; 20. **128.** $2x-y+6=0$; $x-4y=4$; $2x-3y+2=0$. **129.** $y=x+2$; $x-5y=6$; $y=-x$; $2y=x$. **130.** $\sqrt{10}$. **131.** The point moves along the sides of a square bounded by the straight lines: $x-3y=\pm 5$, $3x+y=\pm 5$. **133.** $h_1=h_2=\frac{6}{\sqrt{5}}$. **134.** $\left(\frac{3}{5}, \frac{19}{5}\right)$, $\left(-\frac{9}{5}, \frac{17}{5}\right)$. **135.** (4, 5). **136.** (0, 2), (4, 0), (2, 4), (—2, 6). **137.** $y-x=2$; $x+2y=4$; $2x+y=8$. **138.** $B(2, 1)$, $C(-1, -5)$. **139.** $y=2x+6$, $\frac{12}{\sqrt{5}}$; $\angle DAB\approx 53°$. **140.** $x^2+y^2+8x-6y=0$; A and O are on the circle, B is outside it. **141.** $x^2+y^2+4x-6y=0$. **143.** (0, 0), (—2.5, 2.5). **144.** $(x-1)^2+(y-1)^2=1$ or $(x-5)^2+(y-5)^2=25$. **145.** $\tan\alpha=-2.4$, $\alpha=112°37'$. **146.** $(x+4)^2+(y+1)^2=25$. **147.** $x^2+y^2-8y=0$. **149.** $y=\frac{4}{3}x$ and $y=0$. **150.** $y^2=x(a-x)$. **151.** $(x-3)^2+y^2=9$. **152.** $x^2+\left(y-\frac{a}{3}\right)^2=\frac{a^2}{9}$. **153.** $x^2+y^2=a^2$. **154.** $x^2+y^2=ax$. **155.** $x^2+y^2-6y-9=0$. **156.** (1) (3, —2), $R=6$; (2) $\left(-\frac{5}{2}, \frac{7}{2}\right)$, $R=4$; (3) $\left(0, -\frac{7}{2}\right)$, $R=\frac{7}{2}$. **157.** $x^2+y^2+4y=0$; (0, 0), (2, —2), (—2, —2). **158.** $x^2+y^2+ax+ay=0$. **159.** $y=0$, $15x+8y=0$. **160.** 90°. **161.** $x+y=3$. **162.** $x^2+y^2+ax=0$. **163.** $(x-2)^2+y^2=16$. **164.** $x^2+y^2=2ax$. **165.** $a=4$; $b=2$; $c=2\sqrt{3}$; $\varepsilon=\frac{\sqrt{3}}{2}$. **166.** (1) $\frac{x^2}{25}+\frac{y^2}{9}=1$; (2) $\frac{x^2}{36}+\frac{y^2}{27}=1$. **167.** $b=1.4$; 3; 4; 4.8; 5; $\varepsilon=0.96$; 0.8; 0.6; 0.28; 0. **168.** $a=150{,}000{,}000$ km; $\varepsilon=\frac{1}{60}$. **169.** $\frac{x^2}{16}+\frac{y^2}{4}=1$; $\varepsilon=\frac{\sqrt{3}}{2}$; $r=4-\sqrt{3}$; $r_1=4+\sqrt{3}$. **170.** $\frac{x^2}{64}+\frac{y^2}{28}=1$; $r=11$; $r_1=5$. **171.** $4\sqrt{3}$. **172.** $\sqrt{0.4}$. **173.** $\left(\frac{2}{7}, \pm\frac{4\sqrt{3}}{7}\right)$. **174.** $\left(-\frac{15}{4}, \pm\frac{\sqrt{63}}{4}\right)$. **175.** $\frac{x^2}{36}+\frac{y^2}{4}=1$. **176.** $\frac{x^2}{4}+\frac{y^2}{3}=1$. **178.** $\frac{x^2}{a^2}+\frac{y^2}{b^2}=1$ or $\frac{x^2}{b^2}+\frac{y^2}{a^2}=1$. **179.** $\frac{x^2}{9}+\frac{y^2}{5}=1$, or $\frac{x^2}{5}+\frac{y^2}{9}=1$. **180.** $\frac{x^2}{34}+\frac{y^2}{9}=1$; $\varepsilon=\frac{\sqrt{3}}{2}$, $r=3$, $r_1=9$. **181.** $\sqrt{2(a^2+b^2)}$. **182.** $\left(\pm\frac{4\sqrt{2}}{3}, \frac{1}{3}\right)$ and (0, —1). **183.** (—5, 7). **184.** $(\pm\sqrt{15}, \pm 1)$.

185. $x^2+4y^2=16$. **186.** $\frac{x^2}{9}+\frac{y^2}{8}=1$. **187.** $\varepsilon=\frac{\sqrt{5}}{2}$, 53°08′. **188.** $r=1$, $r_1=9$. **189.** (1) $\frac{x^2}{16}-\frac{y^2}{9}=1$; (2) $\frac{x^2}{20}-\frac{y^2}{4}=1$. **190.** $\frac{x^2}{12}-\frac{y^2}{4}=1$; $2\sqrt{3}$ and $6\sqrt{3}$. **191.** $\frac{x^2}{16}-\frac{y^2}{9}=1$. **192.** $x^2-y^2=a^2$. **193.** $(0, \pm a\sqrt{2})$; 90°. **194.** $y+2=\pm\frac{\sqrt{2}}{2}x$. **195.** b; $2 \arctan \frac{b}{a}$. **196.** $\frac{ab}{\sqrt{b^2-a^2}}$; $b > a$. **197.** (1) $\varepsilon=2$; (2) $\varepsilon=\sec\alpha$. **198.** $y\leqslant-3$, $y<-|x|$. **199.** $\frac{x^2}{4}-\frac{y^2}{12}=1$. **200.** $x^2-\frac{y^2}{3}=1$ (for $x>0$). **201.** $x^2-y^2=a^2$. **202.** $\frac{x^2}{a^2}-\frac{y^2}{b^2}=1$. **203.** $\frac{x^2}{16}-\frac{y^2}{9}=1$ $\left(\text{or } \frac{x^2}{9}-\frac{y^2}{16}=-1\right)$. **204.** (0, 0) and $(6, \pm 2\sqrt{3})$. **205.** $y=\pm\frac{4}{3}(x+5)$. **206.** $(-9.6, \pm 3/5\sqrt{119})$. **207.** $(\pm\sqrt{6}, \pm\sqrt{2})$. **208.** (—4, 3) and $\left(-\frac{4}{7}, -\frac{3}{7}\right)$. **209.** $\frac{x^2}{16}-\frac{y^2}{48}=1$. **210.** $\frac{x^2}{a^2}-\frac{y^2}{3a^2}=1$ (for $x>0$). **211.** $y=3-\frac{x^2}{4}$. **212.** $y^2=8(x+2)$. **214.** (1) $y^2=9x$; (2) $y=-x^2$. **215.** $y=\frac{a}{b^2}x^2$. **216.** $\left(x-\frac{p}{2}\right)^2+y^2=p^2$; $\left(\frac{p}{2}, \pm p\right)$. **217.** $y=-\frac{x^2}{2}$. **218.** $(3, \pm 3\sqrt{2})$. **219.** 40 cm. **221.** $y^2=px$. **222.** $y^2=4ax$ and $y=0$. **224.** $y^2=8(2-x)$. **225.** $y=x-\frac{x^2}{4}$; $O_1(2, 1)$. **226.** (1) $y^2=-4x$; (2) $y=x^2$. **227.** $y^2=-3x$. **228.** (0, 0), $(6, \pm 2\sqrt{3})$. **229.** $x=0$; $x+y+2=0$. **230.** $y=-\sqrt{3}(x+1)$; $\frac{16}{3}$. **231.** $r=7.4$; $d=9.25$. **232.** Directrices $x=\pm 3.2$; $\varepsilon=1.25$; $r=10.25$; $d=8.2$. **233.** $\frac{x^2}{4}+y^2=1$. **234.** $x^2-y^2=12$. **235.** Conjugate diameter $y=-\frac{x}{2}$; $a_1=b_1=\sqrt{10}$. **236.** Conjugate diameter $4y+x=0$; 31°. **237.** The equation of the diameter $y=\frac{b}{a}x$; its length $\sqrt{2(a^2+b^2)}$. **238.** $y=1.5x$. **239.** $y=2$. **240.** $8x-9y+25=0$. **241.** $y=2x+3$. **243.** (1) $x\pm 2\sqrt{3}y=8$; (2) $2x\pm y=1$; (3) $x\pm 2y=-2$. **245.** $x-y=\pm 5$. **246.** $y=\pm 2x+6$. **247.** $x+y=\sqrt{a^2+b^2}$. **249.** $y=2x\pm 4\sqrt{2}$. **250.** Equation of the normal MN: $a^2y_0x-b^2x_0y=c^2x_0y_0$. Putting $y=0$, find the abscissa of the point N of intersection of MN and OX: $x_1=\varepsilon^2x_0$. Then $FN=x-\varepsilon^2x_0=\varepsilon r$, $F_1N=c+\varepsilon^2x_0=\varepsilon r_1$, i.e. the normal MN divides FF_1 in the ratio $r:r_1$, and therefore is a bisector. 252. The normal to the parabola $y^2=2px$ has the equation $y_0x+py=y_0(p+x_0)$. Putting $y=0$, we find $x_1=p+x_0$, $FM=x_1-\frac{p}{2}=\frac{p}{2}+x_0=FM$, i.e. $\angle FMN=$

$=\angle FNM$. **253.** $(\pm 3.2, \ \pm 2.4)$. **254.** The diameters $y=x$ and $y=-\frac{x}{4}$; the angle $59°02'$. **255.** $y=\frac{x}{4}$. **256.** $4x-y=6$. **257.** $\arctan 3 \approx 71°31'$. **259.** $x+y+2=0$. **260.** (1) $O_1(1, 2)$, (2) $\tan\varphi=\frac{3}{4}$. **261.** (5) $X^2+4Y^2=16$; (6) $Y^2=4X$; (7) $X^2-4Y^2=4$; (8) $Y=\frac{1}{2}X^2$. **262.** (1) $X^2+4Y^2=16$; (2) $X^2-4Y^2=16$. **263.** $X^2-Y^2=8$. **264.** (1) $XY=6$; (2) $XY=-6$; (3) $XY=4$; (4) $XY=-6$. **268.** Equation of the jet: $y=16(x-x^2)$; at $x=0.75$ m $y=3$ m. **269.** $y=b\left(1-\frac{x^2}{a^2}\right)$. **270.** $x^2+y^2+4x=0$. **271.** (1) $45°$; (2) $\arctan 2$. **272.** $y=x\tan\varphi-\frac{gx^2}{2v_0^2\cos\varphi}$. **273.** $y^2=24x+3x^2$ (hyperbola). **275.** (1) Ellipse; (2) hyperbola. **276.** (1) $\frac{X^2}{5}+\frac{Y^2}{2}=1$, $O_1(3, -1)$; (2) $X^2-Y^2=9$; (3) $Y^2=2X$; (4) $X^2=4Y$. **277.** $X^2+2Y^2=4$. (1, 1) and $(-1, -1)$. **278.** $(x+1)^2+y^2=4$. **279.** $(x-3)^2+(y-3)^2=2$. **280.** $x+3y=0$. **281.** $y^2=4(x+4)$. **283.** $\frac{(x-2)^2}{16}+\frac{y^2}{12}=1$. **284.** $x^2+y^2-ax-by=0$. **285.** $\frac{a\sqrt{5}}{2}$. **286.** The base $AB=2a$, altitude $OD=\frac{a}{\sqrt{5}}$, area $\frac{a^2}{\sqrt{5}}$. **287.** Take for the origin point O which divides AB in the ratio $AO:OB=m$, and the straight line OB for the axis OX; let $OB=a$, then the coordinates of the points A and B will be: $A(-ma, 0)$, $B(a, 0)$. The equation of the required line $(m-1)x^2+(m-1)y^2=2max$; for $m \neq 1$ a circle: $x^2+y^2=\frac{2ma}{m-1}x$; for $m=1$ a straight line: $x=0$. **288.** Take O for the origin, and OB for the axis OX. The equation of the required line: $(a-b)(x^2+y^2)=2abx$; for $a \neq b$ a circle: $x^2+y^2=\frac{2ab}{a-b}x$; for $a=b$ a straight line: $x=0$. **289.** $2(k^2x^2+y^2)=a^2(k^2+1)$; an ellipse for $k \neq 1$, a circle $x^2+y^2=a^2$ for $k=1$. **290.** $\frac{x^2+10x}{25}+\frac{y^2}{9}=0$. **291.** $3a^2\sqrt{3}$. **292.** $\arctan\frac{3}{4} \approx 36°52'$. **293.** $(\pm a, \pm a)$. **294.** $A(\sqrt{6}; 0)$; $B(2, -2)$, $C(-2\sqrt{2}, \sqrt{2})$; the area of $\triangle ABC=\sqrt{2}+\sqrt{3}+\sqrt{6}$. **296.** $2\sqrt{2}$; $y=x-2$. **297.** $\frac{2+\sqrt{3}}{2}$. **298.** $\left(x-\frac{p}{2}\right)^2+y^2=\frac{9p^2}{16}$. **299.** $ax-by+a^2+b^2=0$; $d=\frac{|ab|}{\sqrt{a^2+b^2}}$. **300.** Subtracting the equations termwise, we get $4(y-x)=(y+x)(y-x)$; hence (1) $y=x$; (2) $x+y=4$; consequently, the points of intersection of the parabolas lie either on the straight line $y=x$, or on $x+y=4$; we find: $x_1=2$; $x_2=-6$; the chord length

$8\sqrt{2}$. **301.** 30. **302.** $x^2+y^2=a(x+y)$. **303.** $\frac{(x-2)^2}{4}+y^2=1$, an ellipse with the centre (2, 0). **304.** $xy=4$. **305.** $y=\frac{x^2-6x+25}{8}$. **306.** $X^2-Y^2=4$; $O_1(2, -3)$. **307.** $\frac{(x-2.5)^2}{2.25}-\frac{y^2}{4}=1$, a hyperbola with the centre (2.5, 0). **308.** Let $M(x, y)$ be a point of the ellipse. Then $FM+F_1M=AF+AF_1$ or $\sqrt{(x-a)^2+(y-a)^2}+\sqrt{(x+a)^2+(y+a)^2}=4a$; $3x^2-2xy+3y^2=8a^2$; on rotating the axes through 45°: $X^2+2Y^2=4a^2$. **309.** $\cos\varphi=\frac{1}{\sqrt{1+\tan^2\varphi}}=\frac{2}{\sqrt{5}}$; $\sin\varphi=\frac{1}{\sqrt{5}}$; the new equation $X^2-Y^2=4$. **310.** $3x^2+8xy-3y^2=20$; by rotating the axes through the angle $\varphi=\arctan\frac{1}{2}$ it is reduced to the form $X^2-Y^2=4$ (see 309). **311.** $y^2=2px+(\varepsilon^2-1)x^2$. **313.** (1) a pair of straight lines $y=\pm 2x$; (2) a point (0, 0); (3) an imaginary circle; (4) a point (3, 4); (5) a pair of straight lines $x=0$, $y=-x$; (6) a pair of straight lines $y=\pm 4$; (7) a pair of straight lines $y=x$ and $y=\frac{x}{2}$. **314.** (1) (1, —1), $\frac{X^2}{6}+\frac{Y^2}{4}=1$; (2) (2, 1), $X^2-Y^2=9$; (3) $2X^2+5XY+2Y^2=8$. **315.** (1) $\frac{X^2}{24}+\frac{Y^2}{4}=1$; (2) $\frac{X^2}{4}-\frac{Y^2}{6}=1$. **316.** (1) $\frac{X^2}{8}+\frac{Y^2}{4}=1$; (2) $\frac{X^2}{8}-\frac{Y^2}{4}=1$. **317.** (1) $Y^2=2\sqrt{5}X$; (2) a pair of straight lines $x-2y=3\pm 1$. **318.** (1) $3y=2x-7\pm(x-2)$; (2) a point (2, —1); (3) $4y=-2x-3\pm 1$. **319.** $4X^2-Y^2=8$; centre (2, 0); $\tan\varphi=-1/2$. **320.** $5(x-1)^2+(y-2)^2=9$. **321.** Rotating the axes through —45° we get; $Y=\frac{X^2}{a\sqrt{2}}+\frac{a}{2\sqrt{2}}$. The equation $\sqrt{x}+\sqrt{y}=\sqrt{a}$ defines an arc AB of this parabola (Fig. 91), on which $x\leqslant a$ and $y\leqslant a$. **322.** $(x-m)^2+(y-n)^2-\varepsilon^2(x\cos\alpha+y\sin\alpha+q)^2=0$; $A+C=2-\varepsilon^2$; $\delta=1-\varepsilon^2$. **323.** (1) A pair of straight lines $x\pm 2y=0$; (2) a point (—2, 2); (3) a pair of straight lines $y=x$, $x+6y=0$. **324.** (1) $\frac{X^2}{12}+\frac{Y^2}{4}=1$; (2) $\frac{X^2}{20}-\frac{Y^2}{5}=1$. **325.** (1) $Y^2=4\sqrt{2}X$; (2) straight lines: $x+y=2\pm 1$. **326.** (1) $y=x-2\pm 1$; (2) $3y=x-5\pm 2(x+1)$. **327.** (1) $7x^2-2xy+7y^2-48x-48y+144=0$; (2) $x^2+4xy+y^2+6x+6y-18=0$. **328.** $(x-y)^2-2a(x+y)+a^2=0$; $Y^2=a\sqrt{2}X$. **329.** $x^2-4xy-y^2-4x+8y-12=0$; $X^2-Y^2=3.2\sqrt{5}$. **335.** (1) $r=\frac{a}{\cos\varphi}$; (2) $r=\frac{a\sin\alpha}{\sin\varphi}$. **336.** $r=\frac{a\sin(\beta-\alpha)}{\sin(\beta-\varphi)}$. **337.** $r=2a\cos\varphi$. **338.** (1) $r_{max}=5$ at $\varphi=135°$, 315°; $r_{min}=1$ at $\varphi=45°$, 225°; $r=3$ at $\varphi=0°$ 90°, 180°, 270°; (2) $r_{max}=3$ at $\varphi=0°$, 120°, 240°; $r_{min}=1$ at $\varphi=60°$, 180°, 360°; (3) $r_{max}=2$ at $\varphi=90°$,

210°, 330°; $r_{min}=0$ at $\varphi=30°$, 150°, 270°. **339.** (1) $r_{max}=a$ at $\varphi=30°$, 150°, 270°; $r=0$ at $\varphi=0°$, 60°, 120°, 180°, 240°, 300°; (2) $r=a$ at $\varphi=45°$, 225°; $r=-a$ at $\varphi=135°$, 315°; $r=0$ at $\varphi=0°$, 90°, 180°, 270° (see Fig. 87 on p. 386). **340.** (1) $r^2=\frac{a^2}{\cos 2\varphi}$; (2) $r=a$; (3) $r=\frac{p}{\cos(\varphi-\alpha)}$; (4) $\tan\varphi=1$; (5) $r=\alpha\cos\varphi$; (6) $r^2=a^2\cos 2\varphi$. **341.** (1) $x=a$; (2) $x^2+y^2=2ay$; (3) $xy=a^2$; (4) $x+y=2a$; (5) $(x^2+y^2-ax)^2=a^2(x^2+y^2)$. **342.** (1) $\frac{x^2}{25}+\frac{y^2}{9}=1$; (2) $\frac{x^2}{16}-\frac{y^2}{9}=1$; (3) $y^2=6x$. **343.** $r=\frac{a}{\sin\varphi}\pm b$. **344.** $r=OB\pm AB=\frac{a(1\pm\sin\varphi)}{\cos\varphi}$ or in Cartesian coordinates $y^2=\frac{x(x-a)^2}{2a-x}$. **345.** $FM^2=r^2+a^2-2ra\cos\varphi$; $F_1M^2=r^2+a^2+2ra\cos\varphi$; $FM^2\cdot F_1M^2=(r^2+a^2)^2-4r^2a^2\cos^2\varphi=b^4$; hence $r^4-2a^2r^2\cos 2\varphi=b^4-a^4$. **346.** $r=a(1+\cos\varphi)$; $(x^2+y^2-ax)^2=$ $=a^2(x^2+y^2)$. **347.** Let C be the centre of the fixed circle, C_1 the centre of the displaced circle, and $M(\varphi, r)$ a moving point. Since $\angle OCC_1=\angle MC_1C=\varphi$ and $CO=C_1M=\frac{1}{2}a$, then $OM \parallel CC_1$. Projecting the polygonal line $COMC_1$ on CC_1, we get: $\frac{a}{2}\cos\varphi+r+\frac{a}{2}\cos\varphi=a$. Hence $r=a(1-\cos\varphi)$. **348.** (1) $r_{max}=5$ at $\varphi=0°$, 180°; $r_{min}=1$ at $\varphi=90°$, 270°; (2) $r_{max}=4$ at $\varphi=90°$, 210°, 330°; $r_{min}=2$ at $\varphi=30°$, 150°, 270°; (3) $r=a$ at $\varphi=0°$, 180°; $r=-a$ at $\varphi=90°$, 270°; $r=0$ at $\varphi=45°$, 135°, 225°, 315°. **350.** $r=\frac{ab\sin(\beta-\alpha)}{a\sin(\varphi-\alpha)+b\sin(\beta-\varphi)}$.

351. (1) $\frac{x^2}{4}+y^2=1$; (2) $\frac{x^2}{4}-y^2=1$; (3) $y^2=x$. **352.** $r^2=2c^2\cos 2\varphi$; $(x^2+y^2)^2=2c^2(x^2-y^2)$. In Fig. 84: $c\sqrt{2}=a$. **353.** $r=b+a\cos\varphi$. **354.** From $\triangle OAM$: $r=OM=OA\cos\varphi$, but from $\triangle OAB$: $OA=2a\sin\varphi$; hence $r=a\sin 2\varphi$. **358.** Let point A be on the axis OX, point B on OY, and $\angle OAB=t$. Then $x=BM\cos t=BC\cos^2 t=$ $=a\cos^3 t$, $y=AM\sin t=AC\sin^2 t=a\sin^3 t$; thus, $x=a\cos^3 t$, $y=a\sin^3 t$; hence $x^{\frac{2}{3}}+y^{\frac{2}{3}}=a^{\frac{2}{3}}$. **360.** $y^2=\frac{px^2}{p+x}$. **361.** $(3y^2+x^2)^2=$ $=4x^2(a^2-y^2)$. **362.** In polar coordinates: $r=OM=AB=BD\sin\varphi=a\times$ $\times\tan\varphi\cdot\sin\varphi$; in Cartesian coordinates: $y^2=\frac{x^3}{a-x}$ (Fig. 89). **365.** Denoting the angle between OA and OX by t, we find $x=2a\cot t$, $y=2a\sin^2 t$. Eliminating, t we get $y=\frac{8a^3}{x^2+4a^2}$. **367.** $\begin{cases} x=a(t-\sin t), \\ y=a(1-\cos t). \end{cases}$

368. $\begin{cases} x=a(\cos t+t\sin t), \\ y=a(\sin t-t\cos t). \end{cases}$ **369.** $y=x\cot\frac{x}{a}$.

370. $\begin{cases} x=(R+r)\cos t-r\cos\dfrac{(R+r)t}{r}, \\ y=(R+r)\sin t-r\sin\dfrac{(R+r)t}{r}, \end{cases}$ where t is the rotation angle of the centre line. **371.** $\begin{cases} x=(R-r)\cos t+r\cos\dfrac{R-r}{r}t, \\ y=(R-r)\sin t-r\sin\dfrac{R-r}{r}t. \end{cases}$

374. $X=\sum X_i=8$; $Y=\sum Y_i=-2$; $OM=\sqrt{64+4}=2\sqrt{17}$. **375.** $\sqrt{8+2\sqrt{3}}$. **379.** (1) $\boldsymbol{c}=\dfrac{\boldsymbol{a}+\boldsymbol{b}}{2}$; (2) $\boldsymbol{a}=2\boldsymbol{c}-\boldsymbol{b}$. **380.** $\boldsymbol{c}=\dfrac{2}{3}(\boldsymbol{a}-\boldsymbol{b})$. **881.** $\boldsymbol{m}+\boldsymbol{p}=\boldsymbol{n}$; $\overrightarrow{OB}=3(\boldsymbol{m}+\boldsymbol{n})$; $\overrightarrow{BC}=3(\boldsymbol{n}-\boldsymbol{m})$; $\overrightarrow{EO}=3(\boldsymbol{m}-\boldsymbol{n})$; $\overrightarrow{OD}=3(2\boldsymbol{n}-\boldsymbol{m})$; $\overrightarrow{DA}=6(\boldsymbol{m}-\boldsymbol{n})$. **382.** $\overrightarrow{AC}=2(\boldsymbol{n}-\boldsymbol{m})$; $\overrightarrow{OM}=2\boldsymbol{n}+\boldsymbol{m}$; $\overrightarrow{ON}=3\boldsymbol{m}+\boldsymbol{n}$; $\overrightarrow{MN}=2\boldsymbol{m}-\boldsymbol{n}$. **383.** $6\sqrt{3}$. **384.** $X=X_1+X_2+X_3=-3$; $Y=\sum Y_i=6$; $OM=\sqrt{9+36}=3\sqrt{5}$. **885.** (1) $\boldsymbol{a}=3(\boldsymbol{c}-\boldsymbol{b})$; (2) $\boldsymbol{c}=2\boldsymbol{b}-\boldsymbol{a}\sqrt{3}$. **386.** $OM=r=5\sqrt{2}$; $\cos\alpha=0.5\sqrt{2}$, $\cos\beta=-0.3\sqrt{2}$, $\cos\gamma=0.4\sqrt{2}$. **387.** $r=7$, $\cos\alpha=\dfrac{2}{7}$. **388.** $\beta\approx 52°$ or $128°$. **389.** $M(3\sqrt{2},\ 3,\ -3)$, $\boldsymbol{r}=3(\sqrt{2}\boldsymbol{i}+\boldsymbol{j}-\boldsymbol{k})$. **390.** $\boldsymbol{u}=2\boldsymbol{i}-6\boldsymbol{j}+3\boldsymbol{k}$, $u=7$. **391.** $\overrightarrow{OC}=\boldsymbol{i}-2\boldsymbol{j}+\boldsymbol{k}$, $OC=\sqrt{6}$, $\overrightarrow{AB}=\boldsymbol{k}-4\boldsymbol{j}-\boldsymbol{i}$; $AB=3\sqrt{2}$. **392.** The end-point $B(4,\ -2,\ 5)$ or $B_1(4,\ -2,\ -7)$, $\cos\alpha=\dfrac{2}{7}$; $\cos\beta=-\dfrac{3}{7}$; $\cos\gamma=\pm\dfrac{6}{7}$. **393.** $\boldsymbol{a}=2\boldsymbol{b}-0.8\boldsymbol{c}$. **394.** $u=3\sqrt{5}$, $\cos\alpha=-\dfrac{2}{3\sqrt{5}}$. **895.** $\cos\alpha=\cos\beta=\cos\gamma=\dfrac{1}{\sqrt{3}}$. **396.** $45°$ or $135°$. **397.** $D(4,\ 0,\ 6)$. **398.** $\boldsymbol{c}=2\boldsymbol{b}-2\boldsymbol{a}$. **399.** $135°$. **400.** $B=C=45°$. **401.** $\cos\varphi=\dfrac{1}{\sqrt{10}}=0.316$; $\varphi=71°35'$. **402.** $\cos\varphi=\dfrac{2}{\sqrt{5}}=0.894$; $\varphi\approx 26°37'$. **403.** $60°$. **404.** arccos 0.8. **405.** $90°$. **406.** $\text{pr}_{\boldsymbol{b}}\boldsymbol{a}=\dfrac{4\sqrt{2}}{3}$. **407.** 2. **408.** (1) $2+\sqrt{3}$; (2) 40. **409.** $(\boldsymbol{a}+\boldsymbol{b})^2=a^2+b^2+2ab\cos\varphi$ (law of cosines); $(\boldsymbol{a}+\boldsymbol{b})^2+(\boldsymbol{a}-\boldsymbol{b})^2=2a^2+2b^2$ (property of diagonals of a parallelogram). **410.** 7. **411.** $R=\sqrt{(\boldsymbol{a}+\boldsymbol{b}+\boldsymbol{c}+\boldsymbol{d})^2}=100\sqrt{4+2\sqrt{2}}\approx 253$ N. **412.** $\sqrt{7}$ and $\sqrt{13}$. **413.** $\cos(\widehat{\boldsymbol{a},\ \boldsymbol{m}})=\dfrac{(2\boldsymbol{m}-\boldsymbol{n})\,\boldsymbol{m}}{\sqrt{(2\boldsymbol{m}-\boldsymbol{n})^2}\cdot 1}=\dfrac{5}{2\sqrt{7}}$;

$\cos(\widehat{a, n}) = -\frac{2}{\sqrt{7}}$. **414.** $\frac{5}{6}$. **415.** $\overrightarrow{OM} = 2(\boldsymbol{i}+\boldsymbol{j}+2\boldsymbol{k})$; $\overrightarrow{ON} = 2(\boldsymbol{i}+2\boldsymbol{j}+\boldsymbol{k})$; $\cos\theta = \frac{5}{6}$. **416.** $\cos\varphi = \frac{2}{\sqrt{7}}$. **417.** $\cos\varphi = 0.26\sqrt{10}$; $\varphi \approx 34°42'$. **418.** $D(-1, 1, 1)$; $\varphi = 120°$. **419.** $\mathrm{pr}_a b = \frac{\overrightarrow{AB}\cdot\overrightarrow{CD}}{AB} = -6$. **420.** $OM = \sqrt{(2\boldsymbol{n}+\boldsymbol{m})^2} = \sqrt{7}$; $ON = \sqrt{(3\boldsymbol{m}+\boldsymbol{n})^2} = \sqrt{13}$; $\cos\varphi = \frac{\overrightarrow{OM}\cdot\overrightarrow{ON}}{OM\cdot ON} = \frac{17}{2\sqrt{91}} = \frac{17}{19.08} \approx 0.891$; $\varphi = 27°$. **421.** 120°. **423.** 80 J, $\cos\theta = \frac{4\sqrt{2}}{15}$. **424.** $a\sqrt{6}$. **425.** $\cos\varphi = -\frac{1}{4}$. **426.** $\boldsymbol{a}\times\boldsymbol{b}$ equals: (1) $-6\boldsymbol{j}$; (2) $-2\boldsymbol{k}$; (3) $6\boldsymbol{i}-4\boldsymbol{j}+6\boldsymbol{k}$. The area equals: (1) 6; (2) 2; (3) $2\sqrt{22}$. **427.** 24.5. **428.** $\sqrt{21}$ sq. units, $h = \sqrt{4.2}$. **429.** (1) $2(\boldsymbol{k}-\boldsymbol{i})$; (2) $2\boldsymbol{a}\times\boldsymbol{c}$; (3) $\boldsymbol{a}\times\boldsymbol{c}$; (4) 3. **430.** The area of a parallelogram constructed on the diagonals of a given parallelogram is twice the area of the given parallelogram. **431.** $50\sqrt{2}$. **432.** $1.5\sqrt{2}$. **433.** $3\sqrt{17}$, $S_\triangle = \frac{3\sqrt{17}}{2}$ sq. units. **434.** $S_\triangle = 7\sqrt{5}$ sq. units, $BD = \frac{2\sqrt{21}}{3}$. **435.** $|\boldsymbol{a}+\boldsymbol{b}| = |\boldsymbol{a}-\boldsymbol{b}| = \sqrt{5}$, $S = \sqrt{6}$ sq. units. **437.** 1.5. **438.** $V = 51$, left-handed. **439.** $V = 14$ cu. units, $H = \frac{7\sqrt{3}}{3}$. **441.** $\boldsymbol{c} = 5\boldsymbol{a}+\boldsymbol{b}$. **443.** $\frac{2\sqrt{2}}{3}$. **444.** $V = 14$ cu. units, $H = \sqrt{14}$. **445.** $\boldsymbol{c} = \boldsymbol{a}+2\boldsymbol{b}$. **446.** $V = |(\boldsymbol{a}+\boldsymbol{b})\cdot[(\boldsymbol{b}+\boldsymbol{c})\times(\boldsymbol{a}+\boldsymbol{c})]| = 2|\boldsymbol{abc}|$. **447.** $(\boldsymbol{m}\times\boldsymbol{n})\cdot\boldsymbol{p} = |\boldsymbol{m}\times\boldsymbol{n}|\cdot 1\cdot\cos\alpha = \sin\alpha\cos\alpha = \frac{1}{2}\sin 2\alpha$. **449.** 52. **451.** $\cos\alpha = \frac{2}{7}$, $\cos\beta = \frac{3}{7}$, $\cos\gamma = \frac{6}{7}$. **452.** $x+4y-2z=2$. **453.** $x+y=2\alpha$. **454.** $x-y+z=\alpha$. **455.** $2y-3z+7=0$. **456.** $3y+2z=0$. **457.** $2x+y=0$. **458.** $\frac{x}{a}+\frac{z}{c}=1$. **459.** $x+y+z=4$. **460.** $\frac{x}{4}+\frac{y}{3}+\frac{z}{2}=1$. **462.** $\cos\alpha = \frac{2}{3}$; $\cos\beta = -\frac{2}{3}$; $\cos\gamma = \frac{1}{3}$; $\alpha = 48°11'$, $\beta = 131°49'$, $\gamma = 70°32'$. **463.** $x-2y-3z+14=0$. **464.** $3x-4z=0$. **465.** $x+y=4$. **466.** $\frac{x}{2}+\frac{y}{4}+\frac{z}{4}=1$. **467.** (1) 45°; (2) 78°30′. **468.** $x-2y-3z=4$. **469.** $2x+3y+4z=3$. **470.** $2x+y+z=a$. **471.** $2x-2y+z=2$. **472.** $2x-y+z=5$. **473.** $3x-y=0$ and $x+3y=0$. **474.** 3. **475.** $\sqrt{6}$. **476.** $2\sqrt{2}$. **477.** (1) $x-2y+2z=11$ and $x-2y+2z=-1$; (2) $x+y-2z=0$ and $x+y+z=0$. **478.** (1) $x-8y+9z=21$; (2) $x-y+2z=0$ and $x-y-z=0$. **479.** (1, −1, 2). **480.** $3x-4y+z=11$. **481.** $2y-5z+10=0$ **482.** The equation of the plane: $x+y-2z=0$; the angle between this plane and the plane $z=0$: $\cos\varphi=\frac{\sqrt{6}}{3}\approx 0.8165$; $\varphi=35°15'$. **483.** $\frac{|a|}{\sqrt{3}}$. **484.** $y=\pm z$. **485.** $\frac{2abc}{\sqrt{a^2b^2+a^2c^2+b^2c^2}}$. **486.** $2x+2y+z=20$ and $2x+2y+z+4=0$. **487.** $7x+14y+24=0$. **488.** (1) (5, 4, 0) and (7, 0, 2); (2) (0, —4, 0) and (2, 0, 2). **489.** $x=-z+3$, $y=-z+5$; $\frac{x-3}{1}=\frac{y-5}{1}=\frac{z}{-1}$. **490.** $\frac{x-4}{-1}=\frac{y-3}{1}=\frac{z}{1}$. **491.** $\boldsymbol{P}\{0, 0, 1\}$. **492.** (1) $\boldsymbol{P}=\boldsymbol{i}$; (2) $\boldsymbol{P}=\boldsymbol{i}+\boldsymbol{k}$; (3) $\boldsymbol{P}=\boldsymbol{j}+\boldsymbol{k}$. **493.** $\frac{x+1}{3}=\frac{y-2}{4}=\frac{z-3}{-5}$; $\cos\alpha=0.3\sqrt{2}$; $\cos\beta=0.4\sqrt{2}$; $\cos\gamma=-0.5\sqrt{2}$. **494.** $x=2$, $z=3$. **495.** In t seconds the coordinates of the point M will be: $x=4+2t$; $y=-3+3t$; $z=1+t$; $\frac{x-4}{2}=\frac{y+3}{3}=\frac{z-1}{1}$. **496.** (1) $x=-2+t$, $y=1-2t$, $z=-1+3t$; (2) $x=1+t$, $y=1-t$, $z=2+t$. **497.** (1) $\frac{x-a}{0}=\frac{y-b}{0}=\frac{z-c}{1}$, which means: $\begin{cases} x=a \\ y=b; \end{cases}$ (2) $z=c$ and $\frac{x-a}{m}=\frac{y-b}{n}$. **498.** $\cos\varphi=\frac{1}{\sqrt{3}}$. **499.** $\cos\varphi=\frac{11}{26}$. **501.** The direction vector $\boldsymbol{P}=\boldsymbol{N}\times\boldsymbol{N}_1=\boldsymbol{i}+3\boldsymbol{j}+5\boldsymbol{k}$. The equations of the straight line $\frac{x+4}{1}=\frac{y-3}{3}=\frac{z}{5}$. **502.** $3x+2y=0$; $z=4$. **503.** $0.3\sqrt{38}$. **504.** $\frac{4\sqrt{2}}{3}$. **505.** (4, 2, 0), (3, 0, 2), (0, —6, 8). **506.** $x=6-3z$, $y=-2z+4$; $\frac{x-6}{-3}=\frac{y-4}{-2}=\frac{z}{1}$; the traces: (6, 4, 0), (0, 0, 2). **507.** $\frac{x}{1}=\frac{y+4}{2}=\frac{z}{3}$. **508.** $\boldsymbol{P}\{0, 1, 0\}$. **509.** $\boldsymbol{P}\{1, 1, 2\}$; $\alpha=\beta=\arccos\frac{1}{\sqrt{6}}$. **510.** $y=-3$; $2x-z=0$. **511.** Reduce the equations to the canonical form: $\frac{x}{1}=\frac{y+7}{2}=\frac{z-5}{2}$ and $\frac{x}{2}=\frac{y-4}{3}=\frac{z}{6}$; $\cos\varphi=\frac{20}{21}\approx 0.952$; $\varphi=17°48'$. **512.** Representing the equations of the given straight line in the form $\frac{x-2}{2}=\frac{y}{2}=\frac{z-\frac{1}{3}}{3}$, we get the equation of the required straight line: $\frac{x+1}{2}=\frac{y-2}{2}=\frac{z+2}{1}$. **513.** $A(0, +1, 0)$, $\overrightarrow{AM}\{3, -1, 4\}$, $\boldsymbol{P}\{1, 2, 2\}$, $d=\sqrt{17}$. **514.** $\sin\theta=\frac{1}{\sqrt{6}}$. **515.** For both straight lines $Am+Bn+Cp=2\cdot 2+1(-1)+(-1)\cdot 3=0$, but the point of the first one (—1, —1, 3) does not lie in the plane, while the point of the second one (—1, —1, —3) does. **516.** $y+z+1=0$ $\left(\text{the equations of the straight line may be rewritten as } \frac{x-2}{0}=\frac{y-1}{1}=\frac{z}{1}\right)$. **517.** $x-2y+z+5=0$. **518.** $8x-5y+z-11=0$. **519.** $x+2y-2z=1$. **520.** $\frac{x}{3}=\frac{y}{1}=\frac{z}{1}$; 17°33′. **521.** (5, 5, —2). **522.** (6, 4, 5). **523.** (5, 5, 5). **524.** (3, 3, 3). **525.** $d=\frac{\overrightarrow{AA_1}PP_1}{|P\times P_1|}=\frac{1}{\sqrt{3}}$. **526.** $x+2y-5z=0$. **527.** $\frac{x-2}{-9}=\frac{y-1}{8}=\frac{z}{11}$. **528.** (1, 1, 2); 70°. **529.** (—1, 2, 2), 30°. **530.** (6, 2, 0). **531.** (3, —1, 1). **532.** $x-y-z=0$. **533.** (—1, 3, 1). **534.** $\frac{x-1}{5}=\frac{y}{-4}=\frac{z+1}{-1}$. **535.** The points on the straight lines $O(0, 0, 0)$ and $A(2, 2, 0)$; their direction vertors: $\boldsymbol{P}\{0, 0, 1\}$ and $\boldsymbol{P}_1\{2, -1, 2\}$, $d=\frac{\overrightarrow{OA}PP_1}{|P\times P_1|}=\frac{6}{\sqrt{5}}$. **536.** (1) $C(1.5, -2.5, 2)$, $R=2.5\sqrt{2}$; (2) $C(0, 0, a)$, $R=a$. **537.** $(x-1)^2+(y+1)^2+(z-1)^2=1$. **538.** $x^2+y^2+z^2=8x$. **539.** $x^2+y^2+z^2-a(x+y+z)=0$. **541.** $y^2=2ax-x^2$. **542.** $x^2+y^2=2ax$, $x^2+z^2=2ax$, $y^2+z^2=a^2$. **544.** (1, 7, 2), $R=4$. **545.** $(3Y-2Z)^2=12(3X-Z)$. **546.** (1) $y=0$; $x^2=a^2-az$ (parabola); (2) $x=0$; $y^2=a^2-az$ (parabola); (3) $z=h$; $x+y=\pm\sqrt{a(a-h)}$ (a straight line parallel to $x+y=a$ (see Fig. 63 on p. 372)). **547.** Cylindrical surface $2x^2+(y-z+2)^2=8$, the shape of the shadow $\frac{x^2}{4}+\frac{(y+2)^2}{8}=1$ is an ellipse. **548.** $2x-y+3z-7=0$. **549.** $x^2+(y+4)^2+z^2=4$. **550.** $\frac{(x-2)^2}{36}+\frac{(y+4)^2}{18}=1$. **553.** $(x-z)^2+(y-z)^2=4(x-z)$. **554.** $x=4$, $z\pm y=2$. **555.** $\frac{x^2+y^2}{a^2}=\frac{z^2}{c^2}$. **556.** $h^2x^2=2pz[h(y+a)-az]$. **557.** (0, a, 0), the directrix is a circle $z=a$, $x^2+(y-a)^2=a^2$. **558.** The vertex (0, 0, 0), the directrix is a parabola $z=h$; $x^2=2hy$. **559.** For $z=0$ $x=\pm a$; for $y=h$ $x^2+y^2=a^2$; for $x=\pm c$ straight lines $z=\pm\frac{\sqrt{a^2-c^2}}{h}y$, i.e. the surface is generated by a moving straight line parallel to the plane YOZ and intersecting the circle ABC (see Fig. 69 on p. 374) and the axis OX. **560.** (a) $z=x^2+y^2$; (b) $\sqrt{y^2+z^2}=x^2$. **561.** (1) $z=e^{-(x^2+y^2)}$; (2) $z=\frac{4}{x^2+y^2}$. **562.** $9(x^2+z^2)=16y^2$. **563.** $x^2+z^2=z(y+a)$. **564.** (a) $x^2+z^2=y^2$; (b) $z^2=x^2+y^2$. **565.** Rotating the axes OX and OY about the axis OZ through 45°, we obtain the equations of the surface and the plane in the form $2Z^2=X^2-Y^2$, $X=a\sqrt{2}$. Hence the section: $X=a\sqrt{2}$, $\frac{Y^2}{2a^2}+\frac{Z^2}{a^2}=1$ an ellipse with the semi-axes $a\sqrt{2}$ and a. **566.** $\frac{x^2+y^2}{a^2}+\frac{z^2}{c^2}=1$. **567.** (a) 3.84π; (b) $\frac{45}{4}\pi$. **568.** (a) $\frac{x^2+y^2}{a^2}-\frac{z^2}{c^2}=1$ (hyperboloid of one sheet); (b) $\frac{x^2}{a^2}-\frac{y^2+z^2}{c^2}=1$ (hyperboloid of two sheets).

570. $\begin{cases} \frac{x}{4}+\frac{z}{6}=\frac{1}{3}\left(1+\frac{y}{2}\right), \\ \frac{x}{4}-\frac{z}{6}=3\left(1-\frac{y}{2}\right) \end{cases}$ and $\begin{cases} \frac{x}{4}+\frac{z}{6}=1-\frac{y}{2}, \\ \frac{x}{4}-\frac{z}{6}=1+\frac{y}{2}. \end{cases}$

571. $x=\frac{a}{c}[(c-z)\cos t+(c+z)\cos(t+\alpha)]$, $y=\frac{a}{c}[(c-z)\sin t+(c+z)\sin(t+\alpha)]$; hence: $\frac{x^2+y^2}{2a^2}-\frac{z^2}{c^2}(1-\cos\alpha)=1+\cos\alpha$; at $\alpha=90^\circ$ $\frac{x^2+y^2}{2a^2}-\frac{z^2}{c^2}=1$; at $\alpha=120^\circ$ $\frac{x^2+y^2}{a^2}-\frac{3z^2}{c^2}=1$; at $\alpha=180^\circ$ $\frac{x^2+y^2}{4a^2}-\frac{z^2}{c^2}=0$ (cone). **572.** $x^2+y^2=az$. **574.** $\begin{cases} x+y=4, \\ x-y=z; \end{cases}$ $\begin{cases} x+y=2z, \\ x-y=2. \end{cases}$ **575.** $\frac{x^2}{2a^2}+\frac{y^2+z^2}{a^2}=1$. **576.** $x^2+y^2-z^2=-2a^2$ (hyperboloid of two sheets). **577.** $x=-\frac{z^2+y^2}{4a}$. **578.** $9x=\pm 13z$. **579.** $4y=\pm 3z$. **580.** (1) A sphere with the centre (0, 0, a) and radius $R=a$; (2) paraboloid of revolution about OZ; (3) cylinder; (4) hyperbolic paraboloid; (5) cone; (6) parabolic cylinder; (7) cone; (8) paraboloid of revolution; (9) cone; (10) cylinder. **581.** $\begin{cases} x+y=2+z, \\ x-y=2-z; \end{cases}$ $\begin{cases} x+y=3(z-2), \\ 3(y-x)=z+2. \end{cases}$

582. $x^2+y^2=2az$. **583.** $z=a-\frac{x^2+y^2}{2a}$. **584.** $2y=\pm 3z$.

585. $\begin{cases} 3x+4y=24, \\ 3x-4y=12z; \end{cases}$ $\begin{cases} z=0, \\ 3x=4y. \end{cases}$ **586.** 26. **587.** —38. **588.** 7. **589.** $2a$. **590.** 1. **591.** $\sin(\alpha+\beta)\cdot\sin(\alpha-\beta)$. **592.** —10. **593.** $4a$. **594.** $-2b^2$. **595.** $-2x$. **596.** $-4a^3$. **597.** 144. **598.** 72. **599.** $(x-y)(y-z)(x-z)$. **600.** 1. **601.** $\sin(\beta-\alpha)$. **602.** 10. **603.** They lie on the straight line $y=x+2$. **604.** (1) $\begin{vmatrix} x & y & 1 \\ x_1 & y_1 & 1 \\ x_2 & y_2 & 1 \end{vmatrix}=0$; (2) $\begin{vmatrix} x & y & 1 \\ 2 & 3 & 1 \\ -1 & 5 & 1 \end{vmatrix}=0$. **605.** 10.

606. amn. **607.** $a(x-z)(y-z)(y-x)$. **608.** $4\sin\alpha\sin^2\frac{\alpha}{2}$. **610.** (1) $x_1=2$, $x_2=3$; (2) $x_1=0$, $x_2=-2$. **611.** $x=5$; $y=-4$. **612.** $x=\frac{4}{a}$; $y=1$. **613.** $x=0$; $y=2$. **614.** $x=m$; $y=2m-n$. **615.** 5; 6; 10. **616.** —1; 0; 1. **617.** $7k$; $8k$; $13k$. **618.** $5k$; $-11k$; $-7k$. **619.** $x=y=z=0$. **620.** Incompatible. **621.** Indeterminate: $x=\frac{2+5z}{3}$,

$y=\frac{5-7z}{3}$. **622.** Incompatible. **624.** 2; -1; -3. **625.** 1; -1; 2. **626.** $2k$; k; $-4k$. **627.** $x=y=z=0$. **628.** $-k$; $13k$; $5k$. **629.** Indeterminate: $y=7-3x$, $z=18-7x$. **630.** (1) $12+5i$; (2) a^2+b^2; (3) $5-12i$; (4) $-2+2i$; (5) i; (6) $1+i$. **634.** (1) $2\left(\cos\frac{3\pi}{4}+i\sin\frac{3\pi}{4}\right)$; (2) $2\cos\frac{\alpha}{2}\left(\sin\frac{\alpha}{2}+i\sin\frac{\alpha}{2}\right)$. **640.** (1) $32i$; (2) 64; (3) $4(1-i)$; (4) $2(3+2\sqrt{2})i$; (5) $8i$. **641.** $\sin 3\alpha=3\sin\alpha\cos^2\alpha-\cos^3\alpha$, $\cos 3\alpha=\cos^3\alpha-3\sin^2\alpha\cos\alpha$. **642.** $\cos\frac{k\pi}{3}+i\sin\frac{k\pi}{3}$; $k=0, 1, \ldots, 5$. **643.** (1) 1, $\frac{-1\pm i\sqrt{3}}{2}$; (2) $-i$, $\frac{i\pm\sqrt{3}}{2}$; (3) $\pm i$, $\frac{\pm\sqrt{3}\pm i}{2}$; (4) $1+i$; $-1.36+0.365i$; $0.365-1.36i$. **644.** (1) $\pm\frac{1+i}{\sqrt{2}}$; (2) $\sqrt[6]{2}(\cos\varphi+i\sin\varphi)$; $\varphi=45°$, $165°$, $285°$; (3) $\pm 2(\sqrt{3}+i)$, $\pm 2(-1+i\sqrt{3})$. **645.** (1) -2, $1\pm i\sqrt{3}$; (2) $\pm 1\pm i$. **646.** (1) $\ln 2+\pi i$; (2) $\frac{1}{2}\ln 2+\frac{\pi i}{4}$; (3) $\frac{\pi i}{4}$; (4) $\ln\sqrt{x^2+y^2}+i\arctan\frac{y}{x}$; (5) $\frac{3}{2}\ln 2-\frac{\pi}{4}i$. **647.** $\frac{\sin\frac{nx}{2}\sin\frac{n+1}{2}x}{\sin\frac{x}{2}}$. **648.** $\frac{\sin\frac{nx}{2}\cos\frac{n+1}{2}x}{\sin\frac{x}{2}}$. **650.** (1) $\frac{7-24i}{25}$; (2) $2b(3a^2-b^2)i$. **651.** (1) $4\sqrt{2}e^{\frac{\pi i}{4}}$; (2) $2e^{\frac{2\pi i}{3}}$; (3) $\sqrt{2}e^{-\frac{\pi i}{4}}$. **652.** (1) $5(\cos 0+i\sin 0)$; (2) $e^{-\frac{\pi i}{2}}$; (3) $2e^{-\frac{3\pi i}{4}}$. **654.** Points inside a circle with centre $C(z_0)$ and $r=5$. **655.** (1) $8i$; (2) $512(1-i\sqrt{3})$; (3) -27. **657.** (1) $\frac{\pm 1\pm i}{\sqrt{2}}$; (2) $\cos\varphi+i\sin\varphi$, where $\varphi=0°$, $72°$, $114°$, $216°$, $288°$. **658.** (1) 2, $-1\pm i\sqrt{3}$; (2) $\pm 2i$, $\pm\sqrt{3}\pm i$; (3) ± 3, $\pm 3i$. **659.** $\frac{\sin 2nx}{2\sin x}$. **660.** (1) -1, 2, 3; (2) 5, $\frac{-1\pm i\sqrt{5}}{2}$. **661.** (1) $x_1=3$, $x_2=4$, $x_3=-2$; (2) $x_1=1$, $x_2=-2$, $x_{3,4}=\pm i\sqrt{2}$; (3) $x_1=-2$, $x_{2,3}=\pm\frac{1}{3}$; (4) $x_1=1$, $x_{2,3}=\pm\frac{i}{2}$. **662.** (1) $\Delta=\frac{49}{4}>0$, $u_1=2$, $v_1=1$, $z_1=3$, $z_{2,3}=\frac{-3\pm i\sqrt{3}}{2}$; (2) $\Delta=0$, $z_1=4$, $z_2=z_3=-2$. **663.** (1) $\Delta<0$, $\varphi=60°$, $z_1=4\cos 20°$, $z_{2,3}=4\cos(20°\pm 120°)$.

665.

α	β	$f(\alpha)$	$f(\beta)$	k	k_1	$\Delta\alpha$	$\Delta\beta$
1	2	—10	4	14	31	0.71	—0.13
1.71	1.87	—3.2	0.36	22	26	0.14	—0.01

$1.85 < x < 1.86.$

666. 2.15; 0.524; —2.66. **667.** (1) 1.305; (2) 4 and 0.310; (3) —0.682*l*; (4) $x_1=1.494$, $x_2=-0.798$ (x_1 is found by the formula $x=\sqrt[4]{2x+2}$, and x_2 by the formula $x=\frac{x^4+3x-2}{5}$). **668.** (1) —6, $-1\pm i\sqrt{2}$; (2) —1, 2, 2. **669.** (1) $\Delta=\frac{1225}{4}>0$, $u_1=3$, $v_1=-2$, $z_1=1$, $z_{2,3}=\frac{-1\pm 5i\sqrt{3}}{2}$; (2) $\Delta=-4<0$, $\varphi=45°$, $z_1=2\sqrt{2}\cos 15°=1+\sqrt{3}$, $z_2=-2$, $z_3=1-\sqrt{3}$; (3) $\Delta=0$, $z_1=-2$, $z_{2,3}=1$; (4) putting $x=z-2$, we get $z^3-3z+2=0$; $\Delta=0$; $z_1=-2$, $z_2=z_3=1$; $x_1=-4$, $x_2=x_3=-1$. **670.** 1.76 and —2.15. **671.** (1) 1.17; (2) 3.07. **672.** 1.67. **675.** $0\leqslant x<1$. **681.** $x_1=0$, $x_2=4$. **683.** (1) $x\geqslant-2$; (2) $-3\leqslant x\leqslant 3$; (3) $0\leqslant x\leqslant 4$. **684.** (1) $-4\leqslant x\leqslant 0$; (2) $-1\leqslant x\leqslant 3$. **685.** (1) $x\geqslant 0$; (2) $x\leqslant 4$. **686.** (1) $2k\pi\leqslant x\leqslant(2k+1)\pi$; (2) $-4\leqslant x\leqslant+4$. **687.** (1) $f(0)=1$, $f(1)=1$, $f(-1)=3$, $f(2)=3$, $f(a+1)=a^2+a+1$. **688.** (1) $b+a$; (2) $2ah$. **689.** $\frac{b+a}{b^2+ab+a^2}$. **690.** $F(4, 3)=19$, $F(3, 4)=-25$. **691.** (1) even; (2) odd; (3) even; (4) odd; (5) odd; (6) neither odd, nor even. **692.** $\frac{f(x_1)+f(x_2)}{2}>f\left(\frac{x_1+x_2}{2}\right)$. **693.** $\log_a x$. **694.** a^x. **696.** $2<x\leqslant 3$. **700.** (1) $|x|\leqslant 2$; (2) $-1\leqslant x\leqslant 3$; (3) $-\frac{\pi}{4}+k\pi\leqslant x\leqslant\frac{\pi}{4}+k\pi$; (4) $|x|\geqslant 2$. **701.** (2) $6x^2+2h^2$; (3) $4(2-a)$. **702.** Variation of the variable $\alpha=\left(-\frac{1}{2}\right)^n$ is shown graphically in Fig. 39. $|\alpha|<0.001$, as soon as $n>\frac{3}{\log 2}$ or $n>\frac{3}{0.3}=10$; $|\alpha|<\varepsilon$, as soon as $n>\frac{\log\frac{1}{\varepsilon}}{\log 2}$. **703.** $x=2$; $\frac{2}{3}$; $1\frac{1}{5}$; $\frac{6}{7}$; $1\frac{1}{9}\ldots\to 1$. $|x-1|<0.01$,

as soon as $n \geqslant 50$; $|x-1| < \varepsilon$, as soon as $n > \frac{1-\varepsilon}{2\varepsilon}$. **704.** $x=4$; 3.1; 3.01; ... $\longrightarrow 3+0$; $x=2$; 2.9; 2.99; ... $\longrightarrow 3-0$. **705.** $x=6$; 5.1; 5.01; ... $\longrightarrow 5+0$; $x=4$; 4.9; 4.99; ... $\longrightarrow 5-0$;
$x=-1$; -1.9; -1.99; -1.999; ... $\longrightarrow -2+0$;
$x=-3$; -2.1; -2.01; -2.001; ... $\longrightarrow -2-0$.

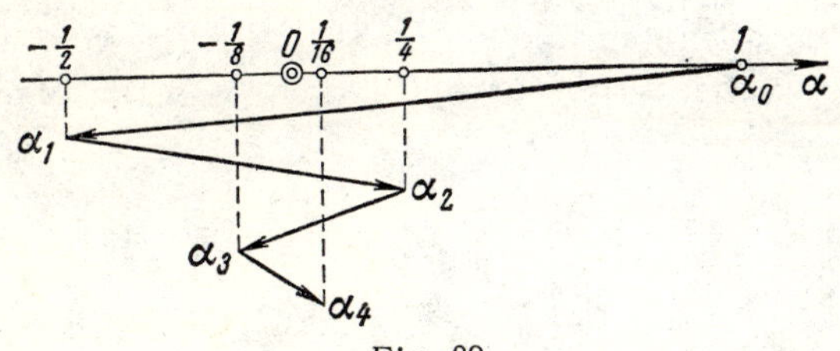

Fig. 39

707. $\delta=\frac{\varepsilon}{2}$. **708.** $\delta=0.01$. **712.** For $|x| > 2500.5$. **713.** For $|x| > 7.036$.
715. $\lim\limits_{n\to\infty} x$ in (1) is equal to 1, in (2) to -1, in (4) to 0, in (5) to 2, in (6) to 0, in (3) does not exist.

716.

x	3; 2.1; 2.01; ... $\longrightarrow 2+0$
$\frac{3}{x-2}$	3; 30; 300; ... $\longrightarrow +\infty$

; $\lim\limits_{x\to 2+0} \frac{3}{x-2} = +\infty$.

x	1; 1.9; 1.99; ... $\longrightarrow 2-0$
$\frac{3}{x-2}$	-3; -30; -300; ... $\longrightarrow -\infty$

; $\lim\limits_{x\to 2-0} \frac{3}{x-2} = -\infty$.

717.

x	1; 0.1; 0.01; ... $\longrightarrow +0$
$2^{\frac{1}{x}}$	2; 2^{10}; 2^{100}; ... $\longrightarrow +\infty$

; $\lim\limits_{x\to +0} 2^{\frac{1}{x}} = \infty$.

x	-1 -0.1; -0.01; ... $\longrightarrow -0$
$2^{\frac{1}{x}}$	$\frac{1}{2}$; $\frac{1}{2^{10}}$; $\frac{1}{2^{100}}$; ... $\longrightarrow 0$

; $\lim\limits_{x\to -0} 2^{\frac{1}{x}} = 0$.

718. (1) $\lim\limits_{x\to\infty} \frac{2}{x} = 0$; (2) $\lim\limits_{x\to +0} \frac{2}{x} = +\infty$; $\lim\limits_{x\to -0} \frac{2}{x} = -\infty$;

(3) $\lim_{x \to +\infty} 3^x = \infty$; (4) $\lim_{x \to -\infty} 3^x = 0$; (5) $\lim_{x \to +0} \log x = -\infty$; (6) $\lim_{x \to 90^\circ - 0^\circ} \tan x = +\infty$; $\lim_{x \to 90^\circ + 0^\circ} \tan x = -\infty$. **724.** $AB \longrightarrow \infty$, $CB \longrightarrow \infty$, $\angle BCD \longrightarrow 0^\circ$, $\angle ACB \longrightarrow 180^\circ$.

725. $x = 5$; 4.1; 4.01; 4.001; ... $\longrightarrow 4+0$;
$x = 3$; 3.9; 3.99; 3.999; ... $\longrightarrow 4-0$;
$x = -0.5$; -1.4; -1.49; -1.499; ... $\longrightarrow -1.5+0$;
$x = -2.5$; -1.6; -1.51; -1.501; ... $\longrightarrow -1.5-0$.

729. Only the first variable has a limit: $\lim_{n \to \infty} x = 1$, in the rest of the cases $\lim_{n \to \infty} x$ does not exist. The graph shown in Fig. 39 can be transformed to depict the behaviour of the first variable. To this end the origin O should be shifted to the left by 1, $-\frac{1}{2}$ replaced by $+\frac{1}{2}$, $-\frac{1}{8}$ by $+\frac{7}{8}$ and so on. The graph for the second variable $x = (-1)^n + \frac{1}{2^n}$ for $n = 0, 1, 2, \ldots$ is given in Fig. 40. **730.** (1) 0;

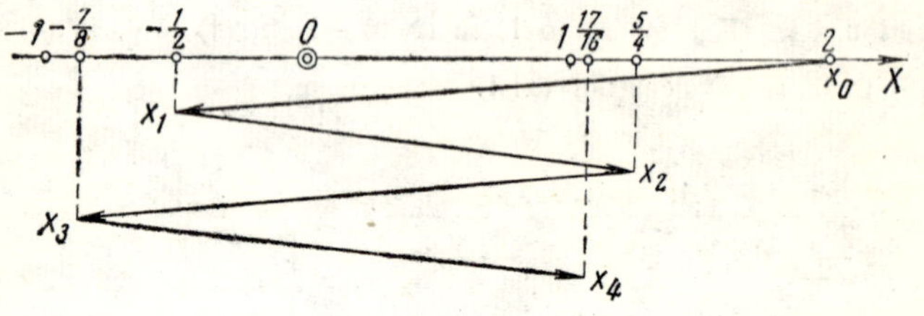

Fig. 40

(2) ∞; (3) ∞; (4) 0; (5) 2; (6) 0; (7) 0 for $a > 1$, $\frac{1}{2}$ for $a = 1$, a for $0 < a < 1$. **733.** 1. **734.** (1) -0.6; (2) 1. **735.** 4. **736.** 1. **737.** $\frac{3}{2}$. **738.** $\frac{1}{2}$. **739.** $-\frac{1}{\sqrt{2}}$. **740.** $\frac{2}{3}$ **741.** $-\frac{1}{2}$ for $a > 0$, and ∞ for $a < 0$. **742.** $\frac{2}{3}$. **743.** $\frac{m}{3}$. **744.** 1. **745.** $-\frac{1}{2}$. **746.** (1) $\frac{2}{3}$; (2) -2.5. **747.** 0. **748.** ∞. **749.** -2. **750.** $-\frac{3}{2}$. **751.** $\frac{1}{\sqrt{2}}$. **752.** $\frac{1}{6}$. **753.** $\frac{1}{4}$. **754.** -12. **755.** -1. **756.** $\lim_{x \to \pi+0} \frac{|\sin x|}{\sin x \sqrt{1-\cos x}} = -\frac{1}{\sqrt{2}}$. **757.** 2.5.

758. $\sqrt{3}$. **759.** -4. **760.** 2. **761.** $-\frac{1}{56}$. **762.** $-\sqrt{2}$. **763.** 4. **764.** $\frac{1}{3}$. **765.** 1. **766.** $\frac{1}{4}$. **767.** 2. **768.** $6\sqrt{2}$. **769.** $2\cos x$. **770.** (1) 1; (2) $-\frac{1}{2}$. **771.** $\frac{1}{2}$. **772.** $\frac{1}{2}$. **773.** $\frac{1}{3}$. **774.** 8. **775.** $\lim_{x\to-0}\frac{\sqrt{2}\,|\sin x|}{x}=-\sqrt{2}$. **776.** 4. **777.** $\frac{m^2}{2}$. **778.** 3. **779.** $\frac{1}{4}$. **780.** (1) $-2\sin x$; (2) $-\frac{1}{2}$. **781.** 1. **782.** 1.5. **783.** $\frac{1}{2}$. **784.** 1. **785.** $\frac{1}{2}$. **786.** $\frac{1}{4}$. **787.** -3. **788.** $\frac{2}{\pi}$. **789.** -2. **790.** $-\frac{1}{4}$. **791.** $\frac{1}{2}$. **792.** 0. **793.** $\frac{1}{2}$. **794.** $-\frac{1}{2}$. **795.** -1. **796.** (1) $\frac{1}{20}$; (2) 3. **797.** (1) $\frac{3}{4}$; (2) 2 [put in (1) $x=t^{12}$, and in (2) $1+2x=t^4$]. **798.** $-a$. **799.** (1) -1; (2) -0.2. **800.** (1) 3; (2) $\frac{3}{2}$. **801.** (1) 1; (2) $-\frac{1}{2}$. **802.** (1) -2; (2) -0.1. **803.** (1) -2.5; (2) 1.5. **804.** (1) $-\sqrt{2\pi}$; (2) -1. **805.** (1) 2nd; (2) 3rd. **806.** (1) 4th; (2) 1st; (3) 3rd. **807.** 2nd. **809.** As $\alpha\to0$ $(1+\alpha)^3-1\approx3\alpha$. **810.** (1) 2.5; (2) $\frac{a}{b}$; (3) 1.5. **811.** 2nd and 3rd. **812.** (1) 2nd; (2) 3rd; (3) 1st. **815.** (1) at $x=0$; (2) at $x=\frac{2n-1}{2}\pi$; 3) at $x=\pm2$. **816.** At $x=2$ the first three conditions are fulfilled, while the fourth is not.

817. (1) $y=\begin{cases}-1 & \text{for } x<-1\\ 1 & \text{for } x>-1;\end{cases}$ (2) $y=\begin{cases}x-1 & \text{for } x<-1,\\ x+1 & \text{for } x>-1.\end{cases}$

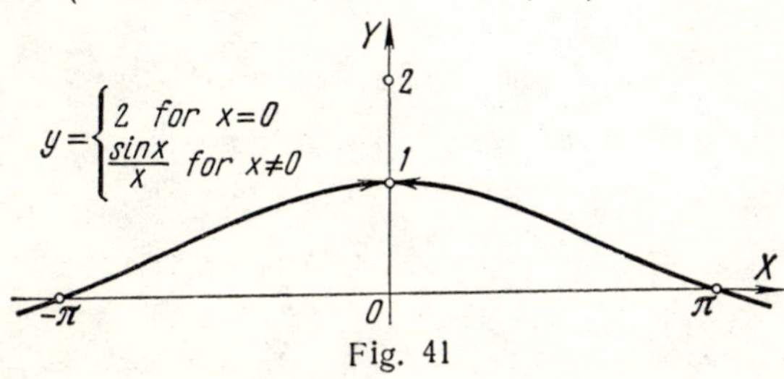

Fig. 41

At $x=-1$ the functions have a discontinuity of the 1st kind (only the second condition of continuity is fulfilled). **818.** At $x=0$ only the fourth condition is not fulfilled (Fig. 41). **819.** A discontinuity at $x=0$. $\lim_{x\to+0}y=\infty$, $\lim_{x\to-0}y=0$, $\lim_{x\to\infty}y=1$ (Fig. 42). **820.** Discontinuities at $x=\pm2$. **821.** (1) A discontinuity of the 1st kind at $x=0$, and

$\lim\limits_{x\to+0} y=0$, $\lim\limits_{x\to-0} y=1$, $\lim\limits_{x\to+\infty} y=\frac{1}{2}$, $\lim\limits_{x\to-\infty} y=\frac{1}{2}$ (Fig. 43); (2) A discontinuity of the first kind at $x=a$, and $\lim\limits_{x\to a-0} y=-\frac{\pi}{2}$, $\lim\limits_{x\to a+0} y=\frac{\pi}{2}$, $\lim\limits_{x\to\pm\infty} y=0$; (3) $y=\frac{x^2}{2}$ for $x>1$ and $-\frac{x^2}{2}$ for $x<1$; at $x=1$ a discontinuity of the first kind, and $\lim\limits_{x\to1-0} y=-\frac{1}{2}$, while $\lim\limits_{x\to1+0} y=\frac{1}{2}$.

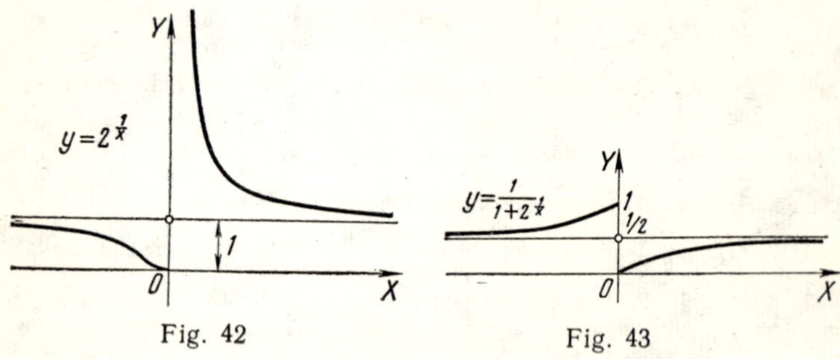

Fig. 42 Fig. 43

822. The equation $x^2-y^2=0$ defines y as an infinite number of single-valued functions of x, two of them $y=x$ and $y=-x$ being continuous. The rest of them (discontinuous) are defined by the equation $y=x$ on some intervals of the axis OX, and by the equation $y=-x$ on the others. An even function with discontinuities at $x=\pm1, \pm2, \pm3, \ldots$ may be defined as:

$$y=\begin{cases} -|x| & \text{for } 2n-1<x<2n \\ +|x| & \text{for } 2n<x<2n+1, \end{cases}$$

an odd one as:

$$y=\begin{cases} -x & \text{for } 2n-1<x<2n, \\ +x & \text{for } 2n<x<2n+1, \end{cases}$$

where $n=0, \pm1, \pm2, \pm3, \ldots$.
823. A discontinuity of the 2nd kind at $x=-2$. $\lim\limits_{x\to-2-0} y=+\infty$, $\lim\limits_{x\to-2+0} y=-\infty$, $\lim\limits_{x\to\pm\infty} y=1$. **824.** At $x=0$ only the fourth condition of continuity is not fulfilled; at $x=\pm2$ the third and the fourth. **825.** The points of discontinuity: (1) $x=0$; (2) $x=2$; (3) $x=0$; (4) $x=0$; (5) $x=\pm2$ and $x=0$. **826.** Infinite number of functions. Out of them (1) continuous ones: $y=\sqrt{4-x^2}$ and $y=-\sqrt{4-x^2}$; (2) the required

discontinuous function is

$$y=\begin{cases} -\sqrt{4-x^2} & \text{for } |x|\leqslant 1, \\ +\sqrt{4-x^2} & \text{for } 1<|x|\leqslant 2. \end{cases}$$

827. $x=0$ and $y=1$. **828.** (1) $x=0$ and $y=x$; (2) $x=-1$ and $y=x-1$; (3) $y=1$. **829.** (1) $x=0$, $y=-1$; (2) $x=0$ and $y=x-1$; (3) $x=-\frac{n}{m}$ and $y=\frac{a}{m}$. **830.** (1) $x=-\frac{1}{2}$ and $y=-2$; (2) $y=x$; (3) $y=-x$. **831.** (1) $y=\pm x$; (2) $x+y=-a$; (3) $y=x\pm\pi$; (4) $y=-\frac{\pi}{4}$. **832.** (1) $y=0$, (2) $y=\pm 2x$, (3) $x=0$ and $y=x$. **833.** Parabolas: (1) $y=\frac{x^3}{3}$; (2) $y=x^2$. **834.** (1) $x=0$ and $y=1$; (2) $x=0$ and $y=-x$. **835.** (1) $x=-2$, $y=\frac{1}{2}$; (2) $x=1$ and $y=-\frac{x+1}{2}$; (3) $x=2, x=-2$, $y=1$ (Fig. 44); (4) $x=1$, $x=-1$ and $y=-x$. **836.** $\frac{1}{e^5}$. **837.** (1) $e^{-\frac{1}{3}}$;

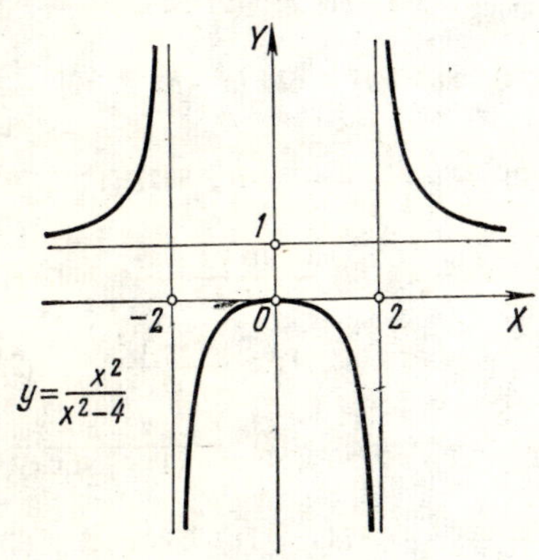

Fig. 44

(2) e^4. **838.** (1) e^2; (2) e^{-4}. **839.** (1) e^{-1}; (2) e^{-2}. **840.** (1) 3; (2) e^3. **841.** $\frac{1}{\sqrt{e}}$. **842.** (1) 1; (2) -1; (3) $2\ln a$. **843.** 3 and 4. **844.** (1) e^6; (2) $\frac{1}{e\sqrt{e}}$. **845.** (1) $\frac{1}{e^2}$; (2) -3. **846.** $\frac{1}{\sqrt{e}}$. **847.** (1) $\frac{1}{x}$; (2) -2. **848.** (1) $3x^2$; (2) $4x^3$; (3) $\frac{1}{2\sqrt{x}}$; (4) $\cos x$; (5) $-\frac{1}{x^2}$; (6) $-\frac{1}{2x\sqrt{x}}$;

(7) $-\frac{2}{x^3}$; (8) $\frac{1}{\cos^2 x}$; (9) $-\frac{3}{x^4}$; (10) $\frac{1}{\sqrt{1+2x}}$; (11) $-\frac{3}{(3x+2)^2}$; (12) $\frac{x}{\sqrt{1+x^2}}$. **849.** (1) $(x-2)^2$; (2) $\frac{b}{a}$. **850.** (1) $(x^2-1)^2$; (2) x^3-2x. **851.** (1) $1+\frac{1}{\sqrt{x}}$; (2) $1-\sqrt{\frac{a}{x}}$. **852.** (1) $-\frac{30}{x^4}$; (2) $-\frac{x^2+2x+3}{x^4}$. **853.** (1) $\left(1-\frac{1}{x^3}\right)^2$; (2) $3\left(1-\frac{1}{\sqrt{x}}\right)$. **854.** (1) $\frac{2}{\sqrt[3]{x^2}}-\frac{1}{\sqrt[4]{x^3}}$; (2) $\frac{2}{3x}\left(\frac{1}{\sqrt[3]{x}}-\frac{1}{\sqrt[3]{x^2}}\right)$. **855.** (1) $\frac{1-x}{x^4}$; (2) $\frac{2}{x}\left(\frac{1}{\sqrt[3]{x}}-\frac{1}{\sqrt[4]{x}}\right)$. **856.** (1) $2\sin^2\frac{x}{2}$; (2) $-\tan^2 x$. **857.** (1) $x(2\cos x-x\sin x)$; (2) $\frac{x(\sin 2x-x)}{\sin^2 x}$. **858.** (1) $-\frac{x\sin x+2\cos x}{x^3}$; (2) $\frac{2x}{(x^2+1)^2}$. **859.** (1) $\frac{1}{(1-4x)^2}$; (2) $\frac{4x-\sin 2x}{4x\sqrt{x}\cos^2 x}$. **860.** (1) $\frac{1}{1-\sin x}$; (2) $\frac{1}{2\sqrt{x}(\sqrt{x}+1)^2}$ **861.** (1) gt; (2) $2a\sin^2\frac{t}{2}$. **862.** 1; 0; 4. **863.** 8.25. **864.** -90. **865.** (1) $-6bx(a-bx^2)^2$; (2) $\frac{1}{3\sqrt[3]{x}}\left(\frac{1}{\sqrt[3]{x}}+1\right)$. **866.** (1) $\frac{2x-1}{2x^6}$; (2) $\frac{1}{x}\left(\frac{1}{\sqrt{x}}-\frac{1}{\sqrt[3]{x}}\right)$. **867.** (1) $2\cos^2\frac{x}{2}$; (2) $-\cot^2 x$. **868.** (1) $x(2\sin x+x\cos x)$; (2) $\frac{x(\sin 2x+x)}{\cos^2 x}$. **869.** (1) $\frac{\cos x-2x\sin x}{2\sqrt{x}}$; (2) $\frac{ds}{dt}=\frac{1}{2}+\frac{2}{t^2}$. **870.** (1) $\frac{(x^2+1)^2}{x^4}$; (2) $\frac{4x}{(x^2+1)^2}$. **871.** (1) $-\frac{1}{x\sqrt[3]{x}}\left(1+\frac{1}{\sqrt[3]{x}}\right)^2$; (2) $-\frac{2+\sin x}{(1+2\sin x)^2}$. **872.** $-\frac{1}{3}$. **873.** -1; $-\frac{1}{9}$; $-\frac{1}{25}$. **874.** (1) $6\cos 6x$; (2) $b\sin(a-bx)$. **875.** (1) $\frac{1}{2}\left(\cos\frac{x}{2}-\sin\frac{x}{2}\right)$; (2) $-2\sin\frac{x}{3}$. **876.** (1) $-20(1-5x)^3$; (2) $\frac{2}{\sqrt[3]{4+3x}}$. **877.** (1) $\frac{10x}{(1-x^2)^6}$; (2) $-\frac{x}{\sqrt{1-x^2}}$; (3) $-2\tan 4x\sqrt{\cos 4x}$. **878.** $\frac{2\sin^2 x}{\sqrt{2x-\sin 2x}}$. **879.** $4\sin^3 x\cos x$. **880.** (1) $\sin 2x$; (2) $-\sin 2x$; (3) $2\tan x\sec^2 x$. **881.** $\frac{3}{\sqrt{2}}\sin 2x\sin\left(x-\frac{\pi}{4}\right)$. **882.** $3\tan^4 x$.

883. $\dfrac{-\sin 2x}{4\sqrt[4]{(1+\cos^2 x)^3}}$. **884.** $\dfrac{\cos\sqrt{x}}{2\sqrt{x}}$. **885.** $\pm(\sqrt{1-\sin 2x}+\sqrt{1+\sin 2x})$; plus for $\cos 2x>0$; minus for $\cos 2x<0$, and at $\cos 2x=0$ y' does not exist $\left(\lim\limits_{x\to\frac{\pi}{4}-0} y'=\sqrt{2}\right.$, and $\left.\lim\limits_{x\to\frac{\pi}{4}+0} y'=-\sqrt{2}\right)$. **886.** $\dfrac{20\sin 4x}{(1+\cos 4x)^6}$. **887.** $-\dfrac{\cot^2\frac{x}{3}}{\sin^2\frac{x}{3}}$.
888. $\sin x(1+\sec^2 x)$. **889.** $\dfrac{2x^2-1}{\sqrt{x^2-1}}$. **890.** $\dfrac{1-x}{x^2\sqrt{2x-1}}$. **891.** $-\sin\dfrac{2t}{a}$.
892. (1) $\dfrac{dr}{d\varphi}=-\dfrac{a\sin 2\varphi}{\sqrt{\cos 2\varphi}}$; (2) $\dfrac{dr}{d\varphi}=\dfrac{2\sin^2 2\varphi}{\sqrt{2\varphi+\cos^2\left(2\varphi+\frac{\pi}{4}\right)}}$.
893. $f'\left(\dfrac{\pi}{2}\right)=\dfrac{ab}{\sqrt{a^2+b^2}}$, $f'(\pi)=0$, $f'\left(\dfrac{3\pi}{2}\right)=-\dfrac{ab}{\sqrt{a^2+b^2}}$.
894. $\dfrac{1}{\sqrt{3}}$. **895.** $\dfrac{4\cos^2 2x}{\sqrt{4x+\sin 4x}}$. **896.** $\dfrac{x(2-3x^2)}{\sqrt{1-x^2}}$. **897.** $-\sin 4x$.
898. $-\dfrac{2\sin 6x}{\sqrt[3]{(1+\cos 6x)^2}}$. **899.** (1) $\sec^6 x$; (2) $3x^2\sin 2x^3$.
900. $\dfrac{4\cos 2x}{(1-\sin 2x)^2}$. **901.** $\dfrac{ds}{dt}=\dfrac{\sin^2\frac{t}{4}}{2\sqrt{\frac{t}{2}-\sin\frac{t}{2}}}$. **902.** $\dfrac{dr}{d\varphi}=\dfrac{1}{2}\cos\varphi$.
903. $-\dfrac{2(3x+1)}{x^3\sqrt{4x+1}}$. **904.** $-\sqrt{\dfrac{\pi}{6}}$. **905.** $k=\tan\alpha=\pm 4$.
906. $y=8-4x$, $x-4y=2$. **907.** $y=x+\dfrac{2}{3}$. **908.** $y=0$ and $y=\pm\dfrac{1}{2}(3x-1)$. **909.** $y=-\dfrac{x}{2}+2$. **910.** $y=\pi-x$. **911.** 45° and 135°.
912. $\arctan\dfrac{4}{3}$. **913.** (1) $\dfrac{1}{2}$, 2, $\dfrac{\sqrt{5}}{2}$, $\sqrt{5}$; (2) $\dfrac{2}{3}$, $\dfrac{3}{2}$, $\dfrac{\sqrt{13}}{3}$, $\dfrac{\sqrt{13}}{2}$. **915.** $y=x^2-3x+4$. Parameter b is found from the condition $y'=2x+b=4+b=1$, and c from the condition that (2, 2) is the point of tangency. **916.** $y=-4x+8$, $y=-\dfrac{1}{4}x-2$; $\varphi=\arctan\dfrac{15}{8}\approx 62°$. **917.** $y=4x$, $y=-4x+16$. **918.** $x\pm 4y=8$. **919.** $y=\pm(3x+8)$ and $y=0$. **920.** $\dfrac{4}{\sqrt{17}}$. **921.** 40°54′ or 139°6′. **922.** (—2, —4).

923. $\left(\frac{1}{2}, \frac{17}{4}\right)$. **924.** 1; 1; $\sqrt{2}$; $\sqrt{2}$. **925.** 11°20′ and 7°7′. **926.** $y'_{-}=-1$, $y'_{+}=1$. **927.** $y'_{-}=-\frac{1}{2}$; $y'_{+}=\frac{1}{2}$. **928.** $y=x$ and $y=-x$. **929.** $y=\pm\frac{x-\pi}{\sqrt{2}}$; 109°30′. **930.** $x=0$. **931.** $x=2$. **932.** $x=0$. **933.** $x=2$. **934.** $y-1=\pm\left(x-\frac{\pi}{2}\right)$. **935.** $x=-1$. **936.** $y=\pm 4x$; 28°. **937.** (1) $\ln x+1$; (2) $-\frac{\ln x}{x^2}$; (3) $\frac{0.4343}{x}$. **938.** (1) $\frac{(x+1)^2}{x^3}$; (2) $\frac{2(x+1)}{x(x+2)}$. **939.** (1) $-\tan\frac{x}{2}$; (2) $\cot x\cos^2 x$. **940.** $\frac{1}{2\sqrt{x^2+x}}$. **941.** $\frac{4a^2x}{a^4-x^4}$. **942.** $\frac{2}{x(1-x^2)}$. **943.** $\frac{1}{\cos x}$. **944.** $\frac{2}{1-4x^2}$. **945.** $\frac{1}{\sqrt{a^2+x^2}}$. **946.** $\frac{1}{2+\sqrt{x}}$. **947.** (1) $-\frac{2\cot^2 x}{\sin x}$; (2) $\frac{2}{x-ax^5}$. **948.** $y=x-1$. **949.** Mutually tangent at the point $\left(\sqrt{e};\ \frac{1}{2}\right)$. **950.** (1) $2x+3^x\ln 3$; (2) $(2x+x^2\ln 2)\,2^x$; (3) $x(2+x)\,e^x$. **951.** (1) $a^{\sin x}\cos x\ln a$; (2) $-2xe^{-x^2}$; (3) $2x(1-x)\,e^{-2x}$. **952.** $e^{\frac{x}{2}}+e^{-\frac{x}{2}}$. **953.** $\frac{1}{2}e^{\sqrt{x}}\left(1+\frac{1}{\sqrt{x}}\right)$. **954.** $\frac{2e^x}{(1-e^x)^2}$. **955.** $\frac{1}{a}e^{\frac{x}{a}}\left(\cos\frac{x}{a}-\sin\frac{x}{a}\right)$. **956.** (1) $-2e^{-x}\sin x$; (2) $-\frac{x}{1+x}$. **957.** $\frac{(x-1)^2}{x^2+1}$. **958.** $2a\,(e^{2ax}-e^{-2ax})$. **959.** $-\ln a$. **960.** 26°35′. **962.** (1) $x^x(\ln x+1)$; (2) $x^{\sin x}\left[\cos x\ln x+\frac{\sin x}{x}\right]$. **963.** $-\tan x\sin^2 x$. **964.** $-\frac{1}{2\sqrt{x^2-x}}$. **965.** $-\frac{1}{x\sqrt{1+x^2}}$. **966.** $\frac{\cos x}{\sqrt{1+\sin^2 x}}$. **967.** $\frac{1}{x(1-x^2)}$. **968.** $\cot 2x$. **969.** $\frac{\cot 2x}{1-\sin 2x}$. **970.** $\frac{\tan x}{1+\cos x}$. **971.** $-\frac{x}{\sqrt{ax+x^2}}$. **972.** $-\frac{x}{a}e^{-\frac{x}{a}}$. **973.** $\frac{1}{2}\left(e^{\frac{x}{a}}-e^{-\frac{x}{a}}\right)$. **974.** $-\frac{4}{(e^x-e^{-x})^2}$. **975.** $\frac{2e^{2x}}{\sqrt{e^{4x}+1}}$. **976.** $\frac{2}{e^{4x}+1}$. **977.** $x^{\frac{1}{x}}\,\frac{1-\ln x}{x^2}$. **978.** 16. **979.** $y=-\frac{x}{2}$. **980.** $\sqrt{\frac{1-x}{1+x}}$. **981.** $\frac{x^2}{1+x^2}$. **982.** $-\frac{1}{\sqrt{x-4x^2}}$. **983.** $\frac{a}{|a|\sqrt{a^2-x^2}}$. **984.** $\frac{a}{a^2+x^2}$. **985.** $\frac{1}{\sqrt{x-x^2}}$. **986.** $-\frac{1}{1+x^2}$. **987.** (1) $2\sqrt{1-x^2}$;

(2) $\frac{3e^{3x}}{\sqrt{1-e^{6x}}}$. **988.** $\frac{2}{1-x^4}$. **989.** $\frac{1}{2x\sqrt{x-1}}$. **990.** $\arctan\frac{x}{a}$.
991. $\frac{1}{2\sqrt{x-x^2}}$. **992.** $\frac{1}{2x\sqrt{6x-1}}$. **993.** (1) $\frac{2x}{|x|\sqrt{2-x^2}}$; (2) $\frac{1}{x^2+x^4}$.
994. $2e^x\sqrt{1-e^{2x}}$. **995.** $\arccos x$. **996.** $\frac{4e^{2x}}{1-e^{8x}}$. **997.** $\sqrt{\frac{4}{t}-1}$.
998. $\sqrt{\frac{2}{x}-4}$. **999.** $\frac{\pi}{4}-1$. **1000.** (1) $\sinh 2x$; (2) $\tanh^2 x$;
(3) $\sqrt{\cosh x+1}$. **1001.** 1.5. **1002.** (1) $\tanh x$; (2) $-\frac{4}{\sinh^2 2x}$.
1003. (1) $\coth^2 x$; (2) $\frac{2}{\sinh 2x}$. **1004.** (1) $\frac{1}{\cosh x}$; (2) $4\sinh 4x$.
1005. $x+1.175y=2.815a$. **1006.** $y=3.76x+3.89$. **1008.** (1) $\frac{1-x}{x^2\sqrt{x^2-1}}$;
(2) $\tan^3 x$. **1009.** $\frac{\sqrt{4x-1}}{2x}$. **1010.** $\frac{dx}{dt}=\frac{2e^t(e^t-1)}{e^{2t}+1}$.
1011. $\frac{x}{\sqrt{x^2-4x}}$. **1012.** $\frac{ds}{dt}=\tan^5 t$. **1013.** $\frac{\pi a}{2}$.
1014. (1) $\frac{x^2+a^2}{x(x^2-a^2)}$; (2) $2\cos(\ln x)$. **1015.** $\frac{1}{15}$. **1017.** $-\frac{1}{3a}$.
1021. (1) $2\cos 2x$; (2) $2\tan x\sec^2 x$; (3) $\frac{1}{(1+x^2)^{3/2}}$. **1022.** (1) $-4\sin 2x$;
(2) $-\frac{24}{x^5}$; (3) $-(x\cos x+3\sin x)$. **1023.** (1) $-\frac{1}{x^2}$; (2) $e^{-t}(3-t)$;
(3) $\frac{2a(3x^2-a^2)}{(x^2+a^2)^3}$. **1024.** $-\frac{2}{(2-t)^{3/2}}$. **1025.** (1) $\left(-\frac{1}{a}\right)^n e^{-\frac{x}{a}}$;
(2) $\frac{(-1)^{n-1}(n-1)!}{x^n}$; (3) $\frac{(-1)^{n-1}1\cdot3\cdot5\ldots(2n-3)}{2^n\sqrt{x^{2n-1}}}$. **1026.** (1) $n!$;
(2) $\sin\left(x+n\frac{\pi}{2}\right)$; (3) $2^{n-1}\cos\left(2x+n\frac{\pi}{2}\right)$. **1028.** (1) $-2e^x\sin x$;
(2) $xa^x(x^2\ln^2 a+6x\ln a+6)$; (3) $2\sin x+4x\cos x-x^2\sin x$.
1029. (1) $2e^{-x}(\sin x+\cos x)$; (2) $\frac{2}{x}$; (3) $x\sin x-3\cos x$.
1030. $f'''(x)=\frac{x+3a}{a^3}e^{\frac{x}{a}}$; $f^{(n)}(x)=\frac{x+na}{a^n}e^{\frac{x}{a}}$; $f^{(n)}(0)=\frac{n}{a^{n-1}}$.
1031. $1, m, m(m-1), m(m-1)(m-2), \ldots, m(m-1)\ldots(m-n+1)$.
1035. (1) $2e^{-x^2}(2x^2-1)$, (2) $\frac{2\cot x}{\sin^2 x}$; (3) $\frac{x}{(4-x^2)^{3/2}}$. **1036.** (1) $a^x(\ln a)^n$;
(2) $(-1)^n\frac{2^n\cdot n!}{(1+2x)^{n+1}}$; (3) $-2^{n-1}\cos\left(2x+n\frac{\pi}{2}\right)$. **1037.** $\frac{\pi}{6}$; $-\frac{\sqrt{3}}{6}$;
$\frac{7\sqrt{3}}{36}$. **1038.** (1) $e^x(x^3+9x^2+18x+6)$;

(2) $\frac{1}{a^3}\left(6a^2\cos\frac{x}{a}-6ax\sin\frac{x}{a}-x^2\cos\frac{x}{a}\right)$; (3) $-xf^{IV}(a-x)$.

1041. By the Leibnitz rule $f^{(n)}(x)=x^2e^{-\frac{x}{a}}\left(-\frac{1}{a}\right)^n+$ $+n\cdot 2xe^{-\frac{x}{a}}\left(-\frac{1}{a}\right)^{n-1}+\frac{n(n-1)}{1\cdot 2}2e^{-\frac{x}{a}}\left(-\frac{1}{a}\right)^{n-2}$. Hence, $f^{(n)}(0)=\frac{n(n-1)}{a^{n-2}}(-1)^{n-2}=\frac{n(n-1)}{a^{n-2}}(-1)^n$. **1042.** $f'(x)=$ $=-2xe^{-x^2}=-2xf(x)$. Using then the Leibnitz rule, $f^{(n)}(x)=$ $=[-2xf(x)]^{(n-1)}$ and so on. **1044.** (1) $-\frac{x}{y}$; (2) $\frac{p}{y}$; (3) $\frac{b^2x}{a^2y}$. **1045.** (1) $-\frac{2x+y}{x+2y}$; (2) $\frac{2x-y}{x-2y}$. **1046.** (1) $-\sqrt[3]{\frac{y}{x}}$; (2) $\frac{e^{-x}+y}{e^y+x}$. **1047.** $-\frac{e\sin y+e^{-y}\sin x}{e^x\cos y+e^{-y}\cos x}$ **1048.** $\frac{1}{y^2}+1$. **1049.** $\frac{1}{3}$. **1050.** (1) $-\frac{a^2}{y^3}$; (2) $\frac{2(y-a)}{(x-b)^2}$; (3) $\frac{m(m+n)y}{n^2x^2}$, **1051.** $-\frac{b}{a^2}$. **1052.** $y=3-x$ and $y=x-1$. **1053.** $\left(\frac{40}{9}, \frac{40}{9}\right)$ and (40, 40). **1054.** (1) $\frac{xx_0}{a^2}+\frac{yy_0}{b^2}=1$; (2) $yy_0=p(x+x_0)$. **1055.** $x+y=\pm\frac{a}{\sqrt{2}}$. **1056.** arctan 3. **1057.** (1) $-\frac{b^2x}{a^2y}$; (2) $\frac{x^2-ay}{ax-y^2}$. **1058.** (1) $-\frac{a^2}{y^3}$; (2) $-\frac{R^2}{(y-\beta)^3}$; (3) $-\frac{2(1+y^2)}{y^5}$; (4) $-\frac{6a^2}{(x+2y)^3}$. **1059.** $2y=-x-3$ and $2y=x+1$. **1060.** $x+2y=4\sqrt{2}$. **1061.** $1-\frac{1}{e}$. **1062.** $e(e-1)$. **1063.** ± 2.

1064. (1) $dy=nx^{n-1}dx$; (2) $dy=3(x-1)^2\,dx$. **1065.** (1) $dy=\frac{x\,dx}{\sqrt{1+x^2}}$; (2) $ds=gt\,dt$. **1066.** (1) $dr=4\sin^2\varphi\,d\varphi$; (2) $dx=-\frac{2dt}{t^3}$. **1067.** (1) $\sin 2t\,dt$; (2) $\sin u\,du$. **1068.** (1) $-\frac{a^3\,dx}{x^2(a^2+x^2)}$; (2) $\frac{(\alpha+1)\,d\alpha}{\alpha}$; (3) $-\frac{1}{2}\sin\frac{\varphi}{2}\,d\varphi$; (4) $-\frac{dx}{x\sqrt{x^2-1}}$. **1070.** (1) 0.04; (2) 0.05. **1071.** (1) $dV=3x^2dx=0.75$; $\frac{dV}{x^3}=0.006$ or 0.6%; (2) $d=\frac{3b\,ds}{8f}$. **1072.** (1) $dx\leqslant\frac{0.1\cdot 2}{5x\sqrt{x}}<0.005$; (2) the error in measuring the radius should not exceed $\frac{1}{3}$% **1073.** (1) $S=\pi R^2$, $\Delta S\approx dS=2\pi R\,dR$; (2) $V=\frac{4}{3}\pi R^3$, $\Delta V\approx dV=4\pi R^2dR$. **1074.** (1) $\frac{(2-x)\,dx}{x^3}$;

(2) $b \sin(a-b\varphi)\,d\varphi$; (3) $-\frac{t\,dt}{\sqrt{1-t^2}}$. **1075.** (1) $-\tan x\,dx$; (2) $\frac{du}{2u\sqrt{4u-1}}$; (3) $-2e^{-2t}dt$. **1076.** (1) $\frac{dx}{2\sqrt{x}}$; (2) $\tan^2\alpha\,d\alpha$; (3) $b(1+e^{-bt})\,dt$. **1077.** (1) $\Delta y = 3x^2\Delta x + 3x\Delta x^2 + \Delta x^3 = -0.2376$, $dy = 3x^2\,dx = -0.24$; (2) $dl = -\frac{14}{\pi} \approx 4.46$ cm; (3) $|dx| \leqslant \frac{x^2 \cdot 0.1}{4} \leqslant 0.006$. **1078.** (1) $4y^2 = x^3$; (2) $y^2 = x\left(\frac{x}{3}-1\right)^2$. **1079.** (1) $\frac{x^2}{a^2}+\frac{y^2}{b^2}=1$; (2) $x^{\frac{2}{3}} + y^{\frac{2}{3}} = a^{\frac{2}{3}}$. **1080.** (1) $x^2 - y^2 = 1$; (2) $y = \frac{1}{1+x^2}$. **1082.** $x = \frac{3at}{1+t^3}$, $y = \frac{3at^2}{1+t^3}$. **1083.** $y = x + \frac{(4-\pi)a}{2}$. **1084.** $x+y = \frac{a}{\sqrt{2}}$. **1085.** (1) $-\frac{1}{a\sin^3 t}$; (2) $\frac{t^2+1}{4t^3}$; (3) $-\frac{1}{4a\sin^4\frac{t}{2}}$. **1086.** (1) $y = -x^2-2x$; (2) $(y+2)^3 = x^2$. **1087.** $x+y = a\left(\frac{3\pi}{2}+2\right)$. **1088.** $y = x - \frac{a\pi}{2\sqrt{2}}$. **1089.** (1) $-\frac{1}{4\sin^3 t}$; (2) $\frac{3t^2-1}{4t^3}$; (3) $\frac{3}{4e^t}$. **1090.** $x = at - \frac{gt^2}{2}$; $\frac{dx}{dt} = a - gt$; $\frac{d^2x}{dt^2} = -g$; in $t = \frac{a}{g}$ sec, $x = \frac{a^2}{2g}$ (the highest point). **1091.** $\frac{dx}{dt} = t^2 - 4t + 3$; $t_1 = 1$; $t_2 = 3$.

1095. $v = \frac{dx}{dt}$; $\frac{dv}{dt} = w$; multiply termwise. **1096** $2v\frac{dv}{dt} = 2a\frac{dx}{dt} = 2av$; hence $w = \frac{dv}{dt} = a$. **1097.** $x = 10 + 20t - \frac{gt^2}{2}$; $\frac{dx}{dt} = 20 - gt$; $\frac{d^2x}{dt^2} = -g$. At the highest point $\frac{dx}{dt} = 0$; $t = \frac{20}{g} \approx 2.04$ sec. **1098.** $\frac{dh}{dt} = \frac{a}{\pi h(2R-h)} = \frac{a}{\pi r^2}$. **1099.** $\frac{dx}{dt} = k(A-x)$. **1100.** $d(\omega^2) = 2\omega\,d\omega$, $\frac{d(\omega^2)}{d\varphi} = 2\omega\frac{d\omega}{d\varphi} = 2\omega\frac{d\omega}{dt}\frac{dt}{d\varphi} = 2\omega\varepsilon\frac{1}{\omega} = 2\varepsilon$. **1101.** The roots of the function: 1; 3. The root of the derivative $f'(x) = 2x-4$ is 2; $1 < 2 < 3$ **1102.** Not applicable, since at $x=0$ the function has no derivative. **1103.** Because the point $x=0$ is a corner (two tangents). **1104.** The slope of the chord (AB): $k = \frac{9-1}{3+1} = 2$; $f'(x) = 2x = 2$, $x = 1$; at the point $x=1$ the tangent is parallel to the chord. **1105.** $f(b) = b^2$, $f(a) = a^2$, $f'(c) = 2c$; substitute this into the Lagrange formula $b^2 - a^2 = (b-a)\cdot 2c$; hence $c = \frac{b+a}{2}$. **1106.** $c = \frac{9}{4}$ **1108.** At $x = \frac{\pi}{2}$ there is a corner point on the arc, at which the function has no derivative. **1109.** The function is continuous and has a derivative inside the interval [0, 2], but is discontinuous at its right-hand end-point. **1110.** Let $s=f(t)$ be the equation of motion, and t_1 and t_2 the initial and final moments of motion respectively. By Lagrange's theorem, between t_1 and t_2 there can be found t_3 for which $\frac{f(t_2)-f(t_1)}{t_2-t_1}=f'(t_3)$, i.e. $40=f'(t_3)=\frac{ds}{dt}$ at the moment t_3. **1111.** $\Phi'(x)=\begin{vmatrix} 1 & f'(x) & 0 \\ b & f(b) & 1 \\ a & f(a) & 1 \end{vmatrix}$. Since $\Phi(b)=\Phi(a)=0$ and the function has a derivative $\Phi'(x)$ in the interval (a, b), then, according to Rolle's theorem, between a and b we can find $x=c$ for which $\Phi'(c)=0$, i.e. $\begin{vmatrix} 1 & f'(c) & 0 \\ b & f(b) & 1 \\ a & f(a) & 1 \end{vmatrix}=0$; hence $f(b)-f(a)=(b-a)f'(c)$. The function $\Phi(x)$ is the doubled area of $\triangle AMB$, where M is any point on the arc AB. **1112.** $\frac{b^3-a^3}{b^2-a^2}=\frac{3c^2}{2c}$; hence $c=\frac{2(a^2+ab+b^2)}{3(a+b)}$. **1113.** The slope of the tangent is $\frac{dy}{dx}=\frac{f'(t)}{\varphi'(t)}$, and at the point $t=c$ $k=\frac{f'(c)}{\varphi'(c)}$. The slope of the secant is $k_1=\frac{y_2-y_1}{x_2-x_1}=\frac{f(b)-f(a)}{\varphi(b)-\varphi(a)}$; according to Cauchy's theorem, between a and b there exists $t=c$ for which $k_1=k$, i.e. the tangent is parallel to the chord. And since $\varphi'(t)\neq 0$, we have $\varphi(a)<\varphi(c)<\varphi(b)$ (or vice versa), and the point of tangency is situated inside the arc. **1117.** $c=\sqrt{\frac{a^2+ab+b^2}{3}}$. **1118.** (1) $\sqrt{\frac{4}{\pi}-1}$; (2) $\sqrt{1-\frac{4}{\pi^2}}$; (3) $\frac{1}{\ln 2}$. **1119.** (1) $\frac{\pi}{4}$; (2) $\sqrt[3]{\left(\frac{15}{4}\right)^2}\approx 2.4$. **1120.** The function $y=|x-1|$ has no derivative at $x=1$. **1121.** At the point $x=-\frac{1}{2}$. **1122.** 3. **1123.** $\frac{1}{2}$. **1124.** $\frac{1}{na^{n-1}}$. **1125.** 1. **1126.** $\frac{a^2}{b^2}$. **1127.** $\frac{1}{2}$. **1128.** $\frac{1}{6}$. **1129.** 3. **1130.** (1) ∞; (2) 0. **1131.** 0. **1132.** 0. **1133.** 3. **1134.** 2. **1135.** 0. **1136.** 0. **1137.** 1. **1138.** 1. **1139.** e^3. **1140.** Of the 2nd order. **1144.** $a-b$. **1145.** $\frac{1}{3}$. **1146.** $\frac{1}{8}$. **1147.** $\ln\frac{a}{b}$. **1148.** $\frac{1}{\sqrt{3}}$. **1149.** 1. **1150.** 1. **1151.** $-\frac{1}{3}$. **1152.** -2. **1153.** $\frac{1}{e}$. **1154.** $\frac{1}{6}$. **1155.** e^3. **1160.** At $x=-2$ $y_{\min}=1$. **1161.** At $x=-2$ $y_{\min}=-\frac{16}{3}$; at $x=2$ $y_{\max}=+\frac{16}{3}$; the points of intersection with OX: $x_1=0$; $x_{2,3}=$

$=\pm 2\sqrt{3}\approx\pm 3.4$. **1162.** At $x=-1$ $y_{max}=1\frac{2}{3}$; at $x=3$ $y_{min}=-9$; the points of intersection with OX: $x_1=0$, $x_{2,3}\approx 1{,}5\pm 3.3$. **1163.** At $x=\pm 2$ $y_{max}=5$; at $x=0$ $y_{min}=1$; at $y=0$ $x\approx\pm 2.9$. **1164.** At $x=0$ $y=0$, an inflection; at $x=3$ $y_{min}=-6\frac{3}{4}$. **1165.** At $x=-2$ $y_{max}=-2$; at $x=2$ $y_{min}=2$; the asymptotes: $x=0$ and $y=\frac{x}{2}$. **1166.** At $x=0$ $y_{min}=-1$ (a cusp); the points of intersection with OX: $x=\pm 1$. **1167.** At $x=0$ $y_{max}=1$; as $x\longrightarrow\infty$ $y\longrightarrow 0$, i.e. $y=0$ is an asymptote. The curve is symmetric about the axis OY (why?). **1168.** At $x=1$ $y_{max}=-4$; at $x=5$ $y_{min}=4$; the asymptotes $x=3$ and $y=x-3$. **1169.** At $x=0$ $y_{min}=0$; at $x=\frac{2}{3}$ $y_{max}=\frac{4}{27}$ **1170.** At $x=4$ $y_{max}=1$, at $y=0$ $x=3$ or $x=5$; at $y=-3$ $x=-4$ or 12. **1171.** At $x=0$ $y_{max}=1$; the asymptote $y=0$. Symmetric about OY. **1172.** At $x=\frac{\pi}{12}$ $y_{max}=\frac{\pi}{12}+\frac{\sqrt{3}}{2}\approx 1.1$; at $x=\frac{5\pi}{12}$ $y_{min}\approx 0.4$. **1173.** At $x=\frac{\pi}{3}$ $y_{max}=$ $=\frac{4\pi}{3}-\sqrt{3}\approx 2.45$; at $x=-\frac{\pi}{3}$ $y_{min}=\sqrt{3}-\frac{4\pi}{8}\approx -2.45$. The asymptotes $x=\pm\frac{\pi}{2}$. **1174.** At $x=1$ $y_{max}=1$; as $x\longrightarrow 0$ $y\longrightarrow-\infty$; as $x\longrightarrow\infty$ $y\longrightarrow 0$. The asymptotes: $x=0$ and $y=0$. The point of intersection with OX: $1+\ln x=0$, $\ln x=-1$, $x=e^{-1}\approx 0.4$. **1175.** At $x=\frac{1}{2}$ $y_{min}=\frac{1}{2}-\frac{\pi}{4}\approx -0.28$; at $x=-\frac{1}{2}$ $y_{max}\approx 0.28$. The asymptotes: $y=x\pm\frac{\pi}{2}$. **1176.** (1) At $x=2$ $y_{max}=\frac{2}{e}$. The asymptote: $y=0$. (2) At $x=\frac{1}{e}$ $y_{min}=-\frac{1}{e}$; $\lim\limits_{x\to+0} y=0$ (an end-point); at $x=1$ $y=0$. **1177.** (1) At $x=0$ $y_{min}=0$ (a corner); at $x=\pm\sqrt{\frac{4n+1}{2}\pi}$ $y_{max}=1$; (2) at $x=0$ $y_{min}=0$ (a corner). **1178.** $y_{min}=\frac{1}{2}$ at $x=\frac{\pi}{4}$; $\frac{3\pi}{4}$; $\frac{5\pi}{4}$; ...; $y_{max}=1$ at $x=0$; $\frac{\pi}{2}$; π; $\frac{3\pi}{2}$ .... **1179.** The domain of the curve is $x\leqslant 1$; $y_{max}=\frac{1}{2\sqrt{2}}$ at $x=\frac{1}{2}$; $y=0$ at $x_1=0$ and $x_2=1$. **1180.** At $x=2$ $y_{max}=\sqrt{2}$; the domain of the curve is $x>0$. **1181.** The asymptotes: $x=1$ and $x=4$ (discontinuities); $y_{min}=-\frac{1}{9}$ at $x=-2$, $y_{max}=-1$ at $x=2$. **1182.** At $x=1$ $y_{min}=1.5$. The curve asymptotically approaches the parabola $y=\frac{x^2}{2}$ and the axis OY. **1183.** At $x=0$ and $x=2$ $y_{min}=\sqrt[3]{4}\approx 1.6$; at $x=1$ $y_{max}=2$ (the cusps are located at the points of minimum). **1184.** At $x=0$ $y_{infl}=0$; at $x=1$ $y_{max}=0.2$; at $x=3$ $y_{min}=-5.4$. **1185.** At $x_1=-2$ $y_{max}=0$, at $x_2=-1.2$ $y_{min}\approx -1.1$, at $x=0$ $y_{infl}=0$. **1186.** At $x=2$ $y_{max}=\frac{1}{2}$, at $y=0$ $x=1$, the asymptotes are the coordinate axes. **1187.** At

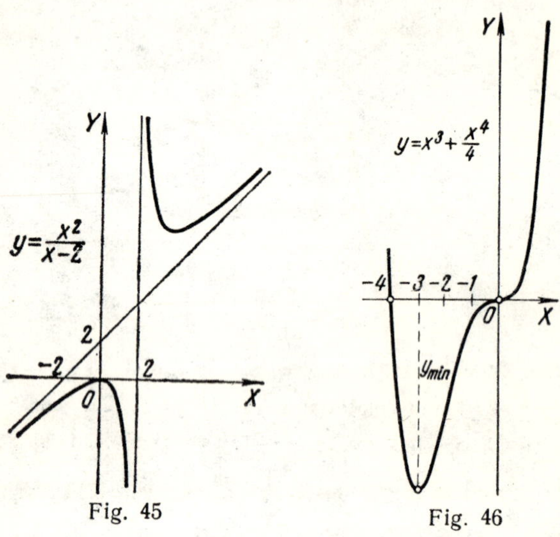

Fig. 45

Fig. 46

$x=-3$ $y_{max}=-4.5$, at $x=0$ $y_{infl}=0$, at $x=3$ $y_{min}=+4.5$, the asymptotes: $y=x$ and $x=\pm\sqrt{3}$. **1188.** At $x=\frac{\pi}{4}+k\pi$ $y_{max}=1$; at $x=\frac{\pi}{2}+k\pi$—discontinuities. **1189.** At $x=\frac{\pi}{4}+2k\pi$ $y_{max}=\frac{\pi}{4}+2k\pi-\frac{1}{2}\ln 2$. **1190.** (1) At $x=1$ $y_{min}=\frac{1}{2}\ln 2-\frac{\pi}{4}$; (2) at $x=-1$ $y_{max}=1$, at $x=0$ $y_{min}=0$ (a corner with slopes $k=\pm 2$). **1191.** At $x=0$ $y_{min}=0$; at $x=2$ $y_{max}=\frac{4}{e^2}\approx\frac{1}{2}$; the asymptote: $y=0$. **1192.** At $x=-1$ a cusp $y_{min}=2$, at $x=0$ $y_{max}=3$, at $y=0$ $x\approx 4$. **1193.** At $x=2$ $y_{max}=4$; at $y=0$, $x_1=0$, $x_2=4$. **1194.** At $x=-1$ $y_{min}=-4$; at $y=0$ $x_1=1$, $x_2=-3$. **1195.** At $x=0$ $y_{min}=0$; at $x=-2$ $y_{max}=\frac{4}{3}$; at $y=0$ $x_1=0$, $x_2=-3$. **1196.** At $x=-1$ $y_{min}=-4$; at $x=-3$ $y_{max}=0$. **1197.** At $x=0$ $y_{max}=0$; at $x=2$ $y=\pm\infty$; at $x=4$ $y_{min}=8$;

the asymptotes: $x=2$ and $y=x+2$ (Fig. 45). **1198.** At $x=-3$ $y_{min}=-6.75$; at $x=0$ $y_{infl}=0$; at $y=0$ $x_1=0$, $x_2=-4$ (Fig. 46). **1199.** At $x=\pm 2$ $y_{min}=-4$; at $x=0$ $y_{max}=0$; at $y=0$ $x_1=0$, $x_{2,3}=\pm\sqrt{8}\approx\pm 2.8$. **1200.** At $x=0$ a cusp $y_{max}=0$; at $x=1$ $y_{min}=-1$; at $y=0$ $x_1=0$, $x_2=3\frac{3}{8}$ (Fig. 47). **1201.** At $x=-1$ $y_{max}=2$; at $x=1$ $y_{min}=0$; at $x=0$ $y=1$. The asymptote: $y=1$. **1202.** At $x=-1$ $y_{min}=-\frac{1}{\sqrt{e}}\approx -0.6$; at $x=1$ $y_{max}\approx 0.6$; the axis OX is the asymptote. **1203.** At $x=2$ $y_{min}=2(1-\ln 2)\approx 0.6$; the axis

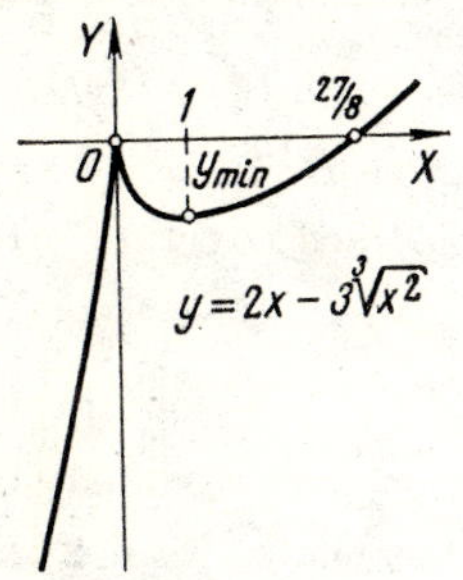

Fig. 47

OY is the asymptote; at $x=1$ $y=1$; at $x=e^2\approx 7.4$ $y\approx 3.4$. **1204.** At $x=0$ a cusp $y_{max}=0$; at $x=2$ $y_{min}=-3\sqrt[3]{4}\approx -4.8$; at $x=5$ $y=0$. The graph is similar to the one shown in Fig. 47. **1205.** At $x=+\frac{\pi}{6}$ $y_{max}=\frac{\sqrt{3}}{2}-\frac{\pi}{6}\approx 0.34$; at $x=-\frac{\pi}{6}$ $y_{min}\approx -0.34$; at $x=\pm\frac{\pi}{2}$ $y=\mp\frac{\pi}{2}=\mp 1.57$. **1206.** At $x=\frac{\pi}{4}$ $y_{min}=\frac{\pi}{2}+1\approx 2.57$; at $x=\frac{3\pi}{4}$ $y_{max}=+3.71$; the asymptotes: $x=0$ and $x=\pi$. **1207.** At $x=-\frac{1}{2}$ $y_{max}=-\frac{1}{2}+\frac{3\pi}{4}\approx 1.85$; at $x=\frac{1}{2}$ $y_{min}\approx 1.28$; at $x=0$ $y=\frac{\pi}{2}$. The asymptote: $y=x$. **1208.** At $x=1$ a cusp $y_{min}=1$; at $x=0$ $y=2$, at $x=2$ $y=2$. **1209.** At $x=\frac{\pi}{6}$ and $\frac{5\pi}{6}$ $y_{max}=1.5$; at $x=\frac{\pi}{2}$ $y_{min}=1$. **1210.** At $x=0$ $y_{min}=0$, at $x=1$ $y_{infl}=1$. **1211.** $x=e$, $y_{max}=\frac{1}{e}\approx 0.4$; at $y=0$ $x=1$. The asymptotes: $x=0$ and $y=0$. **1212.** At $x=-3$ $y_{min}=6$; at $x=-2$ $y=\infty$ (a discontinuity); at $x=-1$ $y_{max}=2$. The points of intersection with the axes: $x=0$, $y=1.5$; $y=0$, $x=\pm\sqrt{3}\approx\pm 1.7$. The asymptotes: $x=-2$ and $y=2-x$. **1213.** At

$x=1$ $y_{min}=2$, at $x=-1$ $y_{max}=-2$, at $x=0$ (a discontinuity). The asymptotes: $y=x$ and $x=0$. **1214.** (1) At $x=0$ $y=a$. The points of intersection with the axis OX: $x=\frac{\pi}{2}+k\pi$. The extrema: at $x_1=$ $=\frac{3\pi}{4}+2k\pi$ a minimum, at $x_2=\frac{7\pi}{4}+2k\pi$ a maximum. The curve is a graph of damped oscillations; it is inscribed in the curves $y=\pm ae^{-x}$ on which the extrema are found. Begin construction with the curves $y=\pm ae^{-x}$. The axis OX is the asymptote. (2) At $x=-1$ $y_{max}=2$, at $x=0$ a point of inflection, at $x=1$ $y_{min}=-2$, at $y=0$ $x_1=0$, $x_{2,3}\approx\pm 1.3$. **1215.** At $x=1$ $y_{min}=3$; at $x=2$ $y=\infty$ (a discontinuity); at $x=4$ $y_{infl}=0$; at $x=0$ $y\approx 3.6$. **1216.** At $x=-2$ $y_{min}=0$; at $x=-4$ $y_{max}=0.8$; at $x=1$ $y_{max}\approx 2.8$; OX is the asymptote. **1217.** At $x=\pm 1$ $y_{max}=1$; at $y=0$ $x=\pm\frac{1}{\sqrt{2}}\approx\pm 0.7$. The asymptotes: the axes OX and OY. **1218.** At $x=0$ $y_{max}=1$; at $x=1$ $y_{min}=0$; at $y=0$ $x=\pm 1$. **1219.** At $x=-1$ $y_{min}=\frac{1}{3}$; at $x=1$ $y_{max}=3$; at $x=0$ $y=1$; the asymptote: $y=1$. **1220.** At $x=-1$ $y_{max}=1$, at $y=0$ $x_1=0$, $x_2=-4$, the domain of the curve is $x\leqslant 0$. **1221.** (1) At $x=-2$ $y=\infty$ (a discontinuity); at $x=-3$ $y_{infl}=0$; at $x=0$ $y_{min}\approx 6\frac{3}{4}$; the asymptotes: $x=-2$ and $y=x+5$. (2) $y_{min}=0$ at $x=2n\pi$, $y_{max}=\sqrt{2}$ at $x=(2n+1)\pi$. At the points of minimum y' does not exist (corner points). **1222.** 30 m$\times$60 m. **1223.** 5 and 5. **1224.** $\frac{ah}{4}$. **1225.** $\frac{a}{6}$. **1226.** 4 m$\times$4 m$\times$2 m. **1227.** 20 cm. **1228.** 60°. **1229.** $\frac{18}{\pi+4}\approx 2.5$. **1230.** $\cos\alpha=\frac{1}{m}$ $\left(\text{provided } \frac{1}{m}\leqslant\frac{a}{AB}, \text{ where } a \text{ is the projection of } AB \text{ on the direction of the railway}\right)$. **1231.** 18 m from the brighter light source. **1232.** In $\frac{a}{2v}$ hours the minimum distance will be equal to $\frac{a}{2}$ km. **1233.** $x=\frac{D}{2}$, $y=\frac{D\sqrt{3}}{2}$. **1234.** $\sqrt{3}\approx 1.7$ times. **1235.** $l\approx 5.6$ m; determined as a maximum of the function $l=\frac{2.4}{\sin\alpha}+\frac{1.6}{\cos\alpha}$. **1236.** $v_{max}=\frac{128\pi}{9}$ dm³ at the height $x=2$ dm. **1237.** $S_{max}=R^2$ at the height $x=\frac{R}{\sqrt{2}}$. **1238.** (1, 1). **1239.** $\sqrt{ab}$. **1240.** At $x=2$ m. **1241.** 4 cm and $\sqrt{3}\approx 1.7$ cm. **1242.** $x=1.5$. **1243.** The section is a square with the side $\frac{D}{\sqrt{2}}$. **1244.** At $\alpha=2\pi\sqrt{\frac{2}{3}}$ radians $\approx 294°$. **1245.** $F=\frac{\mu P}{\cos\alpha+\mu\sin\alpha}$; $\tan\alpha=\mu=0.25$, $\alpha\approx 14°$.

1246. (1) $y=x^2$, $y''=2>0$; the curve is convex down everywhere; (2) $y=x^3$, $y''=6x$, the curve is convex down for $x>0$ and up for $x<0$, $x=0$ is a cusp; (3) $y=e^x$, $y''=e^x>0$ is convex down everywhere, (0, 1) is the point of intersection with OY; (4) $y=\ln x\ (x>0)$, $y''=-\frac{1}{x^2}<0$, the curve is convex up everywhere, (1, 0) is the point of intersection with OX; (5) (0, 0) is the point of inflection. **1247.** The points of inflection: (1) $\left(2, -\frac{8}{3}\right)$; (2) $\left(\pm\frac{1}{\sqrt{2}}, e^{-\frac{1}{2}}\right)$; (3) $\left(\pm\sqrt{3}, \pm\frac{\sqrt{3}}{2}\right)$ and (0, 0); (4) at $x=-\frac{\ln 2}{2}\approx -0.35$. **1252.** The domain $x>-2$. The points of intersection with the axes: $(-1, 0)$ and $(0, \ln 2)$; y increases everywhere, the curve is convex up. The asymptote is $x=-2$. **1253.** $y>0$, $y=0$ is the asymptote. **1254.** (1) Symmetric about OX. The domain: $x\geqslant 0$. The upper branch is convex down, the lower one up. Both branches contact OX at the point (0, 0). The curve is called the semicubical parabola (forming the letter K together with the axis OY); (2) the same as the previous curve, but shifted by three units left. **1255.** (1) At $x=0$ $y_{max}=-1$, the asymptotes: $x=-2$, $x=2$ and $y=0$ (three branches); (2) at $x=1$ $y_{max}=2$, at $x=-1$ $y_{min}=-2$, intersects with OX at $x=\pm\sqrt{3}$, a point of inflection at $x=\pm\sqrt{2}$, the asymptotes: OX and OY. **1256.** (1) The domain: $x>0$; at $y=0$ $x=1$; the asymptotes: OX and OY. At $x=e$ $y_{max}=1$; (2) at $x=1$ $y_{max}=1$, at $x=2$ $y_{infl}=\frac{2}{e}\approx\frac{2}{3}$, the axis OX is the asymptote, at $x=0$ $y=0$. **1257.** (1) At $x=0$ $y_{min}=2$; the asymptotes: $x=-2$ and $x-y=0$; (2) symmetric about OY, at $y=0$ $x=\pm\frac{\sqrt{2}}{2}\approx\pm 0.7$, at $x=\pm 1$ $y_{min}=-1$, the asymptote: the axis OY. **1258.** (1) The domain: $x>0$; at $x=1$ $y_{min}=1$; convex down; the asymptote: the axis OY; (2) OY is the axis of symmetry, at $x=0$ $y_{min}=a$; convex down everywhere. The curve is termed the *catenary*. **1259.** (1) At $x=0$ $y_{max}=0$, at $x=\sqrt[3]{4}\approx 1.6$ $y_{min}\approx 2.1$, at $x=-\sqrt[3]{2}\approx$ ≈ -1.3 $y_{infl}\approx -0.8$, the asymptotes: $x=1$ and $y=x$; (2) at $x=-1$ $y_{min}=-3$, at $y=0$ $x=-\sqrt[3]{0.25}\approx -0.6$, the asymptotes: the axes OX and OY. **1260.** (1) Symmetric about OX and OY, the domain is $|x|<\sqrt{2}$, at $x=\pm 1$ $y_{ex}=\pm 1$, at $y=0$ $x=0$ or $\pm\sqrt{2}$; (2) on the branch $y=x+\frac{2}{\sqrt{x}}$ $y_{min}=3$ at $x=1$, the branch $y=x-\frac{2}{\sqrt{x}}$ intersects OX at $x=\sqrt[3]{4}\approx 1.6$, both branches have asymptotes: $y=x$ and $x=0$. **1261.** At $x=-2$ $y_{min}=-\sqrt[3]{16}\approx -2.52$, at $x=2$ $y_{max}\approx 2.52$ (both points are cusps), the axis OX is the asymptote since $y=\frac{8x}{(x+2)^{4/3}+(x^2-4)^{2/3}+(x-2)^{4/3}}\to 0$ as $x\to\pm\infty$. **1262.** Symmetric about OX; the domain: $x \geqslant 0$; the asymptote: the axis OX ($\lim\limits_{x \to \infty} y = 0$); at $x = 1$ extremum $y_{\text{ex}} = \pm \frac{1}{e} \approx \pm 0.3$. **1264.** (1) $\frac{x^3}{3} + x^2 + \ln x + C$; (2) $2x^5 - \frac{1}{x^3} + C$. **1265.** (1) $\frac{1-x}{x^2} + C$; (2) $\frac{x^2}{2} + 2\ln x - \frac{1}{2x^2} + C$. **1266.** (1) $x\left(\frac{2}{3}\sqrt{x} + \frac{3}{4}\sqrt[3]{x}\right) + C$; (2) $2\sqrt{x} - 4\sqrt[4]{x} + C$. **1267.** (1) $\frac{2x\sqrt{x}}{3} - 3x + 6\sqrt{x} - \ln x + C$; (2) $\frac{3}{4}(x-4)\sqrt[3]{x} + C$. **1268.** (1) $e^x + \frac{1}{x} + C$; (2) $\frac{a^x}{\ln a} - \frac{2}{\sqrt{x}} + C$. **1269.** (1) $-\cot x - \tan x + C$; (2) $-\cot x - x + C$. **1270.** (1) $\int \frac{dx}{\sin^2 x \cos^2 x} = \int \frac{\sin^2 x + \cos^2 x}{\sin^2 x \cos^2 x} dx = \tan x - \cot x + C$; (2) $3\tan x + 2\cot x + C$. **1271.** (1) $\frac{x}{2} - \frac{\sin x}{2} + C$; (2) $\frac{x}{2} + \frac{\sin x}{2} + C$. **1272.** (1) $2\arctan x - 3\arcsin x + C$; (2) $\frac{x^3}{3} - x + \arctan x + C$. **1273.** (1) $\frac{x^4-1}{2x^2} - 2\ln x + C$; (2) $3\sqrt[3]{x} + \frac{2}{\sqrt{x}} + C$. **1274.** (1) $\frac{2(x+2)}{\sqrt{x}} + C$; (2) $4\ln x - \frac{8}{\sqrt{x}} - \frac{1}{x} + C$. **1275.** (1) $\ln x - \frac{1}{x} - \frac{1}{2x^2} + C$; (2) $x + \cos x + C$. **1276.** (1) $e^x + \tan x + C$; (2) $\frac{a^x}{\ln a} - \frac{1}{4x^4} + C$. **1277.** $\cos x - \cot x + C$. **1278.** $\tan x - x + C$. **1279.** $\frac{1}{3}\sin 3x + C$. **1280.** $-2\cos\frac{x}{2} + C$. **1281.** $-\frac{1}{3}e^{-3x} + C$. **1282** $\frac{1}{5}\tan 5x + C$. **1283.** $2\left(e^{\frac{x}{2}} - e^{-\frac{x}{2}}\right) + C$. **1284.** $\frac{1}{6}(4x-1)^{3/2} + C$. **1285.** $-\frac{(3-2x)^5}{10} + C$. **1286.** $-\frac{1}{8}(5-6x)^{4/3} + C$. **1287.** $-\sqrt{3-2x} + C$. **1288.** $\frac{1}{b}\cos(a-bx) + C$. **1289.** $\ln(x^2 - 5x + 7) + C$. **1290.** $\frac{1}{2}\ln(x^2+1) + C$. **1291.** $-0.1\ln|1-10x| + C$ **1292.** $-\frac{1}{6}\ln|1-3e^{2x}| + C$. **1293.** $\ln|\sin x| + C$. **1294.** $-\ln|\cos x| + C$. **1295.** $\ln|\sin 2x| + C$. **1296.** $-\frac{1}{3}\ln|1+3\cos x| + C$. **1297.** $\frac{1}{2}\ln|1+2\sin x| + C$. **1298.** $\ln|1+\ln x| + C$. **1299.** $\frac{\sin^3 x}{3} + C$. **1300.** $-\frac{\cos^4 x}{4} + C$. **1301.** $-\frac{1}{3\sin^3 x} + C$. **1302.** $\frac{1}{2\cos^2 x} + C$. **1303.** $\frac{2-\cos x}{\sin x} + C$. **1304.** $\frac{\sin^2 x}{2} + C$. **1305.** $-e^{\cos x} + C$. **1306.** $\frac{1}{3}e^{x^3} + C$. **1307.** $-\frac{1}{2}e^{-x^2} + C$.

1308. $2e^{\sqrt{x}}+C$. **1309.** $\frac{1}{3}\sqrt{(x^2+1)^3}+C$. **1310.** $\frac{1}{4}\sqrt[3]{(x^3-8)^4}+C$.
1311. $\frac{1}{2}\sqrt[3]{(1+x^3)^2}+C$. **1312.** $-\sqrt{1-x^2}+C$. **1313.** $-\sqrt{1+2\cos x}+C$.
1314. $\frac{2}{3}\sqrt{(1+\ln x)^3}+C$. **1315.** $\frac{1}{6}(1+4\sin x)^{3/2}+C$.
1316. $-\frac{1}{40}(1-6x^5)^{4/3}+C$. **1317.** $2x+\frac{1}{2}(e^{2x}-e^{-2x})+C$. **1318.** $\frac{\sin^4 x}{4}+C$.
1319. $-\frac{1}{2}\sqrt{1-4x}+C$. **1320.** $-\frac{1}{b}\sin(a-bx)+C$. **1321.** $\frac{1}{4}(1+3x)^{\frac{4}{3}}+C$.
1322. $-\frac{1}{7}(1-2x^3)^{\frac{7}{6}}+C$. **1323.** $\sqrt{1+x^2}+C$. **1324.** $\frac{\sin x-2}{\cos x}+C$.
1325. $2\ln|\sin x|-\cot x+C$. **1326.** $e^{\sin x}+C$. **1327.** $-\frac{1}{3}\ln|1-x^3|+C$.
1328. $\frac{1}{2b(a-bx)^2}+C$. **1330.** (1) $0.1\ln\left|\frac{x-5}{x+5}\right|+C$; (2) $\frac{1}{3}\arctan\frac{x}{3}+C$.
1331. (1) $\arcsin\frac{x}{2}+C$; (2) $\ln(x+\sqrt{x^2+5})+C$.
1332. (1) $\ln|x+\sqrt{x^2-4}|+C$; (2) $\frac{1}{\sqrt{3}}\arctan\frac{x}{\sqrt{3}}+C$.
1333. (1) $\arcsin\frac{x}{\sqrt{5}}+C$; (2) $\frac{1}{6}\arctan\frac{x^3}{2}+C$. **1334.** (1) $\frac{1}{2}\arcsin\frac{x^2}{\sqrt{3}}+C$;
(2) $\frac{1}{2ab}\ln\left|\frac{bx-a}{bx+a}\right|+C$. **1335.** (1) $\frac{1}{2}\arcsin\frac{2x}{\sqrt{3}}+C$;
(2) $\frac{1}{4}\ln(x^4+\sqrt{x^8-1})+C$. **1336.** (1) $2.5\ln(x^2+4)-\arctan\frac{x}{2}+C$;
(2) $\frac{3}{2}\ln(x^2-4)-\ln\left|\frac{x-2}{x+2}\right|+C$. **1337.** (1) $\sqrt{x^2+1}+\ln(x+\sqrt{x^2+1})+C$;
(2) $-\sqrt{1-x^2}+\arcsin x+C$. **1338.** $x-\arctan x+C$. **1339.** $\frac{x^3}{3}+3x-$
$-\frac{3\sqrt{3}}{2}\ln\left|\frac{x-\sqrt{3}}{x+\sqrt{3}}\right|+C$. **1340.** $\arctan(x+2)+C$.
1341. $\frac{1}{2}\arctan\frac{x-3}{2}+C$. **1342.** $\ln(x+1+\sqrt{x^2+2x+3})+C$.
1343. $\arcsin\frac{x+1}{\sqrt{2}}+C$. **1344.** $\arcsin\frac{x-2}{2}+C$. **1345.** $\frac{2}{\sqrt{3}}\arctan\frac{2x+3}{\sqrt{3}}+C$.
1346. $\frac{1}{\sqrt{2}}\arcsin\frac{4x-3}{5}+C$. **1347.** $\frac{1}{\sqrt{3}}\ln|3x-1+\sqrt{9x^2-6x+3}|+C$.
1348. $\sqrt{3}\left(\arctan\frac{x}{\sqrt{3}}+\ln\left|\frac{x-\sqrt{3}}{x+\sqrt{3}}\right|\right)+C$. **1349.** $\arcsin\frac{x}{\sqrt{2}}+$

$+\ln(x+\sqrt{2+x^2})+C$. **1350.** $2\ln(x^2+5)-\sqrt{5}\arctan\frac{x}{\sqrt{5}}+C$.

1351. $x+\frac{1}{\sqrt{2}}\ln\left|\frac{x-\sqrt{2}}{x+\sqrt{2}}\right|+C$. **1352.** $\frac{x^3}{3}-2x+2\sqrt{2}\arctan\frac{x}{\sqrt{2}}+C$.

1353. $\arcsin(e^x)+C$. **1354.** $\arctan(2x^2)+C$. **1355.** $0.2\arctan\frac{x+2}{5}+C$.

1356. $\frac{1}{2}\arctan\frac{x-1}{2}+C$. **1357.** $\arcsin\frac{x+2}{3}+C$. **1358.** $\frac{1}{2}\ln(x^2+x+1)-$
$-\frac{1}{\sqrt{3}}\arctan\frac{2x+1}{\sqrt{3}}+C$. **1359.** $\frac{1}{2}\ln(2x+1+\sqrt{4x^2+4x+3})+C$.

1360. $x\ln|x|-x+C$. **1361.** $\frac{x^2}{2}\ln|x-1|-\frac{1}{2}\left(\frac{x^2}{2}+x+\ln|x-1|\right)+C$.

1362. $\frac{1}{2}e^{2x}\left(x-\frac{1}{2}\right)+C$. **1363.** $\frac{x^2+1}{2}\arctan x-\frac{x}{2}+C$.

1364. $x^2\sin x+2x\cos x-2\sin x+C$. **1365.** $\frac{1}{2}e^x(\sin x-\cos x)+C$.

1367. $x[(\ln|x|-1)^2+1]+C$. **1368.** $-x\cot x+\ln|\sin x|+C$.

1369. $-\frac{\ln|x|+1}{x}+C$. **1370.** $2\sqrt{1+x}\arcsin x+4\sqrt{1-x}+C$.

1371. $x\arcsin x+\sqrt{1-x^2}+C$. **1372.** $-e^{-x}(x^3+3x^2+6x+6)+C$.

1373. $x\ln(x^2+1)-2x+2\arctan x+C$. **1374.** $\frac{x}{2}(\cos\ln x+\sin\ln x)+C$.

1375. $\frac{2}{3}\sqrt{x^3}\left(\ln|x|-\frac{2}{3}\right)+C$. **1376.** $-2e^{-\frac{x}{2}}(x^2+4x+8)+C$.

1377. $x\arctan x-\frac{1}{2}\ln(1+x^2)+C$. **1378.** $x\tan x+\ln|\cos x|+C$.

1379. $\frac{1}{2}e^x(\sin x+\cos x)+C$. **1380.** $4\sqrt{2+x}-2\sqrt{2-x}\arcsin\frac{x}{2}+C$.

1381. $-\frac{1}{2}\left(\frac{x}{\sin^2 x}+\cot x\right)+C$. **1382.** $x\arctan\sqrt{2x-1}-\frac{\sqrt{2x-1}}{2}+C$.

1384. $3x+4\sin x+\sin 2x+C$. **1385.** $\frac{3x}{2}+\cos 2x-\frac{\sin 4x}{8}+C$.

1386. $\frac{3x}{8}+\frac{\sin 2x}{4}+\frac{\sin 4x}{32}+C$. **1387.** $\frac{x}{8}-\frac{\sin 4x}{32}+C$. **1388.** $\frac{3x}{128}-\frac{\sin 4x}{128}+$
$+\frac{\sin 8x}{1024}+C$. **1389.** $\frac{x}{16}-\frac{\sin 4x}{64}+\frac{\sin^3 2x}{48}+C$. **1390.** $-\cos x+\frac{2}{3}\cos^3 x-$
$-\frac{\cos^5 x}{5}+C$. **1391.** $\frac{\sin^3 x}{3}-\frac{\sin^5 x}{5}+C$. **1392.** $\frac{1}{4}\sin^4 x-\frac{1}{6}\sin^6 x+C$.

1393. $\sin x-\sin^3 x+\frac{3}{5}\sin^5 x-\frac{1}{7}\sin^7 x+C$. **1394.** $7x+14\sin x+$
$+3\sin 2x-\frac{8\sin^3 x}{3}+C$. **1395.** $-\frac{1}{\sin x}-\sin x+C$. **1396.** $\frac{1}{\cos x}+\cos x+C$.

1397. $\frac{1}{2}\ln|\tan x|+C$. **1398.** (1) $\ln\left|\tan\frac{x}{2}\right|+C$; (2) $\ln\left|\tan\left(\frac{x}{2}+\frac{\pi}{4}\right)\right|+C$.

1399. $\frac{1}{2}\left[\ln\left|\tan\frac{x}{2}\right|+\ln\left|\tan\left(\frac{x}{2}+\frac{\pi}{4}\right)\right|\right]+C$. **1400.** $\int\frac{dx}{\sin x-\cos x}=$ $=\int\frac{dx}{\sin x-\sin\left(\frac{\pi}{2}-x\right)}=\frac{1}{\sqrt{2}}\int\frac{dx}{\sin\left(x-\frac{\pi}{4}\right)}=\frac{1}{\sqrt{2}}\ln\left|\tan\left(\frac{x}{2}-\right.\right.$ $\left.\left.-\frac{\pi}{8}\right)\right|+C$. **1401.** $\frac{\tan^2 x}{2}+\ln|\cos x|+C$. **1402.** $-\frac{\cot^2 x}{2}-\ln|\sin x|+$ $+C$. **1403.** $-\frac{1}{8}(\cos 4x+2\cos 2x)+C$. **1404.** $\frac{1}{2}\left[\frac{\sin(m+n)x}{m+n}+\right.$ $\left.\frac{\sin(m-n)x}{m-n}\right]+C$ for $m\neq n$ and $\frac{x}{2}+\frac{1}{4m}\sin 2mx+C$ for $m=n$. **1405.** (1) $\frac{1}{4}\sin 2x-\frac{1}{16}\sin 8x+C$; (2) $\frac{1}{2}\left[\frac{\sin(m-n)x}{m-n}-\frac{\sin(m+n)x}{m+n}\right]+C$ for $m\neq n$ and $\frac{x}{2}-\frac{1}{4m}\sin 2mx+C$ for $m=n$. **1406.** $-\frac{1}{12}\cos 6x-\frac{1}{8}\sin 4x+$ $+C$. **1407.** (1) $\frac{5}{16}x-\cos x\left(\frac{\sin^5 x}{6}+\frac{5\sin^3 x}{24}+\frac{5\sin x}{16}\right)+C$. **1408.** (1) $\frac{\cos x}{2\sin^2 x}+\frac{1}{2}\ln\left|\tan\frac{x}{2}\right|+C$; (2) $-\frac{\sin x}{2\cos^2 x}+\frac{1}{2}\ln\left|\tan\left(\frac{x}{2}+\frac{\pi}{4}\right)\right|+C$.

1409. $\frac{11x}{2}+3\sin 2x+\frac{9}{8}\sin 4x+C$. **1410.** $\frac{3}{8}x-\frac{1}{4}\sin 2x+\frac{1}{32}\sin 4x+C$.

1411. $\frac{x}{16}-\frac{\sin 4x}{64}-\frac{\sin^3 2x}{48}+C$. **1412.** $\sin x-\frac{2\sin^3 x}{3}+\frac{\sin^5 x}{5}+C$.

1413. $\frac{\cos^5 x}{5}-\frac{\cos^3 x}{2}+C$. **1414.** $7x-14\cos x-3\sin 2x+\frac{8\cos^3 x}{3}+C$.

1415. $\frac{1}{2}\ln|\tan x|-x+C$. **1416.** $\frac{1}{8}(2\sin 2x-\sin 4x)+C$.

1417. $\frac{1}{\cos x}+\cos x+\tan x+C$. **1418.** $-\frac{1}{4}\cos\left(2x+\frac{\pi}{6}\right)+\frac{1}{4}x+C$.

1419. (1) $\frac{x^3}{3}+x^2+4x+8\ln|x-2|+C$; (2) $\frac{x^3}{3}-a^2x+a^3\arctan\frac{x}{a}+C$; (3) $\frac{x^3}{3}+\frac{a^3}{3}\ln|x^3-a^3|+C$. **1420.** $\ln\frac{C(x-2)^2}{|x-3|}$. **1421.** $\ln\left|\frac{(x-1)^3}{x+2}\right|+$ $+C$. **1422.** $\ln\left|\frac{Cx^3(x-1)}{x+1}\right|$. **1423.** $\frac{x^2}{2}+4x+\ln\frac{(x-1)^8}{|x|}+C$.

1424. $\frac{1}{x}+\ln\left|\frac{x-2}{x}\right|+C$. **1425.** $\frac{1}{a^2}\ln\left|\frac{x-a}{x}\right|+\frac{x-a}{ax^2}+C$.

1426. $\ln|Cx(x-1)|+\frac{2}{x-1}$. **1427.** $\ln\left|\frac{x-2}{x+1}\right|-\frac{2}{x+1}+C$.

1428. $\frac{5}{2}\ln|(x^2+2x+10)|-\arctan\frac{x+1}{3}+C$.

1429. $2\ln|(x^2-0.2x+0.17)|-5\arctan\frac{10x-1}{4}+C$.

1430. $\ln|x+1|\sqrt{x^2+4}+C$. **1431.** $3\ln\frac{\sqrt{x^2-2x+5}}{|x|}+2\arctan\frac{x-1}{2}+C$.
1432. $\frac{1}{24}\ln\frac{(x+2)^2}{x^2-2x+4}+\frac{1}{4\sqrt{3}}\arctan\frac{x-1}{\sqrt{3}}+C$. **1433.** $\ln\frac{\sqrt{x^2+1}}{|x+1|}-\frac{1}{x+1}+\arctan x+C$. **1434.** (1) $\frac{1}{2b^3}\left(\arctan\frac{x}{b}+\frac{bx}{x^2+b^2}\right)+C$; (2) $\frac{1}{8b^4}\left[\frac{x(5b^2+3x^2)}{(x^2+b^2)^2}+\frac{3}{b}\arctan\frac{x}{b}\right]+C$. **1435.** (1) $-\frac{x+9}{8(x^2+2x+5)}-\frac{1}{16}\arctan\frac{x+1}{2}+C$; (2) $\frac{1}{8}\left[\frac{(x-3)(3x^2-18x+32)}{(x^2-6x+10)^2}+3\arctan(x-3)\right]+C$. **1436.** $\ln\frac{\sqrt{x^2+1}}{|x+1|}+\frac{x-1}{x^2+1}+C$. **1437.** $\frac{x-2}{4(x^2+2)}+\frac{\sqrt{2}}{8}\arctan\frac{x}{\sqrt{2}}+C$. **1438.** $\frac{1}{a}\ln\left|\frac{x}{x+a}\right|+C$.
1439. $\frac{1}{a-b}\ln\left|\frac{x+b}{x+a}\right|+C$. **1440.** $\frac{1}{2}\ln\left|1-\frac{2}{x}\right|+C$.
1441. $\frac{1}{10\sqrt{3}}\ln\left|\frac{x-\sqrt{3}}{x+\sqrt{3}}\right|-\frac{1}{5\sqrt{2}}\arctan\frac{x}{\sqrt{2}}+C$. **1442.** $\frac{1}{x}+\frac{1}{2}\ln\left|\frac{x-1}{x+1}\right|+C$. **1443.** $\frac{1}{4}\int\frac{4+x^2-x^2}{x(4+x^2)}\,dx=\frac{1}{4}\ln\frac{|x|}{\sqrt{4+x^2}}+C$.
1444. $\ln\left|\frac{C(x-2)^3}{x-1}\right|$. **1445.** $\ln|C(x-1)\sqrt{2x+3}|$.
1446. $\ln\left|\frac{C(x-1)^3}{(x+2)^2(x-2)}\right|$. **1447.** $3\ln\left|\frac{C(x-1)}{x+2}\right|-\frac{2}{x+2}$.
1448. $2\ln\left|\frac{C(x-2)}{x}\right|-\frac{1}{x-2}$. **1449.** $\ln\frac{|x|}{\sqrt{x^2-2x+2}}+2\arctan(x-1)+C$. **1450.** $\frac{1}{a}\ln\frac{\sqrt{x^2+a^2}}{|x|}+\frac{1}{a}\arctan\frac{x}{a}+C$.
1451. $\frac{1}{3}\ln\frac{|x+1|}{\sqrt{x^2+2}}+\frac{1}{3\sqrt{2}}\arctan\frac{x}{\sqrt{2}}+C$.
1452. $\frac{1}{24}\ln\frac{(x-2)^2}{|x^2+2x+4|}-\frac{1}{4\sqrt{3}}\arctan\frac{x+1}{\sqrt{3}}+C$.
1453. $-\frac{1}{2}\left[\frac{x+2}{x^2+2x+2}+\arctan(x+1)\right]+C$.
1454. $\frac{1}{5}\ln\left|\frac{x}{x+5}\right|+C$. **1455.** $\frac{1}{3}\int\frac{x^2+3-x^2}{x^2(x^2+3)}\,dx=-\frac{1}{3x}-\frac{1}{3\sqrt{3}}\arctan\frac{x}{\sqrt{3}}+C$. **1456.** $\frac{1}{2}\int\frac{x^2+1-(x^2-1)}{(x^2+1)(x^2-1)}\,dx=\frac{1}{4}\ln\left|\frac{x-1}{x+1}\right|-\frac{1}{2}\arctan x+C$. **1457.** $\frac{1}{3}\int\frac{x^2+1-(x^2-2)}{(x^2+1)(x^2-2)}\,dx=\frac{1}{6\sqrt{2}}\ln\left|\frac{x-\sqrt{2}}{x+\sqrt{2}}\right|-\frac{1}{3}\arctan x+C$. **1458.** $\frac{x+2}{5}\sqrt[3]{(3x+1)^2}+C$.

1459. $\frac{2x+1}{12}(2\sqrt{2x+1}-3)+C.$ **1460.** $6\left[\frac{\sqrt{x}}{3}-\frac{\sqrt[3]{x}}{2}+\sqrt[6]{x}-\right.$ $\left.-\ln\left(1+\sqrt[6]{x}\right)\right]+C.$ **1461.** $\frac{2}{15}(3x^2-ax-2a^2)\sqrt{a-x}+C.$

1462. $\frac{3}{4}\left[\frac{\sqrt[3]{(x^4+1)^2}}{2}-\sqrt[3]{x^4+1}+\ln\left(\sqrt[3]{x^4+1}+1\right)\right]+C.$

1463. $\frac{(x^2-4)\sqrt{x^2+2}}{3}+C.$ **1464.** $\mp\arcsin\frac{1}{x}+C$ ($-$ for $x>0$ and $+$ for $x<0$). **1465.** $\ln\left|\frac{Cx}{x+1+\sqrt{2x^2+2x+1}}\right|.$

1466. $-\frac{1}{a}\sqrt{\frac{2a-x}{x}}+C.$ **1467.** $\ln\left|\frac{C(x+1)}{1+\sqrt{x^2+2x+2}}\right|.$

1468. $\frac{1}{2}\left[x\sqrt{a^2-x^2}+a^2\arcsin\frac{x}{a}\right]+C.$ **1469.** $\frac{x}{4\sqrt{4+x^2}}+C.$

1470. $2\arcsin\frac{x}{2}-\frac{x}{4}(2-x^2)\sqrt{4-x^2}+C.$ **1471.** $\frac{x^3}{3a^2\sqrt{(a^2+x^2)^3}}+C.$

1472. $\int\sqrt{4-(x-1)^2}\,dx$ is solved by the substitution $x-1=2\sin t$, $\int\sqrt{4-4\sin^2 t}\,2\cos t\,dt=2\arcsin\frac{x-1}{2}-\frac{(x-1)\sqrt{3+2x-x^2}}{2}+C.$

1473. $\frac{x}{\sqrt{2-x^2}}-\arcsin\frac{x}{\sqrt{2}}+C.$ **1474.** $\frac{1}{2}(x+5)\sqrt{x^2+2x+2}-3.5\times$ $\times\ln|x+1+\sqrt{x^2+2x+2}|+C.$ **1475.** $-\sqrt{3-2x-x^2}-\arcsin\frac{x+1}{2}+C.$

1477. $\frac{x-a}{2}\sqrt{2ax-x^2}+\frac{a^2}{2}\arcsin\frac{x-a}{a}+C.$ **1478.** $\frac{1}{3}\ln\left|\frac{\sqrt[4]{1+x^3}-1}{\sqrt[4]{1+x^3}+1}\right|+$ $+\frac{2}{3}\arctan\sqrt[4]{1+x^3}+C.$ **1479.** $-\frac{\sqrt[3]{(2-x^3)^2}}{4x^2}+C.$ **1480.** $\frac{m+1}{n}+$ $+p=\frac{-2+1}{2}+\frac{3}{2}=$ integer; putting $x^{-2}+1=t^2$, we get: $\int\frac{x^{-2}x^{-3}\,dx}{(x^{-2}+1)^{\frac{3}{2}}}=-\int\frac{t^2-1}{t^2}\,dt=-\frac{1+2x^2}{x\sqrt{1+x^2}}+C.$ **1481.** $\frac{m+1}{n}=\frac{3+1}{2}=$ $=$ integer; putting $a-bx^2=t^2$, we get: $\frac{1}{b^2}\int\frac{t^2-a}{t^2}\,dt=\frac{2a-bx^2}{b^2\sqrt{a-bx^2}}+C.$

1482. $\frac{(x-2)\sqrt{2x-1}}{3}+C.$ **1483.** $\frac{(3x+1)^{\frac{2}{3}}}{2}+(3x+1)^{\frac{1}{3}}+$ $+\ln\left|(3x+1)^{\frac{1}{3}}-1\right|+C.$ **1484.** $x-2\sqrt{x}+2\ln(\sqrt{x}+1)+C.$

1485. $-0.3(2x+3a)\sqrt[3]{(a-x)^2}+C$. **1486.** $2\sqrt{x-2}+\sqrt{2}\arctan\sqrt{\frac{x-2}{2}}+C$. **1487.** $\frac{3(x^2+1)}{2}\left(\frac{\sqrt[3]{(x^2+1)^2}}{5}+\frac{\sqrt[3]{x^2+1}}{4}+\frac{1}{3}\right)+C$. **1488.** $\ln(1+\sqrt{(1+x^2)})+\frac{1}{1+\sqrt{1+x^2}}+C$.

1489. $x^2+\frac{1}{3}\sqrt{(4-x^2)^3}+C$; here it is advantageous first to rationalize the denominator. **1490.** $\mp\sqrt{\frac{x+2}{x}}+C$ ($-$ for $x>0$ and $+$ for $x<-2$). **1491.** $\arccos\frac{1}{x-1}+C$. **1492.** $2\arcsin\frac{x}{2}-\frac{x}{2}\sqrt{4-x^2}+C$. **1493.** $2\arcsin\sqrt{\frac{x}{2}}-\sqrt{2x-x^2}+C$.

1494. $\frac{2+x}{2}\sqrt{4x+x^2}-2\ln|x+2+\sqrt{4x+x^2}|+C$.

1495. $-\frac{x+6}{2}\sqrt{5+4x-x^2}+\frac{17}{2}\arcsin\frac{x-2}{3}+C$. **1496.** $-\frac{\sqrt{1+x^2}}{2x^2}+\frac{1}{2}\ln\frac{\sqrt{1+x^2}+1}{|x|}+C$. **1497.** $-\frac{\sqrt{1+x^2}}{x}+C$. **1498.** Putting $1-x^3=t^2$, we find:

$$\int\frac{x^2\,dx}{x^3\sqrt{1-x^3}}=\frac{2}{3}\int\frac{dt}{t^2-1}=\frac{1}{3}\ln\left|\frac{\sqrt{1-x^3}-1}{\sqrt{1-x^3}+1}\right|+C.$$

1499. Putting $x=\frac{1}{t}$, we find:

$$-\int\frac{dt}{\sqrt{3-2t-t^2}}=-\int\frac{dt}{\sqrt{4-(t+1)^2}}=\arccos\frac{x+1}{2x}+C.$$

1500. $\frac{1}{2}\ln(e^{2x}+1)-2\arctan(e^x)+C$. **1501.** $\frac{1}{3}\tan^3x-\tan x+x+C$.

1502. $\frac{e^{2x}}{2}-2e^x+4\ln(e^x+2)+C$. **1503.** $\ln\left|\tan\frac{x}{2}\right|+C$.

1504. $\frac{1}{2}\arctan\left(\frac{1}{2}\tan\frac{x}{2}\right)+C$. **1505.** $\frac{1}{5}\ln\left|\frac{2\tan\frac{x}{2}+1}{\tan\frac{x}{2}-2}\right|+C$.

1506. $-\frac{\cot^3x}{3}-\cot x+C$. **1507.** $\frac{1}{2}\arctan\left(\frac{\tan x}{2}\right)+C$.

1508. $e^x+\ln|e^x-1|+C$. **1509.** $\frac{\tan^4x}{4}-\frac{\tan^2x}{2}-\ln|\cos x|+C$.

1510. $e^x+\frac{1}{2}\ln\left|\frac{e^x-1}{e^x+1}\right|+C$. **1511.** $\frac{1}{\sqrt{2}}\arctan\left(\frac{\tan\frac{x}{2}}{\sqrt{2}}\right)+C$.

1512. $\frac{\tan^3 x}{3}+\tan x+C.$ **1513.** $\frac{1}{2}\arctan(2\tan x)+C.$

1514. $\frac{1}{4}\ln\left|\tan\frac{x}{2}\right|+\frac{1}{8}\tan^2\frac{x}{2}+C.$ **1515.** $\frac{1}{2}\ln\left|\tan\frac{x}{2}\right|-$ $-\frac{1}{4}\cot^2\frac{x}{2}+C.$ **1516.** $2\ln|e^x-1|-x+C.$ **1517.** $\frac{1}{2}(\tan x+$ $+\ln|\tan x|)+C.$ **1518.** (1) $\frac{\sinh 6x}{12}-\frac{x}{2}+C$; (2) $\frac{x}{2}+\cosh 2x+$ $+\frac{\sinh 4x}{8}+C.$ **1519.** (1) $\sinh x+\frac{\sinh^3 x}{3}+C.$ **1520.** $\ln|\cosh x|+C.$

1521. $-\frac{1-\cosh x}{\sinh x}+C.$ **1522.** $-\left(\frac{x}{2}+\frac{\sinh 2x}{4}+\frac{\sinh^2 x}{2}\right)+C.$

1523 and **1524.** See Problem 1366. **1525.** $\frac{x}{4\sqrt{4+x^2}}+C.$

1526. $-\frac{x}{5\sqrt{x^2-5}}+C.$ **1527.** $\frac{\cosh^3 3x}{9}-\frac{\cosh 3x}{3}+C.$ **1528.** $\frac{\sinh 4x}{32}-$ $-\frac{x}{8}+C.$ **1529.** $\frac{\sinh^5 x}{5}+C.$ **1530.** $x-\coth x+C.$

1531. $2\sqrt{\cosh x-1}+C$ (first multiply both the numerator and denominator of the integrand by $\sqrt{\cosh x-1}$). **1532.** $\frac{\sinh x-2}{\cosh x}+C.$

1533. $\frac{3}{2}\ln|x+\sqrt{x^2-3}|+\frac{x}{2}\sqrt{x^2-3}+C.$ **1534.** $\ln|x+\sqrt{x^2+3}|-$ $-\frac{\sqrt{x^2+3}}{x}+C.$ **1535.** $2\sqrt{x+1}+\ln\left|\frac{x+2-\sqrt{1+x}}{x}\right|+C.$

1536. $\frac{(\arctan x)^2}{2}+C.$ **1537.** $\frac{1}{a^2}\ln\left|\frac{x+a}{x}\right|-\frac{1}{ax}+C.$

1538. $\tan\left(\frac{x}{2}-\frac{\pi}{4}\right)+C.$ **1539.** $2\arcsin\sqrt{x}+C$ (put $x=\sin^2 t$).

1540. $ab\arctan\left(\frac{b}{a}\tan x\right)+C.$ **1541.** $\frac{1}{4}\left(x^2+x\sin 2x+\right.$ $\left.+\frac{1}{2}\cos 2x\right)+C.$ **1542.** $\ln|C(e^x+1)|-x-e^{-x}.$ **1543.** $\int\sqrt{\frac{1-x}{1+x}}\,dx=$ $=\int\frac{1-x}{\sqrt{1-x^2}}\,dx=\arcsin x+\sqrt{1-x^2}+C.$ **1544.** $-\frac{\cot^3 x}{3}+C.$

1545. $x\tan x+\ln|\cos x|-\frac{x^2}{2}+C.$ **1546.** $\ln\left|\tan\frac{x}{2}\right|+\cos x+C.$

1547. $-\frac{1}{b}\arctan\frac{\cos x}{b}+C.$ **1548.** $3x^{\frac{1}{3}}-12x^{\frac{1}{6}}+24\ln\left(x^{\frac{1}{6}}+2\right)+$

$+C$. **1549.** $\frac{b-3ax}{6a(ax+b)^3}+C$ (put $ax+b=t$). **1550.** $-\frac{1}{x}+\arctan x+C$. **1551.** $-\frac{1}{\tan x+1}$ (divide both the numerator and denominator by $\cos^2 x$ and put $\tan x=t$). **1552.** $\frac{2}{b}\sqrt{a+b\ln x}+C$. **1553.** $\frac{1}{3b(n-1)(a-bx^3)^{n-1}}+C$; for $n\neq 1$ and $-\frac{1}{3b}\ln|a-bx^3|+C$ at $n=1$. **1554.** Singling out a perfect square in the radicand, put $x+1=\sqrt{2}\sin t$ (or use the method of indefinite coefficients); $\frac{x+1}{2}\sqrt{1-2x-x^2}+\arcsin\frac{x+1}{\sqrt{2}}+C$.

1555. $-\frac{2\sqrt{x}+1}{(\sqrt{x}+1)^2}+C$. **1556.** $\frac{1}{2}\ln\frac{x^2}{1+x^2}-\frac{\arctan x}{x}+C$.

1557. $\frac{1}{2}\arctan\frac{e^x}{2}-\frac{1}{2}x+\frac{1}{4}\ln(4+e^{2x})+C$. **1558.** $\ln\left|\frac{C\sqrt{2x+1}}{1+\sqrt{2x+1}}\right|$.

1559. $x+\cot x-\frac{1}{3}\cot^3 x+C$. **1560.** $-\frac{\sqrt{4-x^2}}{x}-\arcsin\frac{x}{2}+C$.

1561. (1) $\frac{1}{2\sqrt{3}}\ln\left|\frac{\sqrt{3}+\cot x}{\sqrt{3}-\cot x}\right|+C=\frac{1}{2\sqrt{3}}\ln\left|\frac{\sin\left(x+\frac{\pi}{6}\right)}{\sin\left(x-\frac{\pi}{6}\right)}\right|+C$;

(2) $\frac{1}{2\sqrt{3}}\ln\left|\frac{\sqrt{3}+\tan x}{\sqrt{3}-\tan x}\right|+C$. **1562.** (1) Rationalize the denominator: $\frac{2}{3a}\left[(x+a)^{\frac{3}{2}}-x^{\frac{3}{2}}\right]+C$; (2) $\frac{1}{2}[x\sqrt{x^2+1}+\ln(x+\sqrt{x^2+1})+x^2]+C$. **1563.** $\frac{x^2}{2}+x+\frac{1}{x}+\ln\left|\frac{C(x-1)^2}{x}\right|$ **1564.** $-\frac{1}{3}\left(\frac{x+2}{x}\right)^{\frac{3}{2}}+C$ $\left(\text{put } x=\frac{1}{t}\right)$.

1565. $\frac{2}{3}\arctan\sqrt{x^3-1}+C$ (put $x^3-1=t^2$). **1566.** $\frac{1}{2}[x+\ln|\sin x+\cos x|]+C$. **1567.** $2[\sqrt{x}\arcsin\sqrt{x}+\sqrt{1-x}]+C$.

1568. $\tan^2 x+C$ or $\frac{1}{\cos^2 x}+C_1$. **1569.** $\int\frac{\cos^2 x-\sin^2 x}{\sin^4 x}dx=-\int\cot^2 x\,d(\cot x)+\int d(\cot x)=\cot x-\frac{\cot^3 x}{3}+C$. **1570.** $-\cot x\ln(\cos x)-x+C$. **1571.** $e^{-x}+\frac{1}{2}\ln\left|\frac{e^x-1}{e^x+1}\right|+C$. **1572.** $\frac{1}{4}\tan^4 x+C$ (put tan

$x=t$). **1573.** $\ln|x|-\frac{x+1}{x}\ln|x+1|+C$. **1574.** $\int\sqrt{1-\sin x}\,dx=$ $=\pm\int\frac{\cos x\,dx}{\sqrt{1+\sin x}}=\pm 2\sqrt{1+\sin x}+C$ (+ for $\cos x>0$ and — for $\cos x<0$). **1575.** $\frac{1}{\sqrt{2}}\arctan(\sqrt{2}\tan x)+C$.

1576. $\frac{1}{2}\int\frac{d(x^2)}{(x^2+1)(x^2-2)}=\frac{1}{6}\int\frac{x^2+1-(x^2-2)}{(x^2+1)(x^2-2)}d(x^2)=\frac{1}{6}\ln\frac{|x^2-2|}{x^2+1}+C$.

1577. $-2e^{-\sqrt{x}}(\sqrt{x}+1)+C$. **1578.** $2\sqrt{x}\arctan\sqrt{x}-\ln|1+x|+C$.

1579. $\sqrt{\tan x}+C$ (put $\tan x=t$). **1580.** $\ln|x|-\frac{x^2+1}{2x^2}\ln(x^2+1)+C$.

1581. $\frac{1}{\ln a}\arctan(a^x)+C$. **1582.** $2(\sqrt{x}+\cos\sqrt{x})+C$.

1583. $\frac{2(x+7)}{3}\sqrt{x+1}+2\sqrt{2}\ln\frac{|\sqrt{x+1}-\sqrt{2}|}{\sqrt{x+1}+\sqrt{2}}+C$ (put $x+1=t^2$).

1584. $x-\sqrt{1-x^2}\arcsin x+C$. **1585.** $\frac{\sqrt{x^2-1}}{x}$ $\left(\text{put } x=\frac{1}{t}\right)$.

1586. $-\frac{3x^2+3x+1}{3(x+1)^3}+C$ (put $x+1=t$). **1587.** $\sqrt{2ax+x^2}-2a\ln|x+$ $+a+\sqrt{2ax+x^2}|+C$ (p. 192, item 4°). **1588.** $\ln\frac{(2x-1)^2}{|x^2+x|}+C$.

1589. $-\frac{1+\cos x+\sin^2 x}{\sin x}+C$. **1590.** $\frac{1}{16}\ln\left|\frac{C(x^2+2x+2)}{x^2-2x+2}\right|+$ $+\frac{1}{8}\arctan\frac{2x}{2-x^2}$ [the denominator is factorized in the following way: $x^4+4=x^4+4x^2+4-4x^2=(x^2+2)^2-4x^2$ and so on].

1592. $s_5=0.646$, $S_5=0.746$, $\int\limits_1^2\frac{dx}{x}=0.693$. **1593.** 20. **1594.** $2\frac{5}{8}$.

1595. $\frac{14}{3}$. **1596.** $\frac{\pi}{6}$. **1597.** $\frac{\pi}{12a}$. **1598.** $3(e-1)$. **1599.** $\ln(1+\sqrt{2})$. **1600.** $\frac{1}{2}$.

1601 Putting $x=t^2$ and changing the limits accordingly, we get: $\int\limits_2^3\frac{2t\,dt}{t-1}=[2t+2\ln(t-1)]_2^3=2(1+\ln 2)$. **1602.** $\frac{2-\sqrt{3}}{2}$.

1603. $2-\ln 2$. **1604.** $\frac{\pi}{3}-\frac{\sqrt{3}}{2}$. **1605.** $\ln\frac{2e}{e+1}$. **1606.** $\frac{a(\pi-2)}{4}$ (put $x=a\sin^2 t$). **1607.** $\frac{1}{3}$. **1608.** $\frac{\pi a^2}{16}$. **1609.** $2\ln 2-1$.

1610. $\frac{\sqrt{2}+\ln(1+\sqrt{2})}{2}$. **1611.** $\frac{\sqrt{3}-\sqrt{2}}{2}$.

1612. $\ln\frac{3}{2}$. **1613.** (1) $\frac{1}{2}\cdot\frac{\pi}{2}$; (2) $\frac{1\cdot 3}{2\cdot 4}\cdot\frac{\pi}{2}$;

(3) $\frac{1\cdot 3\cdot 5}{2\cdot 4\cdot 6}\cdot\frac{\pi}{2}$. **1614.** $-\frac{a^3}{6}$. **1615.** $\frac{1}{6}$. **1616.** 1. **1617.** $\frac{\sqrt{3}-1}{2}$.

1618. $2\ln 1.5-\frac{1}{3}$. **1619.** $\arctan e-\frac{\pi}{4}\approx 0.433$. **1620.** $\frac{17}{6}$.

1621. $\frac{\pi-2}{4}$. **1622.** $\frac{\pi}{2}-1$. **1623.** $\frac{1-\ln 2}{2}$. **1624.** (1) $\frac{1}{2}\cdot\frac{\pi}{2}$; (2) $\frac{1\cdot 3}{2\cdot 4}\cdot\frac{\pi}{2}$; (3) $\frac{1\cdot 3\cdot 5}{2\cdot 4\cdot 6}\cdot\frac{\pi}{2}$. **1625.** $\frac{32}{3}$. **1626.** πab. **1627.** $\frac{2}{3}$ of the product of the base $(2\sqrt{2ph})$ by the altitude h. **1628.** $\frac{32}{3}$. **1629.** $8\ln 2$.

1630. 1. **1631.** $\frac{16}{3}$. **1632.** 19.2. **1633.** 25.6. **1634.** $8\frac{8}{15}$. **1635.** $\frac{8}{3}$. **1636.** $20\frac{5}{6}$.

1637. πa^2 (see Fig. 60 on p. 361). **1638.** 0.8 (see Fig. 57 on p. 359).

1639. $\frac{(4-\pi)a^2}{2}$; put $x=2a\sin^2 t$ (Fig. 88 on p. 387). **1640.** $2a^2\sinh 1=$ $=a^2(e-e^{-1})\approx 2.35a^2$. **1641.** $3\pi a^2$. **1642.** $\frac{3\pi a^2}{8}$. **1643.** a^2. **1644.** $\frac{3\pi a^2}{2}$.

1645. $r_{max}=4$ at $2\varphi=90°+360°n$, i. e. at $\varphi=45°+180°n=45°$, $225°$; $r_{min}=2$ at $2\varphi=-90°+360°n$, i. e. at $\varphi=-45°+180°n=135°$, $315°$. Adjacent extreme radius vectors at 45° and 135°. The required area equals $\frac{1}{2}\int_{\frac{\pi}{4}}^{\frac{3\pi}{4}}(3+\sin 2\varphi)^2\,d\varphi=\frac{19\pi}{8}$. **1646.** $\frac{3\pi}{4}$. **1647.** $\frac{\pi a^2}{2}$. **1648.** $\frac{\pi a^2}{4}$.

1649. $r=a(\sin\varphi+\cos\varphi)=a\sqrt{2}\cos\left(\varphi-\frac{\pi}{4}\right)$; $r_{max}=a\sqrt{2}$ at $\varphi-\frac{\pi}{4}=0$; $\varphi=\frac{\pi}{4}$; $r_{min}=0$ at $\varphi-\frac{\pi}{4}=\pm\frac{\pi}{2}$, $\varphi=-\frac{\pi}{4}$ and $\frac{3\pi}{4}$. The area $S=\frac{1}{2}\int_{-\frac{\pi}{4}}^{\frac{3\pi}{4}}(a\sqrt{2})^2\cos^2\left(\varphi-\frac{\pi}{4}\right)d\varphi=\frac{\pi a^2}{2}$. The answer is obtained in a simpler way if the Cartesian coordinates are used: $x^2+y^2=$ $=a(x+y)$ is a circle. **1650.** $\frac{7a^2}{4\pi}$. **1651.** $(10\pi+27\sqrt{3})\frac{a^2}{64}$.

1652. $\frac{3}{2}a^2$. **1653.** 36. **1654.** 12. **1655.** $\frac{32}{3}$. **1656.** $\frac{4}{3}$ (see Fig. 56 on

p. 358). **1657.** $\frac{14}{3}$. **1658.** 2. **1659.** $\frac{16}{3}$. **1660.** $17.5-6\ln 6$. **1661.** $2\int_{-1}^{0}-x\sqrt{x+1}\,dx=\frac{8}{15}$ (see Fig. 53 on p. 357). **1662.** $r_{\max}=4$ if $2\varphi=180°+360°n$, $\varphi=90°+180°n=90°$ or $270°$; $r_{\min}=2$ if $2\varphi=0°+360°n$, $\varphi=180°n$; $0°$ or $180°$. The area $S=\frac{1}{2}\int_{0}^{\frac{\pi}{2}}(3+\cos 2\varphi)^2\,d\varphi=\frac{19\pi}{8}$. **1663.** $\frac{3\pi}{4}$. **1664.** $\frac{\pi a^2}{2}$. **1665.** $\frac{\pi a^2}{4}$. **1666.** $\frac{a^2}{4}(e^{2\pi}-e^{-2\pi})=\frac{a^2}{2}\sinh 2\pi$. **1667.** $4ab\arctan\frac{b}{a}$. **1668.** $\frac{11}{8}\pi a^2$. **1669.** πph^2. **1670.** $\frac{8\pi a^2b}{3}$. **1671.** 12π. **1672.** 58.5π. **1673.** $2\pi^2a^2b$. **1674.** $\pi a^3\left(\frac{\sinh 2}{2}+1\right)$. **1675.** $\frac{512\pi}{15}$. **1676.** $\frac{7}{6}\pi a^3$. **1677.** $3\pi^2$. **1678.** $\frac{512\pi}{7}$. **1679.** $\frac{\pi}{4}\left(\frac{5\pi}{3}+\frac{\sqrt{3}}{2}\right)$. **1680.** $\frac{\pi a^3}{6}$. **1681.** $\frac{\pi^2}{2}$. **1682.** $\frac{64\pi}{3}$. **1683.** $\frac{(\pi+2)\pi}{4}$. **1684.** $\frac{4}{3}\pi a^2b$. **1685.** $\frac{32\pi a^3}{105}$. **1686.** 19.2π. **1687.** $\frac{8\pi a^3}{3}$. **1688.** $V=\frac{128\pi}{3}$. **1689.** $5\pi^2a^3$. **1690.** 72π. **1691.** $\frac{112}{27}$. **1693.** $6a$. **1694.** $\frac{670}{27}$. **1695.** $8a$. **1696.** The points of intersection with the axes at $t_1=0$ and $t_2=\sqrt[4]{8}$. $s=\int_{0}^{\sqrt[4]{8}}\sqrt{t^4+1}\cdot t^3dt=4\frac{1}{3}$. **1697.** $\sqrt{6}+\ln(\sqrt{2}+\sqrt{3})$. **1698.** $2a\sinh 1\approx 2.35a$. **1699.** $s=\int_{\frac{3}{4}}^{\frac{12}{5}}\frac{\sqrt{1+x^2}}{x}\,dx$; we put $1+x^2=t^2$; $s=\int_{\frac{5}{4}}^{\frac{13}{5}}\frac{t^2dt}{t^2-1}=\left[t+\frac{1}{2}\ln\frac{t-1}{t+1}\right]_{1.25}^{2.6}=1.35+\ln 2\approx 2.043$. **1700.** The axes are intersected at $x_1=0$ and $x_2=\frac{\pi}{3}$; $s=\int_{0}^{\frac{\pi}{3}}\frac{dx}{\cos x}=\int_{0}^{\frac{\pi}{3}}\frac{\cos x\,dx}{\cos^2 x}=$

$= \int_0^{\frac{\pi}{3}} \frac{d(\sin x)}{1-\sin^2 x} = \ln(2+\sqrt{3}) \approx 1.31.$ **1701.** (1) $4\sqrt{3}$; (2) $\frac{1}{2}\ln(2\cosh 2) \approx 1.009$. **1702.** (1) $8a$; (2) $\pi a\sqrt{1+4\pi^2}+\frac{a}{2}\ln(2\pi + \sqrt{1+4\pi^2})$. **1703.** $\frac{3\pi a}{2}$. **1705.** $\frac{28}{3}$. **1706.** $\ln 3$. **1707.** $2\ln 3-1$. **1708.** $p[\sqrt{2}+\ln(1+\sqrt{2})] \approx 2.29p$. **1709.** $4\sqrt{3}$. **1711.** $\frac{14\pi}{3}$. **1712.** $\pi a^2(\sinh 2+2)$. **1713.** $2\pi\left(1+\frac{4\pi}{3\sqrt{3}}\right)$. **1714.** $2\pi[\sqrt{2}+\ln(1+\sqrt{2})]$. **1715.** $\frac{64}{3}\pi a^2$. **1716.** 3π. **1717.** $4\pi^2 ab$. **1718.** $\frac{34\sqrt{17}-2}{9}\pi$. **1719.** $\frac{62\pi}{3}$. **1720.** $2.4\pi a^2$. **1721.** 29.6π. **1722.** $1.44\cdot 10^6$ N. $1.08\cdot 10^6$ N. **1723.** $\frac{ah^2}{6}$. **1724.** $\frac{2}{3}R^3$. **1725.** $2.4\cdot 10^6$ N **1726.** $J_x=\frac{ab^3}{3}$; $J_y=\frac{a^3b}{3}$. **1727.** $J_x=\frac{ab^3}{12}$; $J_y=\frac{a^3b}{12}$. **1728.** 6.4. **1729.** $M_x=M_y=\frac{a^3}{6}$; $x_c=y_c=\frac{a}{3}$. **1730.** $M_x=\int_0^a \frac{y}{2}y\,dx=0.1ab^2$; $M_y=\int_0^a xy\,dx=\frac{1}{4}ba^2$; $S=\int_0^a y\,dx=\frac{ab}{3}$; $x_c=\frac{3}{4}a$, $y_c=0.3b$. **1731.** $x_c=0$, $y_c=\frac{2\int_0^a \frac{y}{2}y\,dx}{0.5\pi a^2}= \frac{4}{3\pi}a \approx \frac{4}{9}a$. **1732.** (1) $11\,200\pi$ J; (2) $2500\pi R^4$ J. **1733.** $\int_R^{R+h}\frac{mg\,R^2}{x^2}dx = \frac{mg\,Rh}{R+h}$. **1734.** $\frac{10^4\pi R^2H^2}{6} \approx 210$ J. **1735.** 12 410 J. **1736.** 0.24π J. **1737.** $t=\int_0^H \frac{S\,dx}{0.6s\sqrt{2gx}}=100$ sec. **1738.** $t=\frac{R^2}{0.6r^2H^2\sqrt{2g}}\int_h^{H+h} x\sqrt{x}\,dx$, where $h \approx 2$ is the altitude of the additional cone. The computation yields $t \approx 42$ sec. **1739.** $\frac{ah^2}{3}$. **1740.** $17\frac{1}{15}$. **1741.** $\frac{h}{\sqrt{2}}$. **1742.** $2.4\cdot 10^4$ N on each wall. **1743.** $I_x=\int_0^a y^2x\,dy=\int_0^{\frac{\pi}{2}} a^4\sin^2 t\cos^2 t\,dt=\frac{\pi a^4}{16}$.

1744. $x_c=0;\ y_c=\dfrac{\int\limits_0^2 y^2\,dx}{2\int\limits_0^2 y\,dx}=\dfrac{8}{5}$. **1745.** $\dfrac{\pi R^2\cdot 10^4}{H^2}\int\limits_0^H (H-x)^2\,x\,dx\approx$ $\approx 300\pi$ J. **1746.** $\dfrac{p_0 v_0}{k-1}\left[\left(\dfrac{v_0}{v_1}\right)^{k-1}-1\right]\approx 15\,980$ J.
1747. $t=\dfrac{14\pi R^2}{15\cdot s\cdot 0.8}\sqrt{\dfrac{R}{2g}}=\dfrac{400\pi}{3}\approx 419$ sec. **1748.** (1) 1; integrals (2) and (3) diverge; (4) $\int\limits_1^\infty \dfrac{dx}{x^n}=\dfrac{1}{n-1}$ for $n>1$, diverges for $n\leqslant 1$.
1749. (1) 1; (2) $\dfrac{1}{2}$; (3) $\dfrac{\pi}{4}$; (4) 1; (5) $\ln 2$; (6) 16. **1750.** (1) $\dfrac{\pi}{6}$; (2) $\dfrac{\pi}{4}+\dfrac{\ln 2}{2}$; (3) $\dfrac{\pi-2}{8}$. **1751.** (1) $6\sqrt[3]{2}$; (2) diverges; (3) 6.
1752. (1) $\int\limits_0^\infty \dfrac{dx}{\sqrt{1+x^3}}$ converges, since $\dfrac{1}{\sqrt{1+x^3}}<\dfrac{1}{x^{3/2}}$, and $\int\limits_1^\infty \dfrac{dx}{x^{3/2}}$ converges (see Problem 1748); (2) $\int\limits_2^\infty \dfrac{dx}{\sqrt[3]{x^3-1}}$ diverges, since $\dfrac{1}{\sqrt[3]{x^3-1}}>\dfrac{1}{x}$, and $\int\limits_2^\infty \dfrac{dx}{x}$ diverges; (3) $\int\limits_1^\infty \dfrac{e^{-x}\,dx}{x}$ converges, since for $x\geqslant 1$ $\dfrac{e^{-x}}{x}\leqslant e^{-x}$, and $\int\limits_1^\infty e^{-x}\,dx$ converges (see Problem 1749); (4) $\int\limits_1^\infty \dfrac{\sin x\,dx}{x^2}$ converges absolutely, since $\dfrac{|\sin x|}{x^2}\leqslant\dfrac{1}{x^2}$, and $\int\limits_1^\infty \dfrac{dx}{x^2}$ converges (see Problem 1748); (5) $\int\limits_2^\infty \dfrac{x\,dx}{\sqrt{x^4+1}}$ diverges, since for $x>1$ $\dfrac{x}{\sqrt{x^4+1}}>\dfrac{x}{\sqrt{x^4+x^4}}$, and $\int\limits_2^\infty \dfrac{dx}{x\sqrt{2}}$ diverges; (6) $\int\limits_0^\infty e^{-x^2}\,dx=$ $=\int\limits_0^1 e^{-x^2}\,dx+\int\limits_1^\infty e^{-x^2}\,dx$ converges, since for $x\geqslant 1$ $e^{-x^2}\leqslant e^{-x}$, and

$\int_1^{\infty} e^{-x}\,dx$ converges. **1753.** (1) $\int_0^1 \frac{dx}{x^n}=\frac{1}{1-n}$ for $n<1$ and diverges for $n\geqslant 1$; (2) $\int_a^b \frac{dx}{(b-x)^n}=\frac{(b-a)^{1-n}}{1-n}$ for $n<1$ and diverges for $n\geqslant 1$.

1754. π. **1755.** 2. **1756.** $3\pi a^2$. **1757.** $2\pi^2 a^3$. **1758.** $\pi[\sqrt{2}+\ln(1+\sqrt{2})]$. **1759.** $\frac{4\pi}{3}$. **1761.** (1) $\frac{1}{2}$; (2) $\frac{1}{3}$; (3) 1; (4) diverges. **1762.** (1) $\ln(1+\sqrt{2})$; (2) 2; (3) $1-\frac{\pi}{4}$. **1763.** $\frac{1}{2}$. **1764.** 16π. **1765.** 2π. **1766.** (1) $\frac{2}{\pi}$; (2) $\frac{3\ln 2}{\pi}$; (3) $\frac{1}{e-1}$; (4) $\frac{a^2+ab+b^2}{3}$; (5) $\frac{\pi}{4}$. **1768.** (1) $\varepsilon(h)=0$; (2) $|\varepsilon(h)|\leqslant\frac{4}{15}<0.3$. **1770.** $\frac{55}{6}\pi\approx 28.8$ dm³. **1772.** $\ln 2=0.6932$; $|\varepsilon(h)|\leqslant\frac{2\cdot 10^{-4}}{15}<0.0001$. **1773.** 8.16π. **1777.** Approximately 1.22π. **1778.** $R=\frac{1}{2}$. **1779.** $R=\frac{1}{2}$. **1780.** At the vertex (2, 0) $R_1=\frac{1}{2}$; at the vertex (0, 1) $R_2=4$. **1781.** $R=4a$. **1782.** $y_{\max}=\frac{1}{e}$ at $x=1$; $R=e$. **1783.** (4, 4). **1784.** (3, —2). **1785.** (0, 1). **1786.** $27X^2+8Y^3=0$. **1787.** $(2X)^{2/3}+Y^{2/3}=3^{2/3}$. **1788.** $X^{2/3}-Y^{2/3}=(2a)^{2/3}$. **1789.** $X=a\cos t$, $Y=a\sin t$ or $X^2+Y^2=a^2$. **1790.** $k=e^x(1+e^{2x})^{-3/2}$; $k_{\max}=\frac{2}{3\sqrt{3}}$ at $x=-\frac{\ln 2}{2}\approx-0.347$. **1792.** (1) $R=\frac{2}{3}\sqrt{2ar}$; (2) $\frac{a^2}{3r}$; (3) $\frac{r^3}{a^2}$. **1793.** $\frac{1}{2}$. **1794.** 2. **1795.** 1. **1796.** 1. **1797.** (—2, 3). **1798.** $\left(0,\ -\frac{4}{3}\right)$. **1799.** $\left(-\frac{11}{2},\ \frac{16}{3}\right)$. **1800.** $X=\frac{\pi}{4}-\frac{3}{2}\approx-0.7$, $Y=-\sqrt{2}\approx-1.4$. **1801.** $8X^3-27Y^2=0$. **1802.** $X=-t^2\left(1+\frac{t^2}{2}\right)$, $Y=4t\left(1+\frac{t^2}{3}\right)$; to construct the curve and its evolute make a table of values of x, y, X, Y for $t=0$; ± 1; $\pm\frac{3}{2}$. **1803.** $(X+Y)^{\frac{2}{3}}-(X-Y)^{\frac{2}{3}}=4$. **1804.** $(X+Y)^{\frac{2}{3}}+(X-Y)^{\frac{2}{3}}=2a^{\frac{2}{3}}$;

on rotating the axes through 45° this equation takes the form $x_1^{\frac{2}{3}}+y_1^{\frac{2}{3}}=(2a)^{\frac{2}{3}}$, i.e. the evolute of the astroid is also an astroid with doubled dimensions and turned through 45°. **1806.** 21. **1807.** $5t$. **1808.** 7.5. **1809.** 2π. **1810.** $2\sinh 1\approx 2.35$. **1811.** $\frac{3+\ln 2}{2}$. **1812.** $3x+4y=0$; $\frac{d\mathbf{r}}{dt}=4\mathbf{i}-3\mathbf{j}$. **1813.** $y=\frac{4}{3}x-\frac{x^2}{9}$; $\frac{d\mathbf{r}}{dt}=3\mathbf{i}+2(2-t)\mathbf{j}$. **1814.** $\mathbf{w}=\frac{d^2\mathbf{r}}{dt^2}=-2\mathbf{j}$; $w_\tau=\frac{4\,|t-2|}{\sqrt{4t^2-16t+25}}$; $w_n=\frac{6}{\sqrt{4t^2-16t+25}}$; at $t=0$ $w_\tau=1.6$; $w_n=1.2$. **1815.** $\frac{x^2}{a^2}+\frac{y^2}{b^2}=1$; $\mathbf{v}=-a\sin t\,\mathbf{i}+b\cos t\,\mathbf{j}$; $\mathbf{w}=-\mathbf{r}$. **1816.** $\frac{x-t}{1}=\frac{y-t^2}{2t}=\frac{z-t^3}{3t^2}$. **1817.** $\frac{X-x}{1}=\frac{Y-x^2}{2x}=\frac{Z-\sqrt{x}}{\frac{1}{2\sqrt{x}}}$. **1818.** $\frac{x-1}{12}=\frac{y-3}{-4}=\frac{z-4}{3}$. **1819.** $\mathbf{r}=-\mathbf{i}+\mathbf{k}$, $\mathbf{B}=\mathbf{i}+\mathbf{k}$, $\mathbf{N}=-2\mathbf{j}$; $\boldsymbol{\tau}=\frac{-\mathbf{i}+\mathbf{k}}{\sqrt{2}}$, $\boldsymbol{\beta}=\frac{\mathbf{i}+\mathbf{k}}{\sqrt{2}}$, $\mathbf{v}=-\mathbf{j}$. **1820.** $\mathbf{B}=\dot{\mathbf{r}}\times\ddot{\mathbf{r}}=6\mathbf{i}-6\mathbf{j}+2\mathbf{k}$, $\mathbf{N}=(\dot{\mathbf{r}}\times\ddot{\mathbf{r}})\times\dot{\mathbf{r}}=-22\mathbf{i}-16\mathbf{j}+18\mathbf{k}$; the equations of the principal normal: $\frac{x-1}{11}=\frac{y-1}{8}=\frac{z-1}{-9}$, of the binormal: $\frac{x-1}{3}=\frac{y-1}{-3}=\frac{z-1}{1}$, and of the osculating plane: $3x-3y+z=1$. **1821.** $\mathbf{N}=3(\mathbf{i}+\mathbf{j})$, $\mathbf{B}=-\mathbf{i}+\mathbf{j}+2\mathbf{k}$. The equations of the principal normal: $x=y$, $z=0$; of the binormal: $\frac{x-1}{-1}=\frac{y-1}{1}=\frac{z}{2}$. **1822.** Eliminating t, we get $x^2+y^2=z^2$, the equation of a conical surface. $\dot{\mathbf{r}}=(\cos t-t\sin t)\mathbf{i}+(\sin t+t\cos t)\mathbf{j}+\mathbf{k}=\mathbf{i}+\mathbf{k}$; $\ddot{\mathbf{r}}=(-2\sin t-t\cos t)\mathbf{i}+(2\cos t-t\sin t)\mathbf{j}=2\mathbf{j}$; $\mathbf{B}=\dot{\mathbf{r}}\times\ddot{\mathbf{r}}=2\mathbf{i}+2\mathbf{k}$, $\mathbf{N}=4\mathbf{j}$. The tangent: $x=z$ and $y=0$, the principal normal: OY, the binormal: $x+z=0$ and $y=0$. **1823.** At $t=\frac{\pi}{2}$ $\frac{x}{-a}=\frac{z-\frac{b\pi}{2}}{b}$, $y=a$. **1824.** $\cos\alpha=\pm\frac{\sqrt{a}}{\sqrt{a}+\sqrt{b}}$; $\cos\beta=\pm\frac{\sqrt{b}}{\sqrt{a}+\sqrt{b}}$; $\cos\gamma=\pm\frac{\sqrt[4]{4ab}}{\sqrt{a}+\sqrt{b}}$; the choice of sign depends on the choice of direction on each branch of the curve. **1825.** The equation of the helix: $x=\sin 2t$, $y=1-\cos 2t$, $z=2t^2$, where t is the angle of turn (Fig. 48). The unit binormal vector $\boldsymbol{\beta}$ at the point C $\left(\text{for } t=\frac{\pi}{2}\right)$: $\boldsymbol{\beta}=\frac{\pi\mathbf{i}+\mathbf{j}+\mathbf{k}}{\sqrt{2+\pi^2}}$. **1826.** At $t=\frac{\pi}{2}$ $\mathbf{v}=a(\mathbf{i}+\mathbf{j})$, $\mathbf{w}=a\mathbf{i}$.

1827. $\frac{x-2}{1}=\frac{y-2}{1}=\frac{z-8}{8}$. **1828.** $\frac{x-1}{2}=\frac{y-2}{-1}$ and $z=3$. **1829.** $\frac{x-2}{2}=\frac{y}{1}=\frac{z-1}{2}$. **1830.** 120°, 60°, 45°. **1831.** $N=-26\boldsymbol{i}-31\boldsymbol{j}+22\boldsymbol{k}$, $B=16\boldsymbol{i}-12\boldsymbol{j}+2\boldsymbol{k}$; $\frac{x-1}{26}=\frac{y-1}{31}=\frac{z-1}{-22}$; $\frac{x-1}{8}=\frac{y-1}{-6}=\frac{z-1}{1}$. **1832.** $N=-4\boldsymbol{j}-4\boldsymbol{k}$, $B=2\boldsymbol{j}-2\boldsymbol{k}$. The equations of the principal normal: $x=\pi$, $z=y+2$; of the binormal: $x=\pi$, $y+z=6$. **1834.** $\boldsymbol{v}=\dot{\boldsymbol{r}}=$

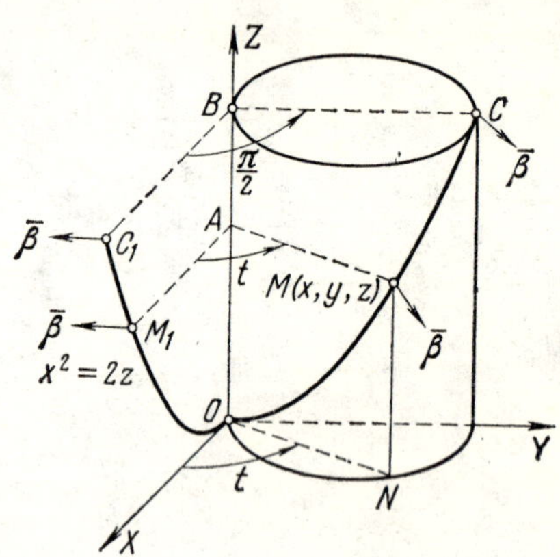

Fig. 48

$=\boldsymbol{i}+(1-2t)\boldsymbol{j}$, $\boldsymbol{w}=\ddot{\boldsymbol{r}}=-2\boldsymbol{j}$, $\frac{1}{R}=\frac{|\boldsymbol{v}\times\boldsymbol{w}|}{v^3}=\frac{2}{v^3}$; $v=\sqrt{2-4t+4t^2}$; $w_\tau=\dot{v}=\frac{4t-2}{\sqrt{2-4t+4t^2}}=-\sqrt{2}$, $w_n=\frac{v^2}{R}=\frac{2}{v}=\sqrt{2}$. **1835.** $\boldsymbol{v}=\dot{\boldsymbol{r}}=-4\sin t\,\boldsymbol{i}+3\cos t\,\boldsymbol{j}=\frac{-4\boldsymbol{i}+3\boldsymbol{j}}{\sqrt{2}}$ $\boldsymbol{w}=\ddot{\boldsymbol{r}}=-\frac{4\boldsymbol{i}+3\boldsymbol{j}}{\sqrt{2}}$, $\frac{1}{R}=\frac{12}{v^3}$; $v=\sqrt{16\sin^2 t+9\cos^2 t}$, $\dot{v}=\frac{7\sin 2t}{2v}$; at $t=\frac{\pi}{4}$ $v=\frac{5}{\sqrt{2}}$, $w_\tau=\dot{v}=\frac{7}{5\sqrt{2}}=0.7\sqrt{2}$, $w_n=\frac{v^2}{R}=\frac{12}{v}=\frac{12\sqrt{2}}{5}=2.4\sqrt{2}$. **1836.** $\boldsymbol{v}=\dot{\boldsymbol{r}}=\boldsymbol{i}+2t\boldsymbol{j}+2t^2\boldsymbol{k}$, $\boldsymbol{w}=2\boldsymbol{j}+4t\boldsymbol{k}$, $v=2t^2+1$, $\frac{1}{R}=\frac{|\boldsymbol{v}\times\boldsymbol{w}|}{v^3}=\frac{2}{(2t^2+1)^2}=\frac{2}{9}$; $w_\tau=\dot{v}=4t=4$, $w_n=\frac{v^2}{R}=\frac{2(2t^2+1)^2}{(2t^2+1)^2}=2$ (at any point). **1837.** First write a matrix of the coordinates of the vectors

$$\begin{array}{c} \mathbf{r} \\ \dot{\mathbf{r}} \\ \ddot{\mathbf{r}} \\ \dddot{\mathbf{r}} \\ \dot{\mathbf{r}}\times\ddot{\mathbf{r}} \end{array} \left\| \begin{array}{ccc} t & t^2 & t^3 \\ 1 & 2t & 3t^2 \\ 0 & 2 & 6t \\ 0 & 0 & 6 \\ 6t^2 & -6t & 2 \end{array} \right\|.$$ Then find: (1) $|\dot{\mathbf{r}}| = \sqrt{1+4t^2+9t^4}$; (2) $|\dot{\mathbf{r}}\times\ddot{\mathbf{r}}| = 2\sqrt{9t^4+9t^2+1}$; (3) $\dot{\mathbf{r}}\ddot{\mathbf{r}}\dddot{\mathbf{r}} = 12$; (4) $\frac{1}{R} = \frac{2\sqrt{9t^4+9t^2+1}}{\sqrt{(1+4t^2+9t^4)^3}} = 2$; (5) $\frac{1}{\rho} = \frac{12}{4(9t^4+9t^2+1)} = 3$. **1838.** $\frac{1}{R} = \frac{\sqrt{2}}{(x+y)^2} = \frac{\sqrt{2}}{4}$; $\frac{1}{\rho} = -\frac{\sqrt{2}}{4}$. **1839.** $\frac{1}{R} = \frac{\sqrt{2}}{3}$; $\frac{1}{\rho} = \frac{1}{3}$. **1840.** For the right-hand helix: $\frac{1}{\rho} = \frac{b}{a^2+b^2}$; for the left-hand: $\frac{1}{\rho} = -\frac{b}{a^2+b^2}$. **1841.** $\frac{1}{R} = \frac{2t}{(2t^2+1)^2} = \frac{2}{9}$; $\frac{1}{\rho} = -\frac{2t}{(2t^2+1)^2} = -\frac{2}{9}$. **1842.** $\mathbf{r} = \frac{y^2}{2}\mathbf{i} + y\mathbf{j} + \frac{y^4}{4}\mathbf{k}$; $\frac{1}{R^2} = \frac{9y^4+4y^6+1}{(y^2+1+y^6)^3} = \frac{14}{27}$; $\frac{1}{\rho} = -\frac{3}{7}$. **1843.** $\frac{1}{R} = \frac{\sqrt{2}}{3}$; $\frac{1}{\rho} = -\frac{1}{3}$. **1844.** (3) The whole plane, except the point (0, 0);

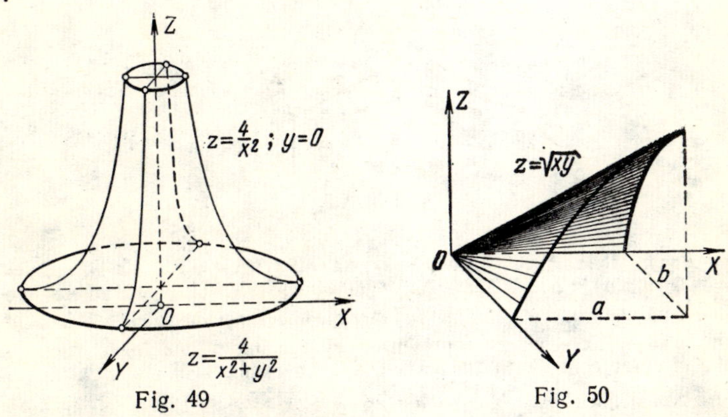

Fig. 49

Fig. 50

(4) $x^2+y^2 \leqslant a^2$; (5) $xy > 0$ (the first and the third quadrants); (6) $x^2+y^2 < 1$; (7) the whole plane, except the straight line $y=x$. Equations (1) and (2) determine paraboloids of revolution; (3) a surface of revolution about the axis OZ of the curve $z=\frac{4}{x^2}$ and $y=0$ (Fig. 49); (4) a hemisphere; (5) a cone which is depicted by taking

the following sections: $x=a$, $z^2=ay$ and $y=b$, $z^2=bx$ (parabolas shown in Fig. 50); (6) a surface of revolution of the curve $z=\frac{1}{\sqrt{1-x^2}}$, $y=0$ about OZ; (7) a cone with the generatrices $y=kx$, $z=\frac{kx}{k-1}$ and the directrices $y=h$, $(x-h)(z+h)=-h^2$ (equilateral hyperbolas) with the vertices on the axis OY and one of the asymptotes in the plane $y=x$ ($x=h$, $y=h$); such hyperbolas are also obtained from the sections $x=h$ or $z=h$ (Fig. 51). **1845.** $s=\sqrt{p(p-x)(p-y)(x+y-p)}$. The domain of the function: $0<x<p$, $0<y<p$ and $x+y>p$, i.e. a set of points inside a triangle bounded by the lines $x=p$, $y=p$ and

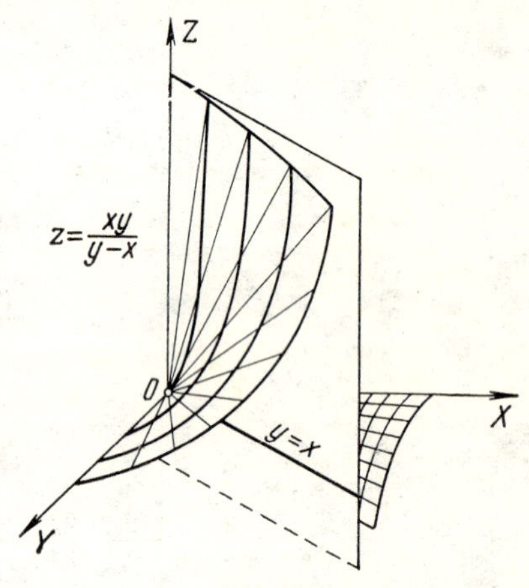

Fig. 51

$x+y=p$. **1848.** $\Delta_x z=(2x-y+\Delta x)\,\Delta x=0.21$; $\Delta_y z=(2y-x+\Delta y)\,\Delta y=-0.19$; $\Delta z=\Delta_x z+\Delta_y z-\Delta x\Delta y=0.03$. **1849.** Being continuous and single-valued in the domain $|y|\leqslant|x|$, the functions $z=+\sqrt{x^2-y^2}$ and $z=-\sqrt{x^2-y^2}$ are represented by the upper and lower surfaces of a circular cone (with the axis OX). An example of a discontinuous function defined by the equation $z=\pm\sqrt{x^2-y^2}$ is the function

$$z=\begin{cases} +\sqrt{x^2-y^2} & \text{for } 0\leqslant x<1 \\ -\sqrt{x^2-y^2} & \text{for } 1\leqslant x<2 \\ +\sqrt{x^2-y^2} & \text{for } 2\leqslant x<3 \end{cases}$$

The straight lines $x=1$, $x=2$, etc. are lines of discontinuity. and so on.

It is depicted by alternate strips of the upper and lower surfaces of the cone. The domain of this function: $|y|\leqslant|x|$, i.e. a set of points inside an acute angle between the straight lines $y=\pm x$ and on these lines. **1854.** (2) The whole plane except the straight line $y=-x$; (3) points inside the ellipse $\frac{x^2}{a^2}+\frac{y^2}{b^2}=1$ and on the ellipse; (4) the whole plane; (5) points inside the angle $|y|\leqslant|x|$ and on its sides; (6) quadrant of the planes $x\geqslant 0$ and $y\geqslant 0$. (2) is a cylindrical surface with the generatrices $z=h$, $x+y=\frac{4}{h}$ and the directrix $z=\frac{4}{x}$, $y=0$ (Fig. 52). (5) and (6) are conical surfaces; surface (4) is a paraboloid.

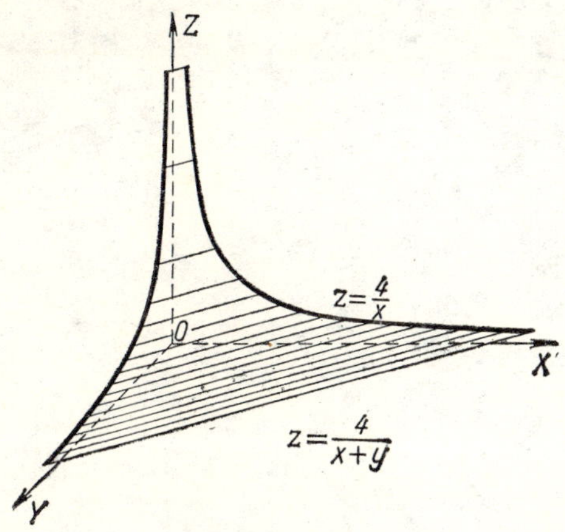

Fig. 52

1858. $3x(x+2y)$; $3(x^2-y^2)$. **1860.** $-\frac{y}{x^2}$; $\frac{1}{x}$. **1861.** $\frac{-y}{x^2+y^2}$; $\frac{x}{x^2+y^2}$. **1862.** $-\frac{y^2}{(x-y)^2}$; $\frac{x^2}{(x-y)^2}$. **1863.** $\frac{\sqrt[3]{t}}{3x(\sqrt[3]{x}-\sqrt[3]{t})}$; $\frac{\sqrt[3]{x}}{3t(\sqrt[3]{t}-\sqrt[3]{x})}$. **1864.** $\frac{\partial c}{\partial a}=\frac{a-b\cos\alpha}{c}$; $\frac{\partial c}{\partial b}=\frac{b-a\cos\alpha}{c}$; $\frac{\partial c}{\partial\alpha}=\frac{ab\sin\alpha}{c}$. **1866.** $\frac{\partial u}{\partial x}=e^{-xy}(1-xy)$; $\frac{\partial u}{\partial y}=-x^2e^{-xy}$. **1867.** $\frac{\partial u}{\partial x}=\frac{5t}{(x+2t)^2}$; $\frac{\partial u}{\partial t}=-\frac{5x}{(x+2t)^2}$. **1868.** $\frac{\partial\alpha}{\partial x}=\frac{t}{2\sqrt{x-x^2t^2}}$; $\frac{\partial\alpha}{\partial t}=\sqrt{\frac{x}{1-xt^2}}$. **1874.** $\frac{\partial z}{\partial x}=-a\sin(ax-by)$; $\frac{\partial z}{\partial y}=b\sin(ax-by)$. **1875.** $\frac{\partial z}{\partial x}=-\frac{y|x|}{x^2\sqrt{x^2-y^2}}$; $\frac{\partial z}{\partial y}=\frac{|x|}{x\sqrt{x^2-y^2}}$. **1876.** $\frac{\partial z}{\partial x}=\frac{3y}{(3y-2x)^2}$; $\frac{\partial z}{\partial y}=-\frac{3x}{(3y-2x)^2}$. **1877.** $\frac{\partial u}{\partial x}=\cot(x-2t)$, $\frac{\partial u}{\partial t}=-2\cot(x-2t)$. **1878.** $\frac{\partial u}{\partial x}=2\sin y\cos(2x+y)$; $\frac{\partial u}{\partial y}=$

$= 2\sin x\cos(x+2y)$. **1885.** (1) 0.075; (2) $-0.1e^2 \approx -0.739$. **1887.** -0.1. **1888.** $1.2\pi\,\mathrm{dm}^3$. **1889.** 0.13 cm. **1890.** (1) $dz = -\left(\frac{y}{x^2}+\frac{1}{y}\right)dx + \left(\frac{1}{x}+\frac{x}{y^2}\right)dy$; (2) $ds = \ln t\,dx + \frac{x\,dt}{t}$. **1891.** $\Delta z = 0.0431$, $dz = 0.04$. **1892.** 0.15. **1893.** $-30\pi\ \mathrm{cm}^3$. **1895.** $\frac{dz}{dt} = -(e^t+e^{-t}) = -2\cosh t$. **1897.** $\frac{dz}{dx} = e^y + xe^y\frac{dy}{dx}$. **1899.** $\frac{\partial z}{\partial u} = \frac{2x}{y}\left(1-\frac{x}{y}\right)$; $\frac{\partial z}{\partial v} = -\frac{x}{y}\left(4+\frac{x}{y}\right)$. **1900.** (1) $\frac{\partial z}{\partial x} = \frac{\partial z}{\partial u}\frac{\partial u}{\partial x} + \frac{\partial z}{\partial v}\frac{\partial v}{\partial x} = m\frac{\partial z}{\partial u} + p\frac{\partial z}{\partial v}$; $\frac{\partial z}{\partial y} = n\frac{\partial z}{\partial u} + q\frac{\partial z}{\partial v}$; (2) $\frac{\partial z}{\partial x} = y\frac{\partial z}{\partial u} - \frac{y}{x^2}\frac{\partial z}{\partial v}$; $\frac{\partial z}{\partial y} = x\frac{\partial z}{\partial u} + \frac{1}{x}\frac{\partial z}{\partial v}$. **1901.** $\frac{\partial u}{\partial r} = \frac{\partial u}{\partial x}\cos\varphi + \frac{\partial u}{\partial y}\sin\varphi$; $\frac{\partial u}{\partial \varphi} = \left(-\frac{\partial u}{\partial x}\sin\varphi + \frac{\partial u}{\partial y}\cos\varphi\right)r$. **1903.** (1) $\frac{dz}{dt} = 2\,[(Ax+By)\cos t - (Bx+Cy)\sin t] = (A-C)\sin 2t + 2B\cos 2t$; (2) $\frac{dz}{dt} = \frac{2e^{2t}}{e^{4t}+1}$. **1906.** (1) $\frac{\partial z}{\partial x} = \frac{\partial z}{\partial u} + \frac{\partial z}{\partial v}$, $\frac{\partial z}{\partial y} = 2\frac{\partial z}{\partial u} - \frac{\partial z}{\partial v}$; (2) $\frac{\partial z}{\partial x} = \frac{\partial z}{\partial u}\cdot\frac{\sqrt{y}}{2\sqrt{x}} + \frac{\partial z}{\partial v}$; $\frac{\partial z}{\partial y} = \frac{\partial z}{\partial u}\cdot\frac{\sqrt{x}}{2\sqrt{y}} + \frac{\partial z}{\partial v}$. **1907.** $\frac{dy}{dx} = \frac{2-x}{y+3}$. **1908.** (1) $-\sqrt[3]{\frac{y}{x}}$; (2) $\frac{2ye^{2x}-e^{2y}}{2xe^{2y}-e^{2x}}$. **1910.** $\pm\frac{3}{4}$. **1911.** -1. **1912.** (1) $(-1, 3)$ and $(-1, -1)$; (2) $(1, 1)$ and $(-3, 1)$. **1913.** $\frac{\partial z}{\partial x} = \frac{3-x}{z}$; $\frac{\partial z}{\partial y} = -\frac{y}{z}$. **1914.** $\frac{\partial z}{\partial x} = \frac{y}{2z}$; $\frac{\partial z}{\partial y} = \frac{x}{2z}$. **1915.** $\frac{\partial z}{\partial x} = -\frac{a}{c}$; $\frac{\partial z}{\partial y} = -\frac{b}{c}$. **1918.** $\frac{dy}{dx} = \frac{x}{4y}$. **1919.** $-\frac{y}{x}$. **1920.** $\frac{x^2+xy+y^2}{xy}$. **1921.** $\frac{1}{2}$. **1922.** $\frac{4}{5}$; $\frac{1}{5}$. **1923.** $\frac{\partial z}{\partial x} = 1$; $\frac{\partial z}{\partial y} = \frac{y}{x-z}$. **1926.** 6; 2; 0; 6. **1929.** $-\frac{6y}{x^4}$; $\frac{2}{x^3}$; 0; 0. **1931.** $\frac{2xy}{(x^2+y^2)^2}$; $\frac{y^2-x^2}{(x^2+y^2)^2}$; $\frac{-2xy}{(x^2+y^2)^2}$. **1938.** (1) $\frac{2}{x^4}(3y^2dx^2 - 4xy\,dx\,dy + x^2dy^2)$; (2) $-\frac{(y\,dx - x\,dy)^2}{xy^2}$.

1942.

$$
\begin{array}{lll|r}
\frac{\partial^2 z}{\partial x^2} = \left(3\frac{\partial}{\partial u} + \frac{\partial}{\partial v}\right)^2 z & & = 9\frac{\partial^2 z}{\partial u^2} + 6\frac{\partial^2 z}{\partial u\,\partial v} + \frac{\partial^2 z}{\partial v^2} & 1 \\
\frac{\partial^2 z}{\partial x\,\partial y} = \left(3\frac{\partial}{\partial u} + \frac{\partial}{\partial v}\right)\left(\frac{\partial}{\partial u} + \frac{\partial}{\partial v}\right) z & & = 3\frac{\partial^2 z}{\partial u^2} + 4\frac{\partial^2 z}{\partial u\,\partial v} + \frac{\partial^2 z}{\partial v^2} & -4 \\
\frac{\partial^2 z}{\partial y^2} = \left(\frac{\partial}{\partial u} + \frac{\partial}{\partial v}\right)^2 z & & = \frac{\partial^2 z}{\partial u^2} + 2\frac{\partial^2 z}{\partial u\,\partial v} - \frac{\partial^2 z}{\partial v^2} & 3 \\
\hline
\frac{\partial^2 z}{\partial x^2} - 4\frac{\partial^2 z}{\partial x\,\partial y} + 3\frac{\partial^2 z}{\partial y^2} & & = -4\frac{\partial^2 z}{\partial u\,\partial v}. &
\end{array}
$$

1943. Writing in the same way as in the previous problem, we get $4\frac{\partial^2 z}{\partial v^2}$.

1945.

$$\left.\begin{aligned}\frac{\partial^2 z}{\partial x^2}&=y^2\frac{\partial^2 z}{\partial u^2}-2\frac{y^2}{x^2}\frac{\partial^2 z}{\partial u\,\partial v}+\frac{y^2}{x^4}\frac{\partial^2 z}{\partial v^2}+\frac{2y}{x^3}\frac{\partial z}{\partial v}\\ \frac{\partial^2 z}{\partial y^2}&=x^2\frac{\partial^2 z}{\partial u^2}+2\frac{\partial^2 z}{\partial u\,\partial v}+\frac{1}{x^2}\frac{\partial^2 z}{\partial v^2}\end{aligned}\right|\begin{aligned}&x^2\\ &-y^2\end{aligned}$$

$$x^2\frac{\partial^2 z}{\partial x^2}-y^2\frac{\partial^2 z}{\partial y^2}=-4y^2\frac{\partial^2 z}{\partial u\,\partial v}+\frac{2y}{x}\frac{\partial z}{\partial v}.$$

1946. $\frac{\partial^2 z}{\partial x^2}+\frac{\partial^2 z}{\partial y^2}$. **1947.** $\frac{\partial^2 z}{\partial x^2}=\frac{2}{1-2y}$; $\frac{\partial^2 z}{\partial x\,\partial y}=\frac{4x}{(1-2y)^2}$; $\frac{\partial^2 z}{\partial y^2}=\frac{8x^2}{(1-2y)^3}$.

1948. 0; 0; $\frac{4}{9t^2\sqrt[3]{t}}$; $-\frac{28x}{27t^3\sqrt[3]{t}}$. **1953.** $d^2u=-\frac{y}{x^2}dx^2+\frac{2}{x}dx\,dy$; $d^3u=\frac{2y}{x^3}dx^3-\frac{3}{x^2}dx^2\,dy$. **1954.** $4a^2\frac{\partial^2 z}{\partial u\,\partial v}$. **1955.** $-v^2\frac{\partial^2 z}{\partial u\,\partial v}+\frac{v^2}{u}\frac{\partial z}{\partial v}$.

1959. $u=\frac{x^2}{2}+x\ln y-\cos y+C$. **1962.** $u=\frac{x}{z}+\frac{1}{x}+\ln y-\arctan z+C$.

1963. $u=xy^2-x+\frac{3y^2}{2}+C$. **1964.** $u=x\sin 2y+y\ln\cos x+y^2+C$.

1965. $u=xy+\frac{\sin^2 y}{x}+y+C$. **1966.** $u=\sqrt{x}\,(1+\sqrt{t^2+1})+C$.

1967. $u=x\ln y-x\cos 2z+yz+C$. **1968.** $u=\frac{x-3y}{z}+C$. **1969.** $y=$

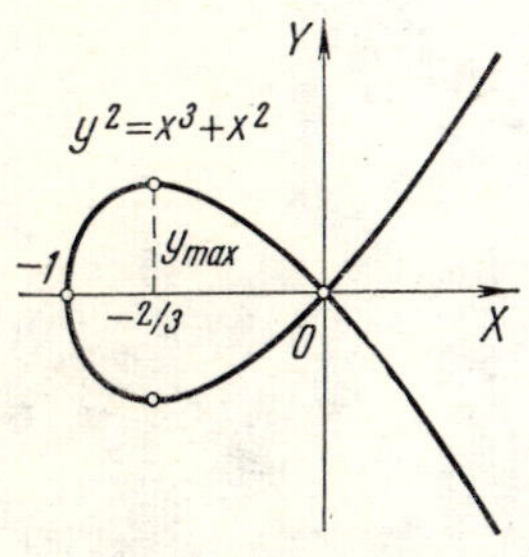

Fig. 53

$=\pm x\sqrt{1+x}$; the domain: $1+x\geqslant 0$; $x\geqslant -1$. Points of intersection with OX: $y=0$, $x=0$ or -1. The singular point $O(0, 0)$ is a node. Extremum of y at $x=-\frac{2}{3}$, $y_{ex}=\mp\frac{2}{3\sqrt{3}}\approx\mp\frac{2}{5}$ (Fig. 53). **1970.** $y=\pm(x+2)\sqrt{x+2}$; the domain $x\geqslant -2$. $(-2, 0)$ is a singular point (a cusp). The points of intersection with the axes: at $x=0$ $y=\pm 2\sqrt{2}$;

at $y=0$ $x=-2$ (Fig. 54). **1971.** $y=\pm x\sqrt{x-1}$. The domain: $x \geqslant 1$ and $x=0$, $y=0$ (a singular isolated point). At $x=1$ $y=0$, at $x=2$ $y=\pm 2$. The points of inflection: $x=\frac{4}{3}$, $y=\pm\frac{4}{3\sqrt{3}}$ (Fig. 55). **1972.** $y=\pm x\sqrt{1-x^2}$; the domain $|x| \leqslant 1$ or $-1 \leqslant x \leqslant 1$. The points of intersection with the axes: at $y=0$ $x_1=0$, $x_2=1$, $x_3=-1$. The sin-

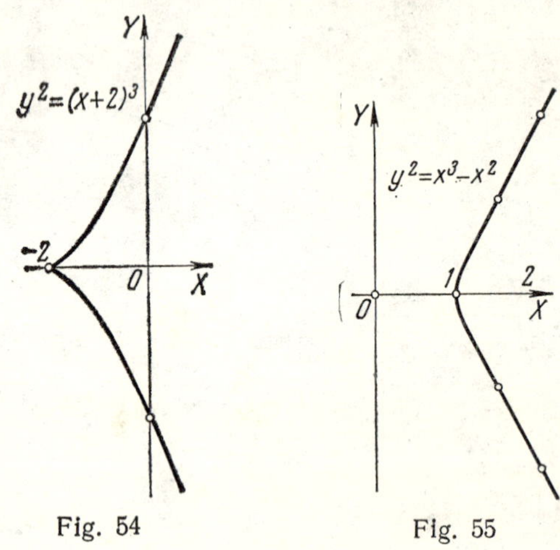

Fig. 54 Fig. 55

gular point $O(0, 0)$ is a node. Extrema at $x=\pm\frac{1}{\sqrt{2}} \approx \pm 0.7$ $y_{ex}=$ $=\pm\frac{1}{2}$ (Fig. 56). **1973.** $y=x\pm x\sqrt{x}$. The domain: $x \geqslant 0$; the points of intersection with the axes: at $y=0$ $x=0$ or $x=1$; the singular

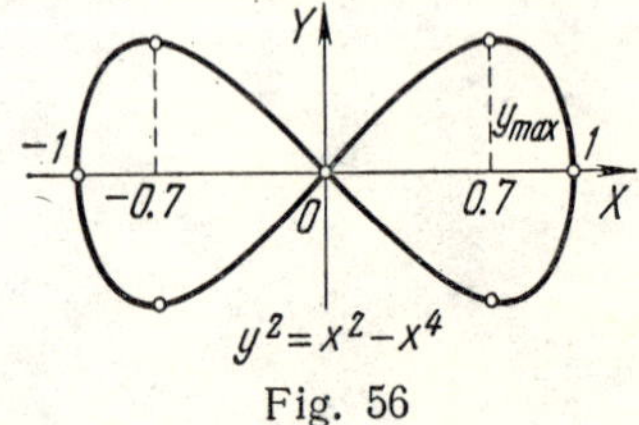

Fig. 56

point $O(0, 0)$ is a cusp of the first kind with the tangent $y=x$. The function $y=x-x\sqrt{x}$ has an extremum: at $x=\frac{4}{9}$ $y_{\max}=\frac{4}{27}$ (Fig. 57). **1974.** $y=\pm(x-2)\sqrt{x}$; $x \geqslant 0$; at $y=0$ $x=0$ or $x=2$; the singular point (2, 0) is a node. The curve has the same shape as the one shown in Fig. 53 but is displaced to the right. **1975.** $y=\pm(x+2a)\sqrt{-\frac{x+2a}{x}}$; the curve is situated in the domain $-2a \leqslant x < 0$, where x and $x+2a$ have opposite signs. $(-2a, 0)$ is a singular point (a cusp); $x=0$ is the asymptote. The curve is a cissoid similar to the one shown in Fig. 89 but displaced to the left by $2a$. **1976.** $y=\pm\sqrt{\frac{x^3-y^3}{3}}$, the domain: $y \leqslant x$. The points of intersection with the axes: at $x=0$ $y=0$ or

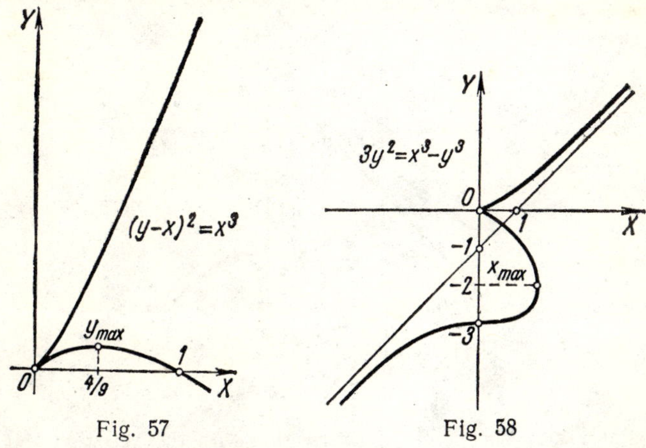

Fig. 57 Fig. 58

$y=-3$. (0, 0) is a singular point (a cusp). Let us find the asymptote $y=kx+b$. Divide the equation by x^3 termwise: $1-\left(\frac{y}{x}\right)^3-3\left(\frac{y}{x}\right)^2\frac{1}{x}=0$. Hence, $k=\lim\limits_{x\to\infty}\frac{y}{x}=1$, $b=\lim\limits_{x\to\infty}(y-x)=\lim\limits_{x\to\infty}\frac{-3y^2}{x^2+xy+y^2}=-1$. Thus, the asymptote is $y=x-1$. An extremum of the function $x=\varphi(y)=\sqrt[3]{y^3+3y^2}$: at $y=-2$ $x_{ex}=\sqrt[3]{4}\approx 1.6$; at $x=0$ $y=-3$ (a point of inflection (Fig. 58)). **1977.** $x^3+y^3-3axy=0$ is the folium of Descartes (see Problem 366). $O(0, 0)$ is a singular point (a node) with the tangents $y=0$ and $x=0$. Let us find the asymptote $y=kx+b$. Bring the equation to the form $1+\left(\frac{y}{x}\right)^3-3a\left(\frac{y}{x}\right)\frac{1}{x}=0$; hence, $k=\lim\limits_{x\to\infty}\frac{y}{x}=-1$, $b=\lim\limits_{x\to\infty}(y+x)=\lim\limits_{x\to\infty}\frac{3axy}{x^2-xy+y^2}=-a$. Thus, $y=-x-a$ is the asymptote (see. Fig. 83). **1978.** $y=\pm\frac{x^2}{\sqrt{x^2-a^2}}$. Symmetric with respect to OX and OY. The domain: $|x|>a$, and $|y|>|x|$. $O(0, 0)$ is a singular isolated point. At $x=\pm a\sqrt{2}$ it has an extremum $y=\pm 2a$. The asymptotes: $x=\pm a$ and $y=\pm x$ (Fig. 59). **1979.** $y=\pm x\sqrt{2-x}$; the

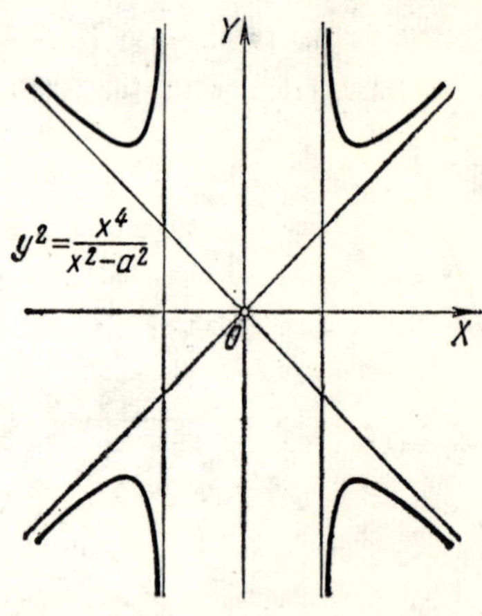

Fig. 59

domain: $x\leqslant 2$. The points of intersection with the axis OX: at $y=0$ $x_1=0$, $x_2=2$. (0, 0) is a singular point (a node). The extrema of y: at $x=\frac{4}{3}$ $y_{ex}=\pm\frac{4\sqrt{2}}{3\sqrt{3}}=\pm 1.08$. (The curve has the same shape as in Fig. 53.) **1980.** $y=\pm\frac{x}{a}\sqrt{a^2-(x-a)^2}$; the domain: $|x-a|\leqslant a$ or $-a\leqslant x-a\leqslant a$ or $0\leqslant x\leqslant 2a$. At $y=0$ $x_1=0$, $x_2=2a$. The point (0, 0) is a cusp. At $y'=0$, $\sqrt{2ax-x^2}+\frac{x(a-x)}{\sqrt{2ax-x^2}}=0$, $x=\frac{3a}{2}$, $y_{ex}=\pm\frac{3\sqrt{3}}{4}a\approx\pm\frac{5}{4}a$ (Fig. 60). **1981.** $y=\pm(x+2)\sqrt{x}$. The domain: $x\geqslant 0$ and an isolated point $(-2, 0)$. A point of inflection at $x=\frac{2}{3}$. The curve is the same as in Fig. 55 but displaced to the left. **1982.** Two domains: (1) $x>0$; (2) $x<-a$. Three asymptotes: $y=x+\frac{3a}{2}$, $y=-x-\frac{3a}{2}$, and $x=0$. A cusp $(-a, 0)$. Extrema of y: at $x=\frac{a}{2}$ $y_{ex}=$

$=\pm\frac{3\sqrt{3a}}{2}\approx\pm 2.6a$. **1983.** $y=\pm\frac{x^2}{2}\sqrt{x+5}$; $x\geqslant -5$. (0, 0) is a point of osculation. Extrema of y: at $x=-4$ $|y|_{max}=8$; at $x=0$ $|y|_{min}=0$ (Fig. 61). **1984.** $y=\pm x\sqrt{x^2-1}$. The domains: $|x|\geqslant 1$ with an isolated point $O(0, 0)$. The graph is the same as in Fig. 55 with a symmetric curve added at the left. **1985.** At $y=0$ $x_1=0$ and $x_2=-4$; at $x=0$ $y_1=0$, $y_2=-1$. (0, 0) is a singular point (a node) with the slope of the tangents $k=\pm 2$. At $x=-\frac{8}{3}$ $y_{max}=1.8$ and at $x=0$ $y_{min}=-1$. The asymptote: $y=x+1$. The curve intersects the

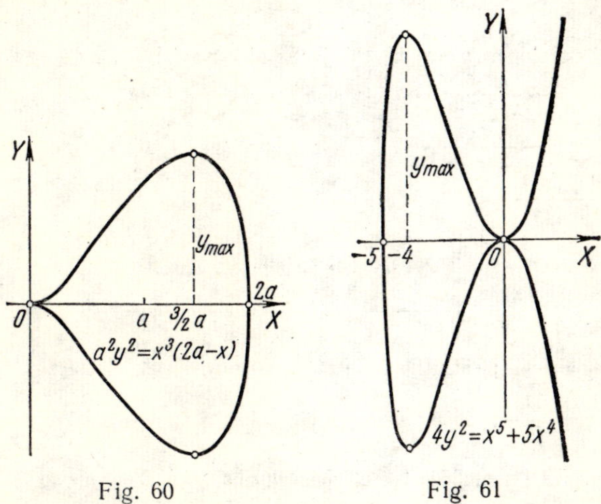

Fig. 60 Fig. 61

asymptote at $x=-0.4$ and then describes a loop passing through the points (0, 0) and (0, -1). **1986.** (1) $y=\pm(x-a)\sqrt{\frac{x}{2a-x}}$; the domain: $0\leqslant x\leqslant 2a$, i.e. the curve is situated where x and $2a-x$ have the same signs. (a, 0) is a singular point (a node) with the tangents $k=\pm 1$. The asymptote: $x=2a$ (Fig. 88). (2) $y=\pm\frac{ax}{\sqrt{x^2-a^2}}$; the domain: $|x|>a$ and $|y|>a$ with an isolated point (0, 0). The asymptotes: $x=\pm a$ and $y=\pm a$. There are no points of the curve between each pair of the asymptotes except for the singular point since $|x|>a$ and $|y|>a$. The curve consists of four symmetric branches approaching the asymptotes $x=\pm a$ and $y=\pm a$. **1987.** (1) $y=\pm x\sqrt{\frac{a-x}{x+a}}$; $-a<x\leqslant a$. The points of intersection with the axis OX: $y=0$, $x_1=0$, $x_2=a$. (0, 0) is a singular point (a node). The

asymptote: $x=-a$. The curve is a strophoid; it is obtained by folding the graph shown in Fig. 88 along the axis OY and then translating this axis to the left by a. (2) Domains: $x \geqslant a$, $x < -a$, and $x=0$. $(0, 0)$ is an isolated point. The asymptotes: $x=-a$, $y=a-x$ and $y=x-a$. At $x=-\frac{a(\sqrt{5}+1)}{2} \approx -1.6a$ $y_{ex} \approx \pm 3.3a$. **1988.** (1) $y=-\frac{x^2}{4}$; (2) $y=\pm 2x$. **1989.** (1) $y=\pm R$; (2) $y=0$ and $y=-x$. **1990.** (1) $y=1$; (2) $y=1$ is the locus of cusps but not the envelope; (3) $y=1$ is both the locus of cusps and the envelope; (4) $y=x-\frac{4}{3}$ is the envelope, $y=x$ is the locus of cusps. **1991.** $x^{\frac{2}{3}}+y^{\frac{2}{3}}=a^{\frac{2}{3}}$. **1992.** $y^2=-\frac{x^3}{x+2}$. **1993.** $(x^2+y^2)^2=4a^2xy$. **1994.** A family of paths $y=x \tan\alpha-\frac{gx^2}{2b^2\cos^2\alpha}$. Their envelope (parabola of "safety"): $y=\frac{b^2}{2g}-\frac{gx^2}{2b^2}$. **1995.** (1) $x^2+y^2=p^2$; (2) $y^2=4x$; (3) $y=1$. **1996.** $y^2=4(x+1)$. **1997.** $x^{2/3}+y^{2/3}=l^{2/3}$. **1998.** $y=-x^2 4/3$. **1999.** $2x+4y-z=3$. **2000.** $xy_0+yx_0=2zz_0$. **2001.** $xy_0z_0+yx_0z_0+zx_0y_0=3a^3$. **2002.** $\frac{xx_0}{a^2}+\frac{yy_0}{b^2}-\frac{zz_0}{c^2}=1$. **2003.** $x+y-z=\pm 9$. **2004.** $\frac{x-3}{3}=\frac{y-4}{4}=\frac{z-5}{-5}$; at the point $(0, 0, 0)$. **2005.** $\cos\alpha=-\cos\beta=\cos\gamma=\frac{1}{\sqrt{3}}$. **2006.** $y=0$, $x+z+1=0$; the surface is represented in Fig. 49 on p. 353. **2009.** The tangent plane: $x-y+2z=\frac{\pi a}{2}$. Its distance from the origin is $\frac{\pi a}{2\sqrt{6}}$. A helicoid is a ruled surface. Straight lines are obtained in the sections $z=h$. At $z=0$ $y=0$; at $z=\frac{\pi a}{4}$ $y=x$; at $z=\frac{\pi a}{2}$ $x=0$; at $z=\frac{3\pi a}{4}$ $y=-x$; at $z=\pi a$ $y=0$ (Fig. 62). **2010.** $z=0$ and $x+y-z=\frac{a}{2}$. **2012.** $\frac{x-4}{4}=\frac{y-3}{3}=\frac{z}{5}$. **2013.** $\cos\alpha=\frac{2}{3}$; $\cos\beta=-\frac{2}{3}$; $\cos\gamma=-\frac{1}{3}$. **2014.** Plane $z+y-x=a$, $p=\frac{a}{\sqrt{3}}$. **2016.** (1) $z=4$; (2) $2x+2y+z=6$. **2017.** $\operatorname{grad} z=-2xi-2yj=-2(i+2j)$. **2018.** (1) $\operatorname{grad} z=\frac{-i+j}{2x}$; (2) $\operatorname{grad} z=\frac{i+j}{2x}$. **2019.** $\operatorname{grad} h=-\frac{x}{2}i-2j$. **2020.** $\tan\varphi=|\operatorname{grad} z|=$

$=\sqrt{\frac{x^2+y^2}{4xy}}=\frac{\sqrt{10}}{4}\approx 0.79$. **2021.** $\frac{du}{dl}=\frac{\sqrt{2}}{2}$. **2022.** $\frac{du}{dl}=2+\sqrt{2}$; grad $u=2\boldsymbol{i}+2\boldsymbol{j}+2\boldsymbol{k}$; $|\text{grad } u|=2\sqrt{3}$. **2023.** grad $u=\pm 4\boldsymbol{i}$. **2024.** $\frac{6}{\sqrt{a^2+b^2+c^2}}$. **2025.** grad $z=0.32\boldsymbol{i}-0.64\boldsymbol{j}$; $|\text{grad } z|=0.32\sqrt{5}$. **2026.** $\frac{du}{dl}=\frac{yz+xz+xy}{\sqrt{3}}=\frac{5}{\sqrt{3}}$. **2027.** grad $u=2(x\boldsymbol{i}+y\boldsymbol{j}-z\boldsymbol{k})$; $|\text{grad } u|=2z\sqrt{2}$. **2028.** grad $u=\frac{x\boldsymbol{i}+y\boldsymbol{j}+z\boldsymbol{k}}{u}$; $|\text{grad } u|=1$ at any

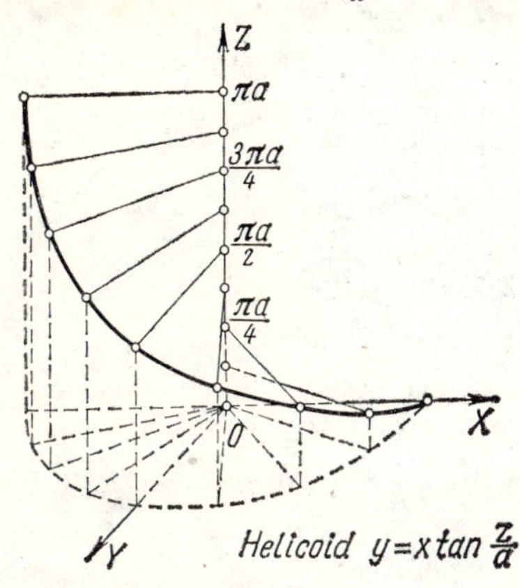

Fig. 62

point. **2029.** $-\frac{3}{\sqrt{a^2+b^2+c^2}}$. **2030.** $z_{\min}=1$ at $x=-4$, $y=1$. **2031.** $z_{\max}=12$ at $x=y=4$. **2032.** $z_{\min}=0$ at $x=1$, $y=-\frac{1}{2}$. **2033.** No extremum. **2034.** $z_{\min}=-\frac{2}{e}$ at $x=-2$, $y=0$. **2035.** $z_{\max}=\frac{3\sqrt{3}}{2}$ at $x=y=\frac{\pi}{3}$. **2036.** $z_{\min}=2$ at $x=y=1$. **2037.** $z_{\max}=-4$ at $x=y=-2$ and $z_{\min}=4$ at $x=y=2$. **2038.** $x=y=\sqrt[3]{2V}$, $z=0.5\sqrt[3]{2V}$. **2039.** $\left(\frac{8}{5}, \frac{3}{5}\right)$, $\left(-\frac{8}{5}, -\frac{3}{5}\right)$. **2040.** It is necessary to find the minimum of the function $z=d^2=x^2+(y-2)^2$ for the condition $x^2-y^2-4=0$. The required points: $(\pm\sqrt{5}, 1)$. **2041.** $R=1$, $H=2$. **2042.** (1) Vertices $(\pm 3, -1)$ and $(0, 2)$; (2) the ray must pass in such a way that $\sin\alpha : \sin\beta = v_1 : v_2$, as it actually happens in nature. **2043.** $z_{\min}=9$ at $x=0$ and $y=3$. **2044.** $z_{\min}=0$ at $x=y=2$. **2045.** $z_{\min}=0$ at $x=0$ and $y=0$.

2046. $z_{min}=0$ at $x=2$, $y=4$. **2047.** $z_{max}=1$ at $x=y=\pm 1$; $z_{min}=-1$ at $x=-y=\pm 1$. **2048.** $V=8$. **2049.** (1) Find the minimum of $d=\frac{x-y+4}{\sqrt{2}}$ or the minimum of $z=x-y+4$ for the condition $4x-y^2=0$. The required point is (1, 2); (2) $2ab$. **2050.** $R=\sqrt{\frac{S}{\pi\sqrt{3}}}$.
2051. Equations of integral curves: (1) $y=\frac{x^3}{3}$; (2) $y=x^3$; (3) $y=-\frac{x^3}{3}$.
2053. $xy'=2y$. **2054.** (1) $y^2-x^2=2xyy'$; (2) $x^2+y=xy'$. **2057.** $y=Cx$, $y=-2x$. **2058.** $xy=C$, $xy=-8$. **2059.** $x^2+y^2=C^2$, $x^2+y^2=20$.
2060. $y=Ce^x$, $y=4e^{x+2}$. **2061.** $y=Ce^{\frac{1}{x}}$. **2062.** $x+y=$ $=\ln|C(x+1)(y+1)|$. **2063.** $r=Ce^{\frac{1}{\varphi}}+a$. **2064.** $s^2=\frac{t^2-1+Ct}{t}$.
2065. $y=Ce^{\sqrt{x}}$, $y=e^{\sqrt{x}-2}$. **2066.** $y=\frac{C\sin^2 x-1}{2}$; $y=2\sin^2 x-\frac{1}{2}$.
2067. $\frac{1}{x}+\frac{1}{y}=C$; $y=-x$. **2068.** General integrals: (1) $y=C(x^2-4)$; (2) $y=C\cos x$. All integral curves of the first equation intersect the axis OX at $x=\pm 2$, and those of the second at $x=(2n-1)\frac{\pi}{2}$ (singular points). **2069.** $y=\frac{x^3}{3}$. **2070.** $\int_0^x y\,dx=a\int_0^x \sqrt{1+y'^2}\,dx$; hence, $y=a\sqrt{1+y'^2}$, $y'=\pm\sqrt{\frac{y^2}{a^2}-1}$; put $y=a\cosh u$, then $a\sinh u\cdot u'=$ $=\pm\sinh u$. Hence: (1) $\sinh u=0$, $\cosh u=1$, $y=a$; (2) $a\,du=\pm dx$, $au=\pm(x+C)$, $y=a\cosh u=a\cosh\frac{x+C}{a}$; at $x=0$ $y=a$ and $C=0$. Thus either $y=a\cosh\frac{x}{a}$ (a catenary) or $y=a$ (a straight line).
2071. $y^2=ax$. **2072.** $y^2=4(x+2)$. **2073.** In 40 min. *Solution* If in t seconds the temperature of the body will be T, then $\frac{dT}{dt}=-k(T-20°C)$, where k is for the present an unknown factor; $\ln(T-20°C)=-kt+C$; at $t=0$ $T=100°C$, therefore $C=\ln 80°C$, $kt=\ln\frac{80°C}{T-20°C}$. Substituting $T_1=25°C$ and $T_2=60°C$ and dividing termwise, eliminate the unknown k: $\frac{kt}{k\cdot 10}=\frac{\ln 16}{\ln 2}$, and $t=40$ min. **2074.** $\sum X_i=-H+T\cos\alpha=0$, $\sum Y_i=-px+T\cdot\sin\alpha=0$; hence, $\tan\alpha=\frac{dy}{dx}=\frac{px}{H}$, $y=\frac{p}{2H}x^2+C$ (parabola). **2075.** Equation of the tangent: $Y-y=y'\cdot(X-x)$. Putting $Y=0$, we find the abscissa of the point A of intersection of the

tangent and the axis OX: $X_A=x-\frac{y}{y'}$. By hypothesis $X_A=2x$; $x=-\frac{y}{y'}$; solving this differential equation, find the required curve $xy=-a^2$ (a hyperbola). **2076.** $x^2+2y^2=c^2$. **2077.** $y^2-x^2=C$. **2078.** $2x^2+3y^2=3a^2$. **2079.** $y=Cx^4$. **2080.** $y=Ce^{-\frac{1}{x^2}}$. **2081.** $2y=\frac{Cx^2}{(1+x)^2}-1$. **2082.** $y=C(x+\sqrt{x^2+a^2})$. **2083.** $y=\frac{C-x}{1+Cx}$. **2084.** $r=C\cos\varphi$, $r=-2\cos\varphi$. **2085.** $\sqrt{y}=x\ln x-x+C$, $\sqrt{y}=x\ln x-x+1$ **2086.** $y=\frac{C\sqrt{1+x^2}}{x+\sqrt{1+x^2}}$, $y=\frac{\sqrt{1+x^2}}{x+\sqrt{1+x^2}}$. **2087.** $xy=-1$. **2088.** $y=ae^{\frac{x}{a}}$. **2089.** $y=\frac{2x}{1-x}$. **2090.** $x^2y=C$. **2091.** Radius vector $OM=\sqrt{x^2+y^2}$, a segment of the normal $MN=\frac{y}{\cos\alpha}=y\sqrt{1+\tan^2\alpha}=y\sqrt{1+y'^2}$. The required curve is either $x^2+y^2=C^2$ (a circle) or $x^2-y^2=C$ (a hyperbola). **2092.** $y=Cx^2$. **2093.** $y-x=Ce^{\frac{x}{y-x}}$. **2094.** $x^2-y^2=Cx$. **2095.** $s^2=2t^2\ln\frac{C}{t}$. **2096.** $y=Cx^3-x^2$. **2097.** $y=\frac{C-e^{-x^2}}{2x^2}$. **2098.** $y=\frac{C-\cos 2x}{2\cos x}$. **2099.** $y=\frac{1}{x\ln Cx}$. **2100.** $y^2=\frac{e^{x^2}}{2x+C}$. **2101.** $\sin\frac{y}{x}+\ln x=C$. **2102.** $y=\frac{x}{C-\ln x}$. **2103.** $y=\ln x+\frac{C}{x}$. **2104.** $y^3=\frac{3}{2x}+\frac{C}{x^3}$. **2105.** $y=\frac{x^2-1}{2}$. **2106.** $s=Ct^2+\frac{1}{t}$; $s=2t^2+\frac{1}{t}$. **2107.** $y=xe^{Cx}$; $y=xe^{-\frac{x}{2}}$. **2108.** $(x-y)^2=Cy$. **2109.** $x^2+y^2=2Cy$. **2110.** $i=\frac{kt}{R}+\frac{kL}{R}\left(e^{-\frac{R}{L}t}-1\right)$. **2111.** Putting $X=0$ in the equation of the tangent $Y-y=y'(X-x)$; find $V_0=-ON=y-xy'$, $ON=xy'-y=OM=\sqrt{x^2+y^2}$. Hence, $y=\frac{x^2-C^2}{2C}$. The mirror must be a paraboloid of revolution. **2112.** $y^2=Cxe^{-\frac{y}{x}}$. **2113.** $y=\frac{\ln C(x+\sqrt{a^2+x^2})}{\sqrt{a^2+x^2}}$. **2114.** For $x>0$ $\sqrt{\frac{y}{x}}=\ln\frac{C}{x}$, for $x<0$ $\sqrt{\frac{y}{x}}=\ln Cx$. **2115.** $y=\frac{x-1}{3}+\frac{C}{\sqrt{2x+1}}$. **2116.** $y=1+\frac{\ln\left|C\tan\frac{x}{2}\right|}{\cos x}$.

2117. $s=t^3(\ln t-1)+Ct^2$. **2118.** $y^2=\frac{1}{1+Ce^{x^2}}$.

2119. $y=2(\sin x-1)+Ce^{-\sin x}$. **2120.** $y=\frac{2x}{1-Cx^2}$; $y=\frac{2x}{1-3x^2}$.

2121. $y^3=x+Ce^{-x}$; $y^3=x-2e^{1-x}$. **2122.** $y=\frac{1}{3\sqrt{1-x^2}-1}$.

2123. $(x-a)^2+y^2=a^2$. **2124.** $y=\frac{\ln Cx}{x}$. **2125.** $y^2=x(Cy-1)$.

2126. $xy=\frac{y^4}{4}+C$. **2127.** $\frac{x}{y}+\frac{y^2}{2}=C$. **2128.** $y=\cos x+\frac{C}{\sin x}$.

2129. $s=\frac{t}{C+t-t\ln t}$. **2130.** $x^2y^2+2\ln x=C$. **2131.** $s=\frac{Ct-1}{t^2}$.

2132. $y=x^2+Cx$. **2133.** $\sin y=x+\frac{C}{x}$. **2134.** $y=\frac{x}{C+2e^{-\frac{x}{2}}}$.

2135. $4x^2+y^2=Cx$. **2136.** $x^3e^y-y=C$. **2137.** $y+xe^{-y}=C$.

2138. $x^2\cos^2 y+y^2=C$. **2139.** $\mu=\frac{1}{x^2}$; $x+\frac{y}{x}=C$. **2140.** $\ln\mu=\ln\cos y$; $x^2\sin y+\frac{1}{2}\cos 2y=C$. **2141.** $\mu=e^{-2x}$; $y^2=(C-2x)e^{2x}$.

2142. $\mu=\frac{1}{\sin y}$; $\frac{x}{\sin y}+x^3=C$. **2143.** $x^3+2xy-3y=C$.

2144. $x^3y-2x^2y^2+3y^4=C$. **2145.** $\frac{x^2\cos 2y}{2}+x=C$. **2146.** $\mu=\frac{1}{y}$; $xy-\ln y=0$. **2147.** $\mu=\frac{1}{x^4}$; $y^2=Cx^3+x^2$. **2148.** $\mu=e^{-y}$; $e^{-y}\cos x=C+x$.

2149. $\ln\mu=-\ln x$; $\mu=\frac{1}{x}$; $x\sin y+y\ln x=C$. **2150.** $y=(C\pm x)^2$. Through the point $M(1, 4)$, the curves $y=(1+x)^2$ and $y=(3-x)^2$. **2151.** $y=\sin(C\pm x)$. Through the point $M\left(\frac{\pi}{2}, \frac{\sqrt{2}}{2}\right)$, the curves $y=\sin\left(x-\frac{\pi}{4}\right)$ and $y=\sin\left(\frac{3\pi}{4}-x\right)$. **2152.** $y=Cx^2+\frac{1}{C}$; singular integrals $y=\pm 2x$. **2153.** (1) $y=x+C$ and $x^2+y^2=C^2$; (2) $x\left(\sqrt{1+\frac{y}{x}}\pm 1\right)^2=C$ or $(y-C)^2=4Cx$. Singular integrals $x=0$ and $y=-x$. Parabolas: for $x>0$ $y\geqslant -x$, for $x<0$ $y<-x$. The parabolas are tangent both to the axis OY and to the straight line $y=-x$. **2154.** (1) $y=1+\frac{(x-C)^2}{4}$; singular integral $y=1$; (2) $x=2p-\frac{1}{p^2}$, $y=p^2-\frac{2}{p}+C$. **2155.** (1) $y=(C+\sqrt{x+1})^2$; singular integral $y=0$; (2) $x=Ct^2-2t^3$; $y=2Ct-3t^2$, where $t=\frac{1}{p}$;

(3) $Cy=(x-C)^2$, singular integrals $y=0$ and $y=-4x$. **2156.** (1) $y=Cx-C^2$; singular integral $y=\frac{x^2}{4}$; (2) $y=Cx-a\sqrt{1+C^2}$; singular integral $x^2+y^2=a^2$; (3) $y=Cx+\frac{1}{2C^2}$; singular integral $y=1$. $5x^{\frac{2}{3}}$. **2157.** $y=1-\frac{(x+C)^2}{4}$; through $M\left(1, \frac{3}{4}\right)$ two curves pass: $y=1-\frac{x^2}{4}$ and $y=x-\frac{x^2}{4}$. **2158.** (1) $x=2p+\frac{3}{2}p^2+C$; $y=p^2+p^3$; (2) $x^2+(y+C)^2=a^2$. **2159.** $y=-\frac{x^2}{4}+Cx+C^2$; $y=-\frac{x^2}{2}$. **2160.** (1) $y=Cx+\frac{1}{C}$; singular integral $y^2=4x$; (2) $y=C(x+1)+C^2$, $y=-\frac{(x+1)^2}{4}$. **2161.** Line segments of the tangent $Y-y=y'(X-x)$ on the coordinate axes: $X_A=x-\frac{y}{y'}$, $Y_B=y-xy'$. By hypothesis $\frac{X_A \cdot Y_B}{2}=2a^2$; $(y-xy')^2=-4a^2y'$, $y=xy' \pm \sqrt{-4a^2y'}$ (Clairaut's equation). Any straight line of the family $y=-Cx \pm 2a\sqrt{C}$ and also the curve determined by the singular integral $xy=a^2$ solve the problem. **2162.** Parabola $(y-x-a)^2=4ax$. **2163.** (1) $y=3\ln x+2x^2-6x+6$; (2) $y=1-\cos 2x$; (3) $y=C_1x+x\arctan x-\ln\sqrt{1+x^2}+C_2$. **2164.** $y=\frac{1}{x}+C_1\ln x+C_2$. **2165.** $y^2=C_1x+C_2$. **2166.** $y=C_1\sin x-x-\frac{1}{2}\sin 2x+C_2$. **2167.** $y^3+C_1y+C_2=3x$. **2168.** $y=C_1x(\ln x-1)+C_2$. **2169.** $\cot y=C_2-C_1x$. **2170.** (1) $y=e^x(x-1)+C_1x^2+C_2$; (2) $x=\frac{1}{\sqrt{C_1}}\arctan\frac{x}{\sqrt{C_1}}+C_2$ (for $C_1>0$), $\frac{1}{2\sqrt{-C_1}}\ln\left|\frac{x-\sqrt{-C_1}}{x+\sqrt{-C_1}}\right|+C_2$ (for $C_1<0$), $C_2-\frac{1}{x}$ (for $C_1=0$). **2171.** $y''=\frac{P}{EI}(l-x)$. For $x=0$ $y=0$ and $y'=0$. $y=\frac{P}{2EI}\left(lx^2-\frac{x^3}{3}\right)$ is the equation of the flexion curve. **2172.** $C_1y=\frac{(C_1x+C_2)^2}{4}+1$. **2173.** $y=a\cosh\frac{(x-b)}{a}=\frac{a}{2}\left(e^{\frac{x-b}{a}}+e^{-\frac{x-b}{a}}\right)$. **2174.** $y=\frac{x^3}{6}$. **2175.** $y=C_1x+C_2-\ln\cos x$; the particular integral $y=-\ln(\cos x)$. **2176.** $y=\frac{x^3}{12}-\frac{x}{4}+C_1\arctan x+C_2$. **2177.** $C_1y^2=1+(C_1x+C_2)^2$. **2178.** $y=(C_1x+C_2)^2$. **2179.** $s=-\frac{t^2}{4}+C_1\ln t+C_2$.

2180. $4(C_1y-1)=(C_1x+C_2)^2$. **2181.** $y=C_2-C_1\cos x-x$. **2182.** See 2177. **2183.** $y=-\ln\cos x$. **2184.** $y=C_1e^x+C_2e^{3x}$. **2185.** $y=(C_1+C_2x)e^{2x}$. **2186.** $y=e^{2x}(A\cos 3x++B\sin 3x)$. **2187.** $y=C_1e^{2x}+C_2e^{-2x}=A\cosh 2x+B\sinh 2x$. **2188.** $y=A\cos 2x+B\sin 2x=a\sin(2x+\varphi)$. **2189.** $y=C_1+C_2e^{-4x}$. **2190.** $x=C_1e^t+C_2e^{-4t}$. **2191.** $\rho=A\cos\frac{\varphi}{2}+B\sin\frac{\varphi}{2}$. **2192.** $s=e^{-t}(A\cos t+B\sin t)$; $s=e^{-t}(\cos t+2\sin t)$. **2193.** $y=C_1e^x+(C_2+C_3x)e^{2x}$. **2194.** $y=C_1\cosh 2x+C_2\sinh 2x+C_3\cos 2x+C_4\sin 2x$. **2195.** $y=C_1e^{2x}+e^{-x}(C_2\cos x\sqrt{3}+C_3\sin x\sqrt{3})$. **2196.** $y=(C_1+C_2x+C_3x^2)e^{-ax}$. **2197.** $y=A\sin x\sinh x+B\sin x\cosh x+C\cos x\sinh x+D\cos x\cosh x$. **2198.** $y=A\cosh x+B\sinh x+C\cos\frac{x}{2}+D\sin\frac{x}{2}$. **2199.** Displacement $x=a\sin\sqrt{\frac{g}{l}}(t-t_0)$; period $T=2\pi\sqrt{\frac{l}{g}}$. **2200.** $x=a\cos\sqrt{\frac{g}{a}}t$; period $T=2\pi\sqrt{\frac{a}{g}}$. **2201.** $x=ae^{-kt}\sin(\omega t+\varphi)$, where $\omega=\sqrt{\frac{g}{l}-\frac{k^2}{4}}$. **2202.** $y=C_1e^{-2x}+C_2e^{-x}$. **2203.** $y=(C_1x+C_2)e^{ax}$. **2204.** $y=e^{-x}(C_1\cos 2x+C_2\sin 2x)$. **2205.** $x=C_1e^{3t}+C_2e^{-t}$. **2206.** $x=C_1\cos\omega t+C_2\sin\omega t$. **2207.** $s=C_1+C_2e^{-at}$. **2208.** $x=e^{-t}(A\cos t\sqrt{2}+B\sin t\sqrt{2})$. **2209.** $y=C_1e^{-x}+(C_2x+C_3)e^{2x}$. **2210.** $y=C_1e^{2x}+C_2e^{-2x}+C_3\cos x+C_4\sin x$. **2211.** $y=(C_1+C_2x)\times\cos 2x+(C_3+C_4x)\sin 2x$. **2212.** $y=\frac{e^x-e^{-x}}{2}=\sinh x$. **2214.** $y=C_1e^{2x}+C_2e^{-2x}-2x^3-3x$. **2215.** $y=C_1e^{-x}+C_2e^{-2x}+0.25\sqrt{2}\times\cos\left(\frac{\pi}{4}-2x\right)$. **2216.** $y=C_1\cos x+C_2\sin x+x+e^x$. **2217.** $y=C_1+C_2e^{-3x}+\frac{3}{2}x^2-x$. **2218.** $y=e^{-2x}(C_1\cos x+C_2\sin x)+x^2-8x+7$. **2219.** $y=C_1e^{2x}+(C_2-x)e^x$. **2220.** $x=A\sin k(t-t_0)-t\cos kt$. **2221.** $y=C_1e^{x\sqrt{2}}+C_2e^{-x\sqrt{2}}-(x-2)e^{-x}$. **2222.** $y=C_1+C_2e^{2x}-\frac{x^3}{6}$. **2223.** $y=\frac{1}{2}e^{-x}+xe^{-2x}+C_1e^{-2x}+C_2e^{-3x}$. **2224.** $x=e^{-kt}(C_1\cos kt+C_2\sin kt)+\sin kt-2\cos kt$. **2225.** $y=C_1+C_2x+(C_3+x)e^{-x}+x^3-3x^2$. **2226.** $y=C_1e^{3x}+\left(C_2-\frac{x}{4}\right)e^{-3x}+C_3\cos 3x+C_4\sin 3x$. **2227.** $x=C_1+C_2\cos t+C_3\sin t+t^3-6t$. **2228.** $y=\left(C_1+\frac{x}{12}\right)e^{-2x}+(C_2\cos x\sqrt{3}+C_3\sin x\sqrt{3})e^x$. **2229.** (1) $x=\left(C_1+C_2t+\frac{t^2}{2}\right)e^{-2t}$; (2) $x=A\cos\frac{t}{a}+B\sin\frac{t}{a}+\frac{1}{a}$. **2230.** In our case $y_1=\cos 2x$, $y_2=\sin 2x$,

$w=2,\ A=-\frac{x}{2}+C_1;\ B=\frac{1}{4}\ln\sin 2x+C_2$, and $y=\left(C_1-\frac{x}{2}\right)\cos 2x+$ $+\left(C_2+\frac{1}{4}\ln\sin 2x\right)\sin 2x$. **2231.** $y=[(C_1+\ln\cos x)\cos x+$ $+(C_2+x)\sin x]\,e^{2x}$. **2232.** $y=(C_1-\ln x+C_2x)\,e^x$. **2233.** $y=C_1\cos x+$ $+C_2\sin x-\cos x\cdot\ln\tan\left(\frac{x}{2}+\frac{\pi}{4}\right)$. **2234.** (1) $y=C_1+C_2e^{-x}-$ $-(1+e^{-x})\ln(1+e^x)+x$; (2) $y=e^{-2x}\left(C_1+C_2x+\frac{1}{2x}\right)$. **2237.** $y=$ $=C_1e^{2x}+C_2e^{3x}+\frac{1}{6}(5\cos 3x-\sin 3x)$. **2238.** $y=(C_1x+C_2)\,e^{-x}+\frac{1}{4}e^x$. **2239.** $y=e^{-\frac{x}{2}}\left(C_1\cos\frac{3x}{2}+C_2\sin\frac{3x}{2}\right)-6\cos 2x+8\sin 2x$. **2240.** $y=$ $=C_1e^{\frac{x}{2}}+C_2e^{-\frac{x}{2}}-x^3$. **2241.** $y=C_1e^x+\left(C_2-\frac{x}{2}\right)e^{-x}$. **2242.** $s=$ $=e^{-t}(C_1\cos t+C_2\sin t)+(t-1)^3$. **2243.** (1) $y=e^{mx}(C_1+C_2x)+$ $+\frac{\cos mx}{2m^2}$; (2) $y=C_1e^{\frac{2x}{n}}+C_2e^{-\frac{2x}{n}}-\frac{2}{n}$. **2244.** $y=A\cos x+B\sin x+$ $+C\cos 2x+D\sin 2x-\frac{1}{2}x\cos x$. **2245.** $y=\left(C_1+C_2x+C_3x^2+\frac{x^3}{6}\right)e^x$. **2246.** $y=\left(\frac{x^2\ln x}{2}-\frac{3x^2}{4}+C_1+C_2x\right)e^{-2x}$. **2247.** (1) $y=C_1\sin x+$ $+C_2\cos x+\frac{1}{2\cos x}$; (2) $y=(C_1-\ln|\sin x|)\cos 2x+(C_2-x-$ $-\frac{1}{2}\cot x\Big)\sin 2x$. **2248.** $y=\left(C_1+\sqrt{4-x^2}+x\arcsin\frac{x}{2}+C_2x\right)e^x$. **2249.** $y=\frac{C-(x+2)\,e^{-x}}{x+1}$. **2250.** $y=1+C\cos x$. **2251.** $y=x\,(1+$ $+C\sqrt{1-x^2})$, linear. **2252.** $y=C\left(1+\frac{x}{\sqrt{1+x^2}}\right)$. **2253.** $s=\frac{e^t+C}{t^2}$. **2254.** $\sqrt{y}=Cx^2-1$. **2255.** $2Cy^2=x\,(C^2x^2-1)$. **2256.** $y=x\ln x-2x+$ $+C_1\ln x+C_2$. **2257.** $y\,(C_2-C_1x)=1$. **2258.** $y=C_1e^{mx}+\left(C_2-\frac{x}{2m}\right)e^{-mx}$. **2259.** $y=\ln x+\frac{C}{\ln x}$. **2260.** $y=xe^{\frac{C}{x}-1}$. **2261.** $y^2=\frac{1}{x+Ce^x}$. **2262.** $y=$ $=(C_1+C_2x)\,e^x+C_3+\frac{x^3}{3}+2x^2+6x$. **2263.** $C_1y=1+C_2e^{C_1x}$. **2264.** $s=$ $=C_1e^{2t}+e^{-t}(C_2+C_3t)-\frac{\sin t}{2}$. **2265.** (1) $s=(t^2+C)\tan\frac{t}{2}$; (2) $y^2=$ $=Cx^2-1$. **2266.** (1) $y=\frac{\sin x+C\cos x}{x}$; (2) $y=e^{-x}\left(C_1+\frac{x}{3}\right)+C_2e^{\frac{x}{2}}\times$

$\times\cos\frac{x\sqrt{3}}{2}+C_3e^{-x}\sin\frac{x\sqrt{3}}{2}$. **2267.** (1) $y=(C_1-\ln\sqrt{1+e^{2x}})\,e^x+$ $+(C_2+\arctan e^x)\,e^{2x}$; (2) $y=C_1e^{\sqrt{cx}}+C_2e^{-\sqrt{cx}}$ and $y=C_1x+C_2$. **2268.** $\frac{a}{\pi g^2}\frac{d^2x}{dt^2}+1000\,x=0$, $x=A\cos\frac{10\sqrt{10\pi}}{\sqrt{a}}gt+B\sin\frac{10\sqrt{10\pi}}{\sqrt{a}}gt$, period $T=\frac{2\pi\sqrt{a}}{10g\sqrt{10\pi}}$. **2269.** $\frac{dT}{dr}=-\frac{k}{4\pi r^2}$; $T=\frac{k}{8\pi r}+C$; k and C are found from the conditions: $20°C=\frac{k}{8\pi 2a}+C$ and $100°C=\frac{k}{8\pi a}+C$; $T=\frac{160°C\,a}{r}-60°C=40°C$. **2270.** (1) $y=C_1x+C_2x^{-1}+C_3x^3$; (2) $y=$ $=\frac{C_1}{x}+C_2x^2$; (3) $y=C_1x^n+C_2x^{-(n+1)}$. **2271.** (1) $y=x^{-2}(C_1+C_2\ln x)$; (2) $y=C_1\cos(\ln x)+C_2\sin(\ln x)$. **2272.** (1) $y=\frac{5x^2}{3}+C_1x^{-1}+C_2$; (2) $y=C_1x^3+\frac{C_2}{x_2}-2\ln x+\frac{1}{3}$. **2273.** (1) $y=C_1x+C_2x^2-4x\ln x$; (2) $y=\frac{C_1+C_2\ln x+\ln^3 x}{x}$. **2274.** (1) $y=\left(\frac{x^3}{6}+C_1x+C_2\right)x^2$; (2) $y=$ $=\frac{x}{2}+C_1\cos(\ln x)+C_2\sin(\ln x)$. **2275.** $x=C_1e^t+C_2e^{-3t}$, $y=-\frac{dx}{dt}=C_1e^t-3C_2e^{-3x}$. **2276.** $x=e^t+C_1+C_2e^{-2t}$, $y=e^t+C_1-C_2e^{-2t}$. **2277.** $x=2e^{-t}+C_1e^t+C_2e^{-2t}$, $y=3e^{-t}+3C_1e^t+2C_2e^{-2t}$. **2278.** $x=$ $=e^t+C_1e^{3t}+C_2e^{-3t}+C_3\cos(t+\varphi)$. **2279.** $x=e^{-2t}(1-2t)$. **2280.** $x=$ $=C_1e^t+C_2e^{-t}+t\cosh t$. **2281.** (1) $u=\varphi(x)+\psi(y)$; (2) $u=y\varphi(x)+$ $+\psi(x)$; 3) $u=x\varphi(y)+\psi(x)$; (4) $u=ax^2\ln y+bxy+\varphi(x)+\psi(y)$. **2282.** $z=y^2(x+y-1)$. **2283.** To reduce the equation $A\frac{\partial^2u}{\partial x^2}+2B\frac{\partial^2u}{\partial x\,\partial y}+$ $+C\frac{\partial^2u}{\partial y^2}=F$ to the canonical form we have to solve the characteristic equation $A\,dy^2-2B\,dx\,dy+C\,dx^2=0$; in two of its integrals: $\varphi(x,y)=\xi$ and $\psi(x,y)=\eta$ take the arbitrary constants ξ and η for new variables and express the given equation as a function of the new variables (see Problems 1941 and 1942). In our example we have to solve the equation $dx^2+4dx\,dy+3dy^2=0$, hence $dy+dx=0$, $dy+3dx=$ $=0$, $y+x=\xi$, $y+3x=\eta$. Expressed in terms of the new variables, the given equation takes the form $\frac{\partial^2u}{\partial\xi\,\partial\eta}=0$. Hence, $u=\varphi(\xi)+\psi(\eta)=$ $=\varphi(y+x)+\psi(y+3x)$. **2284.** Characteristic equation $x^2\,dy^2-$ $-2xy\,dx\,dy+y^2\,dx^2=0$ or $(x\,dy-y\,dx)^2=0$ or $d\left(\frac{y}{x}\right)=0$; $\frac{y}{x}=\xi$. The solutions are equal; we can take y to be equal to η. Thus, the two new variables are: $\frac{y}{x}=\xi$ and $y=\eta$. The equation will take the form (see Problems 1944 and 1945): $\frac{\partial^2 u}{\partial \eta^2}=0$; $u=\eta\varphi(\xi)+\psi(\xi)$ or $u=y\varphi\left(\frac{y}{x}\right)+\psi\left(\frac{y}{x}\right)$. **2285.** $u=y\varphi(y+2x)+\psi(y+2x)$. **2286.** $u=xy+\sin y\cos x$. **2287.** (See Problem 1944.) $u=y\ln x+2y+1$. **2288.** $u=\sqrt{xt}\,\varphi\left(\frac{x}{t}\right)+\psi(xt)$; particular solution $u=\frac{x^2(1+t^3)}{t}$. **2289.** $u=e^{-x}\varphi(x-t)+\psi(x)$; particular solution $u=(x-t)e^{-t}-x$. **2290.** Particular solution $u=x\,at+\frac{1}{3}a^3t^3$. **2291.** $u=\frac{f(x-at)+f(x+at)}{2}+\frac{1}{2a}\int\limits_{x-at}^{x+at}F(z)\,dz$. **2292.** $6-4\ln 2\approx 3.28$. **2293.** (1) $10\frac{2}{3}$ sq. units; (2) 4 sq. units. **2294.** $20\frac{5}{6}$. **2295.** $\frac{9a^2}{2}$. **2296.** $\frac{1}{2}-\frac{1}{e}$. **2297.** (1) $\int\limits_0^a dx\int\limits_0^x dy=-\int\limits_0^a dy\int\limits_y^a dx=\frac{a^2}{2}$; (2) $\int\limits_0^a dy\int\limits_{a-y}^{\sqrt{a^2-y^2}} dx=\int\limits_0^a dx\int\limits_{a-x}^{\sqrt{a^2-x^2}} dy=a^2\left(\frac{\pi-2}{4}\right)$; (3) $\frac{\pi a^2}{4}$. **2298.** (1) $\int\limits_0^1 dx\int\limits_x^{2-x^2} dy=\int\limits_0^1 dy\int\limits_0^y dx+\int\limits_1^2 dy\int\limits_0^{\sqrt{2-y}} dx=1\frac{1}{6}$; (2) $\int\limits_{-2}^0 dy\int\limits_{y^2-4}^0 dx=\int\limits_{-4}^0 dx\int\limits_{-\sqrt{4+x}}^0 dy=\frac{16}{3}$. **2299.** $\left(\frac{\pi}{4}+2\right)a^2$. **2300.** The area of the smaller segment: $\left(\frac{4\pi}{3}-\sqrt{3}\right)a^2\approx 2.457a^2$. **2301.** $\frac{3a^2}{2}\ln 2$. **2302.** $\frac{868}{15}a^2$. **2303.** $\frac{3}{8}\pi a^2$. **2304.** 4.5. **2305.** $\frac{a^2}{6}$. **2306.** $\sqrt{2}-1$. **2307.** $\frac{9}{2}a^2$. **2308.** $8\pi+9\sqrt{3}$. **2309.** $\left(2-\frac{\pi}{4}\right)a^2$. **2310.** $7\ln 2$. **2311.** (1) $\int\limits_a^b dx\int\limits_a^x dy=\int\limits_a^b dy\int\limits_y^b dx=\frac{(b-a)^2}{2}$; (2) $\int\limits_0^a dy\int\limits_{\sqrt{ay}}^{\sqrt{2a^2-y^2}} dx=\int\limits_0^a dx\int\limits_0^{\frac{x^2}{a}} dy+\int\limits_a^{a\sqrt{2}} dx\int\limits_0^{\sqrt{2a^2-x^2}} dy=\frac{a^2(3\pi-2)}{12}$; (3) $\int\limits_0^4 dx\int\limits_{2\sqrt{x}}^{8-x} dy=\int\limits_0^4 dy\int\limits_0^{\frac{y^2}{4}} dx+\int\limits_4^8 dy\int\limits_0^{8-y} dx=\frac{40}{3}$.

2312. $\left(\frac{\pi}{2}, \frac{\pi}{8}\right)$. **2313.** (3, 4.8). **2314.** $\left(\frac{2a}{5}, \frac{a}{2}\right)$. **2315.** $\left(0, \frac{4a}{3\pi}\right)$. **2316.** $\left(0, \frac{256a}{315\pi}\right)$. **2318.** $\frac{17a^4}{96}$. **2319.** $\frac{a^4}{4}$. **2320.** $\frac{a^4}{6}$. **2321.** $\frac{\pi a^4}{8}$.

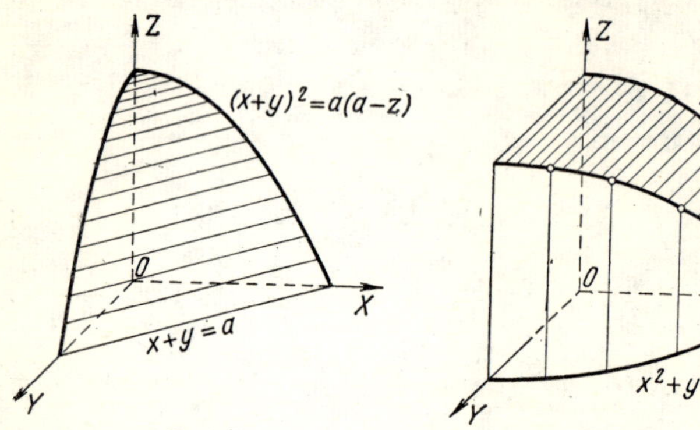

Fig. 63

Fig. 64

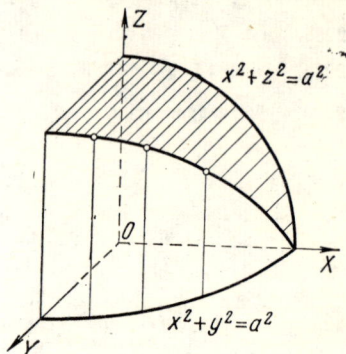

2322. $\frac{\pi a^4}{2}$. **2323.** $\frac{88a^4}{105}$. **2324.** $\left(\frac{3a}{5}, \frac{3a}{8}\right)$. **2325.** $\left(0, \frac{4b}{3\pi}\right)$. **2326.** $\frac{a^4}{30}$. **2327.** 3. **2328.** $\frac{ab(a^2+b^2)}{12}$. **2329.** 47.5. **2330.** $\frac{35\pi a^4}{16}$. **2331.** $42\frac{2}{3}$.

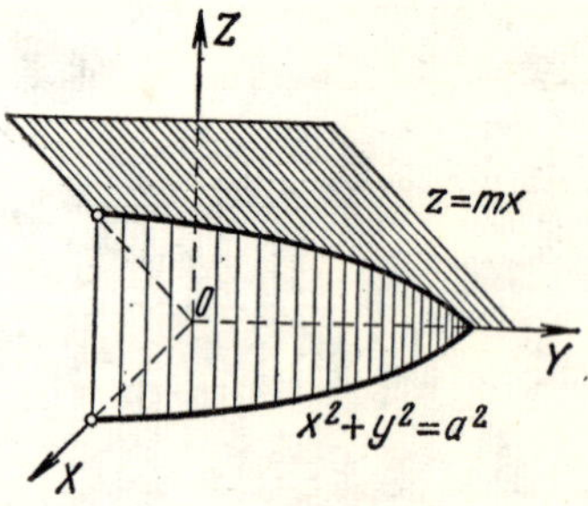

Fig. 65

2332. $\frac{79}{60}a^3$. **2333.** The sections by the plane $z=h$, $x+y=\pm\sqrt{a(a-h)}$ are parallel straight lines, i.e. we have a cylindrical surface (Fig. 63). The required volume $V=2\int_0^a dx \int_0^{a-x} z\,dy=\frac{a^3}{2}$. **2334.** $\frac{16}{3}a^3$ (Fig. 64).

2335. (See Fig. 50 on p. 353.) $\frac{8}{9}a^3$. **2336.** $\frac{a^3}{3}$. **2337.** $\frac{\pi}{12}a^3$. **2338.** $3\pi a^3$.

2339. $V=4\int_0^{\frac{\pi}{2}} m\cos\varphi\, d\varphi \int_0^a r^2\,dr=\frac{4ma^3}{3}$ (Fig. 65). **2340.** $\frac{\pi a^3}{2}$.

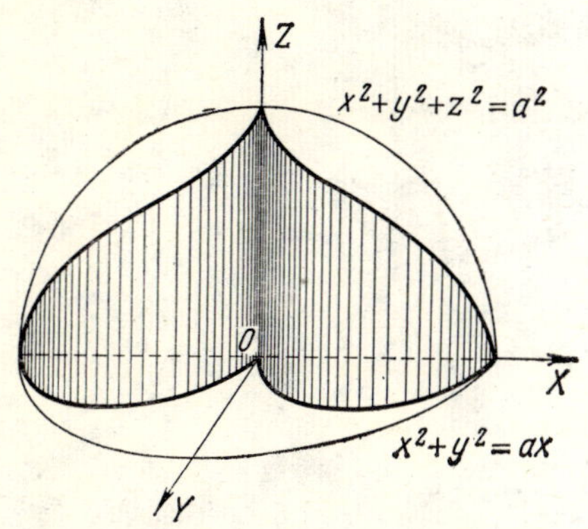

Fig. 66

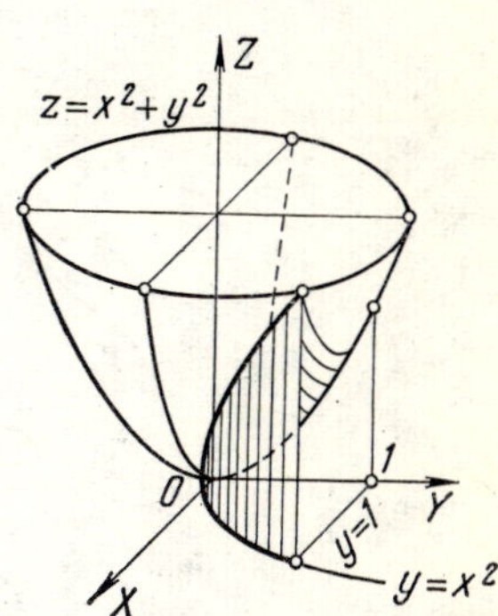

Fig. 67

2341. $4\pi\sqrt{3}\,a^3$. **2342.** $\frac{4a^3}{9}(3\pi-4)$ (Fig. 66). **2343.** $\pi^2 a^3$ (Fig. 62). **2344.** $\frac{16\sqrt{2}}{15}a^3$. **2345.** $\frac{\pi abc}{2}$. **2346.** $\pi abc\left(1-\frac{1}{e}\right)$. **2347.** $\frac{4\pi a^3}{35}$. **2348.** $\frac{8}{15}a^3$. **2349.** $V=2\int_0^1 dx\int_{x^2}^1 z\,dy=\frac{88}{105}$ (Fig. 67). **2350.** $V=$

$$=4\int_0^{3a} dx\int_{\sqrt{ax}}^{2\sqrt{ax}} \sqrt{4ax-y^2}\,dy=3a^3(4\pi-3\sqrt{3})$$ (Fig. 68).

2351. $V=8\int_0^a \frac{b}{a}\sqrt{a^2-x^2}\,dx \int_0^{\frac{b}{a}\sqrt{a^2-x^2}} dy=\frac{16ab^2}{3}$.

2352. $V=4\int_0^a dx\int_0^h \frac{y}{h}\sqrt{a^2-x^2}\,dy=\frac{\pi a^2 h}{2}$, i.e. equal to the area of the conoid base multiplied by half its altitude (Fig. 69). **2353.** $\frac{128}{105}a^3$.

2354. 18π. **2355.** $2\pi a^3$. **2356.** $8\pi \ln 2$ (see Fig. 49 on p. 353). **2357.** $\frac{3}{16}\pi a^3$. **2358.** $\frac{5\pi a^3}{16}$. **2359.** $\frac{4\pi abc}{3}$. **2360.** 13. **2361.** $\frac{8\sqrt{2}}{3}a^2$.

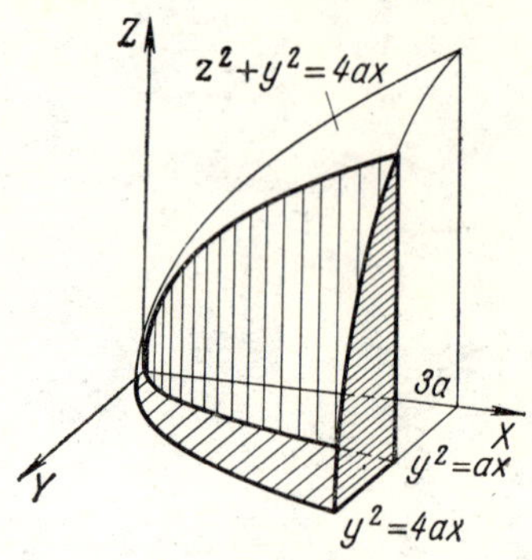

Fig. 68

2362. $2\pi a^2$. **2363.** $\frac{2\pi a^2}{3}(2\sqrt{2}-1)$. **2364.** $2\pi p^2\sqrt{2}$. **2365.** $8a^2$. **2366.** $4a^2(\pi-2)$. **2367.** $\frac{14}{3}\pi a^2$. **2368.** $\sigma=\iint\limits_{(S)}\frac{\sqrt{x^2+y^2+z^2}}{z}\,dx\,dy=$

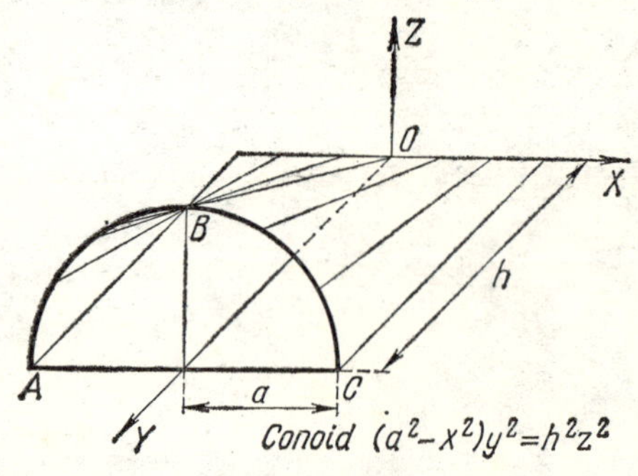

Fig. 69

$=\frac{\pi\beta}{180}R^2\cdot\sin\alpha$; at $\beta=60°$ and $\alpha=30°$ $\sigma=\frac{\pi R^2}{6}$. **2369.** $\frac{\pi a^3}{12}$ (radius of section $r=\frac{a}{\sqrt{3}}$). **2370.** $\frac{2\pi a^3}{3}(2-\sqrt{2})$.

2372. $\int_0^a dx \int_0^{a-x} dy \int_0^{a-x-y} z\,dz = \frac{a^4}{24}$. **2373.** $\left(\frac{a}{4}, \frac{a}{4}, \frac{a}{4}\right)$. **2374.** $\left(0, 0, \frac{a}{3}\right)$. **2375.** $\frac{a^5}{4}$. **2376.** $\frac{\pi a^5}{\sqrt{2}}$. **2377.** (1) $\frac{\pi a^3}{3}$; (2) $\frac{\pi a^3}{60}$. **2378.** $\frac{\pi a^3}{6}(8\sqrt{2}-7)$. **2379.** $\frac{32}{3}\pi$. **2380.** $\frac{\pi a^3}{6}$. **2381.** $\frac{\pi h^4}{4}$. **2382.** $\frac{a^4}{12}$. **2383.** $\left(0, 0, \frac{3a}{8}\right)$. **2384.** $\frac{32\sqrt{2}a^5}{135}$. **2385.** $\frac{a^3}{360}$. **2386.** $6k\pi a^2$, where k is the factor of proportionality.

2387. $\int (x+y)\,dx = \begin{cases} 4 \text{ when taken along the straight line } OA, \\ \frac{10}{3} \text{ when taken along the arc } OA, \\ 2 \text{ when taken along the polygon line } OBA. \end{cases}$

2388. (1) 8; (2) 4. **2389.** $\int (x\,dy + y\,dx) = 8$ in both cases. This is because here $\frac{\partial Q}{\partial x} = \frac{\partial P}{\partial y}$. **2390.** (1) $1.5a^2$; (2) a^2. **2391.** $8a^2$. **2392.** πa^2. **2393.** $\frac{\pi mab}{4}$. **2394.** 0. **2396.** (1) $\frac{5\pi}{6}$; (2) $-\frac{1}{2}$; (3) $2-\frac{1}{\sqrt{3}}$. **2397.** $\frac{2a^3}{3}$. **2398.** πab. **2399.** $\frac{8}{15}$. **2400.** $\frac{3}{2}a^2$. **2401.** $X=0$, $Y=\frac{2kmM}{\pi a^2}$. **2402.** $Y=\frac{kmM}{a^2\sqrt{2}}$. **2403.** $Y=\frac{kmM}{a^2}$. **2404.** (1) -16; (2) $-\frac{52}{3}$; (3) -12. **2405.** (1) $\frac{3a^2}{2}$; (2) $\frac{a^2}{2}$; (3) $\frac{11a^2}{6}$. **2408.** $\frac{3}{8}\pi a^2$. **2409.** $\frac{4}{3}$. **2410.** $\frac{a^3}{2}$. **2411.** $\frac{\pi a^4}{48}$. **2412.** Each part of the formula is equal to $4\pi a^3$. **2413.** Each part of the formula is equal to $\frac{a^4}{3}\left(\frac{4}{5}+\frac{\pi}{16}\right)$. **2419.** Each part of the formula is equal to $\frac{12}{5}\pi a^5$. **2421.** $0.15a^5$. **2422.** No. **2423.** Yes. **2424.** Yes. **2425.** Diverges. **2426.** Diverges. **2427.** Converges, since $\int_1^\infty \frac{x\,dx}{(x+1)^3} = \frac{3}{8}$. **2428.** Converges, since $\int_1^\infty \frac{dx}{1+x^2} = \frac{\pi}{4}$. **2429.** Diverges, since $\int_1^\infty \frac{x}{1+x^2}\,dx = \infty$. **2430.** Converges, since

$$\int_1^\infty \frac{dx}{(2x+1)^2-1} = \left[\frac{1}{4}\ln\frac{x}{x+1}\right]_1^\infty = \frac{1}{4}\ln 2.$$

2431. Converges. **2432.** Converges. **2433.** Converges. **2434.** Converges, since

$\lim\limits_{n\to\infty}\frac{u_{n+1}}{u_n}=\frac{1}{2}<1$. **2435.** Diverges. **2436.** Diverges. **2437.** Converges. **2438.** Diverges. **2439.** Converges. **2440.** Diverges. **2442.** 1. **2443.** $\frac{1}{3}$. **2444.** Converges not absolutely. **2445.** Converges absolutely. **2446.** Converges not absolutely. **2447.** Converges absolutely. **2448.** After the first rearrangement of the terms we get the series in the form: $\left(1-\frac{1}{2}\right)-\frac{1}{4}+\left(\frac{1}{3}-\frac{1}{6}\right)-\frac{1}{8}+\left(\frac{1}{5}-\frac{1}{10}\right)-\frac{1}{12}+\ldots$. Opening the brackets, we obtain a series whose terms are half the terms of the given series. After the second rearrangement any three terms may be expanded as follows:

$$\frac{1}{4n-3}+\frac{1}{4n-1}-\frac{1}{2n}=\frac{1}{4n-3}-\frac{1}{4n-2}+\frac{1}{4n-1}-\frac{1}{4n}+\frac{1}{4n-2}-\frac{1}{4n};\quad \text{for } n=1,\ 2,\ 3,\ \ldots$$

the first four terms form the given series with sum S, and the last two terms with sum $\frac{1}{2}S$. **2449.** Converges. **2450.** Diverges, since $\int\limits_1^\infty\frac{dx}{100x-99}=\infty$. **2451.** Converges, since $\int\limits_1^\infty\frac{x\,dx}{1+x^4}=\frac{\pi}{8}$. **2452.** Diverges since $\int\limits_1^\infty\frac{2x-1}{x^2}dx=\infty$. **2453.** Converges. **2454.** Converges, since $\lim\limits_{n\to\infty}\frac{u_{n+1}}{u_n}=\frac{1}{2}<1$. **2455.** Converges, since $\lim\limits_{n\to\infty}\frac{u_{n+1}}{u_n}=\lim\limits_{n\to\infty}\frac{20n+21}{3(20n+1)}=\frac{1}{3}<1$. **2456.** Converges. **2457.** Converges not absolutely. **2458.** Converges absolutely. **2459.** For $a>1$ converges absolutely, for $a=1$ converges not absolutely, for $a<1$ diverges. **2460.** 1/2. **2461.** 1/4. **2462.** The sum of the series $S(x)=\frac{1}{1-x}$ for $x<1$, the remainder $R_n=S-S_n=\frac{x^n}{1-x}$. On the interval $\left[0,\frac{1}{2}\right]$ $|R_n|<\frac{1}{2^{n-1}}<0.001$, as soon as $n-1>\frac{\log 1000}{\log 2}$; $n\geqslant 11$. **2463.** The series has the sum

$$S=\frac{x}{1-(1-x)}=\begin{cases}1 & \text{for } 0<x\leqslant 1,\\ 0 & \text{for } x=0,\end{cases}$$ and the remainder

$$R_n=\begin{cases}(1-x)^n & \text{for } 0<x\leqslant 1,\\ 0 & \text{for } x=0.\end{cases}$$ For any n the remainder R_n will be greater, say, 0.9 as soon as $x<1-\sqrt[n]{0.9}$, i.e. on the closed interval $[0,\ 1]$ the series converges non-uniformly. But on the interval $\left[\frac{1}{2},1\right]$ it converges uniformly, since then for any x $|R_n|<\frac{1}{2^n}<\varepsilon$ as soon as

$n > \frac{-\log \varepsilon}{\log 2}$; in particular, $|R_n| < 0.01$ for $n \geqslant 7$. **2464.** The remainder of a series with alternating signs is less by modulus than the first rejected term. Therefore, on the interval [0, 1] $|R_n(x)| < \frac{x^{n+1}}{n+1} < \frac{1}{n+1} \leqslant 0.1$ as soon as $n+1 \geqslant 10$ or $n \geqslant 9$. **2465.** The series has the sum $S = \begin{cases} 1+x^3 & \text{for } x > 0, \\ 0 & \text{for } x = 0, \end{cases}$ and the remainder

$$R_n = \begin{cases} \frac{1}{(1+x^3)^{n-1}} & \text{for } x > 0, \\ 0 & \text{for } x = 0. \end{cases}$$

For any n the remainder R_n will be greater, say, 0.1 as soon as $x^3 < \sqrt[n-1]{10} - 1$, i.e. for $x \geqslant 0$ the series converges non-uniformly. But for $x \geqslant 1$ it already converges uniformly, since in this case $|R_n| \leqslant \frac{1}{2^{n-1}} < \varepsilon$ as soon as $n - 1 > \frac{-\log \varepsilon}{\log 2}$; in particular $|R_n| < 0.001$ for $n \geqslant 11$. **2466.** For any non-negative x the terms of the given series are less than, or equal to, the terms of the convergent series $1 + \frac{1}{3} + \frac{1}{3^2} + \frac{1}{3^3} + \ldots$. Hence, the series converges uniformly for all $x \geqslant 0$, $R_n(x)$ is less than the remainder of the number series, i.e. $R_n(x) < \frac{\left(\frac{1}{3}\right)^n}{1 - \frac{1}{3}} = \frac{1}{2 \cdot 3^{n-1}} < 0.01$ as soon as $3^{n-1} > 50$ or $n \geqslant 5$ for any $x \geqslant 0$. **2467.** $|R_n(x)| < \frac{1}{n^2} \leqslant 0.0001$ as soon as $n \geqslant 100$ for any x. **2468.** $u_n = \frac{1}{x+n-1} - \frac{1}{x+n}$. Therefore, $S_n = \frac{1}{x} - \frac{1}{x+n}$; $S = \lim\limits_{n \to \infty} S_n = \frac{1}{x}$ for any $x \neq 0$. In particular, for $x > 0$ $R_n(x) = \frac{1}{x+n} < \frac{1}{n} \leqslant 0.1$ as soon as $n \geqslant 10$. **2469.** For any non-negative x the terms of the given series are less than (or equal to) those of the convergent series $1 + \frac{1}{2} + \frac{1}{4} + \frac{1}{8} + \ldots$. Therefore, the series converges uniformly for all $x \geqslant 0$, $R_n(x) < \frac{\left(\frac{1}{2}\right)^n}{1 - \frac{1}{2}} + \frac{1}{2^{n-1}} < 0.01$ as soon as $2^{n-1} > 100$ or $n \geqslant 8$. **2470.** $-3 \leqslant x < 3$. **2471.** $-\sqrt{5} \leqslant x \leqslant \sqrt{5}$. **2472.** $-\frac{\sqrt{3}}{2} \leqslant x \leqslant \frac{\sqrt{3}}{2}$. **2473.** Converges absolutely along the whole number line. **2474.** $-1 < x \leqslant 1$. **2475.** $-\frac{\sqrt{2}}{3} < x < \frac{\sqrt{2}}{3}$. **2476.** (1) $R=0$; (2) $R=e$. **2477.** $-5 \leqslant x < 3$. **2478.** $1 < x \leqslant 2$. **2479.** $\frac{1}{(1-x)^2}$ for $|x| < 1$. **2480.** $\arctan x$ for $|x| \leqslant 1$. **2481.** $\frac{1+x}{(1-x)^2}$ for $|x| < 1$. **2482.** $(1+x)^m$. **2483.** $-\frac{\sqrt{5}}{2} < x \leqslant \frac{\sqrt{5}}{2}$. **2484.** $-\sqrt{3} \leqslant x \leqslant \sqrt{3}$. **2485.** $-0.1 \leqslant x < 0.1$. **2486.** $-1 \leqslant x \leqslant 1$. **2487.** $-1 \leqslant x < 3$. **2488.** $-1 \leqslant x < 0$. **2489.** $\frac{1-x^2}{(1+x^2)^2}$ for $|x| < 1$. **2490.** $-\ln(1-x)$ for $-1 \leqslant x < 1$. **2491.** $\frac{1-2x}{(1+x)^2}$ for $|x| < 1$. **2492.** (1) $\cos(x-\alpha) = \sin\alpha\left(\frac{x}{1!}-\frac{x^3}{3!}+\frac{x^5}{5!}-\dots\right)+\cos\alpha\left(1-\frac{x^2}{2!}+\frac{x^4}{4!}+\dots\right)$; $|R_n(x)| = \frac{x^n}{n!}\cos\left(\theta x-\alpha+n\frac{\pi}{2}\right)$; (2) $\sin^2 x=\frac{2x^2}{2!}-\frac{2^3x^4}{4!}+\frac{2^5x^6}{6!}-\dots$; (3) $xe^x=x+\frac{x^2}{1!}+\frac{x^3}{2!}+\frac{x^4}{3!}+\dots$; (4) $\sin\left(mx+\frac{\pi}{3}\right)=\frac{\sqrt{3}}{2}\times\left(1-\frac{m^2x^2}{2!}+\frac{m^4x^4}{4!}-\dots\right)+\frac{1}{2}\left(\frac{mx}{1}-\frac{m^3x^3}{3!}+\frac{m^5x^5}{5!}-\dots\right)$. **2493.** $\ln(1+e^{kx})=\ln 2+\frac{kx}{2}+\frac{k^2x^2}{2!2^2}-\frac{k^4x^4}{4!2^3}+\dots$. **2497.** (1) $\ln\frac{1+x}{1-x} = 2\left[x+\frac{x^3}{3}+\frac{x^5}{5}+\dots\right]$; (2) $\ln(2-3x+x^2)=\ln(1-x)(2-x)=\ln 2-\sum_{n=1}^{\infty}(1+2^{-n})\frac{x^n}{n}$; (3) $\ln(1-x+x^2)=\ln\frac{1+x^3}{1+x}=-\left[x-\frac{x^2}{2}-\frac{2x^3}{3}-\frac{x^4}{4}+\frac{x^5}{5}+\frac{2x^6}{6}+\dots\right]=-2\sum_{n=1}^{\infty}\cos\frac{\pi n}{3}\frac{x^n}{n}$. **2498.** $\ln(x+\sqrt{1+x^2}) = x+\sum_{n=1}^{\infty}(-1)^n\frac{1\cdot 3\dots(2n-1)}{2^n n!}\frac{x^{2n+1}}{2n+1}$. **2499.** $e^{\frac{x}{a}}=e\left[1+\frac{x-a}{1!\,a}+\frac{(x-a)^2}{2!\,a^2}+\frac{(x-a)^3}{3!\,a^3}+\dots\right]$, $R_n(x)=\frac{(x-a)^n}{n!\,a^n}e^{1+\theta\left(\frac{x}{a}-1\right)}$. **2500.** $x^3-3x=-2+3(x-1)^2+(x-1)^3$. **2501.** $x^4=1-4(x+1)+6(x+1)^2-4(x+1)^3+(x+1)^4$. **2502.** $\frac{1}{x}=-\frac{1}{2\left(1-\frac{x+2}{2}\right)}=-\frac{1}{2}\left[1+\frac{x+2}{2}+\frac{(x+2)^2}{4}+\frac{(x+2)^3}{8}+\dots\right]$ for $-4 < x < 0$. **2503.** (1) $\cos\frac{x}{2}=\frac{\sqrt{2}}{2}\times$

$$\times\left[1-\frac{\left(x-\frac{\pi}{2}\right)}{1!\,2}-\frac{\left(x-\frac{\pi}{2}\right)^2}{2!\,2^2}+\ldots\right]=\sum_{n=1}^{\infty}\frac{\left(x-\frac{\pi}{2}\right)^{n-1}}{(n-1)!\,2^{n-1}}\cos\frac{(2n-1)\pi}{4};$$

assuming 0! conventionally equal to 1 (see the note on p. 211 to Problem 1760); (2) $\sin 3x=\sum_{n=1}^{\infty}(-1)^n\frac{(3x+\pi)^{2n-1}}{(2n-1)!}$. **2504.** $\sqrt[3]{x}=$ $=-\sqrt[3]{1-(x+1)}=-1+\frac{x+1}{3\cdot 1!}+\frac{2(x+1)^2}{3^2\cdot 2!}+\ldots=-1+\frac{x+1}{3}+$ $+\sum_{n=1}^{\infty}\frac{2\cdot 5\cdot 8\ldots(3n-1)}{3^{n+1}(n+1)!}(x+1)^{n+1}$ for $-2<x<0$. **2505.** (1) $2^x=1+$ $+\frac{x\ln 2}{1!}+\frac{x^2\ln^2 2}{2!}\ldots$; $|R_n|=\frac{x^n\ln^n 2}{n!}2^{\theta x}$; (2) $\cos\left(mx+\frac{\pi}{4}\right)=\frac{\sqrt{2}}{2}\times$ $\times\left[1-\frac{mx}{1!}-\frac{m^2x^2}{2!}+\ldots\right]=\sum_{n=1}^{\infty}\frac{(mx)^{n-1}}{(n-1)!}\cos(2n-1)\frac{\pi}{4}$ (putting $0!=1$).

2506. $x^4-4x^2=(x+2)^4-8(x+2)^3+20(x+2)^2-16(x+2)$.

2507. $\cos^2 x=\frac{1}{4}-\frac{\sqrt{3}}{3}\left[\frac{x-\frac{\pi}{3}}{1!}-\frac{2^2\left(x-\frac{\pi}{3}\right)^3}{3!}+\frac{2^4\left(x-\frac{\pi}{3}\right)^5}{5!}-\ldots\right]+$ $+\frac{1}{2}\left[\frac{2\left(x-\frac{\pi}{3}\right)^2}{2!}-\frac{2^3\left(x-\frac{\pi}{3}\right)^4}{4!}+\frac{2^5\left(x-\frac{\pi}{3}\right)^6}{6!}-\ldots\right]$.

2508. $\sin\frac{\pi x}{3}=\sum_{n=0}^{\infty}\frac{\pi^n(x-1)^n}{3^n n!}\sin\left(\frac{\pi}{3}+n\frac{\pi}{2}\right)$ (putting $0!=1$).

2509. $\sqrt{x}=2\left[1+\frac{x-4}{2^3\cdot 1!}-\frac{(x-4)^2}{2^6\cdot 2!}+\frac{1\cdot 3(x-4)^3}{2^9\cdot 3!}-\frac{1\cdot 3\cdot 5(x-4)^4}{2^{12}\cdot 4!}+\ldots\right]$.

2511. $\arcsin x=x+\frac{1}{2}\cdot\frac{x^3}{3}+\frac{1\cdot 3}{2^2\cdot 2!}\cdot\frac{x^5}{5}+\frac{1\cdot 3\cdot 5}{2^3\cdot 3!}\cdot\frac{x^7}{7}+\ldots$.**2512.** $\sqrt{0.992}=$ $=\sqrt{1-0.008}\approx 1-0.004=0.996$; $\sqrt{90}=\sqrt{81+9}=9\sqrt{1+\frac{1}{9}}\approx$ $\approx 9\left(1+\frac{1}{18}\right)=9.5$. **2513.** $\sqrt[3]{0.991}=\sqrt[3]{1-0.009}\approx 0.997$; $\sqrt[3]{130}=$ $=\sqrt[3]{125+5}=5\sqrt[3]{1+\frac{1}{25}}\approx 5\left(1+\frac{1}{75}\right)=5\frac{1}{15}$. **2515.** $\arctan x=\frac{x}{1}-$ $-\frac{x^3}{3}+\frac{x^5}{5}-\ldots$. **2517.** $\pi=2\sqrt{3}\left(1-\frac{1}{3\cdot 3}+\frac{1}{5\cdot 3^2}-\frac{1}{7\cdot 3^3}+\frac{1}{9\cdot 3^4}\right)=$ $=1.814\sqrt{3}\approx 3.142$. **2519.** (1) $\int\frac{\sin x}{x}dx=C+x-\frac{x^3}{3!3}+\frac{x^5}{5!5}-\ldots$,

(2) $\int \frac{e^x}{x}\,dx = C + \ln x + \frac{x}{1!} + \frac{x^2}{2!2} + \frac{x^3}{3!3} + \ldots$ **2520.** $\Phi(x) = \int_0^x e^{-x^2}\,dx = x - \frac{x^3}{1!3} + \frac{x^5}{2!5} - \frac{x^7}{3!7} + \ldots$; $\Phi\left(\frac{1}{3}\right) \approx \frac{1}{3} - \frac{1}{3^4} \approx 0.419$ with an error $< \frac{1}{2430}$. **2521.** $\Phi(x) = \int_0^x \sqrt[3]{1+x^2}\,dx = x + \frac{1}{3}\cdot\frac{x^3}{3} - \frac{2}{3^2 2!}\cdot\frac{x^5}{5} + \frac{2\cdot5}{3^3\cdot3!}\cdot\frac{x^7}{7} - \ldots$; $\Phi\left(\frac{1}{5}\right) \approx \frac{1}{5} + \frac{1}{3\cdot3\cdot5^3} \approx 0.2008$ with an error $< \frac{1}{3^2\cdot5^6} < 0.0001$. **2522.** Differentiating the equation n times and substituting $x=0$, we get: $y_0^{(n+2)} = n(n-1)\,y_0^{(n-2)}$. Hence, $y_0'' = y_0''' = 0$, $y_0^{IV} = 2\cdot1$, $y_0^{V} = 3\cdot2$, $y_0^{VI} = 0$ and so on. Substituting these values into Maclaurin's series $y = y_0 + \frac{y_0'}{1!}x + \frac{y_0''}{2!}x^2 + \ldots$, we find: $y = 1 + \frac{x}{1} + \frac{x^4}{3\cdot4} + \frac{x^5}{4\cdot5} + \frac{x^8}{3\cdot4\cdot7\cdot8} + \ldots$. **2523.** $y = 1 + \frac{x^2}{2} - \frac{x^3}{3} + \frac{x^4}{6} - \ldots$. **2524.** The solution is a Bessel function of order zero: $I_0(x) = 1 - \frac{x^2}{2^2} + \frac{x^4}{2^2\cdot4^2} - \frac{x^6}{2^2\cdot4^2\cdot6^2} + \ldots$. **2525.** $\sqrt{1.005} \approx 1.0025$; $\sqrt[3]{1.0012} \approx 1.0004$; $\sqrt{0{,}993} \approx 0.9965$; $\sqrt[3]{0.997} \approx 0.999$; $\sqrt{110} = \sqrt{100+10} \approx 10\left(1+\frac{1}{20}\right) = 10.5$; $\sqrt[3]{70} \approx 4\left(1+\frac{1}{32}\right) = 4.125$; $\sqrt[5]{40} \approx 2\left(1+\frac{1}{20}\right) = 2.1$. **2527.** $\pi = 6\left(\frac{1}{2} + \frac{1}{2}\cdot\frac{1}{3\cdot2^3} + \frac{1\cdot3}{2^2\cdot2!\,5\cdot2^5} + \ldots\right) \approx 3(1 + 0.0417 + 0.0047) \approx 3.14$. **2528.** $\pi = 2\left[1 - \frac{1}{3\cdot2^2} + \frac{1}{5\cdot2^4} - \frac{1}{7\cdot2^6} + \ldots\right] + \frac{4}{3}\left[1 - \frac{1}{3\cdot3^2} + \frac{1}{5\cdot3^4} - \frac{1}{7\cdot3^6} + \ldots\right] = \frac{10}{3} + 2\sum_{n=1}^{\infty}\frac{(-1)^n}{2n-1}\times\left(\frac{1}{4^n} + \frac{2}{9^n\cdot3}\right)$. **2532.** $s = 4\int_0^{\frac{\pi}{2}} \sqrt{a^2\sin^2 t + b^2\cos^2 t}\,dt = 4a\int_0^{\frac{\pi}{2}} \sqrt{1-\varepsilon^2\cos^2 t}\,dt = 2\pi a\left[1 - \frac{\varepsilon^2}{2^2} - \left(\frac{1\cdot3}{2\cdot4}\right)^2\cdot\frac{\varepsilon^4}{3} - \left(\frac{1\cdot3\cdot5}{2\cdot4\cdot6}\right)^2\times\frac{\varepsilon^6}{5} - \ldots\right]$, where ε is eccentricity of the ellipse, and a its major

semi-axis (see Problem 1624 and the answer to it). **2533.** $\int\limits_0^{0.5} \sqrt{1+x^3}\,dx=$

$$=\left[x+\frac{x^4}{2\cdot 4}-\frac{x^7}{2^2\cdot 2!7}+\ldots\right]_0^{0.5}=\frac{1}{2}+\frac{1}{2}\cdot\frac{1}{4}\cdot\frac{1}{2^4}-\ldots\approx\frac{65}{128}\approx 0.508$$

with an error $<\frac{1}{7\cdot 2^{10}}$. **2534.** $\Phi(x)=x-\frac{1}{2!}\frac{x^5}{4^2\cdot 5}+\frac{1}{4!}\frac{x^9}{4^4\cdot 9}-\ldots$; $\Phi\left(\frac{1}{2}\right)=\frac{1}{2}-\frac{1}{5\cdot 2^{10}}+\ldots\approx 0.499805$ with an error $<\frac{1}{27\cdot 2^{20}}$.

2535. $y=\frac{x^3}{3}+\frac{x^7}{3^2\cdot 7}+\frac{2\cdot x^{11}}{3^3\cdot 7\cdot 11}+\ldots$. **2536.** Differentiating the equation n times and substituting $x=0$, we get: $y_0^{(n+2)}=-ny_0^{(n-1)}$, hence $y_0=1$, $y_0'=0$, $y_0''=0$, $y_0'''=-1$, $y_0^{IV}=y_0^{V}=0$, $y_0^{VI}=1\cdot 4$, ..., $y=1-\frac{x^3}{3!}+$ $+\frac{1\cdot 4\cdot x^6}{6!}-\frac{1\cdot 4\cdot 7\cdot x^9}{9!}+\ldots$. **2537.** $x=\int\limits_0^s \cos\frac{s^2}{2C}\,ds=s\left[1-\frac{s^4}{2!\,(2C)^2\cdot 5}+\right.$ $\left.+\ldots\right]$, $y=\int\limits_0^s \sin\frac{s^2}{2C}\,ds=\frac{s^3}{2C}\left[\frac{1}{3}-\frac{s^4}{3!\,(2C)^2\cdot 7}+\ldots\right]$, where the constant $C=R\cdot L$, R is the radius of the circular curve, and L the length of the transition curve. The curve is called the *clothoid* (Fig. 92, p. 388). **2538.** $F(x+h,\ y+l)=x^2+xy+y^2+h(2x+y)+l(2y+x)+$ $+h^2+hl+l^2$. **2539.** $x^3+2xy^2=9+11(x-1)+8(y-2)+$ $+3(x-1)^2+8(x-1)(y-2)+2(y-2)^2+(x-1)^3+2(x-1)(y-2)^2$.

2540. $\ln(x-y)=x-(y+1)-\frac{x^2}{2}+x(y+1)-\frac{(y+1)^2}{2}+R_3$, where $R_3=$ $=\frac{(x-y-1)^3}{3\,[\theta x+1-\theta(y+1)]^3}$. **2541.** $\sin(mx+ny)=mx+ny-\frac{(mx+ny)^3}{3!}+$ $+\frac{(mx+ny)^4}{4!}\sin\theta(mx+ny)$. **2543.** $dx=0.1$; $dy=-0.2$; $\Delta z=(2x-y)\,dx+$ $+(2y-x)\,dy+dx^2-dx\,dy+dy^2=-0.63$. **2544.** $\Delta z=-(a\,dx-b\,dy)\times$ $\times\sin(ax-by)-\frac{1}{2!}(a\,dx-b\,dy)^2\cos(ax-by)+R_3$, where $R_3=\frac{1}{3!}\times$ $\times(a\,dx-b\,dy)^3\sin[a(x+\theta\,dx)-b(y+\theta\,dy)]$. **2545.** $x^2y=-1-2(x-1)+$ $+(y+1)-(x-1)^2+(x-1)(y+1)$. **2546.** $\arctan\frac{y}{x}=y-(x-1)y+\ldots$.

2547. $y^x=1+2(y-1)+(x-2)(y-1)+\frac{(y-1)^2}{2}+\ldots$; $1.1^{2.1}\approx 1+$

$+2\cdot 0.1+0.1\cdot 0.1+\frac{0.1^2}{2}=1.215$. **2548.** $dx=-0.01$, $dy=0.02$; $\Delta z=$ $=2yx\,dx+(x^2-2y)\,dy+y\,dx^2+x\,dx\,dy-dy^2+\frac{1}{3}dx^2\,dy\approx -0.1407$.

2549. $\frac{4}{\pi}\sum_{n=1}^{\infty}\frac{\sin(2n-1)x}{2n-1}$. **2550.** $\frac{\pi}{2}-4\sum_{n=1}^{\infty}\frac{\cos(2n-1)x}{(2n-1)^2}$. **2551.** $\frac{\pi^2}{3}+$ $+4\sum_{n=1}^{\infty}(-1)^n\frac{\cos nx}{n^2}$. **2552.** $\frac{3\pi}{4}-\left[\frac{\sin x}{1}-\frac{\sin 2x}{2}+\frac{\sin 3x}{3}-\dots\right]+$ $+\frac{2}{\pi}\left[\frac{\cos x}{1^2}+\frac{\cos 3x}{3^2}+\frac{\cos 5x}{5^2}+\dots\right]$. **2553.** $\frac{4}{\pi}\left[\sin\frac{\pi x}{l}+\frac{1}{3}\sin\frac{3\pi x}{l}+\right.$ $\left.+\frac{1}{5}\sin\frac{5\pi x}{l}+\dots\right]$. **2554.** $\frac{1}{2}+\frac{4}{\pi^2}\left[\frac{\cos\pi x}{1^2}+\frac{\cos 3\pi x}{3^2}+\dots\right]$.

2555. $\frac{l}{4}-\frac{2l}{\pi^2}\left[\cos\frac{\pi x}{l}+\frac{1}{3^2}\cos\frac{3\pi x}{l}+\dots\right]+\frac{l}{\pi}\left[\sin\frac{\pi x}{l}-\right.$ $\left.-\frac{1}{2}\sin\frac{2\pi x}{l}+\dots\right]$. **2556.** (1) $\frac{3}{4}+\frac{4}{\pi^2}\left[\cos\frac{\pi x}{2}-\frac{2}{2^2}\cos\frac{2\pi x}{2}+\right.$ $\left.+\frac{1}{3^3}\cos\frac{3\pi x}{2}+\frac{1}{5^2}\cos\frac{5\pi x}{2}-\frac{2}{6^2}\cos\frac{6\pi x}{2}+\dots\right]$; (2) $\frac{2}{\pi}\left[\sin\frac{\pi x}{2}+\right.$ $\left.+\frac{1}{2}\sin\frac{2\pi x}{2}+\frac{1}{3}\sin\frac{3\pi x}{2}+\dots\right]+\frac{4}{\pi^2}\left[\sin\frac{\pi x}{2}-\frac{1}{3^3}\sin\frac{3\pi x}{2}+\right.$ $\left.+\frac{1}{5^2}\sin\frac{5\pi x}{2}-\dots\right]$. **2557.** $u=\frac{4l}{\pi^2}\sum_{n=1}^{\infty}\frac{1}{n^2}\sin\frac{n\pi}{2}\sin\frac{n\pi x}{l}e^{-\frac{n^2\pi^2a^2t}{l^2}}$.

2558. $u=\sum_{n=0}^{\infty}a_n\cos\frac{2n+1}{2l}a\pi t\sin\frac{2n+1}{2l}\pi x$, where $a_n=\frac{2}{l}\int_0^l f(\xi)\times$ $\times\sin\frac{2n+1}{2l}\pi\xi\,d\xi$. **2559.** $u=\sum_{n=1}^{\infty}b_n\sin\frac{n\pi x}{l}\cos\frac{a\pi^2n^2t}{l^2}$, where $b_n=$ $=\frac{2}{l}\int_0^l f(\xi)\sin\frac{n\pi\xi}{l}\,d\xi$. **2560.** $f(x)=\frac{2}{\pi}\int_0^{\infty}\frac{1-\cos\lambda}{\lambda}\sin\lambda x\,d\lambda$. **2561.** $f(x)=$ $=\frac{2\beta}{\pi}\int_0^{\infty}\frac{\cos\lambda x}{\beta^2+\lambda^2}\,d\lambda$. **2562.** $f(x)=\frac{4}{\pi}\int_0^{\infty}\frac{(1-\cos\lambda)\sin\lambda}{\lambda^2}\sin\lambda x\,d\lambda$.

2563. $\frac{\pi}{2}+\frac{4}{\pi}\left[\cos x+\frac{\cos 3x}{3^2}+\frac{\cos 5x}{5^2}+\dots\right]$. **2564.** $|\sin x|=\frac{2}{\pi}-\frac{4}{\pi}\times$

$\times\left[\frac{\cos 2x}{1\cdot 3}+\frac{\cos 4x}{3\cdot 5}+\frac{\cos 6x}{5\cdot 7}+\ldots\right]$. **2565.** $\frac{4}{\pi}\left[\sin x-\frac{\sin 3x}{3^2}+\right.$ $\left.+\frac{\sin 5x}{5^2}-\ldots\right]$. **2566.** $\frac{l}{2}-\frac{4l}{\pi^2}\left[\frac{\cos\frac{\pi x}{l}}{1^2}+\frac{\cos\frac{3\pi x}{l}}{3^2}+\ldots\right]$.
2567. $\frac{3}{4}-\frac{2}{\pi^2}\left[\frac{\cos \pi x}{1^2}+\frac{\cos 3\pi x}{3^2}+\ldots\right]-\frac{1}{\pi}\left[\frac{\sin \pi x}{1}+\frac{\sin 2\pi x}{2}+\ldots\right]$.
2568. $\sinh l\left[\frac{1}{l}-2l\left(\frac{\cos\frac{\pi x}{l}}{\pi^2+l^2}-\frac{\cos\frac{2\pi x}{l}}{2^2\pi^2+l^2}+\ldots\right)+2\pi\left(\frac{1\cdot\sin\frac{\pi x}{l}}{\pi^2+l^2}-\right.\right.$ $\left.\left.-\frac{2\cdot\sin\frac{2\pi x}{l}}{2^2\pi^2+l^2}+\ldots\right)\right]$. **2569.** $u=\sum_{n=0}^{\infty}a_n\cos\frac{2n+1}{2}t\sin\frac{2n+1}{2}x$, where $a_n=\frac{2}{\pi}\int_0^{\pi}f(\xi)\sin\frac{2n+1}{2}\xi\,d\xi$. **2570.** $f(x)=\frac{2}{\pi}\int_0^{\infty}\frac{\sin\lambda\cos\lambda x}{\lambda}d\lambda$.

APPENDICES

I. SOME REMARKABLE CURVES (FOR REFERENCES)

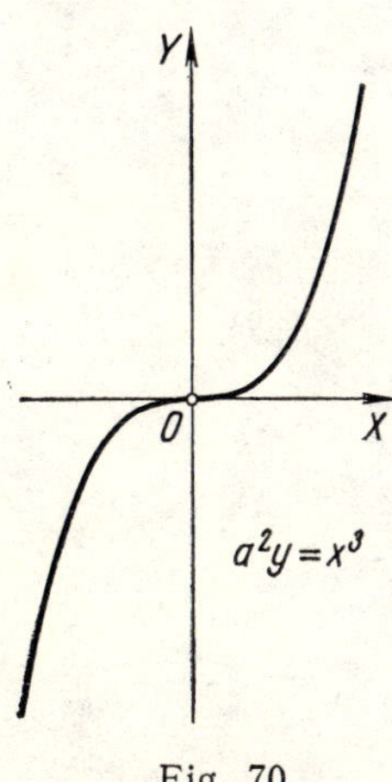

Fig. 70.
Cubic parabola

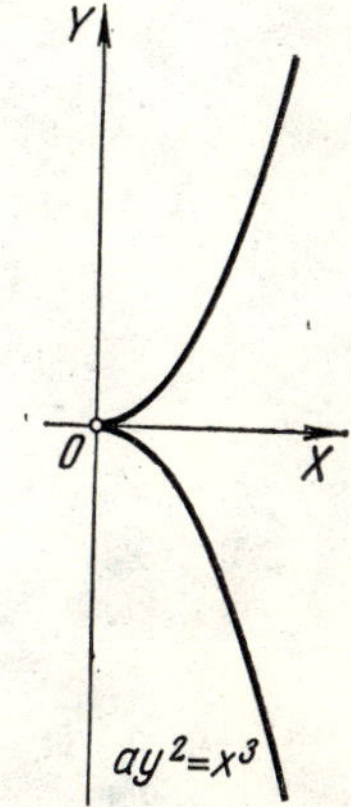

Fig. 71.
Semicubical parabola

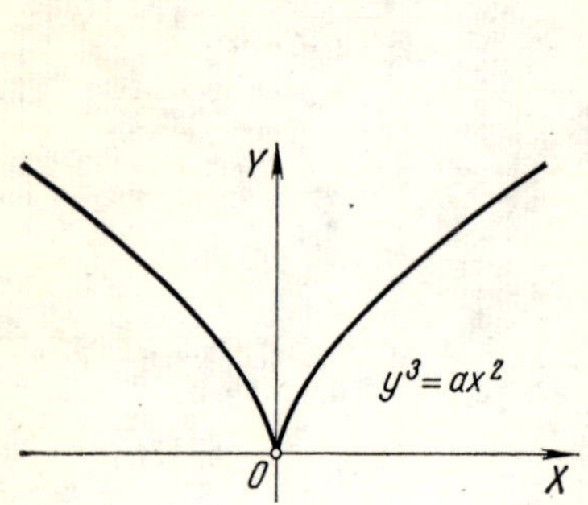

Fig. 72.
Semicubical parabola

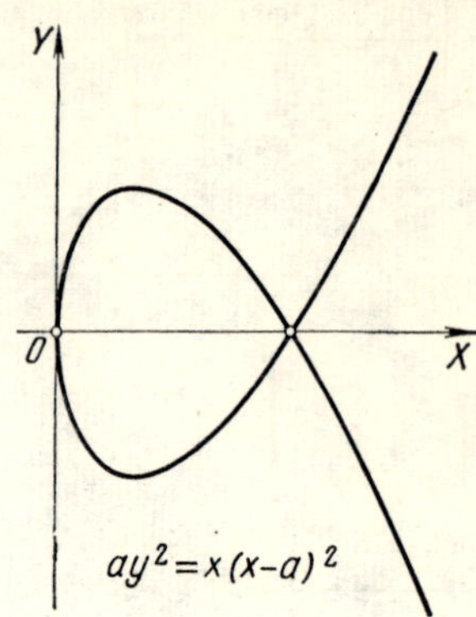

Fig. 73.
Loop parabola

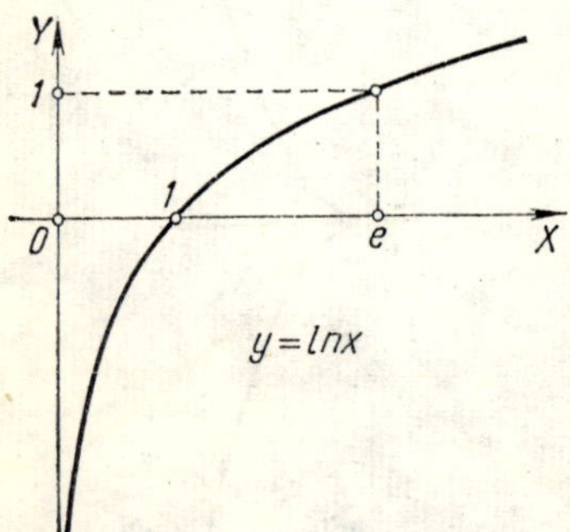

Fig. 74.
Logarithmic curve

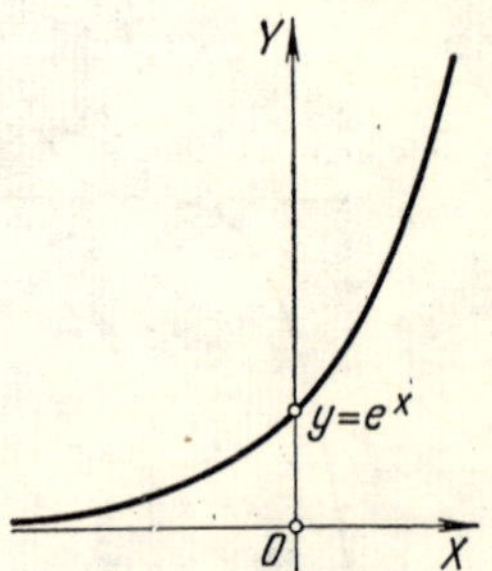

Fig. 75.
Graph of the exponential function

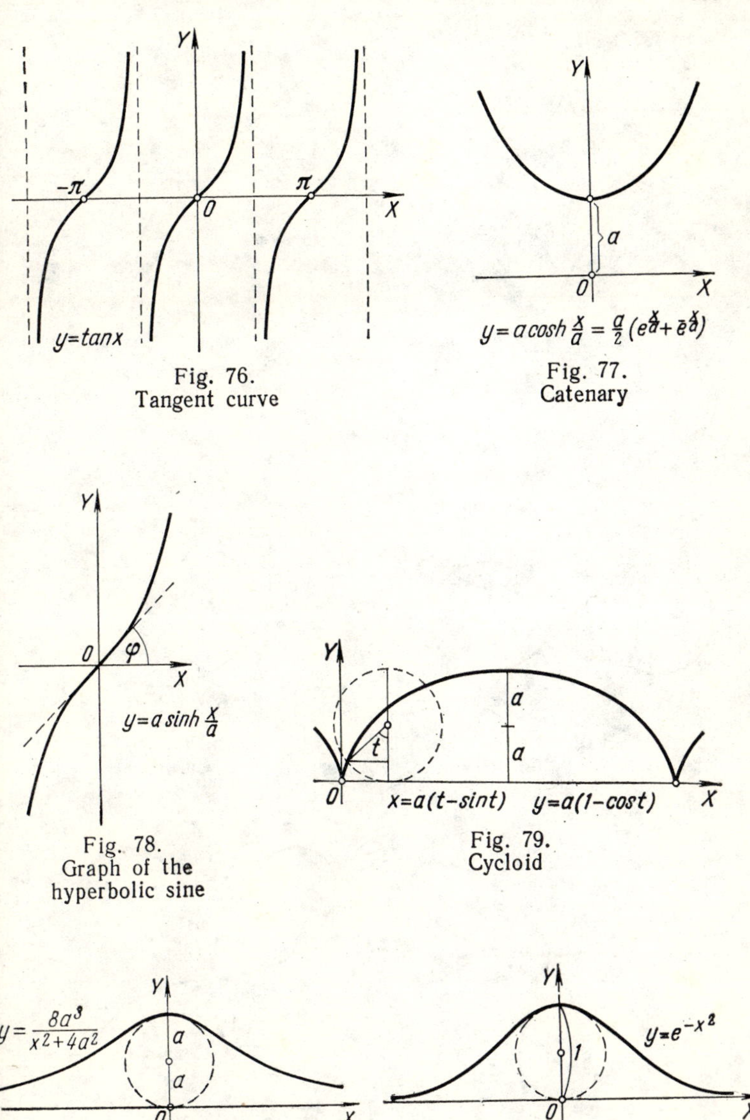

Fig. 76.
Tangent curve

Fig. 77.
Catenary

Fig. 78.
Graph of the hyperbolic sine

Fig. 79.
Cycloid

Fig. 80.
Witch of Agnesi (or versiera)

Fig. 81.
"Probability" curve

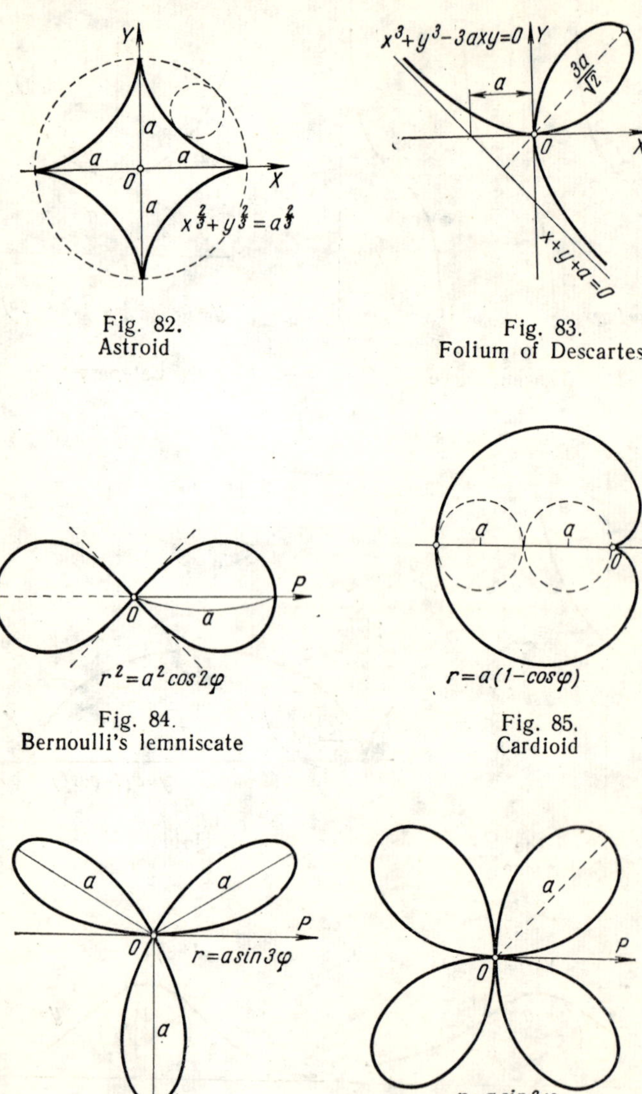

Fig. 82.
Astroid

Fig. 83.
Folium of Descartes

Fig. 84.
Bernoulli's lemniscate

Fig. 85.
Cardioid

Fig. 86.
Three-leafed rose

Fig. 87.
Four-leafed rose

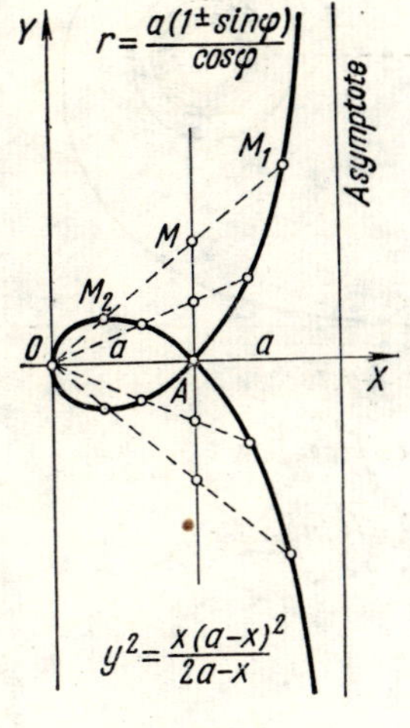

Fig. 88.
Strophoid

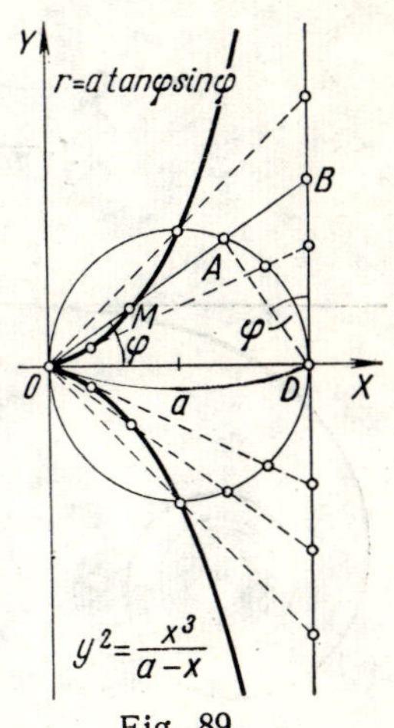

Fig. 89.
Cissoid

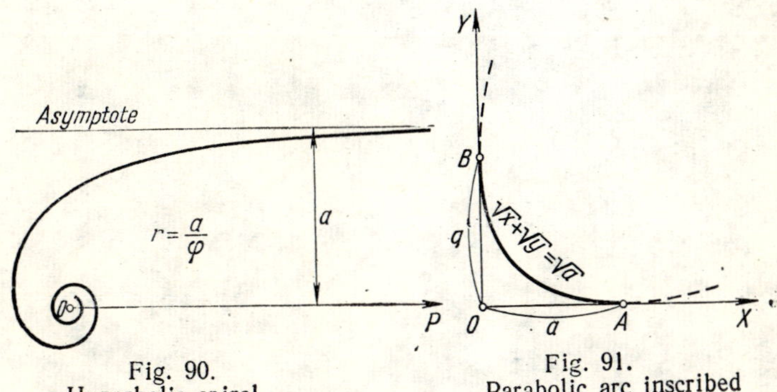

Fig. 90.
Hyperbolic spiral

Fig. 91.
Parabolic arc inscribed in angle XOY.

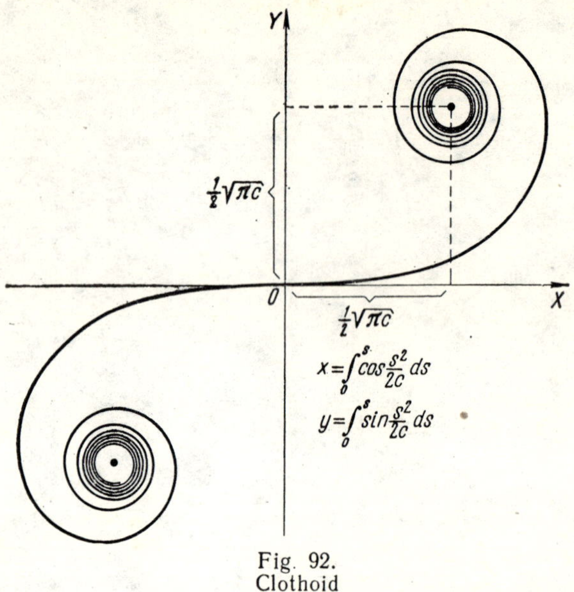

Fig. 92.
Clothoid

II. TABLES

1. Trigonometric functions

$\alpha°$	$\sin\alpha$	$\tan\alpha$	$\cot\alpha$	$\cos\alpha$	
0	0.0000	0.0000	—	1.000	90
1	0175	0175	57.3	1.000	89
2	0349	0349	28.6	0.999	88
3	0523	0524	19.1	999	87
4	0697	0699	14.3	998	86
5	0.0872	0.0875	11.4	0.996	85
6	1045	1051	9.51	995	84
7	1219	1228	8.11	993	83
8	139	141	7.11	990	82
9	156	158	6.31	988	81
10	0.174	0.176	5.67	0.985	80
11	191	194	5.145	982	79
12	208	213	4.705	978	78
13	225	231	4.331	974	77
14	242	249	4.011	970	76
15	0.259	0.268	3.732	0.966	75
16	276	287	487	961	74
17	292	306	271	956	73
18	309	325	3.078	951	72
19	326	344	2.904	946	71
20	0.342	0.364	2.747	0.940	70
21	358	384	605	934	69

$\alpha°$	a radians	$\sin a$	$\tan a$
0	0	0.000	0.000
5.73	0.1	0.100	+0.100
11.5	0.2	0.199	+0.203
17.2	0.3	0.296	+0.310
22.9	0.4	0.389	+0.422
28.7	0.5	0.480	+0.547
34.4	0.6	0.564	+0.684
40.1	0.7	0.644	+0.842
45.0	$\frac{\pi}{4}$	0.707	+1.000
45.8	0.8	0.717	+1.028
51.6	0.9	0.784	+1.260
57.3	1.0	0.842	+1.558
63.0	1.1	0.891	+1.963
68.8	1.2	0.932	+2.579
74.5	1.3	0.964	+3.606
80.2	1.4	0.985	+5.789
86.0	1.5	0.998	+14.30
90.0	$\frac{\pi}{2}$	1.000	—
91.7	1.6	0.999	—33.75
97.4	1.7	0.992	—7.695
103.1	1.8	0.974	—4.292
108.9	1.9	0.946	—2.921
114.6	2.0	0.909	—2.184
120.3	2.1	0.863	—1.711
126.1	2.2	0.808	—1.373

Continued

$\alpha°$	$\sin\alpha$	$\tan\alpha$	$\cot\alpha$	$\cos\alpha$	
22	375	404	475	927	68
23	391	424	356	921	67
24	407	445	246	914	66
25	0.423	0.466	2.145	0.906	65
26	438	488	2.050	899	64
27	454	510	1.963	891	63
28	469	532	881	883	62
29	485	554	804	875	61
30	0.500	0.577	1.732	0.866	60
31	515	601	664	857	59
32	530	625	600	848	58
33	545	649	540	839	57
34	559	675	483	829	56
35	0.574	0.700	1.428	0.819	55
36	588	727	376	809	54
37	601	754	327	799	53
38	616	781	280	788	52
39	629	810	235	777	51
40	0.643	0.839	1.192	0.766	50
41	656	869	150	755	49
42	669	900	111	743	48
43	682	933	072	731	47
44	695	966	036	719	46
45	0.707	1.000	1.000	0.707	45
	$\cos\alpha$	$\cot\alpha$	$\tan\alpha$	$\sin\alpha$	$\alpha°$

$\alpha°$	a radians	$\sin a$	$\tan a$
131.8	2.3	0.745	—1.118
135.0	$\frac{3\pi}{4}$	0.707	—1.000
137.5	2.4	0.676	—0.916
143.2	2.5	0.599	—0.748
149.0	2.6	0.515	—0.602
154.7	2.7	0.428	—0.472
160.4	2.8	0.336	—0.356
166.1	2.9	0.240	—0.247
171.9	3.0	0.141	—0.142
177.6	3.1	0.042	—0.042
180.0	π	0.000	—0.000

$$\sin\frac{\pi}{6}=\frac{1}{2},\quad \cos\frac{\pi}{6}=\frac{\sqrt{3}}{2},$$

$$\tan\frac{\pi}{6}=\frac{1}{\sqrt{3}},\quad \cot\frac{\pi}{6}=\sqrt{3},$$

$$\sin\frac{\pi}{4}=\cos\frac{\pi}{4}=\frac{1}{\sqrt{2}},$$

$$\tan\frac{\pi}{4}=\cot\frac{\pi}{4}=1.$$

α degree	1	2	3	4	5	6	7	8	9
a radians	0.017	0.035	0.052	0.070	0.087	0.105	0.122	0.140	0.157

1 radian = 57°17′45″

2. Hyperbolic functions

x	$\sinh x$	$\cosh x$	x	$\sinh x$	$\cosh x$
0	0	1			
0.1	0.100	1.005	2.1	4.022	4.289
0.2	0.201	1.020	2.2	4.457	4.568
0.3	0.304	1.045	2.3	4.937	5.037
0.4	0.411	1.081	2.4	5.466	5.557
0.5	0.521	1.128	2.5	6.050	6.132
0.6	0.637	1.185	2.6	6.695	6.769
0.7	0.759	1.255	2.7	7.407	7.474
0.8	0.888	1.337	2.8	8.192	8.253
0.9	1.026	1.433	2.9	9.060	9.115
1.0	1.175	1.543	3.0	10.02	10.07
1.1	1.336	1.669	3.1	11.08	11.12
1.2	1.509	1.811	3.2	12.25	12.29
1.3	1.698	1.971	3.3	13.54	13.58
1.4	1.904	2.151	3.4	14.97	15.00
1.5	2.129	2.352	3.5	16.54	16.57
1.6	2.376	2.578	3.6	18.29	18.32
1.7	2.646	2.828	3.7	20.21	20.24
1.8	2.942	3.107	3.8	22.34	22.36
1.9	3.268	3.418	3.9	24.69	24.71
2.0	3.627	3.762	4.0	27.29	27.31

For $x > 4$ assume that $\sinh x \approx \cosh x \approx \frac{e^x}{2}$ (accurate to 0.1).

$$\sinh x = \frac{e^x - e^{-x}}{2}; \quad \cosh x = \frac{e^x + e^{-x}}{2};$$

$$e^x = \sinh x + \cosh x; \quad e^{xi} = \sin x + i \cos x.$$

3. Inverse quantities, square and cubic roots, logarithms, exponential function

x	$\frac{1}{x}$	$\sqrt{x}$	$\sqrt{10x}$	$\sqrt[3]{x}$	$\sqrt[3]{10x}$	$\sqrt[3]{100x}$	$\log x$	$\ln x$	e^x	x
1.0	1.000	1.00	3.16	1.00	2.15	4.64	000	0.000	2.72	1.0
1.1	0.909	05	32	03	22	79	041	095	3.00	1.1
1.2	833	10	46	06	29	93	079	192	3.32	1.2
1.3	769	14	61	09	35	5.07	114	252	3.67	1.3
1.4	714	18	74	12	41	19	146	336	4.06	1.4
1.5	0.667	1.23	3.87	1.15	2.47	5.13	176	0.405	4.48	1.5
1.6	625	27	4.00	17	52	43	204	470	4.95	1.6
1.7	588	30	12	19	57	54	230	530	5.47	1.7
1.8	556	34	24	22	62	65	255	588	6.05	1.8
1.9	526	38	36	24	67	75	279	642	6.69	1.9
2.0	0.500	1.41	4.47	1.26	2.71	5.85	301	0.693	7.39	2.0
2.1	476	45	58	28	76	94	322	742	8.17	2.1
2.2	455	48	69	30	80	6.03	342	789	9.03	2.2
2.3	435	52	80	32	84	13	362	833	9.97	2.3
2.4	417	55	90	34	88	21	380	875	11.0	2.4
2.5	0.400	1.58	5.00	1.36	2.92	6.30	398	0.916	12.2	2.5
2.6	385	61	10	38	96	38	415	955	13.5	2.6
2.7	370	64	20	39	3.00	46	431	993	14.9	2.7
2.8	357	67	29	41	04	54	447	1.030	16.4	2.8
2.9	345	70	39	43	07	62	462	065	18.2	2.9
3.0	0.333	1.73	5.48	1.44	3.11	6.69	477	1.099	20.1	3.0
3.1	323	76	57	46	14	77	491	131	22.2	3.1
3.2	313	79	66	47	18	84	505	163	24.5	3.2
3.3	303	81	75	49	21	91	519	194	27.1	3.3
3.4	294	84	83	50	24	98	532	224	30.0	3.4

Continued

x	$\frac{1}{x}$	$\sqrt{x}$	$\sqrt{10x}$	$\sqrt[3]{x}$	$\sqrt[3]{10x}$	$\sqrt[3]{100x}$	$\log x$	$\ln x$	e^x	x
3.5	0.286	1.87	5.92	1.52	3.27	7.05	544	1.253	33.1	3.5
3.6	278	90	6.00	53	30	11	556	281	36.6	3.6
3.7	270	92	08	55	33	18	568	308	40.4	3.7
3.8	263	95	16	56	36	24	580	335	44.7	3.8
3.9	256	98	25	57	39	31	591	361	49.4	3.9
4.0	0.250	2.00	6.33	1.59	3.42	7.37	602	1.386	54.6	4.0
4.1	244	03	40	60	45	43	613	411	60.3	4.1
4.2	238	05	48	61	48	49	623	435	66.7	4.2
4.3	233	07	56	63	50	55	634	458	73.7	4.3
4.4	227	10	63	64	53	61	644	482	81.5	4.4
4.5	0.222	2.12	6.71	1.65	3.56	7.66	653	1.504	90.0	4.5
4.6	217	15	78	66	58	72	663	526	99.5	4.6
4.7	213	17	86	68	61	78	672	548	110	4.7
4.8	208	19	93	69	63	83	681	569	121	4.8
4.9	204	21	7.00	70	66	88	690	589	134	4.9
5.0	0.200	2.24	7.07	1.71	3.68	7.94	699	1.609	148	5.0
5.1	196	26	14	72	71	99	708	629	164	5.1
5.2	192	28	21	73	73	8.04	716	649	181	5.2
5.3	189	30	28	74	76	09	724	668	200	5.3
5.4	185	32	35	75	78	14	732	686	221	5.4
5.5	0.182	2.35	7.42	1.77	3.80	8.19	740	1.705	244	5.5
5.6	179	37	48	78	83	24	748	723	270	5.6
5.7	175	39	55	79	85	29	756	740	299	5.7
5.8	172	41	62	80	87	34	763	758	330	5.8
5.9	170	43	68	81	89	39	771	775	365	5.9
6.0	0.167	2.45	7.75	1.82	3.92	8.43	778	1.792	403	6.0

Continued

x	$\frac{1}{x}$	$\sqrt{x}$	$\sqrt{10x}$	$\sqrt[3]{x}$	$\sqrt[3]{10x}$	$\sqrt[3]{100x}$	$\log x$	$\ln x$	e^x	x
6.1	0.164	2.47	7.81	1.83	3.94	8.48	785	1.808	446	6.1
6.2	161	49	87	84	96	53	792	825	493	6.2
6.3	159	51	94	85	98	57	799	841	545	6.3
6.4	156	53	8.00	86	4.00	62	806	856	602	6.4
6.5	0.154	2.55	8.06	1.87	4.02	8.66	813	1.872	665	6.5
6.6	152	57	12	88	04	71	820	887	735	6.6
6.7	149	59	19	89	06	75	826	902	812	6.7
6.8	147	61	25	90	08	79	833	918	898	6.8
6.9	145	63	31	90	10	84	839	932	992	6.9
7.0	0.143	2.65	8.37	1.91	4.12	8.88	845	1.946	1097	7.0
7.1	141	67	43	92	14	92	851	960	1212	7.1
7.2	139	68	49	93	16	96	857	974	1339	7.2
7.3	137	70	54	94	18	9.00	863	982	1480	7.3
7.4	135	72	60	95	20	05	869	2.001	1636	7.4
7.5	0.133	2.74	8.66	1.96	4.22	9.09	875	2.015	1808	7.5
7.6	132	76	72	97	24	13	881	028	1998	7.6
7.7	130	78	78	98	25	17	887	041	2208	7.7
7.8	128	79	83	98	27	21	892	054	2440	7.8
7.9	127	81	89	99	29	24	898	067	2697	7.9
8.0	0.125	2.83	8.94	2.00	4.31	9.28	903	2.079	2981	8.0
8.1	124	85	9.00	01	33	32	909	092	3294	8.1
8.2	122	86	06	02	34	36	914	104	3641	8.2
8.3	121	88	11	03	36	40	919	116	4024	8.3
8.4	119	90	17	03	38	44	924	128	4447	8.4
8.5	0.118	2.92	9.22	2.04	4.40	9.47	929	2.140	4914	8.5
8.6	116	93	27	05	41	51	935	152	5432	8.6

Continued

x	$\frac{1}{x}$	$\sqrt{x}$	$\sqrt{10x}$	$\sqrt[3]{x}$	$\sqrt[3]{10x}$	$\sqrt[3]{100x}$	$\log x$	$\ln x$	e^x	x
8.7	0.115	2.95	9.33	2.06	4.43	9.55	940	2.163	6003	8.7
8.8	114	97	38	07	45	58	945	175	6634	8.8
8.9	112	98	43	07	47	62	949	186	7332	8.9
9.0	0.111	3.00	9.49	2.08	4.48	9.66	954	2.197	8103	9.0
9.1	110	02	54	09	50	69	959	208	8955	9.1
9.2	109	03	59	10	51	73	964	219	9897	9.2
9.3	108	05	64	10	53	76	969	230	10938	9.3
9.4	106	07	69	11	55	80	973	241	12088	9.4
9.5	0.105	3.08	9.75	2.12	4.56	9.83	978	2.251	13360	9.5
9.6	104	10	80	13	58	87	982	263	14765	9.6
9.7	103	11	84	13	60	90	987	272	16318	9.7
9.8	102	13	90	14	61	93	991	282	18034	9.8
9.9	101	15	95	15	63	97	996	293	19930	9.9
10.0	0.100	3.16	10.00	2.15	4.64	10.00	000	2.303	22026	10.0

Given in the column "log x" are mantissas of common logarithms.
Natural logarithms of numbers greater than 10 or less than 1 are to be found by the formula

$$\ln(x\cdot 10^k) = \ln x + k \ln 10.$$

$$\ln 10 = 2.303; \qquad \ln 10^2 = 4.605;$$

$$\log x = 0.4343 \ln x; \qquad \ln x = 2.303 \log x.$$

Formulas for approximate taking of roots:

(1) $\sqrt[n]{1+x} \approx 1 + \frac{x}{n} + \frac{1-n}{2n^2} x^2$ for $|x| < 1$.

(2) $\sqrt[n]{a^n + b} \approx a\left(1 + \frac{b}{na^n} + \frac{1-n}{2n^2} \cdot \frac{b^2}{a^{2n}}\right)$ for $\left|\frac{b}{a^n}\right| < 1$.

TO THE READER

Mir Publishers welcome your comments on the content, translation and design of this book.

We would also be pleased to receive any proposals you care to make about our future publications.

Our address is:
USSR, 129820, Moscow I-110, GSP
Pervy Rizhsky Pereulok, 2
Mir Publishers

Printed in the Union of Soviet Socialist Republics

OTHER BOOKS FOR YOUR LIBRARY

1. MULTIPLE INTEGRALS, FIELD THEORY AND SERIES. AN ADVANCED COURSE IN HIGHER MATHEMATICS

B. M. Budak and S. V. Fomin

Covers branches of mathematics increasingly required by physicists, such as multiple, line, and improper integrals, the theory of fields, and power and trigonometric series. Based on lectures read by the authors in the Physics Faculty of Moscow University, the book endeavours to show the connection between the various mathematical concepts and their applications, and wherever possible their physical meaning as well.

Contents. Double Integrals. Triple and Multiple Integrals. Elements of Differential Geometry. Line Integrals. Surface Integrals. Theory of Fields. Tensors. Functional Sequences and Series. Improper Functions. Integrals Depending on Parameters. Fourier Series and the Fourier Integral.

Appendices on (a) Asymptotic Expansions and (b) Universal Computers.

2. DIFFERENTIAL EQUATIONS AND THE CALCULUS OF VARIATIONS

L. Elsgolts

This text is meant for students of higher schools and deals with the most important sections of mathematics—differential equations and the calculus of variations. The book contains a large number of examples and problems with solutions involving applications of mathematics to physics and mechanics.

Contents. First-Order Differential Equations. Differential Equations of the Second Order and Higher. Systems of Differential Equations. Theory of Stability. First-Order Partial Differential Equations. The Method of Variations in Problems with Fixed Boundaries. Variational Problems with Moving Boundaries and Certain Other Problems. Sufficient Conditions for an Extremum. Variational Problems Involving a Conditional Extremum. Direct Methods in Variational Problems.

3. THE THEORY OF FUNCTIONS OF A COMPLEX VARIABLE

A. G. Sveshnikov, A. N. Tikhonov

The book deals with fundamental concepts in the theory of functions of a complex variable and operational calculus, covering such topics as the complex variable, functions of a complex variable, series of analytic functions, analytic continuation, the Laurent series, the calculus of residues and their applications. Serious consideration is given to the principles of conformal mapping and the application of methods of complex-variable theory to the solution of boundary-value problems in hydrodynamics and electrostatics.

Two methods—the sadle-point method and the Wiener-Hopf method—which have found extensive application in physics are treated in considerable detail in the appendix. A valuable feature of the book is the large number of worked examples.

УДК 516 + 517 (076.1) = 20

В. П. Минорский

СБОРНИК ЗАДАЧ ПО ВЫСШЕЙ МАТЕМАТИКЕ

Контрольный редактор Е. Янковский
Издательские редакторы: Н. Привато, Е. Шубина
Художник В. Стуликов
Художественный редактор Н. Зотова
Технический редактор Н. Борисова
Корректоры Б. Русакова Н. Саввон

Сдано в набор 24/X 1974 г.
Подписано к печати 20/I 1975 г.
Бумага тип. № 1 84×108$^1/_{32}$.
6,26 бум. л. усл. печ. л. 21
Уч.-изд. л. 17,60. Изд. № 17/7786.
Цена 1 р. 93 к. Заказ № 1895
Тираж 12 400 экз.
Темплан изд-ва «Мир» 1975 г., пор. № 179

Издательство «Мир»
Москва, 1-й Рижский пер., 2

Ордена Трудового Красного Знамени
Первая Образцовая типография
имени А. А. Жданова
Союзполиграфпрома при Государственном комитете
Совета Министров СССР по делам издательств,
полиграфии и книжной торговли.
Москва, М-54, Валовая, 28

М $\frac{20203-179}{041(01)-75}$ 179—75